THE OCCASIONAL PAPERS OF
THE RHODES-LIVINGSTONE MUSEUM

THE OCCASIONAL PAPERS OF
THE RHODES-LIVINGSTONE MUSEUM
Nos. 1-16

IN ONE VOLUME

REPRINTED ON BEHALF OF
THE INSTITUTE FOR AFRICAN STUDIES
UNIVERSITY OF ZAMBIA
BY
MANCHESTER UNIVERSITY PRESS

© 1974 National Museums Board of Zambia
'Lunda rites and ceremonies' © 1953, 1974, V. W. Turner
'Some African poison plants and medicines of Northern Rhodesia'
© 1955, 1974, W. Gilges
'The material culture of the Ambo of Northern Rhodesia'
© 1964, 1974, Bronislaw Stefaniszyn

Published on the behalf of
THE INSTITUTE FOR AFRICAN STUDIES
UNIVERSITY OF ZAMBIA
P.O. box 900, Lusaka
by
MANCHESTER UNIVERSITY PRESS
Oxford Road, Manchester M13 9PL
ISBN 0 7190 1273 2

Distributed in the U.S.A. by
HUMANITIES PRESS INC
450 Park Avenue South, New York, N.Y. 10016

Printed in Great Britain by
Lowe & Brydone (Printers) Ltd,
Thetford, Norfolk

CONTENTS

Preface *by Ladislav Holy*   *page* vii

Foreword *by Kafungulwa Mubitama*   ix

J. A. Barnes
1 The material culture of the Fort Jameson.Ngoni   1

W. V. Brelsford
2 African dances of Northern Rhodesia   21

C. M. N. White
3 The material culture of the Lunda–Lovale peoples   53

A. M. Jones
4 African music in Northern Rhodesia and some other places   71

A. H. Quiggin
5 Trade routes, trade and currency in East Africa   145

E. Colson
6 Life among the cattle-owning Plateau Tonga *The material
   culture of a Northern Rhodesia native tribe*   167

E. H. Lane-Poole
7 The discovery of Africa *A history of the exploration of Africa as
   reflected in the maps in the collection of the Rhodes-Livingstone
   Museum*   215

C. W. Mackintosh
8 Some pioneer missions of Northern Rhodesia and
   Nyasaland   249

I. M. Fletcher
9 David Livingstone *A short portrait of the great
   missionary-explorer*   297

V. W. Turner
10 Lunda rites and ceremonies   335

W. Gilges
11 Some African poison plants and medicines of
Northern Rhodesia   389

P. I. R. Maclaren
12 The fishing devices of central and southern Africa   427

R. H. Hobson
13 Rubber *A footnote to Northern Rhodesian history*   489

Elliot Pinhey
14 Dragonflies (*Odonata*) of central Africa   539

V. W. Turner
15 Lunda medicine and the treatment of disease   649

Bronislaw Stefaniszyn
16 The material culture of the Ambo of Northern Rhodesia   721

PREFACE

The Occasional Papers of the Rhodes-Livingstone Museum were replaced in 1967 by a new series of Zambia Museum Papers. This was a result of the changes in the organisation of research in Zambia since her independence and a logical consequence of the Livingstone Museum's own role in the research activities taking place in the country. By that time the research into Zambian prehistory, history, ethnography and natural history became a regular part of museum activities and it was systematically carried out by a well qualified and expanding museum research staff. A need to have a regular series, in which the results of the museum research could be published, gave rise to the Museum Papers. The Occasional Papers reprinted here were started in 1948 under different conditions and with a different purpose in mind. Their aim was to give a visitor to the museum more profound information about the collections than could be provided by labels in the display cases. The years during which the Occasional Papers appeared were probably the most active ones in the whole history of the Livingstone Museum. During these years the present museum building in Livingstone was constructed, the exhibition galleries were built, and the museum collections were displayed for the first time in a systematic way. The whole museum staff was for several years fully engaged in a successful completion of this huge and highly demanding task. The research, particularly the research into Zambian prehistory, continued, but the first priority of the museum staff was to build up the museum. Consequently scholars from outside the museum were approached with requests for contributions to the Occasional Papers. All authors of the papers were specialists in their own fields and in their contributions paid attention to various aspects of their own research. As a result all contributions widely surpassed the original modest aims of the papers. Apart from being guides to museum collections, the papers became indispensable sources of information about Zambian traditional culture and history in their own right. Their immense popularity was soon proved by the fact that some of them quickly ran out of print and although a few were reprinted, most of them have been again out of print for quite a long time.

Most of the papers are as significant today as they were some twenty years ago when they first appeared. Many of them are still the only information available on their subject. This in itself warrants their new impression. But the sixteen Occasional Papers of the Rhodes-Livingstone Museum have today yet another significance. In their whole they are a valuable record of an era important for the development of research in Zambia. For this reason they are reprinted together in one volume. By bringing out this volume we not only want to provide anybody seriously interested in Zambian history and culture with an informative source book, but at the same time we want to present a record of scholarly achievements of our predecessors whose efforts have brought Zambia into a leading position in the field of social and historical research in Africa.

To diminish the cost of the publication the papers are reprinted in their original form and no attempt has been made to replace the old name of the country by its new one or to change the names of provinces and various place names to their present form.

Ladislav Holy
former Director of the Livingstone Museum

FOREWORD

Since its inception in the 1930s the Livingstone Museum has contributed to the advancement of knowledge in the fields of history, archaeology, ethnography and natural history in Zambia. The results arising from research work carried out by the staff and affiliates of the Museum have been published in the Robins Series as well as in other forms, the best known of these being the Occasional Papers. The latter include the works of great Africanists such as J. A. Barnes, A. M. Jones, V. W. Turner and E. Colson.

Some of the Occasional Papers were published over two decades ago, but in spite of this the demand for them continues to grow. Unfortunately, scholars have lately found it difficult to acquire some of the numbers, as they were all out of print. It is in order to satisfy the demand for these that the University of Zambia's Institute for African Studies has undertaken to republish all sixteen papers in this one comprehensive volume.

Kafungulwa Mubitana
Director, Livingstone Museum

I

THE MATERIAL CULTURE
OF THE FORT JAMESON NGONI

J. A. BARNES

1948

NGONI WARRIOR
(About 1898)

Drawn by Joan Green after a drawing
in H. H. Johnston's "British Central
Africa".

I

DURING THE 1820s, the rise to power of the Zulu chief Chaka in South Africa led to a number of migrations to the north led by lesser chiefs who wished to avoid a clash with the Zulu armies, or who had already clashed and had been defeated. The descendants of these migrants are to-day living scattered over East Africa, from Lake Victoria to near Lourenço Marques. Many of these still call themselves Ngoni, a term derived from Nguni, a word used to describe themselves while they were still in the south. The leader of one of these Ngoni migrations was Zwangendaba, and it is his descendants who are to be found in Northern Rhodesia and elsewhere at the present time. The only group in this country recognised as Ngoni by the Administration is to be found in Fort Jameson District, under Paramount Chief Mpezeni. Formerly a tribe living in Lundazi District under Chief Magodi was officially called Ngoni, but they are now known to the Administration as Tumbuka. They represent the western salient of the old empire of Mombera, a son of Zwangendaba, whose descendant is now a chief in Nyasaland. This article deals only with the people under Chief Mpezeni.

Zwangendaba led his people northwards, fighting and taking captives as he went, crossed the Zambezi in 1835, an event that happened to coincide with a solar eclipse, and after passing through the present-day Eastern Province, died near Lake Tanganyika in about 1845. His party then split up, one son, Mpezeni, leading his followers south-westwards towards the Bemba and the Wisa in the Northern Province. From there they moved southwards, crossed the Luangwa, and settled in Petauke District. In about 1865 they moved eastwards and settled to the north of the Mpangwe Hills in Fort Jameson District. Some ten years later they went further east, and in 1881, when they were first visited by a European, they had reached a point some fifteen miles south of Fort Jameson. It seems likely that another eastward move was being contemplated when in 1898 they clashed with troops from Nyasaland, and were defeated. Already the territory under the control of Mpezeni stretched across the Luangwa–Shire watershed, and with the establishment of British rule in the same year, that portion of Mpezeni's domain lying across the watershed became detached from the main portion which lay in Northern Rhodesia. The Nyasaland section of the empire is now controlled by two independent Ngoni chieftainships, both in the Fort Manning area of Lilongwe District. In this Territory, the present Paramount Chief is a great-grandson of the first Mpezeni.

Like all the Ngoni groups, Mpezeni's people are the result of much intermarriage between the southern migrants and the Central Bantu people with whom they fought. In particular, Mpezeni's Ngoni intermarried a great deal with the Nsenga of Petauke District, and it is the Nsenga language that is spoken to-day in Ngoni villages, rather than the old Ngoni language, akin to Zulu, which is used only in praises and songs. Cicewa is spoken in some villages which at the time of the arrival of the Europeans had been incorporated only a short time into the Ngoni state and had not had time to lose their own Chewa tongue.

The principal difference between the Ngoni and their surrounding neighbours is in their form of centralised chieftainship, inherited from father to son. Under the Paramount Chief are nine minor chiefs, positions created by the British South Africa Company's administration, and held by descendants in the male line of Zwangendaba and his important officials. Until about 1920 there were divisional headmen in charge of a number of villages, but these posts have now disappeared. In a village there is a headman, an hereditary position in the male line, and often one or two assistants, also hereditary offices, descended from captives of the original headman who had been promoted to responsible office.

In the old days one of the principal ways in which the diverse elements within the Ngoni state were unified was through the regimental system. Regiments were formed every so many years on a national basis to include all the adolescent males in the tribe, whatever their origin. Women were grouped into corresponding regiments. This system broke down after the first World War, when so many young men went away in the fighting. To-day the great exodus is not to war but to work, to the mines of Southern Rhodesia and elsewhere, and the incidence of labour migration is so high that it is not unknown to find a village in which there is no adult male resident. Part of the exodus is seasonal, and many men and women, as well as children, find employment on the tobacco farms of the district and in Fort Jameson Township.

II

THE STAPLE CROP is maize, of which enough is grown to provide in good years for a small surplus for sale to the tobacco farms and the Administration. Tobacco is not grown by Africans for sale, except within the villages, but vegetables and a little rice and finger millet are sold to Europeans. Cattle are kept in the fly-free areas, and play an important but diminishing part in social life as the means of paying bridewealth, but the sale of cattle is not at present a regular affair. Their principal use is as a form of capital investment that can be called up to meet damages and fines awarded by the Courts.

The population of the tribe is about 60,000, the majority living in the Ngoni and Msandile Reserves, both near to Fort

Jameson. The remainder live on the tobacco farms or in Fort Jameson Township. Villages vary in size from settlements of three or four huts to large clusters containing up to 500 people. The average size of a village is about thirty huts with a population of 100.

The Ngoni conquerors reckoned descent in the male line, while most of the people whom they conquered and with whom they married traced descent through the mother. To-day for practical purposes, descent is omnilateral, in that any connection through a male or female ancestor can be made use of as the occasion demands. Clan names, however, are inherited from the father in most Ngoni families. These names are used as surnames for the purposes of the Administration, and as forms of polite address. On marriage, a man and wife may live in either the village of the man or of the woman, although the custom whereby initially they should live in the village of the woman for a few years is still followed by some.

III

IN THE VILLAGE there are dwelling huts, storehouses, pens for the small animals, drying platforms, and cattle byres. The huts are often arranged in rather uneven parallel lines, with all the huts facing the same way. The fences found in other parts of the country enclosing a small courtyard round the hut, are not often seen here. Each married woman has her own hut, and possibly a smaller hut as well, used as a kitchen and sleeping place for visitors and children. Unmarried adolescents of one sex sleep together in modest huts they have built for themselves or else in a hut left empty by a former resident. Where bamboos are available, as in the north and east of the area, they are used to form the framework of a circular hut. The walls are made in two concentric circles, with mud plastered on the inside of the inner circle, but with the outer circle often left unmudded. The walls are made in unbroken circles, doorways being cut out later with an axe. The space between the two circles is used for storing pots and other household goods and is sometimes used for cooking. The bamboos are woven together, split bamboos going horizontally and unsplit ones vertically, so that light is able to pass through the unplastered wall. Open lattice fencing is also found forming part of the outer wall.

Where bamboos are not available, either circular or rectangular huts of poles and mud are made. Rectangular huts are often subdivided with a partition wall, to make a separate sleeping place, while the verandah may be partly walled in to make a cooking shelter protected from the weather. With both bamboo and pole huts, the construction of the walls and roof is the work of men, while women are responsible for plastering walls, floor and verandah, and for collecting the grass for the roof. Pole huts are more often than not plastered on the outside as well as on the inside of the wall, and women like to make designs on them in plasters of different colour, with inscriptions and drawings.

The favourite time for hut building is from June to September, when there is comparatively little work to do in the gardens. A man may undertake the major part of the work himself, but if his wife is co-operative and brews beer, he will also get his friends to come and help him, as a working party. Perhaps fifteen or twenty people will come, the men cutting and carrying poles and fixing them in place, the women bringing grass for thatching. If many people attend, then the walls will be put up, and the thatching started, but if the friends are few, then the beer will be finished while the roof of the house is still not thatched, and the owner will have to finish the work himself. In any case, he will need to offer at a later date, either more beer, or salt, or meat, or sometimes money, to women to come and plaster the walls and floor. Building may however be an operation spread over many months, and if the work is started late in the season, the rains may come before the roof is on. In this case, the building may be left until the following year, when there is again time to spare for building, and good supplies of thatching grass are available. Alternatively, the owner may become discouraged, and use the poles for firewood. A well-built pole hut will last five years and a bamboo hut longer.

Storehouses are built of bamboo or of thick grass, and are sometimes plastered. They have a detachable roof that acts as a lid, and the whole construction is built on a plastered platform about two feet off the ground. Separate storehouses are used for each household and for different crops, maize, finger millet, kaffir-corn and ground-nuts. If a man has two maize gardens, he may keep the produce in separate storehouses. Unmarried and newly-wed persons store with their parents. Storehouses last two or three years.

Byres for the cattle are placed on the edge of the village, with a separate division for calves at the side of the main byre. The robustness with which the byre is built depends on the extent to which there are marauding animals, particularly hyenas, leopards and lions in the vicinity. The usual method of construction is using poles some ten to twenty feet long, placed close together in a circle of about twenty to twenty-five feet in diameter. Thorn branches are placed on the outside of the fence, and the gate is a simple affair of several upright poles leaning in a slot made by two cross-poles. If an anthill is available, the byre will be made round it, so that the cattle may to some extent be able to clamber up out of the mud, which in the wet season may come up to their bellies. The building of a byre is undertaken by the men who will keep their cattle in it, and when a village moves to a new site, this is the first job to be tackled. Each owner of seven or eight head of cattle may have his own byre, but a man with many cattle may share a byre with his brothers. Owners of one or two head keep their cattle with their relatives.

Small domestic animals, such as pigs, goats, sheep and chickens, are kept in the village, near the hut of their owner, and their pens are provided with roofs and sometimes a fence as well, for protection against hyenas. Deserted dwelling huts, whose owners have gone away or have died, are used as shelters for calves and other animals.

Drying platforms are built to provide a stand for reed mats on which flour can be dried in the sun. If no platform has been built, the mats are placed on the ground where the flour is at the mercy of straying animals. Pigeon houses are built on platforms about six feet off the ground, with small holes to allow entry for the pigeons. Chicken houses are also sometimes built in this way, with a ladder to enable the chicken to ascend. The more prosperous villagers may have other buildings, such as latrines, washing shelters, or occasionally open-sided shelters for sitting in and gossiping.

IV

INSIDE THE HOUSE most of the household possessions are kept on the floor. At the back of the hut are the pots of the household, large ten-gallon beer brewing pots, smaller pots for holding the beer when brewed, bowls for drinking beer, wide mouthed pots for washing, small deep pots for cooking porridge and relish, waterpots, ornamented gourds for strong beer, and simple gourd cups for water. With them are also enamel saucepans, basins, mugs, and dishes, and sometimes a kettle. Only the very prosperous have glassware or china crockery.

Pottery is made by women only, and it is not a skill that every woman possesses. In a village there are usually one or two women who make pots, while a few women have a reputation for good pottery that attracts customers to them from a wider neighbourhood. Pots are usually sold for money, salt, or in return for bringing twice the amount of clay needed to make the article required. Petrol and paraffin tins as well as enamel and tinware are also used.

For pot making, clay is chosen from an anthill or marsh, and soaked for three days before being kneaded. The pot is made from a coil, and after smoothing it is ornamented. It is burnt for one day, and may be given a dull black colour by being rubbed with the leaves of the *mbwabwa* tree.

Hung on the walls of the hut or lying on the floor are the different baskets owned by the household. Baskets are made by men, and during the dry season when there is much road repair work to be done it is common to see three or four men spending their evenings after work on the road in making baskets. These baskets are often made to order, but the occasional hawker is seen. Large cuboid baskets are used for transporting mealies and grain, shallow baskets of two feet in diameter are used for winnowing flour, and small hemispherical baskets take the place of plates for

[7]

porridge. These latter are frequently made in pairs, tied together with a string of beads, so that the second basket acts as a lid for the first and keeps the porridge inside warm. For straining beer, a special wide mesh basket is used, either conical or hemispherical in shape. Round and rectangular baskets of various sizes, with flat lids, are also found and are used for carrying small quantities of food on a journey.

In former times, wooden plates were used, but these are now very rare. Wooden spoons are still made and used, and large flat porridge stirrers, with geometrical ornamentation, are common. Wooden hemispherical pats, with a handle, are used for smoothing cooked porridge.

At the back of the hut, or on the verandah outside, are the pestle and mortar used for reducing maize and other cereals to flour. Mortars range in height from one to four feet, the smaller mortars being used by children or for crushing ground-nuts. They are usually of about one foot in diameter, and are made from single blocks of wood, usually from *Afzilia quanzensis* or *Monotes* trees. The inside of the block is hollowed out to leave a receptacle for the maize that is nearly as deep as the mortar is high. The only decoration is a ridge of wood about an inch wide left encircling the base three or four inches from the ground. Pestles are undecorated cylinders of wood, made from *Terminalia sericea* or *Kigelia pinnata* trees. They may be as much as six feet long, and range in thickness from four inches down to the half-inch pestles used by young children playing at pounding.

The hard residue of maize that cannot be reduced to flour by pounding is ground between two stones, and these grinding stones are also kept in the hut. Not every woman has her own grindstones or her own pestle and mortar, and these objects are loaned and borrowed within the village.

Most huts contain some form of chair or stool, but these are sometimes very small indeed, standing only two inches off the ground. Petrol boxes are used to sit on, and deck chairs, known in the vernacular as " sleeping chairs," are common. Carpenters make a small folding chair that is fairly common. European up-right chairs, basket chairs and Morris chairs are sometimes seen, but these are not made locally.

Beds are owned in general by the younger generation only, and then at the rate of one per household. Otherwise, everyone sleeps on the floor on a reed mat. During the day, the mat is rolled up except when needed for drying flour in the sun. These mats are made from reeds that grow near streams. The reeds are split in four, and are threaded with a thin rope made from the inner bark of the *nzizi* tree. Wooden headrests are now a rarity, and if any headrest at all is used, it is a European pillow. Blankets, quilts and, less frequently, sheets, are bought from stores.

[8]

Boys of Simbani Village playing with a toy motor
car made of maize stalks, which is the usual material
used in toy making. Quite elaborate articles can be
made as in this illustration, where the wheels of the
car are free to rotate.

Women pounding maize under a tree in Feni Village.
A flat, winnowing basket is upturned on the ground
and flour is spread out to dry on a mat just visible
round the corner of the nearer hut. Note the dress
of the women, and the rectangular pole houses.

PLATE I   *Photographs by J. A. Barnes*

Funeral of a small child at Kapeza Village. The coffin has been taken out of the house and placed on a reed mat. An old mat has been used, as it will subsequently be placed in the grave with the coffin. The coffin itself is made of a cut-down reed mat, to which fresh bark ropes have been added as lacing to keep the coffin closed and for lowering it into the grave.

The almost universal use of shirts and shorts as clothing by the men can be seen. The man in the foreground on the right is wearing sandals. Such sandals are often made up from discarded outer covers of motor car tyres.

Closing the gate of the cattle byre at Simbani Village. The herdboy has climbed up on to the highest cross-member of the gate, and is inserting the vertical members, stacked against the side of the gateway, in between the two horizontal members. When the gate has been closed in this manner, additional horizontal pieces will be placed through the holes visible in the forked stake, which supports the pole on which the boy is standing. Thorn branches are visible on the outside of the fencing of the byre.

Note the depth of mud in the cattle byre, as indicated by the animals seen inside.

PLATE II

Photographs by J. A. Barnes.

Pounding and winnowing maize at Ziyaye Village. The maize grains are in the cuboid basket seen on the left of the picture, such baskets are called "citundu" (pl. "vitundu"). The grains are placed in the mortar and pounded with the pole held by the woman. The partially reduced grains are then winnowed by the old woman who uses the flat, winnowing basket, called "luŵango" (pl. "maluŵango") which she is seen holding.

She holds the basket at an angle of about thirty degrees from the horizontal, sloping down away from her, and with a tossing motion, separates the husks from the kernels which she puts into two other flat baskets.

In the background are seen rows of dwelling-huts. The little child is seated on a mortar laid on its side.

Storing finger millet, Mbenjele Village. The millet stalks, as they have been brought in from the garden, are seen in the basket on the left of the picture. They are put into a flat basket for pouring into the granary through the hole in the top. When the granary is full a small detachable roof of thatch, or perhaps an old, enamelware basin, will be placed over the hole. The platform construction of the storehouse can be clearly seen.

PLATE III

Photographs by J. A. Barnes.

Brewing beer in Ndawâmbi Village, by a chief's wife. Evidence of prosperity is seen in the ten-gallon drums and the tin bath. In the centre foreground is a calabash gourd beer cup, "cipanda" (pl. "vipanda"), and on the right are two winnowing baskets, and one cuboid basket.

To the right of the fire is a clay beer pot, and some enamelware plates and saucers can just be seen nearby. A gourd water-cup has been put on top of the beer pot, but the woman herself is using an enamelware saucepan as a ladle and stirrer.

Constructing a bamboo house in Amosi Village. The building is still a complete circle. The vertical poles give some idea of the height to which the walls will go. In the background are completed huts. The two poles seen in the right foreground will be used as part of the ring of poles round the outer wall supporting the roof. The woven bamboos will be hammered down to make as tight a weave as possible.

PLATE IV

Photographs by J. A. Barnes.

V

THE CHIEF TOOL for use in the garden is the hoe. Ruins of furnaces for smelting iron ore are still to be seen, but are not now used and are said to have been worked in the old days only by Chewa slaves. Hoe blades are bought in the stores, and hafted with a handle made in the village. Handle making is a man's job, but one that every man knows how to do. Axes are made from blades bought in the store, or else from a worn down hoe blade, with a home-made handle. Adzes are used for mortar making, and young boys make miniature adzes as toys. A pointed blade hafted on to the end of a straight handle is used for making holes in the ground when building.

Sledges and, less commonly, unarticulated carts with solid wheels are made for transporting the harvest from the fields to the village, and for collecting firewood. These are pulled by cattle, not always oxen, using simple yokes made of wood and sinew, with a wooden drawbar.

Hunting is carried on in the dry season, particularly towards the end, when the grass burns easily. Guns of varying degrees of antiquity are used, but none of these are made by Ngoni, although the Chewa still make guns. On a hunt, the rank and file are armed with throwing spears and knobkerries. The gun carriers walk about two hundred yards in front of the main body, who are spread on a single line at right angles to the line of advance. The leader of the hunt walks in the middle of the line, with a responsible person posted on each flank. A started animal, if not shot by the guns, usually turns to run parallel to the line of hunters, who hurl spears and knobkerries at it, and send their dogs after it. The chances of escape for a hunted animal are fairly high. Animals are also trapped, usually with a piece of meat tied to the muzzle of a gun. Hunting with nets is sometimes undertaken in the wet season. Rats are caught in small conical traps baited with beans. The rat chews through a piece of string and releases a green stick, thereby strangling itself.

Shields, once the pride of the Ngoni armies, are not carried on hunts and are infrequently seen.

VI

IT IS only the old men who still wear skin garments, and then only as additions to European style clothing. Men are dressed in khaki shorts and shirts, long trousers, cast-off European clothing, or clothes brought back from the army. Often two shirts are worn on top of one another. Women wear a blouse, a skirt tied on a tape, a cloth wrapped round on top of the skirt, and a small cloth tied round their waist. If carrying a baby, the cloth supporting the child is slung over the left and under the right shoulder, and another cloth may be wrapped round the woman and child under her armpits. Dresses are also worn, and sometimes a singlet under the blouse. Shoes are less common for women than for men. Men wear a variety of European style hats, but women wear only embroidered cloths or berets, or in the case of poorer women, plain bands of cloth.

Children go naked, or may be draped in whatever garment, of whatever size, happens to be available. If the money is there to pay for them, boys are dressed in shorts and shirts, and girls in little dresses.

In the old days, every adult had slit ears, but this custom has died out. Women nowadays pierce their ears if they wish, and it is sometimes difficult to distinguish between a small slit made as a tribal mark and a hole made for individual ornamentation. Earrings, beads, and other ear ornaments are worn, including safety pins. Young girls from time to time make black rectangular marks on their cheeks by pressing on to them strips of *nkholosa* grass. These marks are quite black at first, and gradually lose their colour over a period of a year. Scarification of the face and body is carried out on both men and women for ornament as well as for medication, but there is very little regularity of pattern, save for the inverted crescent mark made between the eyebrows of women. This is the Nsenga tribal mark.

For dancing, most people wear their best clothes, and girls and young women carry whistles on lanyards round their necks. When dancing *ngoma*, the most important tribal dance, miniature shields are carried, and a special type of knobbed stick that is held aloft. Less frequently seen are the wrist and ankle trappings, and skin garments that used to be associated with this and other regimental dances. Nowadays, women's skirts and frocks are sometimes seen worn by men on such occasions.

Single-ended and double-ended drums are used as accompaniments to dancing, while boys play hand pianos. Girls play on a single string fiddle made from a reed. Whistles are bought from the stores. Old fashioned fiddles with gourd resonators are rare.

Boys spend much of their time making and playing with toys of various kinds. Animals, men, and motor cars are fashioned out of mud, while more elaborate motor cars are made from mealie stalks. A favourite toy consists of two wheels, up to six inches in diameter, on an axle with a handle some four or five feet long, terminated in another wheel of the same size. This construction, made of straw, representing the elements of a motor car, is pushed along by boys of ages four to ten.

The well-known game, involving four rows of twelve holes, with three stones in each hole, is played by men, usually in holes scooped out in the ground. A favourite game of girls and boys consists of throwing up beans with one hand and catching them again after moving other beans out of a hole. A boys' game played in the wet season is played with egg-shaped pieces of mud, with a small flange at one end. These pieces are thrown down on to the water, and ought to make an explosive noise.

VII

MAIZE, the main crop, is planted with the first steady rains in November, and is harvested soon after the end of the rains in April or May. Under the influence of the Agricultural Department of the Government, planting in small ridges following the contour is increasingly practised, but prior to the introduction of this and other new agricultural methods in the 1930s, planting was carried out in mounds about three feet in diameter and eighteen inches high. Finger millet is grown on patches of soil on which branches and garden trash have been burnt. However, the *citemene* system, as known in other parts of the country, in which trees are felled over a wide area and burnt to fertilise a small area in the middle, is not practised as a principal method here. Finger millet is the only crop to be planted solely in ash fertilised patches, while the rest of the cleared ground may be planted with beans and nuts, and in the following season, with maize. Gardens last from two up to twenty or more years, depending on the type of soil, and the selection of a garden site is determined to some extent by the nature of the soil and of the vegetation growing on it.

In seepage areas, dry season gardens can be cultivated, and it is in such gardens, fenced in to keep out straying animals, that vegetables are grown for sale to Europeans and in the villages. These sites are also used for early planted maize, which is harvested in January and eaten in the form of green mealies. In the villages themselves, small plots of tobacco and castor oil are grown on old hut sites, while abandoned village sites are used as subsidiary gardens for maize and other crops. Mango, banana, and pawpaw trees are found in villages and on the sites of abandoned villages.

The busiest time of the year in the garden is at the beginning of the rains, when there is much work to be done planting and weeding, and scaring away the monkeys and wild pigs. Later on, in the new year, after the garden has been weeded twice, it is possible to think of enlarging the garden at one edge, and if it is not too late, the newly cleared portion may be planted with a catch crop. Weeding and clearing new ground are both activities that are carried out to some extent co-operatively, either on a mutual help basis between two women, or more frequently in return for beer provided by the owner of the garden. On the day before the party, a few men and women come to the garden and do their share of the work in advance, in the belief that it is better not to have to work and drink on the same day. The next day, the bulk of the party arrive at the garden, and the wife of the owner brings out a pot of beer from the village. When the first half of the garden has been finished, there is a pause, and the beer is drunk. On completion of the whole garden, the party returns to the village and drinking begins in earnest. It is not necessary to have worked in the garden to be able to attend the subsequent drinking, and the well-mannered host will specifically set aside certain pots of beer for those who have not been to the garden.

Towards the end of the rains, there is less cultivating to be done, but the ravages of wild animals become more serious, and many families sleep for two or three months in the garden, returning to the village only to obtain food. Garden shelters are simple open-sided affairs with a thatched roof, but those owners who intend to sleep in their gardens for a long time, build small circular huts as in the village, or conical shelters with the roof reaching to the ground. A few lookout platforms built in trees are used as vantage points for spotting wild animals. If a man has a garden a long way from the village, particularly across a stream which will be in spate in the late rains, he may build a byre for his cattle at the garden.

Maize and ground-nuts are the first crops to be harvested, and later finger millet, root crops, and finally kaffir-corn. Maize is stooked before the cobs are removed, and these are then dried on platforms before being carried to the village to be stored.

The maize is shelled as required, the grains are pounded in a mortar, and then soaked in water for three or four days, if there is time. They are then pounded again, and the flour winnowed out. The residue is ground between two stones. The husks obtained after the first pounding are used as animal fodder, and in beer making. The diligent housewife pounds twice a week, each pounding lasting for about three hours. It is usual for a group of women living as neighbours to pound at the same time, singing together.

The maize flour is dried in the sun, and then put into a pot or basket until required for porridge or beer. Porridge forms the basis of most meals, although in February and March there may not be enough maize left in the storehouses to make this possible. Adults eat porridge in solid form, kneading handfuls of it between their fingers before eating, but infants are fed on fluid porridge made from the ground flour. The herdboys in charge of the cattle may use the milk to make their porridge with. Cooking is women's work, but men by themselves on a journey or working on the tobacco farms will cook porridge for themselves. Green mealies, usually fried, are eaten when available.

Relish is required to go with the porridge, the commonest relishes being pumpkin leaves and hibiscus leaves. There are in addition many wild fruits and leaves searched for in the bush at their appropriate seasons, while the gardens provide pumpkins, cucumbers, various kinds of beans and peas, and edible gourds. The most sought-after relish, and one of the most infrequently found, is meat. Chickens are given to honoured visitors, while beef, mutton, pork, and goat meat are eaten when they can be found. Livestock other than chickens are killed for eating only on cere-monial occasions, such as funerals or marriages, but owners not infrequently kill animals and sell the meat to raise money to pay damages, to finance a journey, or to obtain labour in the garden. Animals that die are usually eaten. Some people keep ducks, pigeons and tame guinea fowl, while such game as is killed on the hunt is divided among the hunters and taken home to be eaten. Owners of guns sometimes hunt by themselves and sell the meat.

Beer drinking is one of the most important social occupations, and a considerable proportion of maize is consumed in this way. Brewing takes six days to complete, but two weeks more are required to prepare the sprouted maize that is an essential ingredient. Once brewed, the beer remains drinkable for two or three days, but the partially brewed beer, of smaller alcoholic content, is also drunk. Beer is brewed for many reasons, for working parties in the garden or housebuilding, for selling at threepence a bowl, or as often as not, just for drinking. Finger millet is used in beer making, and if available, the whole maize flour from a grinding machine, as well as the white maize flour of the village. The beer is brewed in large ten-gallon pots, then poured into smaller four-gallon pots that can be carried about, and from these ladled with a gourd into bowls or ornamental gourd cups. Four-gallon petrol tins are sometimes used instead of pots, and large enamelware mugs instead of bowls. Very rarely, beer is drunk from glasses.

VIII

CATTLE are in the care of herdboys, whose ages range from eight to fourteen. They take the cattle out of the byres in the morning and go off with them to look for pasture. The cattle come back in the early afternoon, when the calves suck, and go off again until about five o'clock in the evening, when they are put back in the byre for the night. The calves are looked after by smaller children, and do not usually go so far away from the village as do the fully grown cattle. In the dry season, after the harvest, when there is no danger of spoiling crops, the cattle wander about very much by themselves, and the boys play or do odd jobs in the village. In these days of village schools, suitable boys are not always free to look after cattle, and in this case girls will do the herding.

Little use is made of the milk except occasionally for use in porridge, and for sale to Europeans. The European market also provides the only use for eggs.

Other specialised activities carried out in the village, apart from those mentioned, are such things as shoe mending, bicycle repairing, and carpentry. These trades are followed by men who learnt them in Southern Rhodesia and elsewhere, and are carried on as part-time occupations. Village stores are modest affairs, with goods for sale that have been bought retail from Indian traders in Fort Jameson, and have been brought out to the village on bicycle. Larger stores on the main roads may be able to buy wholesale, and may employ a tailor making up cloth bought in the store. Shops called in the vernacular " hotels," where tea and scones are sold and perhaps bread, also lie on the main roads.

[17]

After fifty years of European contact, the main changes in the material culture of these people are to be found in clothing, and to a lesser extent in the use of European kitchen utensils. Housing, feeding, and animal husbandry remain much the same as they were before " the Europeans came to worry us." With the increasing attention being paid by the Government towards the development of permanent village sites and the prevention of overstocking, and the growing European interest in African diet, changes in these aspects of their way of life may be expected in the future.

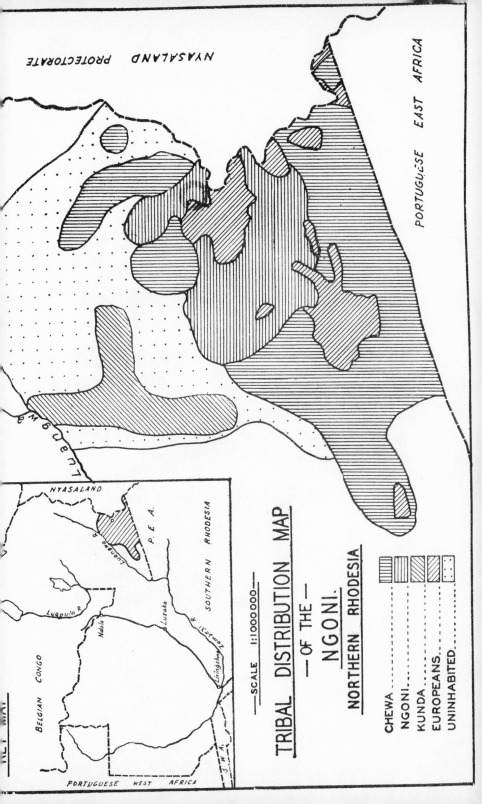

NYASALAND PROTECTORATE

PORTUGUESE EAST AFRICA

Luangwa

TRIBAL DISTRIBUTION MAP
— OF THE —
NGONI.
NORTHERN RHODESIA

— SCALE 1:1000000 —

CHEWA.
NGONI.
KUNDA.
EUROPEANS.
UNINHABITED.

NYASALAND

P.E.A.

SOUTHERN RHODESIA

BELGIAN CONGO

Luapula R.

Luangwa R.

Ndola

Lusaka

Zambesi R.

Livingstone

S.W.A.

PORTUGUESE WEST AFRICA

Photo.—Home News Unit.

Ngoni War Dance.

2

AFRICAN DANCES
OF NORTHERN RHODESIA

W. V. BRELSFORD

1948

INTRODUCTION

It was Havelock Ellis who remarked that to dance was to take part in the cosmic control of the world. The phrase forms a striking reminder that dancing, at least certain forms of dancing, does transport the dancer into an emotional and mental state different from that of his ordinary working life. Modern European ballroom dancing has become a social function and secondarily an " educated form of sex expression ", but in such forms as the ballet, in thematic and in many national dances we see glimpses of prototype dances displaying movements and revealing emotions still indicating that dancing can be life itself but on another plane. The phrase is a metaphysical description of what still happens in many African dances. The self can be lost and the urges of the subconscious acted in ecstatic movements ; consciousness may go and the mind await spiritual possession from another world ; unseen powers are propitiated ; and concord and harmony instilled in the community—all through the dance. In more explicit terms it means that the social and individual life of an African is marked by dances of significance. In the wide social sphere there are dances of birth, initiation, marriage and love, war and secret societies, as well as of pure pleasure and for exhibition. In a sphere we could call that of magic and religion there are dances of worship, to ancestors, the deities and spirits, dances to ensure food, rain and good hunting, dances to exorcise the spirits of sickness and to ensure the safe passage of the dead to the next world. Many Northern Rhodesian dances such as the Ila lion dance have become spectacles. Others, such as the *Kapoya*, have been forbidden because of their erotic content. But the dance as a communicable ecstasy still goes on. In the Eastern Province Nsenga and Chewa girls are " danced into womanhood ",* and in the Northern Province the Bemba still dance the suggestive *Kapombo*, so named after a woman who loved dancing so much she danced until she fell down dead. The dance is still an integral part of African life and accompanies all its functions.

There are several ways in which dances can be classified so as to present an ordered description or discussion. For example they could be classified by subject content such as dances of war or fertility ; or movements such as leaps, lunges and strides could be the basis ; or the types of music could form categories ; or the form of the dance such as single, pair, round or choral dances would give yet another division. But whatever category is used there would

---

* Hambly, W. D.—Phrase used in *Tribal Dancing and Development*.

[22]

be an inevitable overlapping. For example, the *Malaila*, now a dance of triumph, common to many Northern Rhodesian tribes, in addition to being a dance of triumph could be classed also as a leap dance, a choral dance, a weapon dance, a dance in harmony with the body, an image dance, a male only dance, and in several other terms of classificatory distinctions.

In this short paper I propose to treat mainly of subject content which is simple and obvious, but at the same time I want to try and systematise Northern Rhodesian dances by fitting them into wider scientific categories that will need short descriptions. For this purpose detailed descriptions of dances are not necessary. Brief descriptions of many can be found in the books and papers written on Northern Rhodesia. I shall not repeat them but only describe others here that are not on record. This paper will then attempt to gather together a good many Northern Rhodesian dances into simple technical categories that can form a frame of reference. At the same time I shall indicate what seem to be defined geographical or ethnographical divisions in types of dances.

Curt Sachs, whose categories I follow here, divides the dance into two wide sections.* One comprises the " dance in harmony with the body " and the other is the " dance out of harmony with the body ". In both types exhilaration and ecstasy are the result, but in the inharmonious dances such as the convulsive dance they are achieved by mortification of the flesh, whereas the harmonious dances reveal a delight in motor expression that communicates itself to the spectators too. The harmonious dance is again subdivided into " expanded " and " close " dances. Type forms of the expanded dance are leaps, lifts, slaps, strides, skips, lunges and several other movement varieties. These are almost all masculine dances. The " close " dance is a more suppressed feminine dance and often the body remains in one spot with only parts of it moving. The pelvis is rolled, the buttocks are wriggled, the belly is twitched and the breasts swung.

The inharmonious dance is also subdivided into " pure " convulsive dances in which all control is lost of the limbs, which jerk and twitch until the dancer gets into a state of extreme nervous excitement accompanied by wild paroxysms. The "weakened" convulsive dance involves the same movements, but the limbs are always under control, and this dance does not end, as does often the " pure " one, in unconsciousness. The former is a typical secret society dance, whilst the latter is often characteristic of the travelling exhibition dancer who stands for long periods twitching his buttocks and ceaselessly shaking his rattles and rustling his skirts.

All types of dancing can be fitted into these two main divisions, each with its two subdivisions. I shall indicate, in mentioning our Northern Rhodesian dances, to which of these main classes the

---

* Curt Sachs.—*World History of the Dance.*

Photo.—Audrey I. Richards

Bemba Elders dancing Lisonga at a funeral.

Mr. C. M. N. White informs me that the normal pleasure dance of the Lunda, Lovale, Chokwe and Luchazi is the *Kachacha*, a dance of Lovale origin. He says (*in litt.*): " According to the mood of the dancers it may become erotic. It may be danced by men and women or by men only, either round the drums or as a ' front ' dance. It is essentially a social function in which all participate, some for a short time and others for the whole session according to their feelings. The dance alternates movements with posturings, and really the latter provide the essence of the *Kachacha*. They consist in a display of ability to roll the pelvis and hips. This is in fact purely erotic. All the Lovale, Chokwe and Luchazi and to a large extent Lunda indulge in elaborate rollings and wrigglings of this type during intercourse, which are taught to girls at the puberty ceremony and to boys at circumcision if they do not already know them. These rollings have a technical term, *Mutenya*, which is not used much in public except among men who are friends, comparing notes, as it is regarded as obscene, but under the expression *Wino* (skill in dancing) and *Kukina* or *Kubangana* (to dance) they may be discussed quite openly. *Wino* and these two verbs are of course quite general terms for dancing, but their use in connection with the sexual wrigglings and rollings serve to emphasise the close connection between the sexual act and the gestures performed at the *Kachacha*. The latter, as it develops, tends to become a series of solos in which individuals perform their rolls, gradually sinking till sitting on their heels as they do so."

These round and front dances easily develop into couple dances in which all the pairs hold each other and dance together or in which one couple only perform a *pas de deux*. In the *Chikweta*, which the Bemba are said to have learned from the Inamwanga and Iwa, there is the usual row of men facing a row of women. A woman dances towards her opposite number, leads him to the centre and the two dance for a few minutes holding each other by the hips. At a subtle change in the tempo of the drums they part and another woman goes forward to fetch a man. In another Bemba variation, *Muchinko*, learned from the Mukulu, a man dances up to the line of women and leads the whole line to the men. They dance together, then the women go back and another man goes to lead them forward. There are many variations of this type of dance. The *Mangwanya*, said to have been introduced throughout areas in the Northern Province by the Bulungwana (early Swahili slave traders), the men and women periodically and suddenly turn their backs on each other as they dance with bodies close together.

Variations in these round or frontal pleasure dances differ from tribe to tribe. In a common round dance known as *Biliwili* or *Chidika* among the Nsenga, for example, men and women place themselves alternately in the circle. Also there are often sexual differentiations in pleasure dances, but such dances by men alone, as opposed to functional dances such as those of war, are rarer than pure pleasure dances by women alone. The *Yalaula* of the Nsenga is a front dance for young girls only although two boys beat drums. The *Njole* of the Chikunda is also a front pleasure dance for girls alone, but in this case no drums are used, the girls clapping their hands.

The Ngoni have a front pleasure dance known as the *Kandenga* in which the men carry knob-kerries.* In turn a woman dances across to a man, takes his knob-kerry and the man, behind the woman, dances back with her to her place. They return to the centre and dance, the man, behind the woman, with one hand on her shoulder. She then turns and hands him back the club. The *Ngololombe*, circle dance of the Chikunda, is one of the most vigorous of the pleasure dances. The circle comprises alternate men and women. The right hand of the man rests on the shoulders of the woman, his left hand holding reed pan-pipes which he plays with his lips. In addition, balanced by his hold on the woman's shoulder, the man stamps his feet vigorously to mark the time.

Some writers emphasise that the main function of the dance is as a form of play or social ceremonial. Brown† stresses the point that dancing is an activity in which all members of the community can indulge. The effects of the rhythm are to induce a form of self-surrender to the mood of the crowd, to increase personal energy and excitement and to increase the æsthetic sense and to improve the senses of balance and direction. As a social or collective activity the dance stimulates the self-regarding sentiment by its opportunity for exhibition ; it strengthens the sense of social unity in that a dance produces the feeling of good fellowship ; and finally it directs the consciousness of personal value, indicated by ability or personal adornment, into a socially enjoyable activity. Those are sociological and psychological definitions that are far from complete. Some dances excite and culminate in sex : others " sublimate " the sexual instinct—in fact, many dances, especially in European civilisation, are an acknowledgment that physical attraction exists and provides a decorous outlet for it.

The pleasure dances have these characteristics and some of them are displayed in the numerous other types, some of which have traits that overlap to a considerable extent with the pure pleasure dance. Sachs's categories are convenient but not clear cut and, as will be gathered from later descriptions, one dance may embrace many forms.

There is also the point that many dances of the generalised or pleasure type fit into many social occasions. The *Kachacha* may

---

* Rattray, R. S.—*Some Folk Lore Stories and Songs in Chinyanja.* (Published by S.P.C.K.)

† Brown, A. R.—*The Andaman Islanders.*

be danced at a funeral or a wedding or after a witch-finding seance.* The *Ngolombe* is also a general utility dance performed at funerals, weddings or just for pleasure. It might be possible to form yet another category of generalised and specialised dances.

Still another division might distinguish between adult and juvenile dances. The front dance, *Akapole*, of the Luapula valley and the round dance, *Siyaya*, of the Luangwa valley are examples of pleasure dances in which only juveniles normally take part. Thus in order to classify a dance fully some extensive tabulation would be necessary. The terms used in this paper are by no means inclusive.

The Fertility and Erotic Dances.

Such dances still form the most important types in native life. And the fact that sexual acts are often the aftermath of even non-erotic ritual dances supports a vague belief in the minds of some observers that all native dances in which both male and female take part are at least erotic in origin. Some writers with no particular African interest assert that all dancing is sexual in origin. Christian Darnton says† : " Dances originally were directly representational. And since the things they represented were mainly concerned with fertility rites and such-like they were what we nowadays would call lascivious in character. It was only later that they achieved a degree of formalisation and stylisation. Nevertheless the fact remains that a basis of sexual symbolism is shown more or less clearly in every existing dance : must be so, in the nature of things."

So we find eroticism in African agricultural fertility dances. Among the Chewa there used to be separate fertility dances for men and women, in which the men had intercourse with holes in the ground lined with a soft wood and in which a mistress of ceremonies used a wooden penis on the women.

I have watched Sala women perform a dance during which they squirt milk at each other from their breasts. And the *Kanjona* dance of the Eastern Province in which old men dance with young girls and old women with young men also has this emotional substratum indicative of fertility. (Other dances such as the *Ngondo* rainmaking dance of the Inamwanga involved human sacrifice. The accompaniment to this dance was the squeaking made by rubbing a pot, containing seed mixed with human blood, round a native stool. This was inside the chief's hut and the dancers shuffled around outside the hut. Occasionally one of them was seized and strangled to add to the sacrifice.)

---

* White, C. M. N.—*Witchcraft, Divination and Magic.* (Government Printer, Lusaka.)

† Christian Darnton.—*You and Music.* (A Pelican Book.)

[29]

As regards movement and form the erotic dances are mainly in harmony with the body and of the "expanded" type. There is some overlapping as there are "closed" erotic dances in which the woman dance in one spot wriggling buttocks and breasts with the obvious purpose of stimulating sexual excitement in the onlookers. Some of the dances embody the sexual act itself, but I doubt whether the mere fact that the dancers periodically stand or lie in one place for some minutes is sufficient to take the dance out of the "expanded" type and put it into a "closed" one.

I should mention some of the dances in which the sexual act takes place. (These dances are forbidden now.)

There was the *Kafwenka* of the Luangwa valley peoples. Mr. Lane Poole informs me that this was part of the marriage ceremony among the Senga when a girl passed straight out of puberty into marriage. At the end of the *ukwate* or wedding dance the betrothed couple sometimes insinuated themselves under a blanket where consummation took place. This custom, in Mr. Lane Poole's day (prior to 1934), was said to have been introduced from alien tribes. Later, what was once a portion of a marriage rite degenerated into a part of an obscene dance. In the Feira District this dance was known as the *Kashimbo* (not to be confused with the Kaonde dance of the same name). Intercourse took place under a blanket in the centre of the circle, by couples who broke away in turn from the circle of dancers.

The *Butwa* was a secret society based on the Bangweulu-Luapula area.* Its initiates performed all the natural functions in public in front of each other, learned a special dialect and performed sexual intercourse in public without regard to the restrictions of incest or totem. Erotic dances were performed in the open but the main one took place inside a hut. To the sound of a drum the members danced around the confined place or else sat and swayed in tune. When the drum stopped all performed intercourse with whoever happened to be nearest. Then the drum began again, the dance went on until the drum stopped and intercourse again took place. This went on until all the members were exhausted. Beer was not apparently partaken during the dance, although I have been informed that a drug was used to promote and prolong an hysterical state. A strange story is that at some time during the dance the leader of the ceremony used to produce a new born baby out of his legs.

The *Shonongo*, the dance performed by certain sects of the Watch Tower, can best be fully described in the section on new dances. It is a round dance during which the women bend forward and the men effect intercourse with them *a tergo*.

---

* Some information given by Dugald Campbell.—*A Few Notes a Butwa. An African Secret Society.* Man 38, 1914. Also in his book *In the Heart of Bantuland.*

The margin between an erotic dance and actual intercourse is often very narrow and there is little wonder that the act often follows the dance. The same could be said of many native dances as Praetorius said of the seventeenth century Pavan—it is often "an invention of the devil, full of shameful and obscene gestures and immodest movements".

In the Bemba dance, *Muembo*, the action of the dance is symbolic rather than suggestive. It is a front dance and the men in turn approach their opposite number as the line of women shuffle and clap hands. The man puts his hands on the shoulders of the woman and leaps into the air singing—"*Wise chungulo*" ("Come to me to-night"). The women usually do go to the partner after the dance.

The dances range gradually from this symbolic leap to a greater intimacy. The Bisa dance, *Kutupa*, is one of many in which pairs in turn dance in the centre of a round and in which the woman rubs her breasts in turn against the man. Many of the Lamba dances such as the *Muchinko* involved the man catching the woman's breasts during the dance.

The next step is illustrated by the Bemba dance, *Chiropolopo*. This is a round dance, the women on the inside moving in the same direction as the men on the outside. At a change in the tempo of the drums all face inwards, the men stamping and shuffling but the women bending forward and wriggling hips and breasts. Then the women turn to the men, gradually approach them and rub their breasts, first one and then the other, against the man. Both sexes bend their knees in a half-squat as this is being done. As the women turn away to resume the round they kick back at their own buttocks. It is this action that gives the dance its name.

Still greater intimacy is seen in the *Kapoya*, a dance that is common to most of the tribes of the Northern Province. It is a round dance, similar in form to the *Chiropolopo*, but as the drumming changes, the women face inwards, then outwards, to the men without bending. The men clasp the women with both hands round the waist and put one leg between the women's legs. As excitement grows the woman too clasps the man. The couple then wriggle and go through sexual motions, and just before the tempo changes again they gradually bend the knees with a half-squat. The *Shombe* is a similar dance of the Western Province.

The *Kapoya* or *Shombe* is thus a simple, crude dance. Some of the men blow whistles to keep time whilst the women clap, and the intimacy of the clasps increases as the dance goes on. It is even danced in daylight now by schoolchildren, and there have been many complaints by teachers that whole classes are lured away by it. A few chiefs have tried to stop it but it merely grows in popularity. The versions I have witnessed were danced as described, but there is little doubt that sexual intercourse is a frequent result of the unrestrained versions.

[31]

Photo.—Max Gluckman.

Likishi Dancer.—" Kalelwa."

The final stages, before dances in which the sexual act itself is performed as part of the dance itself, are seen in such Luapula valley (and wider areas) dances as the *Mukondo*. This is a circular dance, women inside facing inwards. At a change in tempo of the whistle accompaniment the men clasp the women's loins and genitals and legs are intercrossed.

The last phase of all, actual intercourse during the dance, is instanced by the *Ingwai*, also a dance of the Luapula area. It is also a round dance. The couples face each other and, at one phase of the dance, kick at each others' genitals. In the Ushi area of Fort Rosebery the dance is said to be performed by naked couples with a blanket around them. Intercourse normally takes place after such an exciting dance and often occurs, standing, during the dance. Other such dances are described in the section on modern dances.

Funeral Dances.

These dances have a wide range of form from simple movements expressing grief to some of the most elaborate dances known in Northern Rhodesia. At the one end of the scale there is the dance of the Kaonde in which women merely dance up and down the village, crying and sweeping the ground with small branches. At the other end is the lavish *Nyau* dance of the Chewa and other Eastern Province tribes with its dozens of animal masks and figures. Detailed descriptions of the *Nyau* dance can be found elsewhere.* It is a mimetic or image animal dance with its object as the placation of the spirits of the ancestors. Originally danced only by members of the *Nyau* secret society, its members dancing nude except for elaborate animal masks, it was performed at funerals of chiefs, important personages and members of the society and its members were feared because of their connection with the spirit world. It was the culmination of a long ritual. Now it has almost degenerated into a spectacle. Some of the secret society jargon remains and the animal structures are as elaborate as ever. But nowadays boys are admitted to it, and it is even danced at the puberty rites of girls. The presence of women, who sometimes dance naked among the animal dancers, and the introduction of beer has led to licentiousness, and the missionaries are attempting to have it forbidden. Formerly sexual abstinence was enjoined on members during the period of the dance. Bands of *Nyau* now wander round villages performing the mimetic dances but at the same time they terrify people and rob and steal.

During the war the *Nyau* was a very popular dance among the askari as it does make a good spectacle, but even when it was performed in Lusaka by the 2/6th Northern Rhodesia Regiment it still retained some of its mystery. Mr. Martin Morris, now

---

* Mr. W. H. J. Rangeley, a District Officer in Nyasaland, has written a very detailed description which is to be published. I have also consulted a paper written by Mr. H. N. Parry, a District Officer in Northern Rhodesia.

Assistant Director of Information, tells me that on this occasion a military policeman was unfortunate enough to come across the mask makers in the bush close to the camp. He was severely beaten and tied to a tree, where he languished for forty-eight hours before being found. At the performance no torches were allowed, the light of the moon being the only illumination. Modern models included the Colonel's train and a steamship on Lake Nyasa which rocked realistically. After this performance the Rhodes-Livingstone Museum tried to buy the costumes and masks. But the purchase involved loading at night into a dark railway truck by *Nyau* themselves and similar unloading at Livingstone, an awkward proceeding, so finally an offer of £15 was rejected and the costumes were secretly burned by *Nyau*. The strength of the tradition is still obvious and, as Mr. Rangeley's paper indicates, there is still a wealth of symbolism and myth embodied in it.

At the beginning of this paper I referred to the *Malaila* as a dance of triumph. Mr. Lane Poole reminds me that in the Eastern Province it was originally a dance round the body of a person slain in war. Nowadays throughout both Eastern and Northern Provinces it is invariably danced round the corpse of a lion or leopard when killed or trapped. The main feature of the dance involves the stabbing or beating with sticks of the corpse and insulting it with abusive language. There is to-day more of joy or triumph over an enemy than of sorrow at the loss of a warrior in the dance, but its name, derived from *Kulaila*—to take leave of or say goodbye—indicates its former classification as a funeral dance. It is an example, of which others can be found in this paper, of the form of a dance being retained although the inspiration has gone. In the old *Malaila* there was praise not abuse, and the spears and sticks were used to underline the prowess of the deceased.

Religious Dances.

It is possible to regard many types, for example funeral dances, as religious dances, but I have met one, the *Zikili* of the Swahili of the Ndola District, that can be classed as a purely religious dance. It is a round dance with men in one circle and women in another. In the centre is a flag bearer with a Mohammedan flag which is usually a product of Zanzibar. All the dancers face inwards to the flag and they stamp feet, bending and raising the body, singing " *laila il Allah* " and raising one hand to the forehead at the name of Allah. It is often danced outside the place of worship after a service and is danced in Ndola Township at the end of Ramadan.

Mr. Fox (District Officer) informs me that the *Zikili* is also danced in the Swahili Reserve in the Mporokoso District. It thus seems to be a relic of culture that is slowly being absorbed. Pure Swahili blood is now almost non-existent : the language is being

Ila Lion Dance.

corrupted and strangled but the religion still exists (but does not thrive) in Northern Rhodesia.

War Dances.

In spite of the fact that the war dance is probably the most spectacular of all dances there is little descriptive matter about such dances in Northern Rhodesia. With the cessation of warfare the war dance is one of the few native dances that has lost its inspiration. The Ngoni war dance, during which spears are clashed on cow-hide shields, is now danced on special gatherings at the Paramount's village * ; the Ila war dance is now a spectacle of a mimic battle ; the *Kutomboka* of the Lovale, consisting of solos by armed males who leap, lunge and gesticulate with rolling eyes, was once a war dance but is now performed before a chief on his accession.

Mr. Lane Poole informs me that one typical Ngoni war dance, the *Ngoma* (the name of the large ox-hide drum used), formerly performed on the return of the warriors from a raid or battle, has now degenerated into a sort of " harvest home " dance. It has been taken up by adjoining tribes, such as the Tumbuka, and groups from different villages visit each other when the harvest is in and beer is flowing freely. As performed now it is a front dance with the sexes drawn up in two ranks, women in front and men behind, and the ranks advance and retreat in the same order.

The Ila war dance, which was a mimic battle with most realistic charges, thrusting and hurling of spears and feigning of wounds and death, is still danced. But it is a spectacle now rather than a training. At Christmas time on the Copperbelt bands of young Ila dressed in a rather faded glory of skins, feathers and white war paint dance a poor commercialised version of it for money from house to house.

Research is needed to distinguish between war dances with and without weapons, to classify movements and to trace the functions that the war dance now fulfils. It is possible that this dance, above all others, is becoming a tribal symbol, the typical dance of important tribal occasions such as the death or succession of chiefs. We lack information on these points. (*See* section on hunting dances for note on the part played by females in war and hunting dances.) The handling of weapons is not restricted to war dances. I have mentioned the Ngoni *Kandenga* in which a knob-kerry is employed. Rattray† also mentions the Ngoni marriage dance, *Msindo*, in which the bride dances with a spear in her hand in front of men. It may be significant that both dances are of a warrior tribe.

---

* Mead, M.—*Tradition and Prestige Among the Ngoni*. Africa, October, 1946.

† Rattray, R. S.—*Some Folk Lore Stories and Songs in Chinyanja*. (Published by S.P.C.K.)

Hunting Dances.

Just as the advance of civilisation has meant the doom of the war dance so has the introduction of guns led to the decadence of the hunting dance. The close range shot with the arrow, the thrill and danger of the spear thrust implied a more intimate contact with the dangerous beast. A more urgent need to build up emotional strength through the dance before the hunt was evident, and after the chase the relief equally surged up in triumphal dances. The long range shot seems to require medicine on the gun rather than the emotional keying-up of the hunter.

Also, as with the war dance, the hunting dance has become a spectacle. The Ila lion dance was a favourite with the askari during the war. A clown was introduced and he was killed by the lion after his antics in searching for honey had worked up the spectators into hysterical laughter. Then the hunter and lion danced a *pas de deux*. The hunter failed to kill and had to call in helpers who surrounded the lion. The circle advanced and receded, the hunters springing and cavorting. After the kill there was a wild dance round the body of the lion which was slung on a pole. The tempo of the drums kept pace with the dance.

I have not been able to find a description of the real Ila lion dance. The clown may have been an askari introduction. The part of the women spectators was taken by askari who used army socks rolled up inside their improvised dresses to represent breasts.

One feature, both of the Ila hunting dance and of the war dance, was that the women spectators did not join in the frenzied dances. The women stood in groups chanting but shuffling their feet and gently moving their breasts and buttocks in a very " close " dance. The contrast between the glistening bodies of the leaping, lunging bodies of the warriors or hunters and the solid, gently waving group of women was vivid. It was a picture that perfectly illustrated the sexual division between expanded and close dances, but whether it is typical of other war and hunting dances, I do not know.

Mask and Pole Dances.

In the far west of the Territory are found a group of people, Lovale, Lunda, Luchazi and Chokwe, who have masked dances of a special type. They are known as *Makishi* (plural of the Lovale word *Likishi*—a mask), and since the dancers often perform on a cross-piece between two poles I have, perhaps somewhat arbitrarily, classed the two together. Descriptions of the masks and fantastic costumes made of string which cover the whole body can be found elsewhere*. Mr. C. M. N. White gives me a brief note : " These *makishi* are of two types—the profane or secular like the *Mwana Pwero* (young woman) or *Chiklu* (fool). They are really clowns who come and do comic songs, posture and amuse the public on suitable

---

* *See* notes in the Handbook to the Rhodes-Livingstone Museum.

[37]

Photo.—Home News Unit.

Makishi Pole Dancers,

festive occasions. They are generally serenaded by the women and the latter may do a close shuffle as well. These secular *makishi* are sometimes acrobats and perform on a pole with a cross-piece, or a tree will sometimes do instead. The most skilful of them perform on a tight-rope stretched between two poles. This apparatus is called *Muchapa* and certainly some of the performers who act these secular masques do very nearly dance, and the phrase may be heard in Chokwe ' *Kuhangana Muchapa* '—which might be re-rendered as ' do the tight-rope dance ' or *Muchishi Wamuchapa*—a tight-rope masked performer. These ceremonies usually adorned circumcision ceremonies at which the *makishi* always appear. Some *makishi*, like *Kalębwa* and *Chikunya*, only appear at circum-cision ceremonies, but they do not perform on the tight-rope ; they are essentially cult *makishi*."

Pole dances are not indigenous to any other part of the Territory, indeed even in the west their origin is extra-territorial since the tribes mentioned still retain much of their former Angola culture. Among other tribes a dancer, a Bemba praise singer for example, may climb on the roof of a hut and dance there. Travelling troupes of pole dancers, who are often of the western tribes mentioned, can be seen in Copperbelt towns, and other dancers wearing *makishi* masks are also frequent performers.

New Dances.

The modern ballroom dances, foxtrots, waltzes and so on, are danced regularly, of course, in the compounds of the towns. But in 1938 I saw a foxtrot being danced as part of the ceremonies initiating a new Chief Nkula in the Chinsali District.* It was being danced outside his hut, and he and his councillors were sitting watching it just as they would have one of their own traditional dances. Mouth organs provided the music.

In the same district, at the funeral of a Chief Nkweto†, I watched the proceedings held up whilst the schoolboys did a dumb-bell display whilst the women clapped and sang in time just as at a dance. The clacking dumb-bells kept the rhythm almost as well as the drum.

The *Shabani*, which, as its name implies, comes from Southern Rhodesia, is now danced widely throughout Northern Rhodesia and has been seen as far afield as Johannesburg. It is a round dance and an energetic one too. The women are on the inside and move in the opposite direction to the men, who stamp the ground hard and blow whistles. At a change of tempo all face outwards and the men move outwards, enlarging the circle, still stamping and

---

* Brelsford, W. V.—*Aspects of Bemba Chieftainship*. Communications of Rhodes-Livingstone Institute, No. 2.

† Brelsford, W. V.—*Shimwalule. The Study of a Bemba Chief and Priest.* African Studies, September, 1942.

blowing hard. Then the men turn inwards facing the women, and men and women stamp towards each other. Couples catch each other round the waist but at arm's length, and with the women's buttocks and breasts shaking they bend lower and lower, remaining as low as possible until the tempo changes and the circle is renewed.

The stamping of the feet, possibly the original metronome of the dance, is the noticeable feature of the *Shabani* because it is one of the few mixed dances that includes this feature. It is more typical of the male war and victory dances. Some writers associate the leap (of which the stamp is a degenerate form) with pastoral cultures and go on to state that the farther away from the pastoral life the " closer " typical dances become.* This may be a clue towards the discovery of origins. Southern Rhodesia generally is a more pastoral country than Northern Rhodesia, so the stamp of the *Shabani* may indicate its origin. On the other hand, as Rev. A. M. Jones has pointed out to me (*in litt.*), the stamp in our Morris dances is considered to be a symbolic attempt to make the earth fertile. Later I also describe a puberty rite in which there is a stamp.

Dr. Audrey Richards informed me that she witnessed a Bisa imitation lion dance that at first she thought was indigenous. Later it was described to her as being learnt from " Bwana Strongee ". This turned out to be a reference to the strong man and lion tamer of a circus that had toured the railway area in the late 1920s.

The *Shonongo* dance is associated with certain degenerate sects claiming an unauthorised allegiance to the Watch Tower or Jehovah's Witness movement. Some natives give it a Kaonde origin or it may have been introduced into Northern Rhodesia from outside and adopted by rebels from the cult which is an introduced form of Christianity. No drums are used, the hand-clapping of the women being the only beat although there are special songs. It is a round dance with the women inside. The women wear very short skirts or dresses well above the knees, and the main climax of the dance is when the women bend down and the men have intercourse with them *a tergo*.

This dance is performed by a sect of the movement known as *Chonaule* or *Chisamaliya*. The word *Chonaule* refers to promiscuous intercourse : the name *Chisamaliya* is derived from the Biblical story of the woman of Samaria with whom our Lord, according to the sect, had intercourse.

The *Shonongo* may be restricted in incidence. I first came across it among the Lamba of Ndola. Mr. C. M. N. White has found it among the Kaonde and occasionally among the Mwinilunga Lunda. But it does not appeal to the Balovale people.

---

* Curt Sachs.—*World History of the Dance.*

[40]

The most spectacular of the modern dances is the *Mganda* which, as the Rev. A. M. Jones says, is in essence a burlesque of a military parade.* It started in East Africa during the 1914-1918 war, arrived in Northern Rhodesia via Nyasaland to Fort Jameson, and now it can be seen on the Copperbelt at Christmas time and at other festivities. Mr. Jones describes a procession, headed by a mascot which was a van Heusen collar advertisement carried on a cushion, followed by dancing officers, drummers, trumpeters singing into calabashes, a doctor and stretcher-bearer and a constable. The procession winds to headquarters where the king and his secretary sit. The king controls the dancing, changing the dances and authorising a collection from the spectators, and signalling the stops for refreshments. The dances are round dances with the drummers in the middle and only the performers dance, the spectators refraining from joining in. At the end the king makes a speech congratulating the performers. On the Copperbelt the *Mganda* sometimes becomes a tribal competition, each tribe putting on its procession and each having its own king. The kings sit together at headquarters and one is chosen to be the main judge.

The *Mganda* has thus two distinct phases, the processional dance and the round dances at headquarters.

The incorporation of European figure-heads such as kings, secretaries, and so on, into dances is paralleled by similar figures in many Northern Rhodesian purely native societies. Even self-help societies, such as the Bameetings of the Bangweulu region, have their governors, chief secretaries and medical officers. One is reminded of medieval miracle plays and masques and of more modern carnivals and Morris dances.

The *Mbeni* dance society combined the functions of a dancing organisation with those of a self-help society. Originally a Bemba society, it had chief secretaries, doctors and so on, rather like the *Mganda*. During the native strikes on the Copperbelt in 1935, the *Mbeni* used their organisation to ferment trouble, and during the actual rioting the big red cross on the *Mbeni* doctor's white coat seemed to be a rallying point for the trouble-makers.† Since then the society has faded out, although a dance called *Mbeni* still takes place.

Close Dances.

The close, round or front, dance is in Northern Rhodesia usually a feminine dance although, as Sachs points out, in some cultures men do join in close dances. The solo exhibition dance done by men is, in contrast to the mixed dance, often of the close type. The dances of women at the puberty rites of girls are often of this type, as are

---

* Rev. A. M. Jones.—*The Mganda Dance.* African Studies, December, 1945.

† *See* Report on evidence given to Commission of Inquiry. (Government Printer.)

also some of the dances of welcome given by women. The typical feature seems to be a shuffle. The rows or rounds of women do not take steps but merely shuffle the feet and the line or round sometimes seems to be stationary. Hand-clapping and twitching of the buttocks or breasts are also typical movements.

A noticeable feature of close dancing in Northern Rhodesia is the way in which it sometimes becomes a quiet accompaniment to a violent dance. I have mentioned the close dance of Ila women during the hunting dance. During the Northern Province *Mashya* convulsive dance in which single or couple dancers go through the violent movements, the surrounding circle of men and women merely shuffle and wriggle in accompaniment.

As I have already said, many expanded dances have periods during which they become close dances. There was an old Bisa dance in which couples lay on the ground, quietly, some distance from each other whilst the other dancers threw dust on them. The *Kachacha* as described by White becomes a closed dance as the performers remain stationary but sink gradually on to their heels. On the other hand, the close puberty rite dances among the tribes of the Lovale group tend to become expanded as the initiate emerges from her seclusion, whilst the dances at her grass shelter are strictly close.

Puberty Rite Dances.

We can perhaps distinguish two different types of the close puberty rite dance—that danced by the initiate and that danced by the onlookers or by the person or persons initiating the younger girls.

The *Manchancha* of the Lamba and Kaonde peoples is a front dance performed by the women of a village outside the hut of the girl being initiated. In front of the line of women are three or four elder women who sometimes face the line and sometimes turn their backs to it. The line of women clap hands and shuffle the feet without moving position. The women in front also shuffle to begin with, but as the dance grows in intensity they may occasionally stamp but without moving position. Then the women in front begin to shake their buttocks, slowly at first, but as the dance rises to its peak the wriggling becomes very violent and very rapid. It is a true buttock dance.

Among the Chikunda of the Zambezi Valley, the *Chidikule* dance takes place in the open. Older women surround the initiate and merely shuffle and wriggle without moving position. Women beat the drums at this dance.

The *Mazya a Ndola* is the final stage of the puberty rites among the Nsenga and southern Chewa. The dance is the final phase of rites that may have been going on for six months. The girl initiate stands on a low platform of branches. There she performs a belly dance whilst holding her right bent arm rigid, sometimes clutching a fly-switch. The idea seems to be to wriggle the belly as violently

Women Dancing During Ila Lion Dance.

as possible whilst holding the arm and fly-switch rigid. " The dancing," says Mr. Lane Poole (*in litt.*), " is performed by elderly matrons, gorgeously decorated with bead-work and shells, daubed with pigment of red ochre, brandishing fly-switches and rattling seed pods." The dance of the matrons, which involves much quivering of the belly, seems to be more of the open style than many other puberty dances, although the comparative stillness of the initiate adds the close touch.

The fly-switch also appears in a puberty rite dance of the Soli in the Lusaka District. The girl, holding the switch, merely stands in the centre of a circle of dancing women. One woman beats a drum.

Among some tribes the dances are held either in the seclusion of huts or else in distant places in the bush. The *Manganjo* circumcision dance and the *Musondo* girls' puberty dance of the Swahili are examples of the latter type, and the dances, in separate areas, sometimes go on nightly for over a month.

There are philosophical and practical motives behind the puberty rite dances that I cannot enlarge upon here. As with the war dance, it could be said that the puberty rite dance generates power to pass on, in this case, to the initiate. The dances in seclusion or in remote areas are often a test of endurance, a factor in sexual selection, and the buttock dance which improves general health and perhaps makes parturition easier is especially emphasised at the rites.

An Engagement Dance.

There is a dance known as *Chikombe* among the Chikunda, sometimes performed by the Nsenga of Feira under the name *Chifusi*, in which a betrothed couple sit quietly on a mat whilst married men and women shuffle around them singing. This is a typical close dance, although I have not heard of it outside the Feira District.

Birth Dances.

Mr. Lane Poole has described to me (*in litt.*) the *Nsongwe* dance of the Nsenga and southern Chewa. He describes it as being performed after the birth of the first child and says : " It is a kind of lustration to cleanse the woman after a period of taboo. The active performers are women and the audience are men. The women, entirely nude, assume a squatting posture, raising and lowering their bodies on their heels, accompanying the motion with quivering of their belly muscles. Then, squatting in front of a man she extends his arms in turn, then his legs, simulating the process of washing the limbs. Finally, she embraces the man's neck and draws his head down to her breasts. A good deal of promiscuous fornication follows."

(An African, Mr. Lakement Ngandu, describes a similar dance performed in a kneeling position by women during Nsenga initiation rites. He refers to it as *Mitingu*, after the small calabashes banged on the floor as accompaniment.)

[44]

Dances out of Harmony with the Body

The convulsive dances are typified by distortion and ugly movements. Sachs's two main divisions have been briefly described in the preamble to this paper. Very little is known about these dances in Northern Rhodesia and much research is needed, especially in connection with the pure convulsive dances.

THE PURE CONVULSIVE DANCE

The Demon or Possession Dance.

(This is a type not described as such by Sachs.) It is really pathogenic and also has, judging by the available records, geographical limitations within Northern Rhodesia. Dances performed by those possessed by spirits or demons have been more frequently described from the western and southern areas than from the Northern and Eastern Provinces. Smith and Dale* describe *Busala* dances among the Ila in which it sometimes seems that only the drumming accompaniment serves to turn a fit into a dance. The boundary line between demon dancing and the pathological state of possession is very shadowy. Gouldsbury and Sheane† describe a weird dance which follows the possession of a Bemba by a spirit of a dead chief, and Gluckman mentions‡, but does not describe, curative dances by possessed diviners among the Lozi that may also belong to this class.

A typical curative or exorcism dance is the *Malambo* of the Chikunda or *Mashabi* of the Gowa, both tribes of the Feira District. When a man is sick a diviner may tell the relatives that a spirit of some ancestor is causing the sickness and he orders a *Mashabi* dance in order to find out which spirit has to be propitiated. The sick man is placed on a mat in the open village, the drums are beaten and the people gather and sit around the sick man. One by one the head relative calls out the names of ancestors whilst the drums beat furiously. Soon the " spirit " enters into someone who rises and begins to dance. The sick man is then carried away to his hut, but the dancer goes on wriggling and twirling, faster and faster as the beat of the drums quickens. The end comes when the dancer falls unconscious. The ancestor whose name was called nearest to the dancer being inspired is the one who has caused the sickness and the propitiation has begun.

Rattray§ describes the Ngoni *Kanonomera* dance to cure a person who is ill—" the drums begin to sound, and they are dancing. He who remembers a song sings it ; when one is possessed by a

---

* Smith, E., and Dale, A.—*The Ila Speaking Peoples of Northern Rhodesia.*
† Gouldsbury, C., and Sheane, H.—*The Great Plateau of Northern Rhodesia.*
‡ In appendix to *African Music*, by the Rev. A. M. Jones. Occasional Paper No. 4, Rhodes-Livingstone Museum.
§ Rattray, R. S.—*Some Folk Lore Stories and Songs in Chinyanja.* (Published by S.P.C.K.)

Photo.—*E. Knowles Jordan.*

Girl dancing. Senga Tribe, Luangwa Valley.

spirit, down he falls, and they drag him out of the dance, and deck him with calico and skins of animals, and he again enters the circle and dances. When a person is possessed by a child's spirit, they bind his calico tightly round him that it be strong, because that person is wishing to strip it off and dance naked, as a child does not wear anything. Should a woman be seized by a man's spirit, saying, ' I am so and so ', they deck her with a feather head-dress, and in her hand she holds a little stick (for a spear), and her calico is tied round her waist, and her breasts swing free."

Among the Luchazi, Lwena, Chokwe and to a certain extent among the Lunda, there is a belief in *Makamba*. These, according to White (*in litt.*), are " old, evil spirits of a primitive kind which nearly always affect sexual or reproductive powers or the prowess of hunters ". A diviner is employed to find out which is the *likamba* responsible. Then it must be exorcised to the sound of drums and the patient often goes into a pure convulsive dance, " jerking from the shoulders and hips, frothing at the mouth, perspiring freely and often collapsing exhausted. This jerking is called *tunguta* in Lovale and *zakuka* in Lunda." White goes on to describe how several *makamba* are exorcised.

" In *nkula* the patient jerks and shuffles backwards with jerking buttocks to her house from the gathering several times ; in *katuta* the patient passes and repasses through a covered trench with a hole at either end while onlookers sing and do a close dance and sing until the patient is exhausted. This latter is not called *tunguta*. In *kayongo* the patient jerks into a violent frenzy and ends by decapitating a red cock with his teeth, and may be accompanied by a friend to jerk with him to help him to work up his state of ecstasy. The jerking is said to be the action of the spirit responding to the treatment of exorcism.

" It should be noted that no one ever talks of *tunguta* or *zakuka* as *dancing*. It always seemed to me that the drums as a rule provide music for the dance of the onlookers who sing to address the spirit and that the patient responds with his convulsion not to the drumming but to the singing. The song to the *likamba* is usually a song by the women, and they do most of the dancing except where the *likamba* is affecting the prowess of a hunter, in which case the men predominate."

I think these exorcisms should be classed as dances although, as I indicated before, the boundary line between a convulsive dance and a pathological convulsion may often be very hazy.

The distribution of convulsive dances in Northern Rhodesia is another of the points needing further research. Broadly speaking, possession dances are typical of shaman and witchcraft cultures, but whether tribal distinctions can be made in Northern Rhodesia I do not know. The geographical distribution suggests that there may be subtle differences between groups and tribes distinguishable

[47]

by the strength of the influence of the witch-doctor. That is a cultural difference worth tracing and the pure convulsive dance may be a clue.

THE WEAKENED CONVULSIVE DANCE

This dance can be seen throughout the Territory. It is typical of the wandering solo or troupe dancers and little need be added to the movement description already given in the introductory section. There is often some overlap with the demon dance. Many of the professional dancers, especially among the Lamba and Lala, are said to be possessed by weird or supernatural creatures (*ipinkuwaila*) or by "foreign spirits", but they do not lose consciousness when dancing as do the pure convulsive dancers. But there is one type (again not described by Sachs in my terms) that should be mentioned.

The Ecstatic Self-Mutilation Dances.

The name describes it, and the one description I have is from Mr. F. N. Heath (District Officer) who saw it at Kalindawalo in the Petauke District. It is known among the Chewa as the *Chitika*. It is an individual exhibition dance and at the height of the ecstasy the performer, always a man, slashes his tongue with a knife until the blood flows. That is the main feature of the dance, but the performer seen by Mr. Heath allowed women to place a large wooden mortar on his body and to pound grain in it and for a short time he was buried in the ground.

Dislocation Dances.

Among the Bemba and Lunda of the Luapula there is a dance called *Mashya*, which involves wrenching and the unnatural twisting of the limbs. Sometimes it is performed by a man alone but sometimes a woman joins in too. I have already mentioned that the surrounding dancers perform a quiet close dance. I have not seen this dance and I have not heard of any similar types. According to Sachs such dances would overlap with the close dances of the in-harmony-with-the-body category since they usually involve but short steps, if any at all.

[48]

Photo.—J. P. Murray.

Solo Exhibition Dancer.   Fort Rosebery District.

CONCLUSION

The dances of Northern Rhodesia form a little-known field of study. A few pages in two or three books is almost the full range of published material. The Rev. A. M. Jones* is making studies of African music in Northern Rhodesia. In this paper I have attempted to discuss dancing without mentioning music. It should be remembered that the emotions and ecstasies induced by the dance are brought about as much by the music as by movements, and that the range of instruments is increasing even in the most primitive dances. Police whistles are the invariable accompaniments to the drums in any big dances everywhere. The mouth organ and comb and tissue paper· are common and dance bands with saxophones are now a feature of urban life. The old vocal accompaniments are still heard, the yells of the men and the shrilling of the women. In the western areas among the Lamba I have noted three vocal accompaniments not mentioned elsewhere. A hiss, a hoarse croak in the throat made both with inward and outward breath and also that rude noise with tongue between lips, politely known to us as the " Bronx cheer ". All these noises, even perhaps ankle rattles which are sometimes the sole accompaniment as in the Ngoni *Chitoto* funeral dance, can be classed as accessories. Because, as the Rev. A. M. Jones points out, the typical and essential cross-rhythm of African music can only be obtained on drums or rhythmic equivalents such as beating sticks on a pole. One ancient, and perhaps symbolical, instrumental accompaniment is the tapping of the hoe blade by another piece of iron such as an axe blade. The use of this instrument seems to be restricted to funeral dances and is heard in the *Chisengwe* funeral dance of the Nsenga and Soli and the same dance known as *Nganganga* among the Chikunda. Another usage, new to me, is the banging of *mitungu* calabashes on the ground during the dance of that name, the " tone " being changed by placing the open hand on the opening of the calabash. (Page 21).

Mr. White's description (*in litt.*) of the *Chiyanda*, the "national" dance of the Chokwe, is another illustration of how important and essential drum music is to the dance.

"*Chiyanda* is essentially part of the culture which the Chokwe brought with them from the Western Congo and North-west Angola. It requires the wooden slit-drum used for drum signalling in the Congo and known in Chokwe as *Chikuvu*, since the two-tone system of the drum is used to signal to the dancers to change the pattern of their movements. *Chiyanda* is mainly a dance for women, though male spectators may join in. The women move round the

---

* The Rev. A. M. Jones.—*See* especially *African Drumming* and *The Study of African Musical Rhythms*. Bantu Studies, March, 1934, and December, 1937.

[50]

drums in a circle, singing and with the usual rolling and wriggling until the drum tones change from high to low ; at this, the dancers halt, turn to face inwards, and indulge in remarkable sharp lateral jerks of the pelvis of considerable speed and violence. When the drum tone changes again to high, the circling movement is resumed. Attempts to dance *Chiyanda* with cylindrical drums are always a dismal affair as this cannot get the right tones, and none of the other Balovale people seem to have learned how to do these lateral jerks."

As well as music and accompaniment I have had to leave out any consideration of poetry and song in connection with the dance. This phase alone would form a lengthy and difficult study because the words of the dance songs are often full of symbolic meanings, archaisms and indecent *double entendre*.

Mr. Lane Poole (*in litt.*) makes the point that many dances, especially those connected with puberty rites and marriage, are often only minor incidents in lengthy ceremonies, and to take the dance out of the accompanying circumstances is to give a distorted picture of the dance itself and to make meaningless its symbols and actions. The criticism is valid and the distinction between a rite and a dance is often shadowy, but all I can plead is that such a comprehensive survey is beyond me and would overrun the limits laid down for this small paper.

This discussion is weakened by these omissions, but I hope I have succeeded in indicating that there is scope for the sociological study of dancing. There are social and even tribal themes in dancing. Tucker* has shown that the underlying idea of most Shilluk and Nuer dancing seems to be " warfare ", whilst in Dinka dancing the theme is " cattle ". I have not been able to define so narrowly, but by suggesting that certain geographical areas have very distinctive forms of dancing I have, I hope, laid a trail that should be followed.

As a few final generalisations covering Northern Rhodesia, I could say that tribes in the area to the west of the railway line make use of masks in their dances to a greater extent than do the tribes to the east of the line : that the western dances seem to arouse stronger emotions so that sex and convulsions are more frequent characteristics : also that among western tribes there seems to be a more important role for the diviner in dances. I leave it for future writers to narrow down the field, for if tribal distinctions still remain, then dancing must reflect them.

---

* A. N. Tucker.—*Tribal Music and Dancing in the Southern Sudan.*

3

THE MATERIAL CULTURE
OF THE LUNDA–LOVALE PEOPLES

C. M. N. WHITE

1948

THE TERM LUNDA-LOVALE PEOPLE is a blanket name for a number of groups of people inhabiting the north-west of Northern Rhodesia. Their main areas are the Mwinilunga and Balovale Districts, but large numbers of them also inhabit Barotseland, especially Mankoya, and the Kasempa District.

At least five tribes are represented among them.

The Lunda inhabit much of Mwinilunga and the east bank of the Zambezi in Balovale. They, like the other Lunda-Lovale people, claim a common origin in the country of Mwanchiamvwa in the Belgian Congo. Unlike the other kindred tribes their numbers have been little swelled by immigration. They have a well-defined tribal structure, with Shinde as their superior chief in the Balovale District, Kanongesha as the head of the Mwinilunga Ndembo, and Musokantanda as head of the Mwinilunga Lunda ; the last mentioned resides in the Belgian Congo and his representative in Mwinilunga is Sailunga. The Mwinilunga Lunda tend to live in small scattered villages and to make finger millet their staple crop. The Mwinilunga Ndembo live in larger concentrations, whilst the Balovale Lunda live in large concentrations owing to geographical conditions. The two latter groups have cassava as their staple crop. All the three sections of the Lunda are characterised by marked dialectical variations of language.

The Lwena (often called Lovale) inhabit the west bank of the Zambezi in Balovale, but have spread widely outside their own area. Their superior chief, Kakenge, resides at Lumbala in Angola, the chieftainess, Ndungu, being by common consent the head of the Balovale Lwena. The Lwena are inhabitants of the plains in the river valleys, whereas the Lunda are inhabitants of wooded, often hilly, country. Thus the Lwena are great fishermen, whilst the Lunda are ignorant of fishing and are mainly hunters. The Lovale tribal structure has had a history of perpetual subdivision into minor chieftainships, often held by women, and lacks the cohesion of the Lunda. The traditional diet of the Lwena has always been bulrush millet, but to-day they grow much cassava. The Lwena language, the simplest of this group of languages (termed by Professor Doke " the West-Central Zone of Bantu languages "), has asserted itself vigorously and tended to become the lingua franca of the Lunda-Lovale people in their contacts with the outer world.

The Luchazi are recent immigrants from Angola, the bulk of them having arrived during the last thirty years. Their home in

Angola lay west of Balovale and Kalabo in the Muangai-Cangamba-Lungwevungu areas. They have settled in great numbers along the Manyinga and adjacent rivers in Balovale and southern Mwinilunga, and in Mankoya. Their original tribal structure was extremely slight, and in early days they lived a nomadic existence in Angola, always on the move after a year or two in one place. Their cultivation is closely linked to the presence of *Cryptosepalum* woodlands on the Kalahari contact soils, and it is to such types of terrain that they have gravitated in Northern Rhodesia. The Luchazi include several distinct groups, two of which, the *vaka ndonga* (river people) and *vaka ntunda* (bush people), have settled widely in Northern Rhodesia. Closely allied to them are the Lwimbi, occasionally met with in this Territory, and the Nkangala who linguistically link them to the Mbunda (a closely associated tribe not discussed in this survey).

The Chokwe are also recent immigrants from Angola, mainly from the Kasai watershed. They have settled in many parts of the north-west, particularly in parts of Balovale. Their original tribal structure was more rigid than that of the Luchazi and Lwena, and they did not as a rule have female chiefs. However, these considerations do not affect their settlements in Northern Rhodesia, where there are no Chokwe chiefs. The Chokwe were dwellers in wooded country and knew little of fishing. Their historical fame is chiefly as slave dealers and brigands who plundered all who came their way. To-day their energies have been turned to more peaceful channels, and they must be counted as amongst the most progressive of the Lunda-Lovale peoples ; many of those settled in Northern Rhodesia have come from urbanised areas in Angola and are mechanics and craftsmen who have absorbed something of Latin civilisation.

For the purpose of discussing their material culture all may be treated as a unity, though attention will be drawn to divergences between the tribes in some respects. Originally these divergences were more marked, but now that they have been living together in mixed communities for some time the material culture is tending to become more uniform. But it must not be forgotten that these tribes are not a single homogeneity. The conservative, rather unprogressive Lunda with his tradition of hunting : the enterprising irrepressible Lwena, who lived by fishing : the often primitive, argumentatively stubborn and very industrious Luchazi : and the self-confident Chokwe with his mixed background of highway robbery and trading, and to-day often with his touch of Portuguese culture—and all with their own distinct languages—represent quite separate entities to anyone who has lived among them.

The Ovimbundu do not fall linguistically or ethnologically within these groups, but pockets of them are settled over the north-west and they deserve a passing mention. Many of those in Northern Rhodesia are mechanics and craftsmen or skilled agriculturists, and the citrus, irrigated wheat and vegetable crops which characterise their villages are always worth notice. In their home in Bihe, in the highlands of Angola, they live in open, well-watered hilly country and grow great quantities of maize. For many years they served as the trading intermediaries between the Portuguese on the coast and the more inaccessible tribes of the interior who form our Lunda-Lovale peoples, and in that capacity were often referred to by early writers as Mbali or Vimbali. Thus they form an integral if small part of the mosaic of the north-western tribes ; of interest for their historical associations and their present-day accomplishments, and well worth better acquaintance for the sake of their musical gifts, all too little known.

No exact figures exist of the numbers of the various tribes living in the north-west of the territory. A rough estimate might assess their numbers as Lunda, 30,000 ; Lwena, 60,000 ; Luchazi, 40,000 ; Chokwe, 20,000.

Metal-working, Weapons and Tools

IRON-WORKING is one of the characteristics of the Lunda-Lovale tribes ; but the blacksmith's art has gradually been supplanted by the imported article which can be bought in the store. Nevertheless, there is still quite a keen demand for local ironwork in which the soft iron does not split, as the imported hoe or axe so often does. Apart from hoes, axes, arrow and spear heads, blacksmiths make spare parts such as strikers and triggers for muzzle-loading guns, and the long metal Luchazi pipes.

The blacksmith's art is surrounded by numerous taboos, among which the most important are seclusion of the smelter from the sight of women and abstention from sexual intercourse on the part of the blacksmith whilst working iron.

The iron ore is gathered from one of the known places where there are surface deposits of suitable stones. It is placed in a kiln mixed with charcoal and heated to extract the iron. Bellows with a clay mouthpiece are used to fan the furnace. The iron is then removed and worked on an anvil with hammer and tongs.

Axe heads are usually fashioned with one end tapering off to jut out of the handle and may be detached and used as a crowbar, adze or tin opener. Battle-axes with half-moon shaped blades were formerly used, but are no longer seen to-day. Ornamental axes of miniature size, often resembling the battle-axes, or sometimes with two blades, one below the other, and nearly always ornamented with a pattern of spots and lines, are commonly carried at dances. The blades are usually very thin, and this should distinguish them from the small axes which are sometimes found used for adzing poles.

The normal type of hoe is composed of a flat plate with a projecting tang which is fastened into the handle. The size varies considerably without any special distinction as to the use, but the

[56]

miniature hoes analogous to the miniature axes and carried at dances must be distinguished from the ordinary working hoe. Hoes with a double handle are not infrequently seen among the older Luchazi women, but to-day they seem to be going out of use. They are dragged rather than used for chopping the soil, and are mentioned by Livingstone.

The usual bow is quite long, generally some four feet ; and the string, composed of twisted sinew, is run through an eyelet at each end and then twisted round several times and tied. Arrows are made with shafts of reeds or light wood, the heads being attached by a projecting spike driven into the shaft and tied round with fine bark rope. The majority of arrows are feathered, the feather being split and glued or tied to the shaft. Feathers of guinea fowl and large birds of prey are particularly favoured for this purpose.

Arrows show a great variety of types. The Lunda usually prefer the more orthodox types of leaf-shaped or triangular blade, to which they commonly applied arrow poison obtained from creepers growing in forest patches, which yield a variety of strychnine. Among the Chokwe and Luchazi a greater diversity of shapes of arrow is found, resembling half-moons, spades and axe heads. All these types have distinct names, often quite picturesque, e.g., *timpi lyangombe* (bull's navel) and *matako achizunda* (frog's buttocks). Arrows with barbs are occasionally seen. An arrow with a rounded head of soft wood is also commonly found ; it is usually not feathered and is used for shooting small birds or small mammals. It can only be used at very short ranges, and I have never heard of its being used for stunning monkeys as the Museum Handbook, *p.* 19, states is the case.

Arrows are carried in the hand and quivers are not in use among these tribes.

Spears are widely used, generally for stabbing to finish off wounded game. The head is usually fastened into the haft by a projecting tang, sometimes bound round with metal. Spears with metal butts rather like the blade of an axe in shape are sometimes seen, and also spears made out of a single piece of metal, both blade and shaft being in one piece. The latter are probably an introduction, since long strips of metal such as motor car springs became obtainable. Some spears have a raised hand grip projecting from the shaft about halfway along its length. Fishing spears are commonly used by the Lwena ; they are usually without any flattening of the head, which often has rings or projections and barbules to prevent the fish getting away ; fish are often speared at night by means of flares. The Lwena also sometimes kill fish by shooting them with an arrow into which a bodkin-like head has been fixed.

Almost every man has a knife with a short blade, broad basally and tapering or cut across sharply at the point. The handle is of wood, sometimes ornamented. Most commonly, the knife is merely

[57]

carried in the waist cloth, but rather crude leather sheaths are also found. Mention may be made of the fact that these knives can be given a very keen edge, and before the days of razor blades they were used for shaving and for performing the circumcision operation.

The beheading knife associated especially with the Chokwe and Lwena (*poko yamukwale* or *katana*) is now no longer in use, but may be seen among the heirlooms of some chiefs.

Other metalwork is comparatively little, but mention may be made of a few instances. Large copper crosses, formerly not infrequent at Mwinilunga but now no longer seen in use, are a relic of a form of currency used in past times, and often called slaves' crosses because they were used for buying slaves. Copper wire of industrial manufacture is popular to-day as binding on knives, spears, etc., and brass nails, originally obtained via Angola, were once much used to adorn the stocks of muzzle-loading guns.

Vessels and Receptacles

EARTHENWARE and clay pots and calabashes are the most usual types. Clay pots are rapidly being replaced by imported enamel and metalware. The traditional technique of pot-making was to take pot clay from one of the known sites. The vessel was roughly moulded in the soft clay and then set to dry in the sun. After drying, the pot was smoothed and trimmed with a stone. Finally, the pot was fired with bark chips. The Museum Handbook refers to placing the pots in the rafters of the village shelter or some similar place to dry in the smoke for a week before firing, but this is not general and, if the clay is good for pot making, firing takes place after drying in the sun. Clay pots often have a few geometrical decorations made by marking with a sharp stick.

Reference should be made to a particular type of clay pitcher with a lid and known as *nsaba* (Lunda) or *sapa* (Lwena, Chokwe). This vessel frequently was moulded with a spout for pouring and usually decorated with figures in relief.

Clay vessels were most often used for cooking or, in the case of the pitcher, for holding water. They were also used for medicines and specially small pots were made for this purpose.

Calabashes are universally used for holding water, beer or honey. They are usually grown on waste ground near the village, and a number of different shapes and sizes exist, some having long curved spouts and others a blunt wide mouth. A small calabash with a long narrow spout is used for administering enemas, and another rather larger type serves as a hookah for smokers. In the latter, the calabash holds water whilst the tobacco is placed in an earthenware receptacle attached to the calabash by a reed, and the smoke is drawn through the water. Calabashes cut in half are used to hold meal, dried fish and other objects. Small gourds serve as holders for snuff, tobacco, oil, gunpowder and medicines.

[58]

A number of other miscellaneous vessels are used. Bark trays are commonly seen for carrying root cassava, honeycomb and other long objects, and fresh meat is often brought in on them after a beast has been killed in the field.

Tortoise-shells and horns are often used to hold magical preparations, whether for self-protection or for malevolent purposes. Skin pouches and satchels are not infrequent ; they vary a great deal in workmanship, the old-fashioned types being often of undressed hide with the hair attached, whilst nowadays some degree of tanning is attempted and the influence of European design can be seen.

Basketwork, Mat-making, Ropes, Netting and Weaving

THE COMMONEST TYPES of basket are the tall baskets used for holding meal or grain, etc., and the flat baskets in which meal or other objects are exposed for drying, or which are used to separate chaff from grain by shaking. In the Balovale District the tall baskets (*ihebi* in Lunda, *mbango* in Lwena, *chihele* in Luchazi, *chisoka* in Chokwe) are usually made with tough springy roots known as *jikenge*. These are built up in coils and secured with fine bark rope. At Mwinilunga the usual technique is to use coils consisting of a core of fine grass bound round with a raffia-like grass (*yitendi*). This latter method gives scope to the worker to introduce dyes and patterns into his work.

A wide-mouthed basket with a small stand is used to keep mush clean whilst awaiting the eater, the basket being inverted over the mush.

All these tribes also use a sifting basket—an oblong narrow box-shaped structure with a mouthpiece at one end, and made from palm fronds. It is still in common use in spite of the introduction of the European wire sieve.

Another common type of basket is the *chipau* ; this consists of two oblong shells, one of which fits over the other as a cover. This basket was formerly used especially to carry divining apparatus and charms, and is still often used to-day to carry brush, comb and toilet articles.

The *mutonga* is a long open basket used for carrying fruit, vegetables, cassava roots or dried fish. The rougher type is simply composed of thin criss-crossed cane. A more permanent type has a strong oblong rectangular base to which is attached the boat-shaped receptacle. For ordinary purposes the rough open-work type is the commoner.

Among the Luchazi a large basket is carried on the back, supported by a band round the forehead of the carrier. These baskets are often loaded with firewood or other heavy objects, and rests have to be built—rough platforms as a rule, of shoulder height—between the garden and the village to enable the over-burdened women to rest their loads.

Black dyes are sometimes used to vary the pattern of basketwork, and discarded stubs of indelible pencils are very popular to-day to furnish a violet dye.

Modern developments of basketwork are straw hats, satchels, table mats and even attache cases, which are all to be seen among the younger generation.

In the south of Mwinilunga and in Balovale, mats are made of lengths of papyrus tied together along the edges with bark rope or fibres. Elsewhere in the Mwinilunga District a woven mat is made by criss-cross plaiting of palm leaves. This latter mat (*chikanga*) is woven on a circle, so that when finished the object resembles a hollow cylinder, which is then cut along one side and spread open to form an oblong rectangle, the sides being then trimmed and bound. Ornate patterns are often introduced.

A mat of fine split canes is also sometimes found bound like the papyrus mat and used as a mattress, floor covering or roofing.

Bark rope is universally obtained from certain trees, most often from Musamba, a species of *Brachystegia*. It is plaited to make a strong rope used in snaring large game or for tying heavy loads, the bark rope being well soaked before it is finally plaited. Various plants also yield fine sisal-like fibres used in making smaller snares. Fibres are also used in making nets for fishing and, especially among the Luchazi, a net bag in which cooking pots, etc., are stored and hung up in the rafters of a house, or in which they are carried on a journey.

The weaving of cloth, which was apparently known to these tribes in the past, has vanished completely ; indeed, imported cloth has been known to them for so long through the Ovimbundu traders that this is not surprising. Cotton fibres are occasionally spun for use as sewing cotton, and during the war years one or two energetic youths made open-mesh vests of this cotton fibre, but soon gave up the unequal struggle of weaving their own clothes.

An ornamental type of weaving, usually with a pattern dyed in different shades, is found in the hammocks used by Lwena, Chokwe and Luchazi notables. This type of weaving, done as a rule with sisal-like fibres, has now been adapted to the making of deck chairs, but it seems unlikely to survive, for it is a long and laborious process and its cost disproportionate.

Woodwork and Ivory-work

WOODWORK is usually essentially utilitarian. Stools, wooden pillows and wooden plates were in use since time immemorial. Some stools are carved entirely from wood, whilst others have a hide seat on a wooden frame. Stools are often unadorned, or ornamented with rough geometrical patterns, but highly-carved stools may be met with occasionally. The art of carving realistic figures of human beings and animals is not, however, widespread here, although one or two really notable practitioners have gained a wide publicity outside their own districts, notably the crippled Chamundenda, of Mwinilunga. Paddles for stirring mush are often carefully carved and adorned with geometrical patterns.

Wooden combs with long teeth and ornamental, often figured, handles are in general use among these tribes.

Perhaps the most striking example of wood-carving, however, is the mask of the *likishi* dancer, known as the young woman (*mwana-pwevo*). This is carved from a single piece of wood in a most realistic manner—the hair being made of sisal fibres dyed black ; slits are left for the eyes, the open mouth is arrayed with teeth of bone filed to points in the Lwena style, and the face is marked with characteristic tattooings. Generally, only the front of the face is made of wood, the back and neck being of fibre like the rest of the *likishi* costume ; but I have seen one such mask entirely made of wood, including the top, which was carved to represent the old-fashioned Luchazi hairdressing of nodules of hair anointed with oil and red clay. It was certainly extremely realistic, but must have been most uncomfortable to wear.

Carved figures are also used for magical purposes, and some of the human and animal carvings which figure in the diviner's apparatus exhibit an exceptionally high degree of art.

The European demand for curios has stimulated the carving of human and animal figures, and dolls and various creatures not always easy to identify are occasionally offered for sale, as are carved walking sticks ; but these are rarely used in the village, though a few people do use them for ornamental purposes.

Very little ivory-work is done by the Lunda-Lovale tribes. Elephant are absent from parts of their country, but they evidently preferred to barter any ivory which they got with the Ovimbundu traders in exchange for cloth and gunpowder rather than use it themselves. Ivory handles are sometimes found on fly whisks, but they are more often made of bone.

Preparation of Food

THE STAPLE FOODS of cassava and millet are all prepared as flour by pounding in a wooden mortar, the pounding being done by a woman standing upright and wielding a long pounding-pole.

Beer is prepared from millet in both Balovale and Mwinilunga Districts, and honey beer is also widely used. The calabashes used for ordinary beer are often used also for water, but the ones used for honey beer are usually kept for that purpose only. Bee-keeping is well established among the north-western tribes ; large bark cylinders being placed high in trees for the wild bees to swarm in them. In addition to the above beverages, illicit distilling of spirit from sweet potatoes or cassava is indulged in, a calabash being used with the barrel of a muzzle-loading gun to form a crude retort. Among the Lunda millet was formerly ground by stones, but this practice seems to have gone out of use.

Salt was sometimes obtained from salt pans like Kaimbwe, in the Kasempa District, but among the Lovale and Luchazi ash salt was much used. This latter salt is prepared from certain types of vegetation which grows by streams ; it is gathered, piled up and dried and burned ; the ashes are then placed in calabashes and mixed with water and shaken ; the mouths of the calabashes are then filled with grass and leaves and they are inverted over other calabashes so that the water filters through the grass. This water has absorbed salt from the ashes and is used as a flavouring agent or is evaporated off to leave the salt.

Fire-making, Pipes, Snuff Boxes

THE FLINT AND STEEL is still fairly often seen among these tribes, especially among the Luchazi, who often have quite elegant sets. The tinder is dried vegetable matter or cotton fluff and may be carried in a small calabash used specially to hold it. Fire is some-times made by rubbing two sticks together. But with the advent of the village store these methods of fire-making are becoming obsolete and matches are universal.

Reference has been made above, under receptacles, to the use of the calabash water-pipe or hookah. Among the Luchazi metal pipes are common ; these are often fashioned like the European pipe, but the old-fashioned types have enormously long stems— up to three feet—and large bowls. Luchazi women are keen pipe smokers and are often seen with the short-stemmed pipes. Snuff is widely used, the old-fashioned container being a small calabash, though now a small bottle or a tin is commoner.

Musical Instruments

XYLOPHONES composed of wooden slats fastened upon a wooden framework and with a calabash under each slat to act as a resonator are found ; they are played with two sticks with heads of raw rubber. These xylophones are now quite rare.

The " kaffir piano " consists of a number of metal strips of varying lengths attached to a board. The board may be hollowed or made into a box to produce resonance, or a small calabash may be used as a resonator. This instrument is extremely popular, and nearly everyone plays one at some period of his life.

Small metal bells were sometimes used by hunters or diviners, but these are now extremely rare.

Rattles composed of small gourds containing seeds are often worn on the leg at dances and used also by diviners. The latter also used a double rattle consisting of two spheres of tough fibre with a short stick, as a handle, to join them.

Drums are universally used. The usual type is a hollow wooden cylinder with a skin stretched over one end. The skin is often covered with lumps of wild rubber. The drum is usually warmed by the fire before beating and is beaten by hand, whilst the sides may also be beaten with a stick. Among the Mwinilunga Lunda short drums may be found with solid bases, the only open end of the wooden cylinder being that covered by the skin. Such drums usually have a small aperture in the side, covered with spider's egg case to act as resonator. The hollow wooden drum (*chikuvu*) is now rare ; it is still seen among a few of the Chokwe and Lunda. It is slung between two poles and beaten with sticks which have large heads of wild rubber. One side of the *chikuvu* is thicker than the other and two tones result when it is beaten—a high and a low. It is this type of drum, working upon the combinations of tone, which is used in some parts of Africa for drum signalling, though that is only an ancient memory among the Lunda and Lovale to-day.

A friction drum, known by the Lwena as *ngomapwita*, is also often seen. It consists of a reed or stick passing through a membrane into the drum and produces a squeaky sound. The statement in the Museum Handbook that it is only used by diviners to excite the audience is of doubtful validity. The *ngomapwita* is often used for ordinary purposes of music.

Stringed instruments are extremely rare among the Lunda-Lovale tribes, though they existed in the past and were known as *kalyalya* in Lwena.

Dress and Adornment

ANIMAL SKINS are still sometimes worn by old people, but they are seldom brayed and are usually the skins of duiker or genet worn for want of anything better. To-day, to wear a skin is a mark of extreme poverty. The braying of skins to make karrosses or blankets is known to the Mbunda on the Manyinga, but is probably not indigenous to any other tribes in the district.

Bark cloth is still widely used by the Luchazi as blankets, or sometimes as wearing apparel. It is prepared by soaking the bark stripped from the tree and then hammering it for several days with a wooden mallet with a grooved face to produce the desired thickness. Bark cloth may also be used as the wad in a muzzle-loading gun. Fibre skirts (*zombo*) are worn by the youths at the circumcision ceremony after their scars have healed.

Heavy leather belts were formerly much worn by men, especially for carrying powder pouches, but are now very rare.

Head-dresses of feathers and clay are worn by several of the *makishi* dancers, such as *chikuza* and *kalelwa*. The bead coronets (*muchama*) worn by chiefs in the past are now rarely seen, though a few chiefs still possess them as heirlooms.

Ivory or copper bracelets are not infrequently seen, although the imported articles have largely supplanted them. Wire leg-rings which are coiled several times round the lower part of the leg are still fairly common, especially among the Luchazi. Nose or lip ornaments seem not to be used by these tribes, and ear-rings, when they occur, are always modern importations, though they have been long known.

In necklaces, cowry shells—often a single shell only—are not infrequent, and a round white plaque (*yimba*) is also used for the same purpose. Ancient beadwork is now rare ; among the Mbunda on the Manyinga occur a few ostrich egg bead necklaces which must have come with the original refugees from the Makololo invaders more than a century ago, and are in the nature of heirlooms. The glass or pot beads which were originally worn came in with the Ovimbundu traders via Angola, and the various types have distinctive names often derived from the Mbundu language, but all are rare to-day. Ornamental beadwork seems to have been virtually unknown apart from the royal *muchama* mentioned above. Modern beads are widely worn, however, as necklaces and, by women, round the waist often in large quantities.

Puberty Rites

THE CIRCUMCISION CEREMONIES of the Lunda and Lovale tribes are characterised by the *makishi* dancers—masked dancers who vary from tribe to tribe. It is impossible to describe them in any detail here, and it must suffice to say that they usually wear fibre costumes covering the whole body and have distinctive head-dresses, often very elaborate. To some extent they have to-day degenerated to become itinerant clowns and lost their original status, and this particularly refers to the *mwana-pwevo*. The circumcision enclosure contains a number of ritualistic objects and receptacles of magical preparations to avert evil and, of course, the wooden pens in which the initiates sleep in pairs.

A later ceremony, the *mungongi*, is in the nature of a tribal initiation comparable to freemasonry in its ritual use of special formulae, and on this occasion certain men daubed with white clay walk on stilts. The female initiation ceremony of *chilunga* or *wali* or *nkanga*, which is a puberty ceremony, seems not to be associated with ritualistic objects, although a cylinder of wood is often used to teach the young female how to lie with her future husband in order to give him the greatest satisfaction. At the *chiwila*, the female equivalent of the *mungongi*, stilt-walkers also appear.

Magic and Witchcraft

PROTECTIVE CHARMS are found in a variety of forms. The actual medicine is usually in some sort of receptacle. Among the com-monest of these is the horn of a blue duiker worn round the neck or wrist. Armlets of animal or reptile skin are sometimes worn for the same purpose. Gourds and tortoise-shells are also commonly used as receptacles for magical preparations, and in cases of illness the medicine which they contain is often daubed on to the patient.

Wooden carved figures are used both to protect their owners or to harm others. The carved figure is believed to become animated when the correct spell is applied, usually by inserting a horn of medicine into the head of the figure.

Charms of various types are also placed in gardens to deter thieves from stealing crops, or placed upon the bodies of wives to deter adulterers. The theory being that anyone who interferes with gardens or women so protected will suffer harm as a result. All these are ordinary devices which may be used by any villager, although they are generally obtained in the first place from a professional practitioner.

Among the Lunda-Lovale tribes the possession of witchcraft is generally not accompanied by any overt material objects. Thus the inherent witchcraft evil linked to the female sex consists of small animals with human features, and the various familiar spirits such as *ilomba* (snake), *nkala* (crab), etc., are likewise only visible to the few initiates. There are, however, a few material objects well known. The bodkins used for corpse eating, to prevent the taint of human flesh from reaching the hands, may be cited. There are also certain devices used for causing death or injury which are more particularly the appliances of professional witches or wizards. Perhaps the best known is the night gun, consisting of a barrel fashioned from a human leg or arm bone with a wooden stock. It is primed with a special mixture and generally fired close to the victim, often through a hole in the wall of his hut at night. The victim should then die.

The most usual method of witch-finding was the *ngombo yakusekula*, but the term *ngombo* is a general one and merely means divining apparatus. Thus the axe handle or pounding-stick used to divine the name of a new-born child is termed *ngombo*. The various types of divining apparatus are extremely numerous. The *ngombo yakusekula* consists of a basket with a fairly flat wide mouth : it contains a large assortment of objects, including many carved figures, and such things as claws of eagles, lions or fowls, bones, pieces of dried flesh or placentas, and so on. The figures are often skilfully carved. The whole is covered with the skins of genets or bush babies and shaken, then uncovered. The juxtaposition of the various objects in the basket determines the course of the divination.

Another type of apparatus consists of a duiker skull, which is balanced upon a metal pin and supposed to revolve either clockwise or anti-clockwise according to the course of the divination. In divining witches, white clay was used to mark the innocent and red clay to mark the guilty. A feature of magical apparatus of all types are the red and black seeds (*jikenyenge*) which are affixed to them in many cases.

[65]

The divination of witches has undergone a rapid evolution in recent years coupled with a radical change in the attitude to the discovered witch. Whereas in the past the witch was always put to death, the present method is usually to cure by emetic. Thus the law may be circumvented. In the same way the *ngombo yakusekula* has gone out of fashion, to be replaced by divining by gazing into a meal mortar of medicine or even an old bottle filled with water, or a mirror.

Other objects associated with divination are the rattles mentioned above and the *mwavi* or *mwazi*, a vegetable compound used as an emetic for testing fowls and then the suspect himself.

Miscellaneous

REFERENCE has been made from time to time above to royal insignia : the bead coronet used by the Lunda chiefs, the beheading knife, to which may be added the *ngoma yamukupelo* of the Lovale— a drum carried slung round the neck with a skin at either end and beaten with both hands. No mention, however, would be complete without reference to the *lukano* or crowning bracelet of the Lunda-Lovale chiefs. This is composed of human genitalia. It is kept in a small house along with the other royal emblems and guarded by an old man. It is produced on the day of formally installing the new chief and slipped over his hand and wrist. In theory each new chief should add a new link to the *lukano* on his accession. As the writer has been enabled to examine two of these emblems closely, it may be worth while recording that the *lukano* of Chief Shinde is a dried object in which the individual parts are interlaced together ; whereas in the *lukano* of Chieftainess Ndungu the component parts are each quite separate, well anointed with red clay and castor oil, and each named after a previous holder of the chieftainship.

Objects representing games are rare ; but puzzles are sometimes found, and occasionally boards are carved on which to play the game with some thirty or so holes and stones, seeds, or small fruit as counters.

Cupping horns are commonly used ; in these areas the commonest type is not an animal horn, but the spout of a calabash. They are used for blood-letting to relieve pain in cases of illness, and also to stretch the vulva in some cases at female puberty rites.

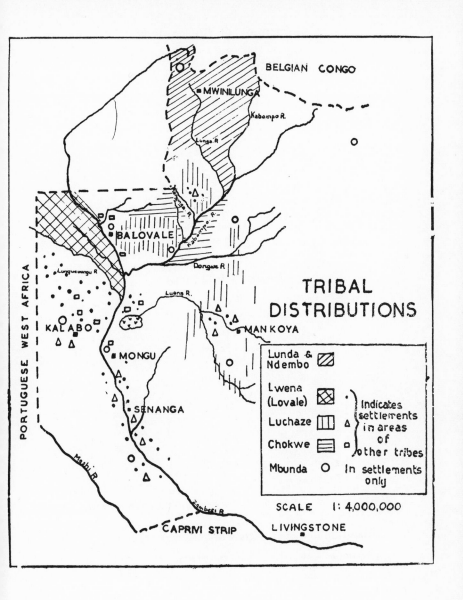

TRIBAL DISTRIBUTIONS

BELGIAN CONGO

MWINILUNGA

Kabompo R.

Lunga. R.

BALOVALE

Dongwe R.

Lungwevungu R.

Luena R.

KALABO

MANKOYA

MONGU

SENANGA

Mashi R.

Zambezi R.

CAPRIVI STRIP

LIVINGSTONE

PORTUGUESE WEST AFRICA

Lunda & Ndembo		
Lwena (Lovale)	·	Indicates settlements in areas of other tribes
Luchaze	△	
Chokwe	□	
Mbunda	○	In settlements only

SCALE 1: 4,000,000

Description of Illustrations.

PLATE I.
(*See overleaf.*)

1. Wooden slit-drum (*Chikuvu*).
2. Likishi mask.
3. Sifting basket (*Musalo*).
4. Porridge paddle (*Mwiko*).
5. Carved comb.
6. Wooden bellows (*Lwazo*).

No. 5 one-fifth (approx.), Nos 1–4 and 6, one-tenth natural size.

Drawn by Joan Green.

PLATE II.
(*See overleaf.*)

1. Arrow heads, showing typical forms :
   A. *Chimbi Lyangombe.*
   B. *Mungamba.*
   C. *Ndavi.*
   D. *Chiyembwoka.*
   E. *Kakweji.*
   F. *Chikenge.*
2. Bow and arrow, showing relative size, method of stringing bow and feathering on arrow.
3. Calabash bubble pipe, decorated with wire (*Mutopa*).
4. Executioner's sword and sheath (*Mukwale*).
5. Water pot (*Mulondo*).

No. 1, one-third natural size ; No. 2 one-twelfth (approx.) natural size ; Nos. 3, 4 and 5, one-fifth natural size.

Drawn by Joan Green.

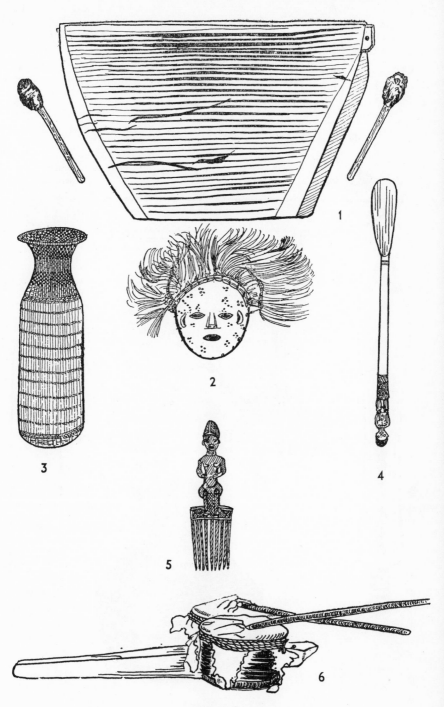

PLATE I.

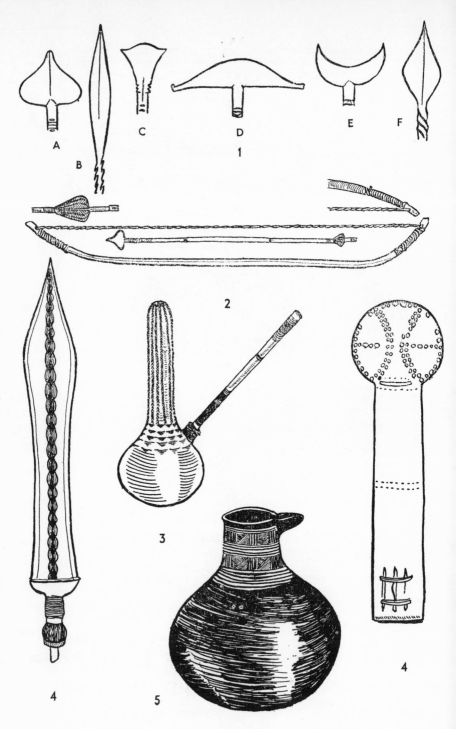

PLATE II.

4

AFRICAN MUSIC IN NORTHERN RHODESIA AND SOME OTHER PLACES

A. M. JONES

1949

The first edition of this pamphlet was called *African Music*. In deference to critics the title is now more limited. But included in this new edition is an Appendix dealing with some music from West Africa, in which are exhibited precisely the same rhythmic principles which characterise African music in Northern Rhodesia.

It is the author's conviction that with a growing body of evidence from different parts of the continent, the principles discussed here will prove to be the specific contribution of Africa as a whole to the world of music.

The paper on AFRICAN MUSIC is partly a reprint of the original " Rhodes-Livingstone Museum Occasional Paper, No. II," published by the Rhodes-Livingstone Institute, and partly reprinted from Essays which appeared in *African Studies*, to the Editor of which we are indebted for permission to reprint.

PART I.

CHAPTER 1.

INTRODUCTION.

NOTE.—This account is based on the musical practice of the following tribes : Bemba, Lala, Swaka, Nsenga, Tonga, Ila and to a limited extent the Lozi—all in Northern Rhodesia. Also to a limited extent of the Manyika of Southern Rhodesia., The practice of different tribes varies, and this limitation must be borne in mind when the terms "African" or "Bantu" are used. At the same time there is evidence to show that underlying variety of practice there is a unity of musical principle which applies everywhere and justifies the term "African Music."

No one will doubt that the African likes to make music, but many may question whether his tunes are really worthy to be classed side by side with the tunes of the West as music.

At the outset of this study it is important to realise that no one with only a nodding acquaintance with Bantu music is in a position to pass judgment upon it. On any quest, the investigator must be unprejudiced ; and the study of African music demands this too. Unfortunately we English people have two strong predispositions when we bring our minds to bear on any music which is not our own. We are prone *to condemn the unfamiliar* ; that is why we hastily turn the knob of our wireless set if haply we light on an Indian broadcast. Secondly, we are predisposed to think that *our own music is the only real music* ; that our scale is nature's own scale and therefore, any other musical system must, in the nature of the case, be more barbaric and less perfect. In this connection it is easy to show that to talk of " nature's own scale " is to talk nonsense. There is no natural scale and any scale has to be a compromise. For nature in music plays a strange trick. By stretching a string and plucking it we can discover nature's octave and nature's fifth. If, however, we tune our piano according to nature's fifths, we find the octaves are all sharp ; if we tune it by nature's octaves, then the fifths will be flat. Nature in fact is imperfect and our Western music with its tempered scale is a vast compromise. This should humble us and we must be prepared to find that other musical systems may be as satisfactory as ours for the purpose of producing beautiful tunes.

It is instructive to compare African and European music. Take *singing* first. The African has both free and metrical solo songs. He has solos with a chorus ; songs in unison, songs in harmony, songs both accompanied and unaccompanied. Take again *the things which make the music*. A European orchestra has instruments falling into defined groups —Woodwind, Strings, Brass, Percussion, and other special things—Piano, Xylophone, Harp, etc. Now the African has stringed instruments, though they are mostly of one string. He has wood-wind instruments, mostly simple flutes. He has no brass, but he plays horns, and after all, brass instruments are developments of the horn. He has percussion ; we are all familiar with the drums, but it may be news to know that the African is far more skilled at drumming rhythms than we are—in fact our banal pom, pom, pom on the drums is mere child's play compared with the complicated and delicate interplay of rhythms in African drumming. Of other effects, while *we* have the piano, the African has the *kalimba* or " kafir piano." Hearing boys strumming on these things one may imagine that they are playing any notes which come to hand. This of course is sheer ignorance on our part. *Kalimba* music is highly developed, and a *kalimba* piece consists of a short tune in harmony repeated many times with an astonishing number of variations. It is indeed highly developed music when played by a good performer.

We see then that the African has already discovered all the main types of vocal music and of sound-producing instruments used by European musicians. His instruments are less complicated, but the musicians' criterion is not that of engineering ; it is simply this ; Do these instruments produce beautiful sounds ? And the answer as far as the African is concerned is—Yes.

Music consists of melody and rhythm. European melodies are for the most part based on definite scales, Major, Minor, etc. The African has no conscious scale. We cannot however say that his music is poor because he knows not our European scales. In melody the question is ; Is the melody a beautiful tune ? If we listen to our carriers sitting round a camp-fire in the evening, singing, we are bound to answer, " Yes it is." Certainly African melody is beautiful. It is not so complicated as ours, but it is simple, strong, incisive and telling. Most European popular tunes need a band to make them sound nice ; but most African melodies are so strong that they can stand being sung without accompaniment.

European rhythm is based on the principle of the *single main beat*, i.e. if a number of people are performing together they all conform to the conductor's main beating. African rhythm is as far advanced beyond this as manhood is from infancy. African rhythm is based on the principle of *multiple main beats*. That is to say that when we listen to an African ensemble we hear not one rhythmic pattern but many distinct rhythms intertwined, each with its own main beat which does not coincide with the main beats of other instruments. So then, drums will all have their own main beats and separate rhythms ; the women are clapping to another rhythm ; everyone is singing to still another rhythm and dancing the while. And thus is built up that magnificent African *Rhythmic Harmony* which, in their system, takes the place of the great tonal harmonies of our orchestras ; but it is none the less thrilling. Yes, the African has some fine music indeed, and the interesting point is that while Europeans have to rehearse and rehearse to produce good music, a simple African village crowd can at a moment's notice, without rehearsal, produce something which as an art form expressing real musical genius, would be hard to surpass.

Music is one expression of the aesthetic sense ; whether it be the highest music or the more homely forms of folk music, if it is true music, it will be a true expression of that soul of art within us that clamours for expression, and so for satisfaction. In this, African music certainly does not fail. While most of us English people, neglecting our own rich store of fine folk music, find expression for our aesthetic sense in tunes, usually banal, imported from America, the African has his own—his very own—folk music, and plenty of it too. Wherever he finds rhythmic acts in daily life he sets them to music. The man at his rock drill, the paddler in his canoe, the woman at her pounding, all translate their rhythmic work to song. And so the genius of African music is that it beautifies the commonplace. We Europeans must seem to the African a drab and musically silent race.

In its social function, too, African music takes its full place. Wherever the African gathers there is music ; and if it be not contaminated with a poor copying of Western tunes, the music made by a crowd is spontaneous, rhythmic, pleasant, in fact it is *music*.

Perhaps this account may arouse in us a new respect for the naive art of the African peoples. Because it is naive and spontaneous, it is honest music. We have indeed some cause for jealousy. For while African music is part of the people's very life, European music cannot now claim that enviable distinction. We do well to esteem—nay even to envy—so rich a treasure house.

CHAPTER 2.

AFRICAN SINGING.

1. TONALITY.

It is natural to inquire at once, " What sort of *scale* does the African use in his music ? Is it like one of ours ? ". The writer of the more superficial type of book on Africa, on the look-out for something arresting, has been known to say that he has " discovered quarter-tones." The author of this essay has often discovered quarter-tones among his choirboys in England because they were too lazy to sing in tune ; the Africans do not sing quarter-tones. They sing notes which are more in tune with nature's intervals than is European singing. For we Europeans have become accustomed to scales played on an instrument like a piano ; now in tuning these instruments the notes of " nature's scale " are flattened or sharpened slightly so as to make every semitone exactly the same size. This is called " equal temperament " and we Europeans have become accustomed to hearing and singing an artificial scale which we have invented. So on hearing the Africans singing we notice their intervals are slightly different from ours. They are in fact a little different but only slightly so.

A more serious theory fairly widely held, is that African music is built on a Pentatonic scale ; that is to say a scale of five notes rather like our Major scale with two notes left out.

Major Scale	*Pentatonic Scales*
(d')t l s fm r d	(d') l s m r d
	(s) m r d l, s,
	(d')t s fm d

[75]

The more musical reader may care to reflect on this thought : granted that the African as we all know regularly uses " te " and " fah " in his music, the acid test of the Pentatonic theory, as far as the first two examples of Pentatonic Scale are concerned, is whether he ever uses " te " and " fah " as *essential melody* notes and not merely as *passing* notes. Clearly if " te " and " fah " are used as essential notes the Pentatonic theory cannot be maintained, for these particular Pentatonic Scales do not contain semitones. Again, in the third example of a Pentatonic scale, " te " and " fah " occur, but " lah " and " ray " are missing. If it can be shown that the African *does* use " lah " and " ray " and also " te " and " fah " in one and the same tune, then again, the Pentatonic theory is inadmissible.

In point of fact the Africans do regularly use all these notes of the scale as essential notes, and not only in singing ; for they both occur on the large *Kalimba*, or kafir piano, where they are not only used as essential melody notes, but also as essential contributors to harmonic progression. One does of course occasionally find pentatonic tunes, but then, any European musician can write a pentatonic tune in Western music. The mere existence of such tunes proves nothing about present African practice, if, as we have said, the African does elsewhere use " te " and " fah " as essential notes.

A more satisfactory theory is that the African scale is a series of conjunct 4ths. Here again we must be cautious for the subject is extremely difficult and the last word has probably not been said. Anyhow we can say this much ; if a European musician makes a tune in accordance with this kind of scale, the African will say, " That is an African tune." The idea is this ; here are some 4ths. :

l	**s**	**f**	**m**	**d**
s	f	m	r	t,
f	m	r	d	l,
m	**r**	**d**	t,	s,

The top and bottom notes in each 4th are the important ones. Compare doh, me, soh, doh' in the European Major scale.

We can make selections from them and group them in several ways, e.g.

$$
\left.\begin{array}{l}\mathbf{s}\\ \mathbf{f}\\ \mathbf{m}\\ \mathbf{r}\end{array}\right\{ \ \left.\begin{array}{l}\mathbf{f}\\ \mathbf{m}\\ \mathbf{r}\\ \mathbf{d}\end{array}\right\{ \ \text{or} \ \left.\begin{array}{l}\mathbf{s}\\ \mathbf{f}\\ \mathbf{m}\\ \mathbf{r}\end{array}\right\{ \ \left.\begin{array}{l}\mathbf{m}\\ \mathbf{r}\\ \mathbf{d}\\ \mathbf{t,}\end{array}\right\{ \ \text{or} \ \left.\begin{array}{l}\mathbf{l}\\ \mathbf{s}\\ \mathbf{f}\\ \mathbf{m}\end{array}\right\{ \ \left.\begin{array}{l}\mathbf{f}\\ \mathbf{m}\\ \mathbf{r}\\ \mathbf{d}\end{array}\right\{ \ \left.\begin{array}{l}\mathbf{m}\\ \mathbf{r}\\ \mathbf{d}\\ \mathbf{t,}\end{array}\right\{
$$

Each of these groups is a different scale ; they are different because they each have different emphasis notes, i.e. those printed in heavier type. These emphasis notes are the chief notes of rest in the melody or the focal points round which the melody moves.

Plate 1*A* shows a tune written by a European, based on the first two scales above. It is taken from the S. Mark's College play "Abu Hassan."

It is on some such underlying principle that the African builds his tunes. But the important fact to realise is that he is utterly unconscious of any organised theory behind his music. He makes his music quite spontaneously and it is with interest and the delight of discovery that the more educated African will listen to a demonstration of the basic principles which underlie his musical practice.

2. MELODY.

A good deal of the vocal music in Northern Rhodesia consists of single melodies without harmony, to be sung by one person, or more usually by voices in unison. These tunes though legion in number have an underlying unity which evades accurate description but which gives them all the characteristic sound of African music. Broadly speaking, the outline of an African tune is like a succession of the teeth of a rip-saw ; a steep rise (not usually exceeding a 5th) followed by a gentle sloping down of the tune ; then another sudden rise—then a gentle sloping down, and so on. The tendency is for the tune to start high and gradually to work downwards in this saw-like manner. There is no key change in the course of the tune (though the writer has come across one or two curious exceptions to this otherwise unexceptionable rule). There is however a distinct feeling in these tunes of hovering over and around a central note or notes, round which the melody seems to be built or towards which it works.

It is important to realise that apart from drumming, nearly all African music is vocal music. This means that African melody has grown up in association with words. Africans rarely, if ever, conceive of melodies in the form of abstract music. Now this has a profound influence on the way the tune is constructed, as the following reasoning will show. All African languages have one common feature which is that every word has its own *tone-pitch* : this means that the word is not merely a series of syllables, but it is a series of syllables *each spoken on a definite pitch of voice*. If you say a bantu word with the wrong pitch on its syllables it is not a word at all : it is meaningless. Every single word and syallable in African languages has its proper tone pitch in the sentence. If, therefore, a word depends for its meaning on the relative highness or lowness with which you say each syllable it is easy to see that if you set these words to a tune, then if the words are to mean anything, the tune must go up or down in conformity with the syllables.

This is precisely what happens in African music wherever possible. It explains why each verse of a song differs slightly in melody. The words of each verse even though they contain the same number of syllables which is unlikely, need separate melodic treatment to make the tune agree with the rise and fall of the syllables. Of course, one of the skills of the song-maker is to choose words which allow the tune to remain more or less constant. How far a melody can jump—a 3rd or 4th or 5th, etc.—when the speech tone varies, has not been determined yet, but it is only in certain cases like fixed metrical choruses where this principle is

[77]

likely to be violated. So powerful is its influence on African vocal music that there is one form of humorous song in which the humour is produced by making the melody for certain syllables run counter to the speech tones. The African thinks this sounds very funny indeed.

The result of all this is that African melody is in a strait-jacket. It is much more restricted in its scope by this very hide-bound system than was European music in the days of Bach and the strict rules of counterpoint. And the liberty of melody is still further restricted by the universal custom of singing *only one note to each syllable*. Anyone who tries to write a tune on these lines will find how very difficult it is to achieve interest and especially balance in melodic form. The African does succeed in doing this, but there is no question that the restrictions of the system have a conservative and limiting effect on the free development of African melody.

3. HARMONY.

When a crowd sings there is usually some harmony. In fact the Bantu have a passionate love of harmony. They are progressing musically in the same way as our forefathers. At their present stage they are moving from unison to harmony and have reached the stage of " organum," that sort of harmony our forefathers delighted in around the years 900–1050 A.D. The idea is that part of the crowd sings the tune, and part of the crowd sings *the same tune* a 4th or a 5th lower. The Bemba for some extraordinary and unexplained reason always sing in organum in *thirds* and never in fourths or fifths. This is most remarkable, for while the 4ths and 5ths are " perfect " intervals, to sing in 3rds involves the recognition that a minor 3rd and a major 3rd are not only consonant intervals but that both alike partake of the quality of " thirdness."

There are indications that the Bantu are already, quite apart from European influence, beginning to take the next step, which is to allow the bass to move independently of the treble, using what we call Oblique and Contrary Motion. Just across the Zambezi, the Manyika have already firmly taken this step and in their folk music harmonies, are just biting at the typical technique of *Polyphony* which technique gave us the glorious vocal music of the Elizabethan age. *Plate 1B* shows a piece of Manyika polyphony. Nothing exhibiting such technical mastery in vocal music has come to the author's notice in Northern Rhodesia.

4. RHYTHM

African songs fall into two main *rhythmic* groups ; those which have a " free " rhythm and those with a " fixed " rhythm. The essential difference is that you cannot beat time (i.e. a regularly recurring rhythm) to the first and you can do so to the second class. If a person is just singing to himself as he walks along, or as he mends his fish-net, he may sing a meandering sort of tune in free rhythm. The *Impango* and *Ziyabilo* songs of the Baila, described on pages 14 and 15 are free rhythm songs.

The vast majority of African songs have a fixed rhythm ; that is to say, you can beat time to them. But when a European says " beat time " he means counting **1,2,3,4,1,2,3,4,** or **1,2,3,1,2,3,** etc. ; in each example the stressed beat is the first one. These of course are only very simple ways of beating time. Sometimes the African uses them but not often. His sense of rhythm is much more developed than ours. Even when he does use them, the words of his songs do not scan metrically nor do they coincide with the beats as is our European custom. Compare these two examples; each has a regular beat, and the speed of the beats is the same for both examples: *See plate two.*

The subtlety of the rhythm of the second song is astonishing: see how the beat falls *right between* two syllables at A and B. If anyone were to ask, " What is the outstanding characteristic of African music ? " the answer is, " A highly developed rhythm."

Now Africans mark the rhythm of their songs by clapping their hands, by beating sticks on a pole lying on the ground when they are in a hut drinking beer, or by drumming. Of these, handclapping is the usual rhythmic accompaniment of singing. The beats in the above example are clapped. While as we have seen, the Bantu do use a *regular* clap, a more typical clapping rhythm is the following:

Each set of 12 is a " bar." Clap it and see what it is like. Note that you have to clap once on each of the numbers 1, 3, 5, 8 and 10. It is not like our rhythms: it is much more interesting, nay infectious, but yet it is quite regular, for the same rhythmic pattern is used for each " bar." A tune with this clapping will be seen on plate 3.

A fundamental feature of African rhythm which we mention here but may not stay to elaborate is this: all African music which is capable of being clapped to, or drummed or played on a *Kalimba* or Xylophone, can be divided into bars containing 4 beats, 6 beats or a multiple of these. A bar of 4 may be followed by a bar of 6 beats. I have never known this principle to be violated: and if a transcriber taking down a tune finds that his tune cannot be so subdivided he may rest assured that he has got it wrong somewhere.

African vocal music is, like our own popular music, always in a state of change. New tunes are always becoming the fashion, and then being replaced by others. A boy who has been absent from his country for some time will, on his return, be all agog to hear the latest " hits." At the same time there is the more traditional type of folk song preserved in the folk stories. At suitable times people will gather in the evening and will relate these folk tales. Most of them have one or more songs inserted by tradition in them. When the narrator is about to start his story he will rehearse the chorus of the songs so that when it occurs, the listeners may take up the refrain without hesitation. As with all folk music, no one knows who made such songs, but there are other classes of songs which are consciously composed. The following very human account made by Robert Kabombo lifts the veil for those who are curious to know how the African sets about making new music.

CHAPTER 3.

SOME TYPES OF AFRICAN SONGS AND HOW THEY ARE MADE

NOTE—This is an account of the songs of the Ila and Tonga tribes.

There are about six classes of African songs as sung by the Ila and Tonga people. They are : *Impango* songs ; *Ziyabilo* songs ; *Inyimbo* ; *Mapobolo* ; *Mapobaulo* ; and *Zitengulo* songs. Each of these classes has its own kind of dancing.

By tribal custom it is incumbent on every young man or woman to compose his own songs. A young man is asked to sing one of his own songs on the day of his marriage. A young woman also is asked to sing one of her own songs on the day she is allowed to wear *musini*. On this occasion this young woman brews beer so that the dressers may drink and sing.

IMPANGO.

This kind is sung by women only, at a beer drink, at work, or on any other occasion when people gather together. Every woman must have her own personal repertoire of *Impango* songs because men are very fond of listening to the singers of such songs.

At a social gathering, when people are settled and they are ready for the singing of *Impango*, one woman will stand to command silence. When all are quiet, one woman will stand up to sing her *Impango*. All the people, both men and women will play close attention to her. If the song is a particularly good one, some of her relatives or friends will stand up and interrupt the song by shouting to praise her and by giving her presents such as a ring, a towel, some tobacco, or a sixpence. This custom of giving presents is called *Kutaila*. If a woman wishes to show her praise but has nothing to give, she may stand up and interrupt the singer by starting to sing an *Impango* of her own. This is called *Kusangila*. When the woman who has interrupted sits down, the first singer will go on with her song.

The *Impango* are sung very high and very fast and have many words. In spite of this and in spite of the fact that there are many rules for the singing of an *Impango*, the owner of the song will never forget it for before a performance she will put in a considerable amount of practice.

No man can sing an *Impango* because they are pitched in the Treble voice and therefore cannot be sung by a man's voice. Some men can remember both the words and tune of an *Impango* but it can never sound right if he sings it on account of his low voice.

[80]

How the Impango are Made.

Making an *Impango* is a difficult task for the women. In each village there will be found some women who are particularly good at the art. A woman who wants to make an *Impango* will first of all think out the words, which will be in praise of her lover, her husband or herself. If her husband has killed some fierce animal, the words will be about this event. If she wishes to praise her husband on the subject of his riches, the words will be framed accordingly.

When she has prepared the words, the woman will call some of her woman friends to help her. Together they will go to a well-reputed maker of *Impango* songs. This lady will ask the woman to sing the first six or more words slowly, and will note the first tone—whether the owner wishes the song to start in a low or high tone. The *Impango* maker will possibly make up a few phrases of music which will suitably follow the first phrase as sung to her. This done, the *Impango* maker now gets to work and composes a complete tune for the whole song. This may take several days. She calls the little party to a practice every evening after supper. When the *Impango* is complete and learnt the practice party is disbanded. The owner of the song will keep on singing it by herself, at home or at work. If she forgets part of it, she will go to one of her friends who was one of the practice party to ask her how the song went. Having mastered it thoroughly, the woman will be proud of her *Impango*. When she is invited to any festival, she will keep on singing it in her heart till the time comes for her to stand up and sing it in public.

Ziyabilo.

This kind of singing is sung by men only and corresponds to the *Impango* sung by women. The *Ziyabilo* and the *Impango* are both sung at similar times such as on a journey, at work, at a beer drink or at any festival. *Ziyabilo* songs always find a welcome audience. In these songs men praise their possessions, their state of life, their travel adventures, how they hunt or how they are happy. It is easy to learn this kind of singing because the song consists of a few words sung over and over again. The pitch of the song is an essential part of it ; thus all *Ziyabilo* must be sung with men's voices just as *Impango* belong to the Treble register. Like the *Impango*, the *Ziyabilo* songs are solos pure and simple and have no chorus, but are sung by one individual. Unlike the *Impango*, the *Ziyabilo* singer may accompany his song with a hand rattle or with a small drum called an *Indandala* which he beats himself.

The same procedure obtains for the singing of *Ziyabilo* as for *Impango*. At a gathering, silence will be commanded, one man will stand and sing his *Ziyabilo*. If the song is a " hit " he may be interrupted by his relations or friends who give presents or by an impecunious adulator who will interpolate a *Ziyabilo* song of his own. When people give these presents they keep on saying their nick-names as they rise to their feet to make the presentation. The man having finished his song, another man will rise and sing his *Ziyabilo*, and so on.

Most of these songs are composed while men are still small boys. Each boy must have two or more of these songs, so that when he grows up he will have a repertoire of the songs of manhood. (Why don't we English people have a similar custom ?—A.M.J.).

While the boys are in the bush minding cattle they may make some short *Ziyabilo* in praise of their father's cattle or any other possessions. There are some boys who are very good at making these songs and they often help their weaker and less musically gifted brethren. Often boys will take the tune of one of their father's *Ziyabilo* and set it to their own words, being careful to see that the words fit the tune. (This raises the complex and little explored subject of the relation between the rise and fall of speech—Tonetics, and the rise and fall of melody—A.M.J.). A boy may practice at any time, when perhaps he is walking alone or when he is with other boys.

Grown up men also make *Ziyabilo* in praise of their riches etc. Some men simply take the tunes of other men's songs and adapt new words according to their fancy. But the words of the song *must* fit the tune. However, it can easily be perceived that such a song has only been arranged and is not a homogeneous composition. Many of the tunes of these songs are brought by visitors from other countries. Men who are not sufficiently musical to make their own *Ziyabilo* may be helped by other men who are good at it.

Some women sing their husband's *Ziyabilo* in good or bad times, though it does not really belong to them to do so. They cannot construct them. A woman is allowed to sing her husband's *Ziyabilo* when her husband has died, and also at the time of his funeral to remind herself how her husband used to sing while he was still alive.

It is easy to understand the words of *Ziyabilo* because this sort of song is sung very slowly.

Inyimbo.

Inyimbo may be subdivided into three classes. First the common *Inyimbo* which are sung at gatherings like beer drinks when they are sung as an accompaniment to dancing by a mixed crowd of adults and young people. Second, those *Inyimbo* which are sung in a *Ciŋande* dance, by young men and young women together. Third, the *Inyimbo* sung in a *Mucinko* dance, danced by young women only. Everyone who is likely to have to join in singing these songs must have his own repertoire. In the *Ciŋande*, common *Inyimbo* are used.

In this kind of singing, women, men and young people sing together. One person at a time will stand up to dance and start his song, then the people will answer and sing it in unison.

Some of this type of song have many words especially those of the women ; the words of the majority of men's *Inyimbo* are few in number. Women are the most zealous in every kind of singing.

[82]

At the time of singing the common *Inyimbo*, people will gather together and sit down. When they are ready they start clapping or beating on pestles with short sticks. When this has got going, one man or woman will stand to start the song, dancing the while in the manner proper to the *Inyimbo*. The owner of the song will first sing it right through, then the people will pick it up and sing it several times. Then the owner will sing it by himself again, and so on till all have had enough. The custom of giving presents is also observed in this type of singing.

The purpose of clapping and beating on pestles is to keep time and to guide the singers. Any person who does not follow the beats cannot be answered when he starts his song, and the crowd will simply laugh at him. (Note the importance of rhythm—A.M.J.). In this sort of singing the grown up people enjoy themselves very much for it is an occasion for praising themselves, their friends or their lovers. If there are some chiefs of importance present, the young men and women should have their own place apart and sing there.

HOW THE INYIMBO ARE MADE.

Inyimbo are made in the same way as the *Impango*, but must be constructed according to the proper idiom of the three types, common *Inyimbo*, *Inyimbo* for the *Ciɲande* dance and the *Mucinko* songs. They are, however, shorter and simpler in wording and so they do not take so long as the *Impango* to compose. A distinct feature of the *Ciɲande* and *Mucinko* songs is that they are short lived. They come into vogue for about four months and then are replaced by new ones.

MAPOBOLO.

This is a very sweet kind of singing, sung slowly and gently. They are sung after the *Impango* songs, when quietness has been secured. One woman at a time will stand in the middle of the gathering to start her *Ipobolo*, then all the people, men and women will answer, the women of course singing an octave higher than the men. This kind of singing is similar to Psalm-chants. During the song, when it is time for the chorus to enter, the owner will make a sign, with a little walk or by raising her hands. This is called *Kuzeema*. The custom of giving presents is used in this style of song. There is no clapping or beating of any kind, but all the people must pay great attention to the song so that they may join in at exactly the right moment. The first person having finished, someone else will stand to sing either another *Ipobolo* or some other kind of song.

HOW THE MAPOBOLO ARE MADE.

Mapobolo are made in the same way as the *Impango* but as the words are few and the tune is short they are easy to make and do not take much time in the making. A woman who wants to make an *Ipobolo* first thinks of the words or tune ; she then tries to sing little by little. When she feels that the song is under way, she sings it to her neighbours. The more musical of these will correct the song and make it right. When they approve the final form, they practice it together till most of them know it, so that when they are invited to a feast they will be able to give a good rendering. This is the way they are made, but each *Ipobolo* must be interesting, and every woman must possess some songs of this kind.

[83]

MAPOBAULO.

This kind of singing was used in old times to sing in fighting ; it was sung by men only. The word *Kupobaula* has two meanings—to slaughter, or to sing happily after having conquered. So it was the *Mapobaulo* which inspired men to bravery. Nowadays as the country is in peace these songs are only sung at the death of important men, expecially those who were leaders in battles. At the time of singing *Mapobaulo*, all the men gather together in a close group and then march together (though they do not keep step). The leader will go in front and start a song. All the men in the group will sing the song bravely, filling their minds with the spirit of fighting.

The words of the *Mapobaulo* are chosen according to the progress of the fighting. Thus some of them were sung when the men were on the way to the fight. Some were sung while the fighting was in progress ; and some were sung when they were returning from the battle, if they had conquered. If they had not conquered they could not sing because they were sorry.

HOW THE MAPOBAULO WERE MADE.

It was the work of the leaders to compose the *Mapobaulo*. These leaders would think of their battles and then formulate some suitable words to make battle songs. Such songs are easy to learn because they are very short, and the same words are repeated over and over again.

ZITENGULO.

This kind of song is sung by women as solos, at the time of a death when they are mourning. It is a very sad song, which makes every singer feel so grief-stricken that tears will roll from her eyes, because she wishes the dead person were alive as he used to be. None of the relatives of the dead person will take the slightest notice of the song. The only people who will listen are those who are not relatives but have come to comfort the mourners.

Some men and women sing *Ziyabilo* at this time though they are not mourning songs. If the dead person is a man, his wife or relatives will sing his *Ziyabilo* songs. If it be a woman, her women relatives will sing her *Impango*, *Inyimbo* or any other type of song which she used to sing while she lived.

HOW THE ZITENGULO ARE MADE.

It is not difficult to compose *Zitengulo* because they are very short, and indeed they are not important for they are sung only at a mourning of a particular person. As soon as a person dies the women will start to mourn, and they will think over carefully the life's work of the deceased. On this they will base their *Zitengulo*. The singers do not help each other in composing this type of song. Each of them by herself will start to sing little by little, adding words and melody till the song is complete. Here is an example of the steps in composing a *Chitengulo* :

[84]

(a)   *Mukwe wa Bama wo wo wo wo wo wo* !

In place of the *wo wo wo wo* the composer next gets an idea :

(b)   *Mukwe wa Bama bama Inamulambo, wo wo wo* etc.

This is again extended to become :

(c)   *Mukwe wa Bama bama Inamulambo omana-milimo omana-milimo* . . . .

Finally the dictates both of rhythm and melody are satisfied with the completed version :

(d)   *Mukwe wa Bama bama Inamulambo omana-milimo Taata omana-milimo.*

Translation.

(a)   Son-in-law of my mother !   (i.e. My husband ! !) *wo wo,*

(b)   Son-in-law of my mother, my mother the mother of Mulambo.

(c)   Son-in-law of my mother, my mother the mother of Mulambo, you hard-working man !

(d)   Son-in-law of my mother, my mother the mother of Mulambo, you hard-working man, my father ! (i.e. my husband !) you hard-working man !

Author's Note.—In the interests both of the study of Bantu music and of posterity, the complete set of examples together with their tunes (and clapping) in the possession of the author ought to be printed in extenso.

It is regrettably impossible to do so in this present essay.

Chapter 4.

DRUMMING.

It is nearly true to say that whenever there is drumming there is dancing : it certainly is true to say that the drums have a social significance not possessed by any other instrument. A wedding, a beer-drink,— any rejoicing without the drums is unthinkable.   They are the very foundation of a social occasion. The dancers dance *to the drums* : it is not the drums which play for them : the singers sing and clap *to the drums* and not vice versa. In fact, the African, unlike the European who treats his drums as an embellishment of music made by other instruments, regards his drumming as *music per se*. The drumming at a dance is the orchestra, and the varied rhythms and tones of the drums not only lead the dancers, they intoxicate them.

Now if a European dance were to be accompanied by drums alone, it needs little imagination to see how intensely boring and banal it would be. Not so with the Bantu : for Bantu drumming is by itself a separate art form. It is cram full of good things ; it never lacks surprises if a good drummer is present. It needs no other instruments to sustain the interest. It is, as an art form, complete in itself.

[85]

From a distance, typical dance drumming sounds to the not-too-inquisitive listener as a dull repetitive *tum*-pi-ti, *tum*-pi-ti, *tum*-pi-ti, *tum*-pi-ti etc. Were he to go close and observe carefully, he would find all sorts of interesting things going on.

The first point to grasp is that African drumming is essentially *harmony*—it is a harmony composed not of notes but of rhythms : and because it is harmony, the drumming as a general rule needs at least two drums ; three is a very usual number.

The second point to grasp is that African drumming is composed of a number of different rhythms played simultaneously but with this one important feature, namely that *the main beats of the rhythms do not coincide.* In this lies the secret of African drumming and it deserves some further explanation.

Suppose there are three European drummers each with a separate drum. The first beats this rhythm over and over again :

The second beats thus :—

and the third man beats this rhythm :—

If a conductor were summoned and conducted all three drums beating simultaneously, his conducting would obviously produce this result :

According to our Western music, the main beats of each instrument must coincide. When the conductor's baton comes down we all know there is a main beat for all the instruments.

Now it so happens that the rhythms given above belong to an African drumming called *Ngwayi*, which is played by the Bemba tribe in Northern Rhodesia. If a Bemba heard the version given above he would just laugh. To him it would sound absurdly childish : in fact he would not call it music at all. For the African has an entirely different way of conducting several instruments playing together.

Let us see how he would conduct these drummers. He would cause the second drummer to beat his main beat *one beat later* than the main beat of the first man. While he would cause the third drummer to make his main beat coincide with the main beat of the first drummer, he would cause him to *start* his rhythm with the first beat of the second drum. Thus the drumming would be :

You notice that it is rather like an English " Round," e.g. " *London's burning* " where each part picks up the tune a bit later than the previous part. But of course it is far more subtle and developed, because the three rhythms are all different, whereas in " *London's burning* " each part sings the same tune. Furthermore the main beat of the second drum is " crossed " with the others. This produces a thrill in the listener : for he can either listen to the main beat of the first and third drums, in which case the beating of the second drum crashes right across it ; or he can fix his attention on the main beat of the second drum, in which case the main beats of the first and third drums form a strong cross rhythm which clamours for recognition and is very stimulating. In fact, these cross rhythms have an effect on the African which is hard to describe ; all we can say is that they are quite intoxicating ; they make every muscle in his body clamour for dancing. This is an effect which we Europeans have never experienced, for we have never tried " crossing " our rhythms. Even syncopation in its jazz forms is utterly different and entirely Western in structure, for *the essence of syncopation is to throw emphasis on the main* beats.

The musical reader may like to know that our African conductor would not be satisfied with this. He would send for a fourth drum whose rhythm would be :

and he would cause it to come in with the second drum, so that its main beat would coincide therewith and so clash with the first and third drums. But note please, that this fourth rhythm is a mixture of triple and duple groups. Now, as all the other drummers have rhythms of triple groups, when the fourth drummer crashes across them with his duple groups the effect is indescribably thrilling. But this is by no means the end of his resources. What else he would do is beyond the scope of this essay : the question is dealt with in detail in Part II. Suffice it to say that he would need a party for hand-clapping to superimpose a new and different cross rhythm. He would need a song to be sung, also with its own peculiar rhythm : and he would not be content till he had those for whom all this really exists—the dancers. For it is the dance with its singing, clapping and drumming which makes the wonderful African ensemble, the flower of his musical genius and the full expression of his aesthetic and social senses.

The above example of drumming is predominantly triple in rhythm though the fourth drum introduces a duple motif. Some drumming is predominantly duple in spirit. But though the Bantu use in all their music both duple and triple rhythms, they seem to refuse to recognise the triple rhythm. If it is isolated and they are asked to sing or tap a triple rhythm, they will naturally and quite unconsciously convert it into duple time. Those of us who have tried to teach Africans English Country dancing or Morris Dancing will know that if the dance has a triple tune it is almost impossible to teach them to move their feet in triple time. They insist on moving them in duple time. The same curious phenomenon occurs in West Africa—see " Music in the Gold Coast " by W. E. Ward, which is an article in the *Gold Coast Review*, Vol. 3, No. 2, July—December, 1927. This is a peculiar and profound mystery.

Sufficient has been said to show the complexity of African drumming. Though it is all built up from simple units of rhythm—little simple drum tunes we might call them—yet when they are combined on the principle of the cross-rhythm they build up an imposing and monumental sound which is as far in advance of our European conductor's petty pulsations as Kilimanjaro (19,000 ft.) is from Snowden (3,560 ft.).

We have devoted a special chapter to Drumming because drumming shows the characteristic rhythmic structure of African music. All African music conforms to the same rules. This may not be apparent where a simple instrument is being played : but so soon as the player starts singing, or someone else starts clapping to his tune, the principle of the cross-rhythms is observed to be present. He who understands drumming has gone far towards the understanding of African music.

Plate 1

A

An African I, from Timbuctoo — I've travelled by land and sea —— To

Bagadad town from Timbuctoo — And glad am I here to be.

B

A POLYPHONIC ROUND

Manyika Story Song. S. Rhod.

VOICE 1.

Ta - - re - - ra Kudya ze u - ro - mbe.

Two top voices should be doubled an octave lower.

VOICE 2

Kwe KweKa Kuyo Ke - ru Kwe-za.

One phrase of 6 pulses.

VOICE 3.

dariko hi, Neji-ra dari-ko hi, Neji-ra

♩. = 120

VOICE 4.

Gomo guru rembire, . Go-mo gu-ru rembi-re,

Probable Translation :

1st voice. It is our custom to eat by begging our way.
(The singers are wandering minstrels).

2nd voice. Scrunch, scrunch! the sound of the millstone grinding millet.

3rd voice. Mr. Frog, please jump!

4th voice. That is the big hill of the Bambile (name of a tribe).

[89]

Plate 2.

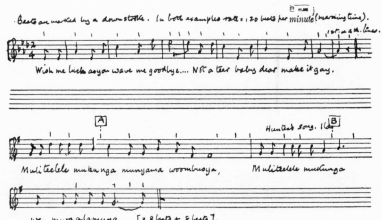

Beats are marked by a down-stroke. In both examples rate = 120 beats per minute (marching time).

Wish me luck as you wave me goodbye.... Not a tear baby dear make it gay.

Muliteelele mukanga munyama woombusya,

Hunted song. 1(a)

Muliteelele mukunga

wa mwaalamuna. [= 8 beats + 8 beats].

Translation :

You will hear the cries of the man who has roused the fury of an animal :

You will hear the cries of the man who has been mauled.

[90]

Plate 3.

A
MEN'S SONG—INYIMBO CLASS.

Each phrase, i e ⌐⊤⌐ ⌐⌐ = 12 pulses
Repeats are essential part of song
Altogether 10 phrases = 4 + 6 (including repeats)

Translation :

My friends, oh ! the movement of the muscles of the cattle as they go along ! as they go along—the cattle went joyfully to the cattle-post : oh ! those cattle, men's helpers ! see how their muscles are moving as they go along.

B
KALIMBA MUSIC.

This is a very simple example

Plate 4.

THE NOTES OF A NDANDI.

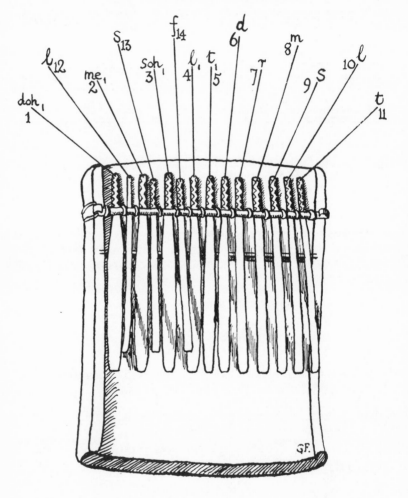

CHAPTER 5.

SOME OTHER MUSICAL INSTRUMENTS.

1. THE KAFIR PIANO OR KALIMBA.

Of all solo instruments this is the most common, though alas the European mouth organ is rapidly displacing it. The Kafir Piano, or *Kalimba* like the representatives of the Harp family is essentially a personal instrument for private pleasure. It is said by the Bantu that when you see a young man going about continually playing his *Kalimba* it is a sure sign that he is in love. However that may be, the *Kalimba* occupies a place in Bantu life of which there is no counterpart in England except it be the mouth organ. At any moment when he feels musically inclined, the African can play to himself on his *Kalimba*. And when he does so, he is producing something far more artistic than the ordianry European would probably concede. To imagine for example that the Kafir Piano player is just playing any notes which come to hand, is sheer nonsense. *Kalimba* music is a fully developed musical form, and though of course we often meet with poor performers, a virtuoso player is a master of music and could hold any musical European spellbound.

Kalimba music consists of a short tune usually with some harmonies, 4ths, 5ths and octaves, which is repeated many times but with this important detail, that it has an astonishing number of variations. Herein lies its charm : for there is something soothing and restful in the constant reiteration of a short piece of beautiful music, whereas any possibility of monotony is removed by the delightfully light and airy nuances produced by the subtle variations.

The ordinary Kafir Piano played about the streets of a town may be but a poor specimen badly out of tune and with its metal notes of unequal length. It has been tampered with perhaps by countless players the generality of whom are as unable to tune a *Kalimba* as an ordinary pianist is to tune his piano. The *Kalimba maker* however is a skilled craftsman and the instrument when it leaves his shop is a thing of beauty. Its tuning indeed involves some of the technique used by a European piano tuner.

Now as the *Kalimba* is played with the thumb nails, and as the music is rapid, it is essential that the little metal prongs which give the sound should not be only in tune but in line or on a sweeping curve, so as not to trip up the thumbs as they move from one note to another. The problem then for the maker is so to adjust the notes that when they are in line they are also in tune. Further he has to make them of such a thickness and springiness that they will not only give a sweet and even sound, each note having the same intensity, but that their main harmonics should harmonise either with the note itself or with one of the other consonant notes. Anyone who has tried to make from an old nail, a note for a Kafir Piano will speedily have discovered what skill is needed for producing this apparently simple instrument.

Kafir Pianos fall into two main classes : the big one, *Ndandi*, which has about 14 notes, and the small one, *Kankobela*, which has about 8 notes. The tuning of these two classes is entirely different and the music played on each is of course different also. The music played on the *Ndandi* is much more elaborate than that of the *Kankobela* as there are more notes at the disposal of the performer.

Let us watch a Kalimba maker tuning a *Ndandi*.

(a) He first makes out of old nails or wire, a number of square rods about 1/8th inch square. He cuts 14 lengths of about 4 inches.

(b) He then beats out by hammering cold, the first note, which is number 9 above. (Plate 4.) He makes it taper and gives it a gentle upward curve. He often stamps a pattern at the head. He puts it in the Kalimba and sees that it gives a good clear note.

(c) He makes number 10 and inserts it, tries it, takes it out and hammers it and so on till it is a tone higher than number 9.

(d) He makes number 11 and tunes it by playing it in succession with numbers 9 and 10 and listening to see if it sounds nice.

(e) Similarly he makes number 8 and tunes it against number 9.

(f) He tunes number 7 against numbers 8, 9, 10, 11.

(g) He makes number 6 and tunes it against numbers 7 and 8.

(h) He makes number 5 and tunes it with number 11 as a true octave.

(i) Now number 4, which he tunes as an octave with number 10.

(j) He tunes number 3 as an octave of number 9.

(k) Number 2 is tuned as an octave of number 8.

(l) Now number 14 is tuned as a perfect 4th, sounded with number 6.

(m) Number 13 is tuned as a unison with number 9.

(n) Number 12 is tuned as a unison with number 10.

If this has been done properly he will find that :

Numbers 1 and 3 make a perfect 5th.

Numbers 4 and 7 make a perfect 4th.

Numbers 5 and 8 make a perfect 4th.

Numbers 2 and 5 make a perfect 5th.

These intervals *must* be in tune. They are constantly used in playing. This is only one example of the method of tuning. It was supplied by a *Kalimba* maker, Nine of Simaubi Village near Mapanza. There are, I believe, other methods. But the actual notes of the instrument will be usually those given above, though there are tribal differences.

The notes of a *Kankobela* (small Kafir Piano) are usually :

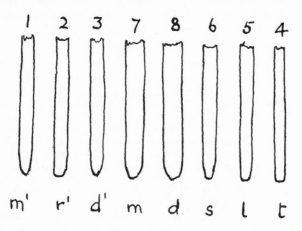

in which :

    1 and 4 sound a perfect 4th.
    2 and 5 sound a perfect 4th.
    3 and 6 sound a perfect 4th.
    3 and 8 are octaves.
    1 and 7 are octaves.
    7 and 4 are a perfect 5th which is a very favourite chord on this
    instrument.

For an example of *Kalimba* music see *Plate 3B*.

2. OTHER INSTRUMENTS.

It is impossible in this handbook to consider in detail the many musical instruments possessed by the Bantu. The purpose of the essay has been rather to give the reader some insight into the basic structure of African music which finds expression in varying degrees of simplicity or complexity in his singing and playing. Apart from the Xylophone, which in the writer's part of the country is seldom used, and anyway is not universal, all the remaining instruments produce one to four notes and so their music is very simple and restricted. These instruments may be placed in three classes—Xylophones, Strings and Blown Instruments.

Xylophones.—The simplest form of the Xylophone is the Lala "*Limba*" make of a large calabash whose mouth is narrowed by a plaster of dung and across which is slung a carefully tuned slab of wood. If this is hit gently by a stick padded with a ball of Native rubber at one end, there issues from the calabash an intense and pervading and very beautiful note. The player makes rhythmic variations not only with his stick but also by placing his left hand over the orifice of the calabash and closing or opening the latter, so making an intermittent rhythm of remarkable penetrating power.

[95]

The full fledged Xylophone is simply a series of these *malimba* arranged on a frame. It may be slung across the front of the body and is played with two drum sticks. The music produced is rapid and is similar to *Kalimba* music. In fact Robert, who wrote chapter 3, says that the Ila Xylophone is tuned to the same notes as a *Ndandi*.

The musical reader may care to experiment with a calabash and a strip of hard wood, and try to produce a note from the calabash by striking the wood. He will probably fail, and by doing so he will realise the skill required in making these instruments. The fact is that the sound is made by setting in vibration the column of air in the calabash, by hitting the wood. But if the wood is to excite the air, when hit it must itself vibrate at the same number of vibrations per second as does the air in the calabash. Looking at these bucolic Xylophones one may be pardoned for failing to realise the exact workmanship required in their making.

Stringed Instruments.—Of these there is a considerable variety, some played by women and some by boys. They are all of very limited range and none have the popularity of the *Kalimba*. They produce but few notes. They may be simple bows with a stretched string, or longer bows with half a calabash inverted and fixed to the middle or the end of the bow. They may be played by plucking or by hitting the string with a short fairly stout stem of dry grass. They all in my experience give a subdued sound and are " private " instruments for personal enjoyment. Often, the one or two prime notes of the string may be increased to as many as four by " stopping " the string, but as there is usually no arrangement as on a violin where the stopped string is pressed on a hard surface, the stopped notes sound dull and lack brilliance. Here it is interesting to note how stringed instruments have almost certainly developed from the hunter's bow ; when the arrow is released there is a twang, and it is easy to see how the Bantu have used this quality of the bow in making music.

Wind Instruments.—The Bantu just like any other race have discovered the principle of the whistle and also of the flute, and therefore they make a variety of reed whistles, reed flutes, and horns of various sizes. Of these there are usually a varied selection in a museum but the writer must confess that he has seldom heard them used. Occasionally small boys make reed flutes sounding about four notes. From time to time one may hear a maiden incarcerated in a hut for from one month to a year as is the Tonga and Ila custom, while away the time by blowing on a horn.

NOTE—There will be noticed on the sides of some drums, e.g. the *Itumba* of the Bemba, on the sides of the calabash resonators of some Xylophones, and on the wooden sound-board of some *Tulimba* (Kafir Pianos) a small piece of white opaque material stretched across a small hole. This material is called in Ci-tonga *Namundelela*, in Lala, *Lemba-lemba* and is the covering of the eggs of a spider known to the Tonga as *Igubilila*. The spider when laying its eggs covers them with this protective material. It is often to be seen high up in the roof timbers of a European house.

When the instrument is played this membrane produces a " sizzing " sound, rather like that produced by singing through a comb covered with tissue paper.

The purpose of the sizzing is to produce a continuous legato sound, and also to amplify it. If there were no membrane the Bantu would say that the sound stops short between each note; they want the sound to run on continuously.

On some *Tulimba* which have no such membrane we notice a number of small pieces of metal either slung on a metal rod inside the wooden sound-board or even attached with wire to its upper surface. The function of these metal pieces is exactly the same as that of the spider's membrane. They produce the required sizzing sound when the instrument is played.

No musician has as yet seriously taken up the study of wind and stringed instruments in Northern Rhodesia, a task which remains to be done. No one knows what further secrets of African musical practice such a study would reveal. But whoever does so would be well advised first to make a general study of singing, drumming and the *Kalimba*, for the music of strings and wind while restricted and adapted to the instrument in question, is part and parcel of the corpus of African music. And to this great volume of music we revert at the end of our study. For a museum is apt to give a wrong impression. With its cases displaying many varieties of instruments it may give one the idea that the African's music is largely instrumental in character or at least dependent on a variety of instruments. As we have seen, this is not so. African music is predominantly singing and drumming with dancing. This is the world of music in which the African lives, moves and has his being: and it is this sort of music which more than any other gives him the very justifiable right to a pride in his national musical heritage and to a place in the musical sun.

RHODES-LIVINGSTONE MUSEUM COLLECTION OF MUSICAL INSTRUMENTS.

(From HANDBOOK *of 1937, compiled by* W. V. *Brelsford).*

Musical instruments out of the Museum show-case, become by reason of the sounds they can produce, one of the " live " influences on native life([1]). Many instruments have a ritual or magical significance which adds to their importance. Most public rites and ceremonies are accompanied by playing and singing, dancing or drumming, and rhythmic work is also lightened by song. The Achikunda paddlers tap the side of the canoe with the paddle to keep time with their songs([2]) and the wielder of hammer or pick will often shout a song to the beat of his tool.

Musical instruments are usually divided into three main groups—percussion, wind and stringed. But the variety of instruments found among primitive peoples do not fall easily into such wide specifications, so following the lead of Dr. Harrison of the Horniman Museum, the first term " percussion " has been ignored and the instruments which usually fall into this group have been rearranged under more suitable heads.

A.—VIBRATION OF BARS AND PLATES, ETC.

(1) *The Xylophone.*—Starting from such primitive methods of making a noise as beating one stick against another, this main group, as well as including the most primitive of instruments, reaches a high development in the Xylophone. Although they are not common they are to be found in the bands of most of the chiefs of the north-west part of the Territory. Exhibits 138 and 139 are from Kasempa, and may be described in the words of Smith and Dale :

" The Xylophone is made of about ten wooden slats fastened lightly with cords, passing through holes in them, upon a frame-work. On the reverse side of the frame are fixed a number of elongated calabashes, of various sizes each under one of the slats ; these are the resonators. If a calabash of suitable size is not to be had, the maker neatly joins two smaller ones together. In the lower two-thirds each calabash has a small hole pierced in it over which is fixed the thin tough web of the *shilubidula* spider. A large bow is fixed on to the instrument, to keep it at a distance from the player's body when playing it. The player stands upright or squats on the ground a cord round his neck supporting the instrument. He plays on the keys with two sticks, the heads of which are covered with string and rubber substance. The tone is sweet, and a good player can produce very pleasant sounds from the instrument."

The slats of wood are " tuned " before they are attached to the frame by cutting, exactly as those of a European xylophone are tuned, by thinning one end of the bar or by flattening the under side([3]).

Exhibit 762 is a type of Wisa Xylophone that is played when a hippopotamus has been killed. It is used also by the Babemba. The wooden slat across the gourd is struck with a stick producing a sound rather like that of a drum.

(2) *The ' Kafir Piano.'*—Next to the drum this instrument is the most common and popular. It is one of the few African musical instruments that seems to have no ritual or magical uses or history. A number of metal tongues are attached to a board and melody is produced by vibrating the free ends of the tongues with the fingers. The keyboard is placed over an empty calabash in order to obtain resonance. Exhibit 110 is a good example of this instrument made by a Lovale native : Exhibit 134 shows a Bemba variety ; Exhibit 426 is a Lunda one and Exhibit 531 is Ila. In the Bemba examples 627 and 664 the wood of the keyboard is hollowed out and inside is fixed an iron rod upon which iron beads move freely, and rattles slightly when the instrument is being played.

The shape, size, number of tongues and methods of obtaining resonance may vary from tribe to tribe. The typical Wisa small piano has 8 tongues and is used with a calabash resonator ; the big Lala ones have 13 tongues. The typical Bemba piano is described above and has 10 tongues, but the fashion is changing and an 11 tongued instrument is coming into favour. The Mambwe often use a complicated instrument that may have been borrowed from Tanganyika tribes. It has an iron bridge between the point of attachment and the free ends, and on the tongues themselves are loose iron rings that jingle. The keyboard is hollow and contains a loose stone that is rattled, and at the back of the keyboard is a small hole which can be stopped or unstopped with the finger. An example has just been acquired for the Museum collection.

When the instrument is first made, the keys should, when in tune, be also in line or on a curve. Occasional tuning, in all varieties, is done by altering the length of the tongue from the point of attachment.

(3) *Bells.*—These native-made instruments in this Territory have a history associated with chieftainship or magic, although nowadays dancers use them on belts or anklets. Their shape is long or conical and they vary from two inches long (Exhibit 561, Ila) to 18 inches (Exhibit 486). The double bells are two bells on a single stem. Exhibit 486, a single bell was once the *lukano* or insignum of chieftainship of the Lunda chief Mburuma, and in the past, minor wars have taken place for the possession or recovery of such *lukano*. Amongst the Lala such double bells as that shown in Exhibit 658 are always kept silent in the relic house of the chief and are only tolled at his death. In former times a commoner found in possession of such a bell was put to death.

Monteiro illustrates double bells, describing them as the hereditary fetishes of kings who used them as signal bells. He also mentions the curious effect obtained by striking the mouths of the bells against the bare stomach whilst they are still reverberating from blows with a stick(4).

" The area of the iron double bell extends from Togo to Lunda and the Marotse, with an enclave in East Africa, and a find in the Zimbalwe ruins "(1).

Exhibit 631 (Nkoya) another double bell was only carried by one of the chief's personal attendants and rung to herald the approach of the chief. Bells were often used by diviners and doctors on their instruments. The *lilamfia* war charm, Exhibit 710, had a single bell attached to it, and in the former Bemba *Zambia* ritual a bell was used(5). In this ritual the blood of a slave was poured into a horn which, as it filled up, overbalanced and rang a bell from whose tolling omens were drawn. The modern *Bamuchapi* witch-finders often included modern bells in their regalia— Exhibit 574.

(4) *Rattles.*—These are often made from empty seed pods or gourds in which pellets are enclosed. A number of such rattles strung along a thong may be used as an anklet for a dancer (Exhibit 764) ; or single ones on sticks like those of Exhibits 511 and 715 may be shaken by a witchdoctor when working up the correct atmosphere for a seance ; or may be used to accompany ritual songs like those of the Ila smith who shakes his rattle and sings after smelting is finished. Exhibits 442 and 459 are double rattles, one on each end of a short stick, made of openwork fibre. Sometimes gourds without handles, as in Exhibit 448, with seeds inside them are used.

(5) *Gongs.*—The term is a loose one but may be taken to include percussion instruments of wood or metal which are hollow. The Balamba use a " sounding boat " (Exhibit 801). Two small heavy pieces of wood are hollowed out almost to the shape of dugout canoes. These are laid on their sides and when struck with stout sticks give forth loud notes. A variation of notes is obtained by striking different parts of the " boats "(6).

B.—DRUMS.

Of all instruments the drum plays the largest part in native life. The drums in African life correspond to the full orchestra of the Europeans. They are the very foundation of African social music. *See* Part II and note (12). Their sound can be heard almost every night as they accompany a dance celebrating some village event, a marriage or a death, or, on a moonlight night, just a dance. They are used for signalling the approach of visitors and calling people to the chief's village.

(1) *Percussion:*—The common drum of the Territory is a hollowed log open at both ends with one or sometimes both open ends covered with a membrane of reptile or animal skin. When the membrane is of buck skin it is put on wet with the hairy side upwards, the hair being shaved off when dry. The membrane is fastened to the drum with small wooden pegs, the type is shown in Exhibit 230 and although they vary much in workmanship there is little difference in shape from tribe to tribe. Exhibit 340 is a good example of Lunda work. The Nkoya and Kaonde tribes are especially noted as drum makers. It is held between the legs when sounded and beaten with the hands. Sometimes the lower part of the palm hits the drum, sometimes the fist and sometimes the finger tips.

Exhibit 319 is a type of drum known as *chikuvu* (Lunda). It is one solid oblong piece of narrow wood hollowed out so that the opening on the top of the long side is only about an inch wide. Specimens are sometimes seen over four feet long. Drums of this kind are used by the Lovale, Lunda, Bemba and allied tribes and they are played with drum sticks, the heads of which are made of native rubber. They are carried by being slung on a long pole.

Resonators are added to many drums in the form of a hole filled with a hollow plug covered with a web made from the spun egg cover of the spider known as *tandabube* (Bemba). Exhibits 665 and 735 are good examples.

Other drums have studs of solid grease, made from the ground nut or from rubber, stuck on to the membrane. By holding a membrane thus studded in front of the fire it is said that it is tightened : also that the fingers stick slightly to this grease and thus sustain the note.

Exhibits 665–667 are a series of Bemba drums. The larger one has a parchment made from the skin of a monitor lizard. The studs on it are of rubber mixed with wax. The two smaller ones have parchment of steinbuck hide. These drums are used together at dances, at a death, or at the end of a beer drink, or at the *kaonge* dance of youths and girls together.

Exhibit 735 is a good piece of work done by Mbwera natives. The drum is carried horizontally and both ends of the log have membranes. The decorations of geometric patterns are worth noting.

Exhibit 800 shows a variation in shape. It is squat and bowl shaped with a membrane both on the wide top and narrow bottom. The membranes instead of being kept taut by a series of wooden pegs as in the other examples, are tightened and joined to each other by a series of hide cords laced round and down the body of the drum. Inside the drum are some seeds which rattle when the drum is struck.

(2) *Friction*—The friction drum is a single membrane instrument which has a reed passing through the centre of the membrane into the drum and sticking out of the hollow end. Exhibits 84 (Lunda work from Mwinilunga) and 440 (from Mankoya) are examples. The player sits with the head away from him and, steadying the instrument with his left hand, slides his right hand, on which there is a piece of wet bark cloth, or a bundle of wet grass, up and down the reed. The vibration of the reed or stick is communicated to the membrane which amplifies it, and the result is a deep booming or sustained rumbling sound. This drum is used by the witchfinder to excite his audience preparatory to the actual witchfinding part of the proceedings. It is also used to announce war, accident or other catastrophe. In the Namwala District when cattle are to be crossed over a river the natives of the Ila tribe send the drum ahead in a canoe and the cattle follow its sound.

C.—STRINGED INSTRUMENTS.

The production of sounds by the vibrating of strings is most commonly instanced in Africa by the " musical bow " which no doubt had its origin in the twanging of the hunter's bow(7). In order to vary the monotony possibly several bows were later used. Ila girls today still play on two bows in the reclusion of their initiation huts. This instrument, Exhibit 827 is known as *mantimbwa* and is only played by girls in the initiation huts(8). It consists of two rough bows cut by the girls and stringed with twisted cord of palm leaf. One bow rests on each shoulder and they are kept in place by a stick passing over each bow under her knees. The strings are twanged with both hands, the cord of one bow being held between the lips in order to vary the sound. The introduction of a resonator amplifies the sound of these primitive instruments. The simplest form of resonator is supplied by placing a part of the bow stave in the mouth, and another simple variation is when, as with the Ila girls, the ends of the bows are placed on an inverted pot, or nowadays, on an inverted tin. Exhibit 294 (Lala) is a bow with a wire string which is tied back to the stave with a loop of wire. This loop is about half way down the string, and a calabash resonator is attached to the stave by this loop. The instrument is held by the left hand at the point where the string is tied back and the string is struck with a straw. The thumb of the left hand presses on the middle of the string in order to alter the pitch, and the sound can also be varied by pressing the calabash on to the chest.

Exhibit 640 (Mambwe) is of the zither type. Strings are stretched across a shallow wooden trough, and in making music the strings are plucked. This example has in addition a large calabash, on which shells are tied, as a resonator.

There are several examples of the class headed by lutes, guitars and violins. Exhibit 376 (from Mkushi) is a derivative from the musical bow with a stiff stave and a gourd resonator. In this Exhibit although there are only two strings a wide range of notes can be obtained by ' fingering ' on the three bridges.

Exhibit 105 is a one-stringed fiddle played with a bow similar to the one illustrated by Livingstone(9). The resonator is a small wooden drum with membranes on top and bottom.

Exhibit 828 is a type of six-stringed instrument, *ubwesela* (Chilamba), the use of which seems to be dying out. The strings are stretched across a board, two pieces of wood being inserted to raise them. One long cord threaded through the holes makes up the six strings and when one is out of tune the whole six have to be readjusted. A calabash resonator is attached and when being played by plucking the one hand is employed in ' fingering ' to alter the pitches.

Exhibit 170 is a very modern looking fiddle from Balovale.

D.—WIND INSTRUMENTS.

Two of the Exhibits in the Museum are of the flute class ; that is to say sound is produced by blowing air across an apperture in a tube. Exhibit 614 is a small duiker horn used by the Bemba in calling duiker. The wide end of the horn is covered with the egg-cover of a spider ; the narrow end is sawn off and the hole left is blown across.

Exhibit 546 is an Ila flute made simply out of a straight reed. Pipes of this sort are used by this tribe to call their herds of cattle.

There are two exhibits of the trumpet class ; air being blown into the mouth-piece, not across it.

Exhibit 612, also Ila is a much longer reed with an open gourd resonator at one end. It is blown at the extreme tip of the tube. It was used by an attendant of Chief Mukobela to announce the sitting of court.

Exhibit 446 is also of the trumpet class. It is a hollow piece of wood and was blown by a witch-finder (*see* section on Witch-finding) preparatory to pointing out the witch. It is blown by a mouthpiece not at the tip but at the side of the tube.

Trumpets made out of elephant tusks or antelope horns have been recorded in the Territory(10). Now that Government takes all ivory no trumpets of elephant tusks are seen.

BULL ROARERS.

Exhibit 829 shows two bull roarers, one made of string and the bulb of a plant and the other made of wood. Such instruments are not uncommon but in most tribes are child's playthings. (11) The Mbunda-Lubale tribes use them in circumcision ceremonies.

Later Note.—The instruments in the Museum are exhibited with photographs showing royal bands and drums, women and men playing instruments and singing and dancing. Each photograph is fully described. Photographs in the *Makishi Collection* show these dances and orchestras.

A collection of records of African music has been started.

These photographs and records are added in an attempt to overcome the " deadness " of a plain collection of instruments.

References.

(1) E. M. Von Hornbostel.—" The Ethnology of African Sound Instruments." *Africa*, Vol. VI, Nos. 2 and 3, April and July, 1933.
(2) S. R. Denny.—" Some Zambesi Boat Songs." *Nada*, No. 14.
(3) Percival R. Kirby.—" The Musical Instruments of the Native Races of South Africa," page 57.
(4) J. Monteiro.—" Angola and the River Congo," 1875. Vol. I, page 203.
(5) " The Awemba Country."—*The Central African Times*, June 10th, 1899.
(6) C. M. Doke.—" The Lambas of Northern Rhodesia," page 361.
(7) H. Balfour.—" The Natural History of the Musical Bow," page 4.
(8) Smith and Dale.—" The Ila Speaking Peoples of Northern Rhodesia," pages 22 and 262.
(9) D. Livingstone.—" Zambesi and its Tributaries," page 93.
(10) Sir H. H. Johnston.—" British Central Africa," page 464 *et seq.* Also C. M. Doke, *op. cit.*, page 367.
(11) C. M. Doke, *op. cit.*, page 367.
(*b*) P. R. Kirby.—essay in " Western Civilisation and the Natives of South Africa."
(12) A. M. Jones.—" African Music—The Mganda Dance," reprinted from *African Studies*, January, 1946.

APPENDIX 2.

NOTES ON THE SOCIAL BACKGROUND OF BAROTSE MUSIC.*

BY MAX GLUCKMAN.

I cannot add to the musical analysis of Mr. Jones, but comment briefly on the social background of music among the Barotse, whom I studied sociologically.

(1) CHIEF'S BANDS.

Throughout North-Western Rhodesia, into Angola and the Congo, all chiefs possess royal bands. In fact, to find out if a particular important man ranks as a chief, one may ask : " Has he drums ? " The greatest chief of this region is the Paramount Chief of Barotseland, the head of the dominant Lozi tribe. Wherever he goes, his band accompanies him, periodically through every night they play at the capital. People far from the capital who meet a man from there, will inquire after the Paramount Chief's health : " are the drums still beating ? " For on his death they fall silent.

Most important of his instruments are the *maoma* (singular, *lioma*), the royal drums of chieftainship. These are huge drums, some carved out of trees three feet in diameter. They vary in size and decorations, and each has its name ; some are eighty years old. The skins are from a bull, and are renewed periodically ; before the drums are beaten, the skins are painted with white and red spots. The wooden cases are carved with crocodiles, men, antelope, lizards.

It is the *maoma* above all which confer kingship (*bulena*). Their lineage is ancient : by tradition, they were taken by Mwanambinyi the miracle-worker, younger brother of Mboo the first Lozi king, from the Mbukushu tribe near the Mashi river ; they lay in Mwanambinyi's royal burial-village, which every Lozi salutes as he passes, until Ngalama, great conquering Lozi king, brought them to his capital. Henceforward, a man was crowned king by being sat upon a particular *lioma*. (See photograph from C. W. Macintosh's *Yeta III : Paramount Chief of Barotseland* of the crowning of Yeta III, which is exhibited in the case containing Barotse Proclamations in the historical section). When the Lozi king Ngombala established a secondary capital in the Nalolo region south of the main capital, the prince or princess (Mulena Mukwae) there was given *maoma*. The Mulena Mukwae alone of other chiefs has *maoma* and is crowned on a *lioma*. In 1934, there was appointed as Mulena Mukwae the daughter of the Mulena Mukwae Matauka who had just died : as she was a member of the royal family on the distaff side, she could not sit on a *lioma* to be crowned, nor use *maoma* in her ceremonies. The people attached to her resented this as cheapening their chieftainship, and this was one of the grounds for petitioning for her replacement. She was replaced by a daughter of Paramount Chief Yeta III.

The *moama*, whose thunder can be heard for many miles across the great plain in which the Lozi live, are not beaten every day. They are used to summon the people urgently to the capital, at the Paramount's coronation, to send the army to war and at the purification of the returned warriors, and on the ceremonial voyages of the Paramount Chief and the Mulena Mukwae out of the flooded plain to their margin capitals and back to their plain capitals when the flood falls (*see* photographs in musical stand and in Barotse Proclamations exhibit). Each of the above situations has its own rhythm, so that many miles away people can tell whether the *maoma*

* For a description of Barotseland, see M. Gluckman, *Economy of the Central Barotse Plain*, Rhodes-Livingstone Paper, No. 7. In D. W. Stirke's *Barotseland*, at pp. 85–92, are recorded the words of different songs of the various Barotse tribes.

announce that the Paramount Chief is about to move out of the plain or is summoning them urgently. Skilled men, including some of the highest councillors, beat the drums. The night before the ceremonial moves, the paramount inaugurates the beating of the *maoma* with his own hand, he is followed by his prime minister, and then by the *Natamoyo* and others in order of rank. Eventually, every man at the capital may for a time have the honour of drumming, until the *maoma* travel in their own barge, the *Nalikwanda*, where only councillors and prices of high rank who are the paddlers take turns in beating them.

The *maoma* are in charge of the third ranking councillor of the kingdom, *Natamoyo*, " The-Giver-of-Life," an elected prince who is chosen for his kindness, for the bearer of this name is a sanctuary for those threatened with punishment, unless they have committed a heinous offence.

Besides the *maoma* these big chiefs have bands which originally consisted of Lozi drums (*mwenduko*) and xylophone, and Simaa xylophone (according to tradition it was some Simaa who by giving fish as a gift to Lozi princes gave rise to Lozi kingship—see *Economy of the Central Barotse Plain*, Rhodes-Livingstone Paper, No. 7, p. 89). Sipopa, the Lozi king who drove out the Basuto Kololo conquerors of Loziland, added Nkoya drums and xylophone including the double-ended drums (*mikubele*). The chiefs still keep a large entourage of Lozi, Simaa, and Nkoya players for their bands : these people are settled in villages which belong to the chiefs. These players are not only virtuosi on their instruments but they should know how to sing the *maloko*, the praise-sayings of chiefs, councillors' names, God, etc. which contain (in original Lozi, a language no longer spoken) Lozi philosophy. These praise-sayings go, e.g. : " the king owns the land and cattle, his prime minister owns the people " ; " as a needle sews together skins to make a kaross, so the chief unites many people." There are many hundreds of these praise-sayings.

The bands escort the great chiefs into the court, and sit before them playing and singing; the councillors respond. When the king travels in the *Notila* barge (see photograph in Barotse proclamations exhibit) some of the instruments are played behind his shelter : this is a modern custom, for he and they used to travel with the *maoma* in the *Nalikwanda* barge. These instruments and the *maoma* are played alternately for short periods during the voyage : but at beginning and end, near the capitals it is the former which are beaten. Again, every night various of these drums, which are kept in a shed (*limbetelo*) in the courtyard of the palace, are beaten at stated intervals, from the sounding of the curfew by the *mwenduko* till it lifts it in the morning.

In recent years, permission has been granted to the Lozi chiefs extablished in the provinces to have xylophone, but not *maoma*. All these chiefs are princes or princesses. Certain foreign chiefs, subject to the Lozi, are also by special privilege allowed to have bands : they are Mwene-Kahari and Mwene-Mutondo (Nkoya), Mwene-ciengele (a Mbunda whose ancestor settled about 120 years ago in Loziland), and the Lunda chief Shinde and certain Lubale chiefs who have now been made independent of the Barotse.

In Lozi courts, there is a fixed order of seating : councillors to the right of the Chief, stewards and princes to the left. Bandsmen have their own part of the court, directly in front of the dais of the chief. Their instruments are a sanctuary for a man threatened with throttling or beating is safe if he can lay hold of a royal drum or xylophone.

Also, the bandsmen are a sanctuary unto themselves. I am told reliably that throughout this region, when the drums encouraged the armies into war and chosen warriors sang songs to excite them, the drummers had nothing to fear, save a chance spear or arrow. If their army broke, no-one would kill them, but they would be seized and added to the conquering royal band. " To kill the drummers would be to kill the chieftainship and the country." Even defeated warriors who sought sanctuary round their drums would be spared to be taken as slaves. The protection of the drums was recognised over a large number of tribes.

In their songs, bold drummers could reprimand the paramount. If he stayed closeted in his courtyard, they would sing to tell him to come before his people ; they could sing asking forgiveness for a delinquent, or to tell the chief they were hungry and wanted meat ; there were songs to tell him that the people were waiting for him to lead them out of the discomfort of the flooded plain, and later back from the margin to their beloved plain. The drummers, many inheriting from fathers and maternal uncles, were respected, honoured and generously treated.

A slit-drum (*moondo*) was beaten to summon councillors to sittings of the court.

(2) CEREMONIES.

Mr. Jones refers to the importance of drums in African life, and this appears in the fact that in any neighbourhood, the number and the quality of drums which particular people own, are known to everyone. But the Lozi, as a people, have not the massed and exciting dances found among the Southern Bantu, except for the royal *ngomalume* dances, and the singing of *liimba* songs by the women. At weddings there are small dances, and at first menstruation and inheritance ceremonies they dance the Mbunda *siomboka* and *lilombola*—shuffling dances in a circle. (See photographs in ceremonial room). There are mourning songs (*katimbo*—Nkoya).

The dance and song to celebrate success in hunting (*manyanga*) is also Mbunda.

Among the most interesting ceremonial dances are those of the *makishi*, masked costumes which are used in the circumcision ceremonies of the Mbunda-Lubale and related tribes.

Semi-ceremonial songs are songs to welcome chief (*liimba*—Lozi), and others found among all tribes of this region. (See photographs in music exhibit).

(3) CURATIVE SONGS AND DANCES.

In Barotseland, curative songs and dances are used for many diseases, whereas among the Zulu, I know only of *isanusi* dances by " possessed " diviners, to divine and to cure those possessed. Among all the Barotse tribes, the drums that sound almost every night, usually indicate that a leech is at work.

The Kwanga *liyala* dancer is a leech who gives his patients medicines in the intervals of a night-long dance. This leech wears a huge mass of skins about his waist, which he swings high as he vibrates his body : he uses hand rattles and dances to drums and a chorus of men and women. (See photograph in music exhibit). The diseases he treats are believed to come from ancestral spirits.

Lubale-Mbunda leeches also treat the *sisongo* and *mahamba* disease with drumming. *Sisongo* strikes the sufferer's limbs with shivering, he is unable to move ; but when the drums begin, he rolls about the ground, all his muscles vibrate, quivering, he flings himself about on the medicines. All who have been treated for *sisongo*, among the crowd of watchers who attend to enjoy the spectacle of the cure, join in the dance, to the refrain :

" The *sisongo* is a madman."

Other curative dances are : *Maimbwe*, *makwasha*, *machoba*, *mawila*, *mandende* (Nkoya) ; *manyanga*, *bikulu* and *malengele* (Mbunda) ; *kanyongo* (Lubale) ; and *lishemba* and *kanyowe* (Makoma, Nyengo and Nwenyi tribes).

(4) ENTERTAINMENT.

Many Barotse play instruments for sheer pleasure, and I have known experts visit me regularly for the delight of entertaining me with new songs on a *Kangombyo* (kafir-piano). This art has royal patronage : one Lozi prince so loved playing that he used to entertain his uncles' wives all day. A Lozi king died of a cut caused by playing one of these instruments.

Matangu are songs of folk-tales or fairy-tales, found in all the Barotse tribes, which are sung by women in the evenings of winter, and by boys and men on long journeys.

[105]

The *sipelu* dance in my experience, as danced by young men and girls, is an attractive jolly affair though I must admit I have only seen it once. However the Lozi authorities, I understand largely instigated by missionaries, have banned it as causing adultery: though one District Commissioner who saw it recorded his opinion that is harmless enough. Boys and girls, or men and women, stand opposite each other in line, and dance out in pairs; amid other steps, they clap hands and bang their bottoms together as in " Boomps-a-Daisy."

Certain *makishi* dancers are acrobats and conjurers, and this is also so of other dancers. The *liyala* leech, in addition to treating diseases, by the reputed power of medicines swallows spears, stabs through his stomach, cuts his tongue and eyes, and so on. I have heard of, but not seen, Nkoya who with flutes induce snakes to leave their holes, and of Nkoya acrobats who dance in high trees. To the west of the Lozi plain, are said to be Mwenyi, Simaa, Nyengo and Nkoya, dancers who dress in suits which enable them to roll about in hot embers: all to music.

(5) WORK-SONGS.

As Mr. Jones generalises of most Africans, the Barotse peoples always break into song to relieve labour, and bring their efforts into time. Paddlers and carriers lighten their long trek with songs, communal parties at work in the fields or at building, chorus as they work.

PART II

Two Critical Essays:

One

AFRICAN DRUMMING

Two

THE STUDY OF AFRICAN MUSICAL RHYTHM

by

A. M. JONES

These essays are reprinted, by permission, from *Bantu Studies,* the Journal of the University of the Witwatersrand, Johannesburg. "African Drumming" was published in that Journal in Vol. 8, No. 1 March, 1934. "The Study of African Musical Rhythm" was published in the same Journal in December, 1937.

PART II

1. AFRICAN DRUMMING.

A Study in the Combination of Rhythms in African Music*.

In January, 1928, in *Africa* Vol. 1, No. 1, there was an article by E. M. Von Hornbostel on African Negro Music, wherein he cited a complicated Xylophone piece (ex. 9, p. 50 of his article : reproduced here in appendix 1), and proceeded to analyse it. This essay is a criticism both of that analysis and also of the conclusions deduced therefrom. The writer hopes that while he has this specific object in view, he will at the same time make clear some of the typical African combinations of rhythm, and indeed he hopes that the reader may catch some of the thrill which the African feels when playing cross rhythms.

We are all acquainted with the apparent inextricable complexity of African rhythms expecially when several instruments or voices are played simultaneously. In fact Hornbostel says in reference to his example, that " the lower part is syncopated past our comprehension." But the writer claims that this idea is false. On *a priori* grounds why should the music of the African be so hyper-developed when all his other arts are so often rudimentary ? But *a priori* grounds are of no use by themselves : we must have facts : here they are. Anyone who cares to take a course of African drumming will speedily be convinced that what he has to play on his own drum is a *perfectly simple* rhythm. The other players are also, for the most part, playing *simple rhythms* : it is the combination of these simple rhythms which makes the glorious African rhythmic harmony, which to the listener often sounds beyond analysis. A phonograph in this field is useless. The writer is convinced that to understand African rhythm, the student must " join an African band " and learn to take his part.

*Like the author of the accompanying article, which appears to me to mark an epoch, I have always felt that the study of African music must be undertaken on the spot, and that the student must himself participate in Native musical performances if he is to arrive at a real understanding of Native musical art.

Although the areas to which my own researches have been restricted, have presented a series of musical problems very different, for the most part, from those faced by Mr. Jones, I have in certain districts come across a number which are identical with his, and having, like him, " gone to school," I have arrived at similar conclusions, and can thoroughly endorse his. Mr. Jones here deals with drumming, and shows how what to the European is apparently highly elaborate syncopation is really the deliberate opposition of simple powerful rhythms. I have had precisely the same experience with South African xylophone playing, finding that what at first seemed to be exceedingly complex was actually formed from simple elements, which, however, were by no means easy for a European to master when they were performed in combination.

Mr. Jones' study, based on research in Northern Rhodesia, is worth the closest attention, for it assuredly reveals the truth concerning some practices about which there has been a good deal of speculation but little real knowledge.

PERCIVAL R. KIRBY.

Let us then go to school. The value of the following examples of drumming will be almost nil, unless the reader procures a friend or two, and they together learn to tap on the table at least one of the pieces.

Here is an example of Bemba drumming called " Ngwayi."

R=right hand.   ♪=120
L=left hand.

Drum No. 1.

R   L   R   R   L

$\frac{3}{16}$ |♪· |♪· |♪ ♪|♪ ‖

Repeat the measure ad infin.

Drum No. 2.

R   R   L   L   R   R   L   L

$\frac{3}{16}$ |♪ ♪|♪ ♪|♪ ♪|♪ ♪|♪ ♪ ‖ ad infin.

Now let us combine them. Drum No. 1 starts. Drum No. 2 has got to get the first beat of his bar to coincide with the *third* beat of No. 1's bar. The African usually does this by beating only the *principal* beat (1st beat of bar) in combination with drum No. 1 who is playing his measures complete, until he feels he has " got the hang of it."

Thus stage 2 is :

Drum 1. $\frac{3}{16}$ |♪· |♪· |♪ ♪|♪ ‖

Drum 2. $\frac{3}{16}$ |♪ ⅂ |♪ ⅂ |♪ ⅂ |♪ etc.

Concentrate on your own drum. When drum No. 2 can hear his own rhythm well, (i.e. when he is convinced that his beat is *not* the 3rd beat of No. 1's bar, but is beat 1 of his own bar), then he can add his other tap (beat 3). The result is :

Drum 1. $\frac{3}{16}$ |♪ |♪· |♪ ♪|♪· ‖

Drum 2. $\frac{3}{16}$ ♪|♪ ♪|♪ ♪|♪ ♪|♪ etc.

[109]

To the outside listener, the combination sounds like :

 etc.

In this example we learn three main facts :

1. The fondness of the African for combining two triple rhythms, the second of which starts on the 3rd beat of the first.
2. The way the second drum " enters " by first tapping out his main beat.
3. There are 12 taps to the phrase. This is a typical African measure.

Example 2. Bemba. " Imbeni."

Drum No. 1.

In this example note :

1. Drum No. 1 starts in triple rhythm and finishes in duple. His part is really

    ♪♪ ♪♪ ♪♪ ♪♪ ♪ ♪ ‖

    Note that he has an odd beat to start with. The reason is that this drumming in essentially duple, consisting of 16 taps to the phrase, and 3 into 16 goes 5 *plus* 1.
2. Drum No. 2 places a duple rhythm against drum No. 1's triple form, i.e. 4 against 3.
3. Drum No. 2 places his first main beat on the 2nd beat of drum No. 1.
4. Drum No. 3 places his first main beat on the 2nd beat of the last bar of drum No. 1's phrase.

The resulting rhythm heard by the listener is :

Who would have thought, on hearing this drumming, that this simple result was brought about by such an extraordinary combination of cross rhythms ?

The above syntheses are *fact*, not theory. The writer claims them to be indisputably accurate, as he has taken his part at each drum.

We now leave this field and turn to the field of speculation, i.e. to Hornbostel's analysis of the phonograph record of the Pangwe Xylophone piece. This analysis is, I believe, almost completely off the track.

Turning to Appendix 1 let us look for some clues.

1. Bars 5, 6, 7 and 8 are the easiest.

Tap out the low Xylo part, ignoring Hornbostel's barring : it is obviously this :

The voice part has the same rhythm, and contains a repetition of the figure marked X. Thus :

The top Xylo part minus Hornbostel's bars is this :

What is this rhythm ? Tap it out and you cannot fail to find it :

---

* The rest should be a crochet rest.

[111]

I can hear an objector saying, " But the bars might equally well be placed in ¾ time thus : "

$\frac{3}{4}$ [musical notation]

[musical notation]

I invite my objector to tap out the rhythm in this way. He must play fair. Hornbostel's transcription has no strong accent marks. Therefore the objector must not introduce any. While he is thus playing the piece, let him ask an observer what rhythm he is tapping out. I leave him to find the answer.

Returning to the 3/8 form written out above, what about the two preliminary crotchets. Are they not out of time ? The answer is that they show where the top Xylo was marking time, in imitation of the two crotchets at the beginning of bar 1. Note that the notes on the score are the same in both cases.

What about the three end crotchets ? These are just a flavour of duple rhythm bringing the phrase to a feeling of rest. The exact analogy can be seen at the end of the Drum No. 1 part of " *Imbeni*." Moreover the same kind of thing, i.e. finding a suitable figure for the end of the phrase, occurs at the end of bars 2, 12, 16, 20, 24.

When we put the two Xylo parts plus the voice part together, we get a rhythmic passage as written in Appendix 2, bars 5, 6, 7, 8. Now when these rhythms are sounded together, a new and resultant rhythm emerges. In this case, the top Xylo carries the main beat of the rhythm, and this resultant rhythm is as follows :

$\frac{3}{8}$ [musical notation]

[musical notation]

How amazingly consistent ! and how simple ! surely we have hit upon the clue to the rhythmic structure of these bars. There is no hyper-complex syncopation here.

2. Bars 9, 10, 11, 12.

The top Xylo part becomes obvious and consistent if barred in *binary* rhythm as follows :

$\frac{4}{8}$ [musical notation]

[musical notation]

So the top Xylo in this variation has changed from triple to duple rhythm—a typical change in playing variations in drumming.

To understand the low Xylo, look at bars 10, 11, 12. There is no doubt as to the rhythm. It is simply this :

$\frac{3}{8}$ ♪♩ ♪♩ ♪♩ ♪ ⊦ ♪♩ ♪♩ ♪♩ ♪ ⊦ ♪♩ ♪♩ ♪ ⊦ ⫽

Putting bar 10 together, we get :

$\frac{4}{8}$ | ♪ ♪ ♪ ♪ | ♪ ♪ ♪ | ↱ | ♪ ♪ ♪ |

$\frac{3}{8}$ ⊦ ♪♩ ♪♩ ♪♩ ♪

Note that the low Xylo enters on *his third beat*. Now playing a " 3 beat-in-the-bar " rhythm against a " 4 beat-in-the-bar " measure is a difficult feat. What does the low Xylo do ? He just beats his 3rd beat only, 4 times before making his rhythmic entry. This is typical of drumming procedure. The low Xylo bar 9 thus becomes :

Top Xy. $\frac{4}{8}$ | ♩ ♩ | ♪ ♪ ♩ | ♪ ♪ ♩ | ♪ ♪ ♪ ♪ ♪ ♪

Low Xy. $\frac{3}{8}$ ♩. | ♪ ⊦ ♩. | ♪ ⊦ ♩. | ♪

he is off now.

Looking at Appendix 2, bars 9–12, we find that the resultant rhythm is again triple, in fact just the same time as bars 5–8.

Here it is :

$\frac{3}{8}$ ♪ | ♫♫ | ♫♫ | ♫♫ | ♫♫ | ♪ ↝ ♪ ♫♫ | ♫♫ | ♪ ♪ etc.

The low Xylo carries the main beat.

3. Bars 1 and 2.

The top part of Bar 1 = top part of bar 9.

Now bar 10 continues the duple rhythm of bar 9. What of bar 2 ? Tap it out from Hornbostel's score. It suggests at once triple rhythm. Quite so : very African : bar 1 in duple, bar 2 in triple rhythm. When this same tune is repeated in bar 9, there is a variation in the second bar of the phrase, bar 10. In this case the duple rhythm does not change as it does in bar 2.

Thus bars 1 and 2, top Xylo become :

Note that the figure ⌐♩♪♪♩⌐ prepares the way for ⌐♩♪♪♪⌐

Bar 2 shows that the low Xylo has a triple rhythm, its strong beat landing on beat 2 of the top Xylo part. (*See* Appendix 2.)

The first three notes of the low Xylo part are once again the preparation for the low Xylo entry on the *third beat of his own bar*, using a 3 rhythm against the top Xylo's 4 rhythm. It is a difficult feat, and to get your arm swinging in the right rhythm helps you to enter at the right moment. The two bars thus become :

Top Xy.

Low Xy.

Where again, is the complex syncopation ?

4. Bars 13, 14, 15, 16.

Bars 13 and 14 correspond to bars 1 and 2, *except* for the last note of the low Xylo in bar 14. What is the significance of this note ?

It is obvious : the low Xylo's beat in bar 14 corresponds with that of the top Xylo. On entering bar 15 he wants to cross the rhythms. He does this by dropping one beat at the end of bar 14.

Thus the low Xylo part is :

There are marks of emphasis in Hornbostel's version in bars 3, 5, 17, 22. Hornbostel with considerable ingenuity justifies these on the ground that it is the *raising* of the arm rather than the actual sound of the strike, that carries the strong accent in African percussion rhythms. If our version be accepted, note that these accented notes practically all fall naturally into position, counting the strike as the accent. My African informant repudiates Hornbostel's notion. In this example, at any rate, it is entirely irrelevant.

The foregoing remarks may lead the reader to think that the piece is complicated. It is *not* : it is just a combination of simple elementary rhythms. We have set out the rhythmic pattern in Appendix 2. Let the reader test any one of the parts by tapping it out. Is it difficult ?

[114]

It will have been perceived that this analysis and that of Hornbostel differ fundamentally. How exactly do they differ ? Hornbostel has treated the piece as though it has a uniform metrical shape, i.e. 6/4 time ; all the voices being in 6/4 time, their principal beats all coincide on the 1st and 4th beats of the bar.

The present writer regards the piece as " poly-rhythmic," i.e. made up of voices each carrying their own inherent rhythm, and having different starting points. This difference is exactly analogous to the difference between polyphony and harmony. Polyphony looks out horizontally, i.e. it pays attention to the ebb and flow of each part individually. The resulting harmony is the result of the part writing of each part considered as a separate melody. Harmony looks out vertically, i.e. it pays attention to the chord effects as such, and the ebb and flow of the parts, considered as melodies is entirely dependent on these effects. There can be no doubt that if we are to solve the problems of African rhythm we must regard it as " poly-rhythmic," i.e. a combination of rhythms having their own starting points and their own individuality.

Finally we have set out in Appendix 3 the musical notation with appropriate barring. The resultant rhythm heard by the listener would be on this pattern :

i.e. 3/8 time throughout.

This can be found by regarding the score vertically and noting the single rhythm which emerges from the combination of rhythms. It is true that when an entry is made in 4/8 time it throws the listener off for the moment, and he wonders what is happening. In fact the listener hears a fundamental 3/8 rhythm which is occasionally topped by a 4/8 time. But he must not be deceived. The fundamental 3/8 time has not changed : the 4/8 rhythm is merely an embellishment. This phenomenon is exactly what happens in drumming. The people go on dancing to the 3/8 time, while one drum will occasionally suddenly hammer out across this time with a 4/8 rhythm, and then relapse again into the main swing of 3/8 time. Therein lies a glorious rhythmic thrill.

A last word about Appendix 3. It is certainly an extraordinary combination of sounds, but what a delightful rhythmic interplay—and all made up by skilful handling of 3 beat bars and 4 beat bars. Can it be said to be " syncopated past comprehension ? "

Appendix 1.

HORNBOSTEL'S ANALYSIS

Appendix 2.

RECONSTRUCTED RHYTHM.

Bar numbers refer to Hornbostel's analysis.

NOTE.—Not one single note value or rest have been altered in rearranging Hornbostel's version. This version is note for note and rest for rest the same as his.

There are 12 quavers to the phrase. This is typically African. On this point alone we agree with Hornbostel.

Appendix 3.

RECONSTRUCTED ANALYSIS.

2. THE STUDY OF AFRICAN MUSICAL RHYTHM.

Those of us who are interested in the study of African rhythm, or indeed of any branch of African music, must view with not a little apprehension the growing use by the Bantu of the gramophone and of European dance rhythms. In towns the old Native rhythms are dying out, and even in the villages, the young men returning from work are introducing western forms of music through gramophone records or through the " Europeans' Dance " which they learnt while at work. Other branches of Native life are receiving their share of investigation, but music lags sadly behind. The writers of books on tribal customs have a habit of mentioning music and then apologising for the fact that as they are not musicians, they feel incompetent to deal with the subject : which of course is a good thing, but it is at the same time a clear call to musicians to bestir themselves. For if something is not done soon, it will be too late.

A certain amount of research work on African music is going on, but it is being done by isolated individuals who pursue their own methods quite independent of one another. The result is that the present state of musical research is chaotic—nothing less than that. No investigator knows on what lines the other man is proceeding ; he does not know what method the other man used in making his transcriptions ; he does not know what criteria the other used in order to test the *accuracy* of his transcriptions. And the natural consequence of this is, that no one investigator can trust the other man's work. He cannot depend upon it for formulating theories, as he does not know what degree of reliability it possesses. This is hopeless and entirely unscientific. We shall never know the secret of African musical rhythms if we go on in this fashion.

Africa is a large country ; tribes living in various parts have widely differing musical practice ; yet there is sufficient evidence to warrant the suspicion that underlying these practices there is a common ground of rhythmic structure. But at present no one can tell what it is. Yet if this suspicion is correct surely it is imperative that there should be a close co-operation between musical researches carried on all over the continent, so that results may be comparable. The writer of this essay feels strongly that the time has come when some body of musicians should draw up a scheme of procedure in investigation of musical problems, and that this body should invite all research workers to conform to this procedure. Were this done, then we should all feel that our transcriptions possessed equal validity and we should feel able to use each other's work in further-ing our own studies.

The particular purpose of this essay is the study of the recording of African *Rhythms*. In whatever branch of music research is done, the investigator is almost at once brought up against the difficulty of putting the music down on paper, not so much because of the melody itself but because of the *rhythm* of the melody. The rhythm is clearly felt, but it is most difficult for a European to " nail it down " and to transcribe it accurately. Yet anyone who has done work on African music knows that African rhythm is absolutely fundamental. It is the purpose of this essay to consider the methods of recording this rhythm, and it is hoped that in the process, some principles of African rhythm may be made clear.

As the writer has experience of the practices of some of the tribes in Northern Rhodesia only, it should be borne in mind that any deductions or conclusions made from musical examples quoted in these pages refer to these tribes only. The tribes are : Tonga, Bemba, Nsenga and Lala.

1. THE PROBLEM OF RECORDING.

The two methods of making transcriptions of African music or percussion playing which are in common use are first direct transcription and second, the making of a gramophone record from which a transcription is made.

Consider the Direct Transcription method. The investigator listens carefully to the music and when he is sufficiently certain that he knows what is being sung or played, he writes it down. The careful person will check his transcription not once nor twice. What exactly happens in this method ? The African music passes through a European ear, is analysed by a European brain which instinctively inherits the musical attitude of the West, and is then duly transcribed. A more subjective process it is hard to imagine. It may be successful in easy passages, by which of course we mean those passages which are similar in structure or melody to European music, but when it comes to hard passages, every one who has tried this method knows that it breaks down. We simply cannot be sure what the African is doing. And it is exactly these hard passages, by which we mean those parts which are characteristic of African as distinct from Western music, that we want to be sure about. For therein undoubtedly lie the secrets of the principles that govern African music. In other words, by the direct transcription method, we can put down what we already know, but in the nature of the case, we can never find out that which is foreign to our experience. At best we can only put down what we *think* the African does. Which of course is useless for scientific purposes. To test the truth of this contention we invite the musical reader to do as we have done. Listen to a party of Africans singing. Write down the apparent melody, taking care to get the rhythm right. Now send for one of the singers, and ask him what words he was singing. Jot these down and try to fit them in to your melody. You will probably be quite non-plussed ; there are far too many syllables. The fact is that the European ear catches merely the *apparent* tune, and in so doing, instinctively moulds it in a westernised shape.

Let us make another test. Select a sensible singer, and let him sing to you. You will first write down all the words he sings under the stave of your blank page of music paper. He then sings repeatedly and you fill in the melody. In this case clearly you have the advantage of knowing that you have to account for every syllable, and your transcription will therefore be far more trustworthy. When you have finished, your singer says that the people always clap to this song. You tell him to sing and clap—but when it comes to marking in on your score the exact positions of the handclaps, you will almost certainly acknowledge yourself beaten. It is here that acquaintance is made with the peculirities of African rhythm, for it is plain that the handclapping by no means follows the natural rhythm either of the tune or the words. Yet the words are rhythmic, the tune is rhythmic, and the clapping is rhythmic. At once we notice that whereas the tune though rhythmic, was somewhat free in its rhythm, the quavers were not always quite quavers, and the rests had a length which defied exact counting, the clapping has a certain and relentless and regular rhythm. It becomes clear therefore, that if only we can get the handclapping correctly marked on our score, we shall be on the way to checking the rhythm of the song ; in fact if our rhythmic transcription of the song agrees with the handclap, it is *quite certain* that it is a correct and scientific transcription. After years of living among the Bantu and listening and struggling to master the clapping, it is possible to attempt to mark in the claps. But even this is possible only if the singer is a fairly educated person who can discipline himself to go slowly and to emphasise the syllables on which the clap occurs, and such persons are rare. It is indeed, incredibly difficult for the experienced musician to write the claps in at all, and quite impossible for him to write in claps of difficult songs, and when all is said and done, all he can say is, " This is what I *think* the African did." Which of course is subjective and quite valueless for scientific research. We do not want to think, we want to *know*.

Here is an example to illustrate the points made in the above paragraph.

The words were first written under a blank stave. Then the melody was sung, first as a whole, then bit by bit, and was noted down with as great care as possible. Next, the singer clapped the hand-clap rhythm. It is a familiar Tonga hand-clap, which the writer always represents as :

1 2 **3** 4 5 **6** 7 **8** 9 **10** 11 12 **1** 2 **3** 4 5 **6** 7   etc.

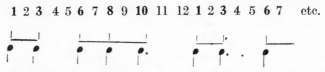

Lastly, an attempt was made to mark in the claps on the manuscript. Bearing in mind that the rhythm of the claps is inexorable, if the reader looks carefully at this example, he will see how inaccurate the first transcription of the rhythm of the song was. And what should it be ? In some places the necessary emendations are clear ; but not so in others. We leave the reader to try to correct the time value of the melody notes. In marking the clapping, attention was fixed on the words and not the time, as it is easier to tell on what syllable rather than on what note a clap occurs. The clap-marks here are as accurate as it was possible for the writer to get them.

Our African now goes on to say that really this song with its hand-clapping is properly only sung at a dance, and is an accompaniment to the drumming. So the Direct Method transcriber goes to listen to this drumming for he realises that his transcription will not be complete unless it contains the drumming correctly put in and related to both the singing and the clapping : in fact he ought to realise that up to this point he has recorded only the embellishment of the real piece, which is the rhythm of the drums. But let it be stated categorically that if our investigator listens to that drumming for a life-time, he will not, by pure listening, be enabled to write down the rhythms of each drum, let alone put it down in correct relation to the singing and clapping. The European is here completely out of his depth. There may be as many as four drum rhythms crossing each other : by this we mean that the first beat of the bar of one drum is not the first beat of the bar of any other drum. Each drum has its own starting point, and the combination of these cross rhythms produces one firm resultant rhythm which is that heard by the outside observer. Added to these four cross rhythms, there is the handclapping which again crosses the drum rhythms, and the singing which crosses them all. The transcriber has to listen to six variant rhythms simultane-ously, and each rhythm has its own main beat which may not coincide with that of any other. This is quite beyond the most brilliant musician. It simply cannot be done. It is in the combination of singing, clapping and drumming that we obtain the full impression of the characteristics of African music, and we cannot fail to realise that it is basically different from our own music. At the same time, here is something natural to the African, and although it is incredible and incomprehensible to us, surely there is here something vital. One feels convinced that the rhythms move according to rule ; the whole pattern is shapely and intensely musical, yet it evades us. In many years of close study, and with the expenditure of not a little brain work, and even after having mastered the drum rhythms of each drum in two seaprate Bemba dance drummings, by learning to play them, the writer has not been able to identify a single example of either handclapping or singing so as to be able to transcribe either of them with certainty in correct relation to the drumming. The subjective method here shows its inherent incapacity to deal accurately with the problem of recording.

From time to time, there appear in magazines or elsewhere, articles on Native music containing examples of tunes which so it is said were heard in such and such a place. If, as is probable, these examples were noted down by direct transcription from listening, one is fairly safe in stating, that they *may* be accurate, but that they are almost certainly wrong at those very points on which we need enlightenment if we are to solve the problems of African rhythm.

The indictment is not yet ended. Consider the Kalimba or " Kaffir Piano." The African learns to play a tune on this instrument by sitting near and watching another player day after day, until he has memorised both the tune and the fingering (or rather, thumbing). The consequence is that all Kalimba tunes have a large number of variants. And this peculiarity of the Kalimba exists not only as between player and player, but is one of the features of the music itself. A good Kalimba player in playing the inevitably short motif over and over again, plays it with a surprising number of variations. Therein lies much of the charm of this music. But therein lies also the difficulty of recording. Kalimba playing proceeds at a great pace ; and it is very rarely that we come across a player who can play the tune at any speed other than the one he has always used. Therefore our direct transcriber has to try and memorise the tune complete. He might possibly do this with a simple tune—it can be done—provided that the player does not put in the variations. But the African will almost certainly put these in, and anyhow, what we mean by a simple tune is often that sort of tune which conforms most nearly to our idea of music. Its value for research purposes is therefore almost negligible. And when all is said and done, and the transcriber flatters himself that he has successfully recorded a Kalimba tune, which he justly regards as a *tour de force*, he can only say, " I am practically certain that this is what was played." He cannot say, "*I know*," and he has no means whereby to measure the accuracy of his transcription. His transcription is an untrustworthy document, and it would be hazarduous to use it for studying those particular points in which African music differs from our own.

Having thus ruled out direct transcription as an impossible method for scientific study, we turn to the second method, whereby a gramophone record is first made. Here we have something which is mechanically accurate. We have no doubt but that the record contains, and when played gives forth, every sound which was produced by the African performers. The record has further the great advantage that it can be played over and over again ; it can also be slowed down so as to give the transcriber a chance of catching the difficult parts. In passing, let it be stated that we are not here considering for a moment the " armchair scientist." To attempt to transcribe records apart from and away from the African performers is sheer futility and is doomed to dismal failure. We have in mind the student who, while having access to his African performers, yet considers that to make a gramophone record of the piece will result in a more accurate transcription.

It is conceivable that he will produce a better transcription. Yet in principle it is difficult to see where this method differs from that of direct transcription. For the same sounds have to go through the same European ears and brain, and whatever difficulties were encountered in the first method, will be met with again here. The passages which are difficult are difficult because they are foreign to us. Our mind cannot cope with them. They defy analysis. Moreover with drumming, instead now of hearing the distinctive timbre of each drum, we are confronted with a dead level of drumming beats, as the gramophone declines to register quality of drumming as distinct from the volume of it. Nor can we decipher which hand the player used for which beat, so that the

[127]

gramophone cannot reveal the *technique* of performance. This applies also to records of Kalimba playing. We cannot tell which thumb the player used for which note : we do not know if there is anything interesting to be learnt here, and even if we slow the machine down as far as possible, it is very doubtful if we could catch many of the lower notes of the tune, which are usually played simultaneously with higher ones, and which being by nature very quiet, as the keys are not large enough to produce a rich sound, would be undecipherable. And even were we to claim to ourselves a measure of success in transcribing the gramophone records, the transcription would only be what we *think* the Africans did, and the worst of it is that we have no external criteria which we may apply to the transcription to test its accuracy. We have to take the transcriber's word for it : a position which would not be tolerated in any other branch of scientific research.

The gramophone was hailed as a great acquisition in the study of African music. It certainly has its uses. It enables us to hear music from many different tribes. We might concede that in this respect it is of value for enthnological purposes. But as the handmaid of the scientific study of African rhythm, it is of no more value than the direct transcription.

To sum up : African music urgently needs research work ; what work is going on has no sort of co-ordination : the little work that has been done in reducing African rhythms to writing is of doubtful value for scientific purposes. It is, one hopes, not uncharitable to say that there is hardly an example of African rhythm in existence on which one would feel safe to build a theory. And the reason for this is first, that there is no common ground of procedure, and second, that the two methods of recording in common use are in the nature of the case, inadequate for the purpose. Research conducted on these lines is far from satisfactory. The whole problem of African rhythm is being viewed constantly through European-tinted spectacles. The subjective element is dominant : the value of the result is more than questionable. It stimulates interest but not conviction. It exposes the problem to wild hypotheses and theories for which there may be not the slightest trace of demonstrable and unassailable evidence.

2. THE SCIENTIFIC APPROACH TO THE PROBLEM OF RECORDING.

All scientific investigation aims at being as completely *objective* as is humanly possible. It is the very opposite of the subjective process. The greatest possible safeguards are taken to eliminate the personality of the investigator. Experiments are planned as objective tests, giving objective results. The validity of the experiment must not rest on any subjective element—this is the scientific ideal. Thus the experiment is capable of repitition by different persons, and should give the same results : and the experiments are so arranged that those results are objective and demonstrable evidence. Further, the scientific investigator in whatever field he is working, tries to arrange his experiments that they shall have results which are mensurable—capable of being measured accurately, and if possible, arithmetically.

[128]

The scientific investigation of African music, therefore, should and must proceed on these lines. It should provide *mensurable* results. This statement may shock those who, regarding music purely from the artistic point of view, feel that it is indefinable, immeasurable, enshrined in the sanctity of the soul. They may feel outraged at the very idea of measuring music with a yard-stick. But let us come down to earth. In so far as music is constructed on regular rhythms, it is based on something which can be counted, and indeed counted with the utmost arithmetical precision. We can count how many movements there are in a piece ; further sub-division tells us how many bars there are in a movement ; and finally not only can we count how many beats there are in a bar, but we Westerns have made our music so mathematical that we can count how many sub-divisions of a beat there are in a beat.

Approaching African music in this scientific frame of mind we find that we are of all investigators, most fortunate. For one of the chief characteristics of African music is its rhythms, which are not only usually present, but also invariably regular in structure. In Northern Rhodesia, for example, however many instruments or voices are employed simultaneously, and on whatever beat of each others' bar they start, the resultant rhythm of the piece has either 6, 8, 12 or 16 beats to the bar. This is common to all four tribes under the writer's notice, and he has never come across an exception to these divisions. It is not necessary at this point to discuss the significance of the word " bar " as here used. It's use will become clear in the musical examples that follow later. It is sufficient to say that the word " bar " is intended to mean the natural division of the piece into regularly recurring rhythmic units.

As we have stated before, nearly all African singing is based on some sort of percussion rhythmic understructure. It may be handclapping. This clapping has invariably a mechanical accuracy. It may be drumming which again is obviously mechanical in its rhythms. It may be a pounding song, where the song follows the relentless rhythm of the pestles. It may be a mining song where the rhythm is that of the striking of the rock drills. It may be a canoe song, in which case the underlying rhythm is the beat of the paddle on the water, or if one prefers, the regularly recurring muscular action of the arms. It may be " beer-drink-chamber-music," where the rhythm is produced by old men sitting round the walls inside a hut and beating on the ground with sticks. In fact one may say, that wherever the African hears regular percussion he instinctively translates it into song. Or conversely, that almost always, wherever there is an African song, there is also some regular *and mensurable* rhythm on which it is based ; further it is an *objective* rhythm and is produced by mechanical means and is therefore able to be measured mechanically.

We have, then, abundant material for our objective recording. How can we arrange our experiments so that we shall obtain a recording which can be measured or counted arithmetically ? If we are to measure the results we ought to be able to *see* them. Both the ear and the perceptive faculty are out of court as being subjective in character. Ovbiously we want a mechanical device. And as all percussion is produced by contact, we have the opportunity to use electricity, which will give us all the

[129]

accuracy that we could possibly look for. There can be no doubt whatever that if the problems of African rhythms are to be solved, we must use recording machines of such a type that the results will be *seen* and not heard, so that we can count and measure them.

All that has been said so far is merely the formal setting down of a growing conviction. Six years ago, the writer decided that if ever Kalimba music were to be recorded accurately, it must be done by an electric machine which would *write* the music on paper. He tried and failed ; but this conviction was not shaken. Later, a study of drumming was attempted. If the reader refers to the previous article on African Drumming he will imagine the mental strivings and manual struggles which were necessary in order to master the examples there quoted. It was perfectly clear at the time, that any serious study of the more difficult drumming could only be done with an electric recorder which would give written results. And you will look in vain in that article for the hand-clapping and singing which accompany the drum examples quoted there. These were beyond the wit of man, but they are by no means beyond the capabilities of electricity. Later still, attention was turned to hand-clapping : the writer trained himself to be able to clap and sing more than one simple African song, but beyond this was the vast expanse of material, often obviously containing passages which were crying out for investigation, totally outside the power of the mind to learn, but surely not beyond the electric recorder if such could be devised. We proceed to the description of such a machine, which has passed its tests, and records with satisfactory precision.

3. APPARATUS FOR ELECTRICAL RECORDING OF RHYTHMS.

The principle of the apparatus is that there shall be a number of pencils arranged side by side which write on a continuous paper drawn along underneath them, thus producing parallel lines. Each percussion instrument taking part in the music is connected electrically with electromagnets placed so that whenever a contact is made, the pencils are drawn away at right-angles to the line they are making, thus marking the exact moment when the percussion was made. Each percussion instrument is connected with its own pencil. The pencils must be truly aligned, so that a contact made say by the first drum and the fourth drum simultaneously, will produce bends in the lines of their respective pencils, immediately above and below each other. In reading the record, therefore, we shall know that marks which are in line with each other, were produced by simultaneous percussion on the respective instruments.

(a) Twenty metal arms of lengths varying in series from 3 inches to 9 inches are mounted side by side on a board, by nails on which each can revolve, passing through a hole drilled in each arm one third of the length from the end of each arm. The arms are one-eighth of an inch thick and are mounted at one quarter of an inch from centre to centre, thus allowing one eighth of an inch gap between each arm. The arms are kept parallel by a stop pin on one side of each, against which they are pressed by a spring pushing against the other side of each arm. The stop pins are driven into the board on which the arms are mounted.

[130]

(b)   At the ends furthest away from the pivots, each arm has a small hole in which a small piece of soft " propelling pencil " lead is placed, the lead being pressed down by a spring fixed to each arm.   The arms are so placed that the pencils are all in a row and exactly opposite one another. Adjustment of this alignment is provided for.

(c)   Below the pencils is a rounded bar of wood over which passes a paper of sufficient width, being fed from a roll underneath, and being wound on a roller.   This winding is done by hand.   The paper moves at about two inches per second.

(d)   At the ends of the arms nearest the pivots are inserted small pieces of malleable iron, and opposite these, mounted on the board, are electromagnets, one to each arm, so placed that if current flows through them, they will pull the arms towards themselves a distance of just less than one-sixteenth of an inch, thus causing the pencils to move just less than one eighth of an inch.   That is, the arms can be moved by their magents without touching the adjacent arms.

(e)   Each magnet is connected by a common wire to one terminal of a car battery.   To the other wire from each magnet is attached a length of flexible insulated wire, at the ends of which are attached small spring brass rings which will fit conveniently tightly over the first finger.

(f)   One arm with its magnet is connected with a small spring contact like a morse tapper, placed in front of the apparatus, and which is the operator's control contact.

(g)   A number of petrol tins corresponding to the number of drums required are connected electrically between themselves and also with the second terminal of the car battery.   The control switch is also connected with this terminal, and in the case of handclapping, where two brass rings are needed, one of these is likewise connected with this terminal of the car battery.

(h)   A switch is provided in the circuit so that the current can be turned on after the music is well under way.

(i)   The cost of the apparatus excluding the car battery is about thirty shillings, if home-made from scrap material.

The following points may be noted :

(a)   Whenever a performer makes a percussion whether of drumming or clapping, the line of this pencil will make a simultaneous deflection.

(b)   In the case of drums, not only the rhythm of each drum but the beats played by each individual hand will be registered.

(c)   The operator hears the resultant rhythm of the music, and taps this out on his control.   This operation is not essential but it helps in the subsequent reading of the record.

(d)   The rhythm of the song is recorded in this fashion :

[131]

The operator writes down the words of the song beforehand. He then makes marks on those syllables which he can recognise easily and quickly when the song is sung.

While the song is being sung, the operator depresses his control key every time the singer sings one of the marked syllables. While doing this, of course, he does not tap out the resultant rhythm. This process may sound difficult but it is easy in practice. The operator does not depend on his ear : he watches the mouth of the singer. This is the only part of the experiment where the subjective element comes in, though as can be seen, that element is reduced to its minimum.

4. PROCEDURE FOR RECORDING.

A drum rhythm which has clapping and singing accompaniment is best chosen as it serves the manifold purpose of :

discovering the rhythm of each drum (say 4 drums) ;

discovering the exact relation of each drum rhythm with the others, i.e. finding the cross rhythms ;

discovering the exact rhythm of the clapping. Quite often this cannot be arrived at by listening. It may be based on duple or triple rhythm, we cannot tell ;

discovering the relation of the clapping rhythm with the drums ;

discovering the rhythm of the song ;

discovering the relations of the clapping with the song melody ;

discovering the relation of the song with the drumming.

In fact we are enabled to make no less than fourteen separate investigations in one operation.

(a) The operator summons a party of drummers, a boy for clapping, a singer (or more) and a European assistant

(b) The operator takes down the words of the song. The singer sings it and the operator takes down the melody, noting approximately though not with excessive care, the rhythm of it.

He makes a clear mark above the syllables which he can recognise easily and quickly. The more syllables he marks, the more accurate and incontrovertible will be the record.

(c) The drummers are supplied with the brass rings, one for each forefinger, the rings being supplied in rotation so that the drum recordings will appear in order on the paper

(d) The operator writes on the paper opposite each pencil, its particular function, e.g. top drum, left ; middle drum, right ; clap ; control, etc.

(e) The clapper is supplied with two rings, one for each hand. In clapping he must clap one ring against the other.

[132]

(*f*) There follows a brief instruction : the players are exhorted to be careful to play firmly on the petrol tins, and also to guard against touching them except when they intend to make a beat. In passing we may say that if several recordings are done of the same drumming, accidental contacts if any, should be apparent by comparison.

(*g*) A short practice is held. The Africans called by the writer found no difficulty in drumming with one finger only of each hand. In fact he was taught a drum rhythm on a table in this very way by an African.

(*h*) The European assistant now takes his place by the paper-roller handle.

(*i*) The drumming is started ; the clapper claps and the singer sings. When it is going nicely, the operator gives a signal to the assistant, and switches on the current. The assistant starts winding the paper, and the operator taps out the main beats of the resultant rhythm. After about 4 seconds the current is switched off, the assistant winds up some paper so as to leave a blank gap, the current goes on again and the operator, watching the mouth of the singer, this time taps out the marked syllables of the song. About four seconds later the current is switched off and the recording is complete.

In less than ten seconds of actual recording, we have made an almost perfect and indisputable record of no less than fourteen different investigations.

(*j*) Each drummer is now asked in turn and separately, to beat his rhythm by himself. The operator notes any salient features about it that strike him. These notes are not essential except in a case of a rhythmic pattern in which a drum beat occurs on each beat of the bar. In which case it will be recorded thus :

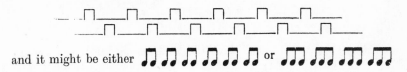

and it might be either 𝅘𝅥𝅮𝅘𝅥𝅮 𝅘𝅥𝅮𝅘𝅥𝅮 𝅘𝅥𝅮𝅘𝅥𝅮 𝅘𝅥𝅮𝅘𝅥𝅮 𝅘𝅥𝅮𝅘𝅥𝅮 𝅘𝅥𝅮𝅘𝅥𝅮 or 𝅘𝅥𝅮𝅘𝅥𝅮𝅘𝅥𝅮 𝅘𝅥𝅮𝅘𝅥𝅮𝅘𝅥𝅮 𝅘𝅥𝅮𝅘𝅥𝅮𝅘𝅥𝅮 𝅘𝅥𝅮𝅘𝅥𝅮𝅘𝅥𝅮

5. DECIPHERING THE RECORD.

In Appendix 1 there is an example of recording made on 1st November, 1936, of a Bémba dance drumming with handclap and song. The name of the drumming is *Ngwayi*, or rather " *Ngwayi*, new style," as the boys have it. It was this same *Ngwayi* which was analysed in the article on African Drumming referred to above. It will be interesting to find how it justifies the name of " *Ngwayi*, new style."

We give first the words of the song, with the syllables marked for tapping, together with the tune as it was noted down before recording.

[133]

Senséntá Mfúmú, sénséntá Mfúmú, wafwola chirànkulé, wafwala ndúwulé

Our concern here so far as music goes, is with the melody, and not the rhythm of the melody. All we want is the notes which are sung to each syllable : we remember that this investigation is to do with rhythm, and not primarily with melody, and therefore we do not object to the subjective method used in transcribing the melody.

Looking at Appendix 1, we note the marks on the control line for giving the main beats of the resultant rhythm. This line is of course purely subjective, being the operator's impression as to what the main beats were. But that does not matter a bit. Its only use is to give us a convenient indication as to where the rhythms start to repeat again. Noting that the Kabitiko drum is beating regularly, twelve beats to the bar as marked by the control, we number the beats accordingly, choosing the beat which is two beats behind the first clap as Beat 1.

Looking at the Kabitiko line we see that we may write it down as a line of quavers (or any other note-value). Is it duple or triple ? Here we consult our notes (see section 4, note *j*) and find it is triple with strong beats as follows :

R L R   L R L   R L R   L R L   etc.

It is interesting to compare this with the rhythm of this drum as analysed in " African Drumming." There it was given as :

R   L   R R L

So in the " new style," the Kabitiko drum has filled out its rhythmic pattern, rather a pity, we think, as the original was so distinctive in comparison with the other drums.

Between the recorded lines of the Kabitiko drum we write in convenient signs to make the rhythm clear, and also to show whether right or left hand were used. We choose to write | for Right, and . for Left.

We turn our attention to the Sensele drum. Now the young gentleman who played this drum was in our presence firmly exhorted by the Kabitiko player, with quite a lot of illustration, that he was to play this rhythm :

etc.

[134]

which you will perceive, is identical with the rhythm for this drum given in " African Drumming." But what do we find on the record ? We mark in the signs to make the rhythm clear, and we find it is unmistakeably this :

♩ ♪♩. ♩ ♪♩. ♩ ♪♩. ♩ ♪♩. etc.
R L R   R L R   R L R   R L R

When the young rascal was faced with this disclosure (which could never have been detected by ear), he merely said, " But that is what I was taught when I originally learnt to play the Sensele part for this dance." So here we have an authentic variant, and incidentally quite an unlooked-for discovery. But the evidence of the pencil line cannot be contradicted. And if any confirmation of it were needed, it lies in the fact that he freely admitted to having played this rhythm.

Further, on the same afternoon, a little later, he suddenly started another variant. Space prevents us from giving the recorder marks, but the rhythm was this :

| ♩ ♩ ♪ ♪ ♪. | ♩ ♪. | ♩ ♪ ♩ ♪ ♪. | ♩ ♪. | = 3 measures.
R L R L R L R   R L R   R L R L R L R   R L R

Altogether then, we have three variants for the Sensele drum. This is characteristic of African drumming. Provided the drums move generally within the limits of their main rhythm, they can make embellishments or variations at will. At least that is our impression, but we want more evidence before we state it as a fact.

We look now at the Kabanga drum ; marking in its rhythm we find that it plays eight quavers followed by a minim, or vice versa, it matters not. This looks duple, but on referring to our notes, we find the stress marks proclaimed it as triple, and it should therefore be written thus :

♫ ♫♫ ♫♫ ♩
LR   LRL   RLR   L

Objection may be taken to the evidence of the notes which we refer to. Here is a loop-hole for error which we admit. Though with only one drum to listen to, we ought to be able to tell, if it is at all regular, whether it is beating a duple or triple rhythm. But the objection remains and we could meet it by placing on the drum a small insulated metal plate connected to a circuit of its own. We could ask the drummer to beat his stressed beats on this plate and the others on the petrol tin. At the time of writing we have not had time to do this.

[135]

The Kabanga drum in places has a slight variation. He plays :

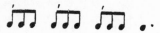

R L   R L R   L R L   R R

There is also another variation on strip B. The recording might be
written either as :

or as :

We had to summon a drummer to our aid. Both rhythms were
tapped out to him and he had no hesitation in accepting the second.
There was no question about it. Here again is an illustration of the
point already alluded to, namely, that variation seems to be permitted so
long as it conforms to the general rhythmic pattern of the original. The
rejected rhythm while covering the same number of beats, has no longer the
" flavour " of the other two variants. By comparing the three we note
that this " flavour " is produced by the entry of the figure on the second
pulse of the group of three pulses, with, therefore, an implied rest on the
first (and strong) pulse. If the reader beats out these two rhythmic
patterns for himself, he will find what a big difference there is between
these two rhythms.

The Itumba drum rhythms as transcribed in Appendix 2 do not
appear in Appendix 1. The reason is that at the time of recording the
writer did not know that a fourth drum should be playing : and anyway,
the paper at his disposal was only just wide enough to record the other
instruments. He therefore obtained the correct placing of the Itumba
drum by causing it to be played subsequently in conjunction with one or
other of the others. The Itumba drum has two very distinct and different
rhythmic figures. This is notable, for the variations in the other drums
in each case have a basic structure which remains unchanged. Great
freedom is apparently allowed to the Itumba player. This is the writer's
impression by observation. There is not yet enough evidence to lay it
down as proven fact. One of the Itumba rhythms has a variant, making
three variants in all. The rhythms are :

(a)

(b)

(c)

L   R L R   L R L   R L R   L

[136]

The clapping rhythm is plain. It is a double clap followed by a pause, a double clap followed by a pause.

Lastly we review the song. First we write in our marked syllables under the control marks to which they belong. We then fill in the other syllables. At once we notice a curious feature. Whereas in the first singing, the song is introduced so that the word *mfu-mu* coincides with the clap, in the second singing, the song is shifted forward so that the clap occurs on *se-nse-nta*. Looking at the numbers of the beats, we see that while the first time, the song began on beat 9, the second time it begins on beat 3, i.e. 6 beats early, and as the complete measure consists of 12 beats, that means that while in one case it begins (to put it conveniently) at the beginning, in the second case it starts in the middle. Several recordings were made, and in each case the song was sung in this odd fashion. Why ? We have found out the fact, but we know not the reason. But we never even suspected the fact itself before the electric recording was made.

The music of *Se-nse-nta* has four notes to be accounted for. Looking at the recording, we find that while *Se* undoubtedly coincides with beat 9*, *Nse* just as clearly does not coincide with beat 10. In fact it falls half way between beats 10 and 11. *Nta* coincides with beat 12, and *mfu-* falls on beat 3 of the next bar. But *Nta* has two notes to it. We have then :

```
9  10  11  12  1  2  3
9   |      12  x     3
```

There is no doubt about it. It is 2 against 3. Four notes of music against six of the drums. The syllables we marked are found to occur in the correct position for this rhythm. Surely we may presume that the fourth note marked x falls halfway between 1 and 2. Additional evidence for this is the fact that when we roughed out the melody we gave these four notes equal value. But it is just these four notes which are interesting. In our rough transcription, we were not sure what exactly was their rhythm. The recorder tells us. We did not mark them 2 against 3, but the record shows this to be the case. The objective method shows its superiority.

We have now reviewed each part separately. We go on to view the record vertically so as to find the relation of the instruments, clapping and singing with each other.

First the drums. Four strips of recording were made and for reference have been lettered A, B, C and D. It is impossible to reproduce them in their entirety. A specimen of the recording is given in Appendix 1.

The order in which the drums are considered is the order in which they are regarded by the Bemba people. From the top drum to the lowest the order being Sensele, Kabitiko, Kabanga and Itumba. The first three

---

*The first entry of *se-nse-nta* on Strip B was tapped a trifle late. Compare the next bar : the strips record many entries of *se-nse-nta*, as stated above, on beat 9.

may be of equal size and are of the familiar shape like a woman's pounding a mortar. They are about 2 feet 6 inches high, open at the lower end, with a thick skin stretched over the top and held down by wooden pegs driven through the skin into the side of the drum. The Itumba is a special drum, about 1 foot 3 inches high and 1 foot in diameter. It is open at the bottom and has a thin skin stretched over the top, studded with little "knobbles" of Native rubber. In the side is a hole about 1 inch in diameter over which is stuck a piece of that opaque covering to a certain spider's eggs which the writer knows as "Lemba-lemba." This drum is always used as an embellishment and is played only by superior players who use many variations in playing. It produces a very low and persistent humming sound.

Reference should be made frequently, in following the analysis given below, to Appendices 1 and 2.

First we note that in the case of each drum, after 12 pulses, the rhythmic figure is repeated. Thus the whole piece is in the form of a 12 pulse measure. Further, the main rhythm of each drum is triple—groups of three. We thus consider the bar to consist of four groups of three.

For purposes of analysis we must choose a starting point from which to count. It does not matter where. Let us therefore call the main beat of Sensele which occurs just before the first clap, Beat 1.

The Sensele drum therefore has its main beats on 1, 4, 7, 10. From strips A, B, C and D, we find that the Kabitiko drum enters with a strong beat on 5, and his main beats are 5, 8, 11, 2. Comparing the relation of the two rythms thus :

$$1 \quad 4 \quad 7 \quad 10$$
$$5 \quad 8 \quad 11 \quad 2$$

we see that there is a cross rhythm here. Kabitiko's main beats are *one beat later* than those of Sensele. The relation of their rhythmic figures is therefore :

This relation holds good also for the variations of both Sensele and Kabitiko. Whatever the variation, the same cross rhythm occurs.

From strips A and B we find that the Kabanga drum starts with two unaccented beats, and then his first main beat occurs on beat 7 of the bar. His main beats are therefore 7, 10, 1, or 7, 10, 1, 3, in the variant. Thus the Kabanga stressed beats coincide with those of Sensele with the interesting exception of the stressed 3 in the variant. Main beats on 1 and 3, with the entry of the figure on 5 (1, 3, 5) indicate a duple touch in the middle of a strongly triple rhythm. This is one of the little ways in which African drumming is made so thrilling and delightful. Across the main triple rhythm come a few beats—just a touch—of duple rhythm played perhaps by only one drum : but quite sufficient to give piquance to the movement. However, as the main beats of Sensele and Kabanga coincide, we see that they are " brothers."

The Itumba drum has two distinctive variations. Strip C shows that one of these starts on beat 10 1/2 with the first main beat on 11, its main beats being 11, 2, 5, 8. The other variation, also on strip C has its first main beat on 5, its stresses being either 5, 8, 11, 1, 3, or if we take the variant of this, 5, 8, 11, (1), 2. Note that the start on 11 in the one case and 5 in the other, simply means that one variation starts exactly half a measure (6 beats) away from the other. We note also that the Itumba repeats the Kabanga's device of a duple interruption in the triple flow, this interruption occurring on beats 1, 3 and the following 5. But Itumba does not always do this (nor does Kabanga). Itumba's variation 5, 8, 11, 1, 2, coincides with Kabitiko's figure :

Once more it is clear that the main triple rhythm can be crossed from time to time, and at the whim of the player, by a momentary duple rhythm, which is thrilling to listen to. It is certain the African enjoys this, for he hammers out these duple beats truly and well. To return to the Itumba, whatever variation is taken, the Itumba and the Kabitiko carry the same main beats. Therefore these, the second and fourth drums, are " brothers."

We see then that the rhythm of Sensele and Kabanga crosses that of Kabitiko and Itumba. And each of these pairs has the same starting point for its first main beat. For Sensele's starting point can be reckoned as either 1, 4, 7, or 10 and 7 is Kabanga's starting point ; while both Kabitiko and Itumba enter on beat 5.

Turning our attention to the Clap, we find its rhythm, which is : clap clap (long pause) clap clap (long pause) clap clap, etc. falls on beats 3 and 6. All strips A, B, C and D witness to the invariable nature of the clap. Now no drum has a single stress on 6, and only two have one on 3, and that only when they are departing from their main rhythm to make the duple interlude. So the clap rhythm is crossing all four drums. Our best drummer says that when he is drumming, he is aware that the clapper is clapping just after the main beat of Kabitiko, which statement agrees with our analysis.

Kabitiko ... 5, 8, 11, 2 ‖ 5, 8, etc.

Clap ... 3, 6,

Incidentally, we expect no sort of help from the African with the analysis of cross rhythms. He knows his own drum and how to incorporate it into the whole ensemble, but he has no analytical sense whatever. He cannot say *what* is happening. This is another reason why mechanical recording is essential.

[139]

Another interesting fact about the entry of the clap is this. The first clap of each group comes in on the beat following the only beat in the measure where there are less than three drums beating simultaneously. Whatever variation is played, it will be found that only two drums are beating on beat 2 in each bar. And the clap enters on beat 3. Whether this fact guides the clapper, we cannot say. He may be listening for this weak beat ; on the other hand beat 3 is the beat following the final strong beat of the Kabitiko rhythmic figure. Were he listening to this figure, which is distinctive, it would be easy for him to come in at the right moment.

Lastly we consider the relation of the song with the clap and drums. From strips B, C and D, we find it consists of 4 complete bars—48 beats, in triple time except for the touches of duple rhythm at the words " *Sensenta.*". Here again we note with interest the inclusion of a duple touch in a triple form. From these strips we find that the song may enter on either beat 9 or beat 3. On strips B and C it enters alternately on 9 and 3. On strip D it enters each time on 9. But in either case, its main beats are 3, 6, 9, 12 and we see at once that the song is the " brother " of the handclap.

There is another point of special interest. Kabitiko and Itumba have a duple interruption on beats 1, 3 and 5, while the song's duple rhythm occurs on either 9, 10½, 12, 1½, 3 or on 3, 4½, 6, 7½, 9, according to its starting point. Thus the duple rhythm of Kabitiko and Itumba has nothing whatever to do with the duple part of the song. But what we do notice particularly is this ; the duple effect of the song is produced in a different way from that of the drums. With the drums it is a case of 6/8 time being changed to 3/4.

While with the song, it is a case of $\circ = \downarrow$ or " 2 against 3."

Drums.

Song.

It is strange that the untutored African should perform by the light of nature these two rhythmic devices—without of course having the least idea of the principle underlying what he is doing.

We have now made the fourteen investigations which we claimed could be made simultaneously on the electric recorder, though in our case we admit that by oversight, we had to make two operations instead of one. We know now the separate rhythms of four drums ; the hands used by each drummer in playing ; the relation of the drum rhythms with each other ; the rhythm of the clapping ; the relation of the clapping with the drums ; the rhythm of the song ; the relation of the clapping with the song ; the relation of the song with the clapping. There remains one big and all-important query. Will these revelations lead us to discover the *basic principle* on which this delightful *Ngwayi* dance music is built.

To this end we proceed to summarise the results of the analysis we have made.

1. SUMMARY OF RHYTHMS.

(The letters at the left of the rhythms refer to the recording strip on which those rhythms appear.)

		Entry on beat	Main beats

Sensele :

			Entry on beat	Main beats
1. A.			1	1, 4, 7, 10.
2. B.				
3. B.	= 1½ Measures.			

Kabitiko :

			Entry on beat	Main beats
1. D.	*		5	5, 8, 11, 2.
2. A.B.C.				

Kabanga :

		Entry on beat	Main beats
1. A.		5	7, 10, 1, 3.
2. B.			
3. B.			7, 10, 1.
			7, 10, 1.

Itumba :

			Entry on beat	Main beats
1. C.	or		5	5, 8, 11, 1, 3.
2. C.				5, 8, 11, 2.
3. C.			10½	11, 2, 5, 8.

Clap :

		Entry on beat	Main beats
A.B.C.D.		3	3, 6.

* The line should consist of :—2 dotted crochets, 1 crochet, 1 quaver, 1 dotted crochet.

Song :   4=6   4=7

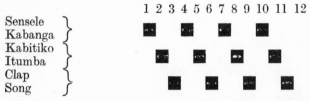

1. B.D.   9   3,   6,   9,   12.

2. B.   3   3,   6,   9,   12.

2. MAIN BEATS OF VOICES, SHOWING CROSS RHYTHMS.

	1	2	3	4	5	6	7	8	9	10	11	12
Sensele Kabanga			■			■			■			■
Kabitiko Itumba					■			■		■		■
Clap Song				■			■			■		■

From these summaries it is tempting to draw general principles. We want a great deal more evidence from the recording of other dance music before accepting generalisations. However, *as far as the piece under review goes*, we put forward the three following conclusions :

From Summary 1 we conclude

" Freedom of variation but restriction of form."

The variation tends to have the same rhythmic feeling of form as the original. (But note the exception of the Itumba alternative). The discussion of the third Kabanga alternative on p. 9 is strong evidence for this conclusion. It would be easier to play the rejected form, but it was rejected doubtless just because it had a different rhythmic feeling. It does not sound a bit the same ; not a bit.

Summary 2 is significant. It is the climax of our investigation. Surely it shows the inner principle of the rhythmic construction of *Ngwayi*. The principle may be stated thus :

" This piece consists of triple units of three pulses. The parts are so disposed that all three pulses are used as main beats, thus creating three cross rhythms. There are four triple units to a measure."

This essay starts with a critical examination of present methods of recording African rhythms. It pleads for scientific mechanical recording providing mensurable results. It proceeds to apply this method : we hope the result justifies the plea. The writer can at least claim of Appendix 2, not that he *thinks* it is right, but that he *knows* it is right.

The writer suggested that this discussion on recording rhythms might give the reader some idea of the features and principles of African rhythms in music as found in Northern Rhodesia. He hopes that the essay has fulfilled its purpose in this respect also.

Lastly he would ask the reader to recollect that he has been studying what can only be described as a perfect art form. It is as perfect in its way as the polyphony of Palestrina : indeed it is analogous in form. It is as perfect as the harmony of the later masters. Here indeed is harmony, but it is rhythmic harmony. It is the harmony of the drums and claps. They are music to the African—and music too, to the European who has ears to hear. In rhythmic beauty and interest it is as far removed from Western music as manhood is from infancy. *Ngwayi* is but one of countless African Dance rhythms. It was not chosen for study because it was the best of its type. And let the reader recollect that he has been studying the African counterpart of European Music for Full Orchestra and Chorus. But it has this to its crown. It is of the people, for the people and by the people. It needs no highly trained performer. Four drums and an untutored village crowd can produce at any moment without rehearsal music that rivals in intensity of interest that of our own masters. And if Bach's music or Beethoven's is divine, the heathen African's dance measures can claim no less a source of inspiration. The writer of Laudate Domimun could hardly have expressed in better words than these, either the universality of genius, or the divine nature of all beautiful things :

Praise Him in the cymbals and dances :

Praise Him upon the strings and pipe.

Praise Him upon the well-tuned cymbals :

Praise Him upon the loud cymbals.

Let everything that hath breath (simple African or cultured Western) praise the Lord.

APPENDIX 2

BEMBA DANCE - NGWAYI   **FULL SCORE**   ELECTRIC RECORDING

[Of each drum, one variation only is given]

5

TRADE ROUTES, TRADE AND CURRENCY IN EAST AFRICA

A. H. QUIGGIN

1949

THE EAST COAST OF AFRICA was visited by traders long before the dawn of history, though Sumerians or Assyrians from the Persian Gulf, Egyptians from the north through the Red Sea, or Indians, helped in their longer voyages by the steady blowing of the monsoons, left little evidence behind. If Somaliland was the " Land of Punt " Egyptian traders about 3,000 B.C. were bringing back from there the incense for which the country was famed, as well as gold and ivory ; and if (as many still believe) Sofala with its hinterland was the " Land of Ophir," gold and ivory were brought from there to Judaea and Phoenicia about 1000 B.C. But the lack of evidence suggests that such early venturers had little contact with the coast and less with the interior of the continent.

ARABS.

In prehistoric as in historic times the Arabs appear to have been the chief traders across the Indian Ocean and to have dominated its western shores. There was fierce rivalry for the valuable trade, and sometimes Yemen, sometimes Axum in Abyssinia, and for some centuries (sixth to ninth) Persia, was in the ascendant, but the coastal trade bringing spices and slaves from the north and ivory from further south was mainly in the hands of the Arabs from the beginning of our era. The *Periplus*, containing instructions for pilots, dated at about 60 A.D., is the earliest written account of the East Coast, which it calls " the Ausanitic Coast " from its former dependence on the Arab state of Ausan. It records the trading establishments along the shores and the trade with the interior organised by Arab captains and agents " who are familiar with the natives and intermarry with them and who know the whole coast and understand the language."*

The chief exports, in exchange for " lances, hatchets, daggers, awls and various kinds of glass," were a great quantity of ivory, rhinoceros horn, tortoise shell and a little palm oil. The slave trade had already begun, but there is no mention of gold. The instructions end at Rhapta, which is assumed to have been in the neighbourhood of Bagamoyo, Dar es Salaam, or possibly Kilwa, beyond which, as was commonly believed, " the unexplored ocean curves around towards the west."

In the first centuries of our era we can thus picture Arab trading posts here and there along the coast, and during the ascendency of Persia there may have been Persian settlements, but the first detailed information of any important migration is that of

* *The Periplus of the Erythraean Sea*, W. H. Schoff, 1912, p. 28.

[146]

the Emozaide in the eighth century A.D. Zaide, who was a heretic, though a descendant of the Prophet, led his followers across Arabia into Africa, and they spread "like a slow plague" down the coast.*

They were followed by a migration of orthodox Moslems escaping from tyranny in Central Arabia, who settled at Mogadishu and at Brava, expelling the heretical Emozaide, who were driven inland. Some time later a boat from Mogadishu was driven by stormy weather to take refuge in the port of Sofala, and the men brought back tales of gold up-country. This led to the establishment of a trading post there, and Arab influence was extended as far south as Inhambane and Cape Corrientes, but it was mainly confined to the coast. The Emozaide, who mixed more and more with the natives, acted as middlemen, bartering the cloth, beads and trade goods brought by sea, for the ivory and gold, skins, cattle and grain carried down by slaves to the coast. To the north there is evidence of traffic between the coast and the Lakes. Further south Rhodesian gold was carried down the Zambesi Valley to Quilimane, or to Sofala by way of the Sabi River. But there is no record of inland settlement earlier than the sixteenth century.

MASUDI.

The "Arab Herodotus" Masudi, traveller and writer of the tenth century, made several voyages down the East Coast in trading vessels and describes its dangers. In all his travels, from the Mediterranean to the China Seas, he had never encountered anything more perilous than the "Sea of Zendj" on his way to Kanbalou (Madagascar), with waves like high mountains, called "blind waves" because they never broke in foam. The Zendj (whom he describes) inhabited the coast from Abyssinia to Sofala, which was the limit of navigation for Arabian and Persian traders, and among the exports were panther skins for saddles and tortoise shell for combs. There was gold in abundance in Sofala, but ivory was more important, quantities being brought back to Oman to be sent to China (for palanquins) and India (for dagger handles and chessmen). The Zendj used neither gold nor silver for ornament, but only iron.

IBN BATUTA.

The intrepid traveller Ibn Batuta tells a little more about the East Coast in the fourteenth century, though he did not go further south than Kilwa. On one of his many pilgrimages to Mecca he made an excursion down to the "country of the Zanuj" (Zendj) calling in at the island of Mombasa. He notes that "the greatest gift bestowed by the people of the country is ivory—they seldom give gold." But he had heard of the gold dust that

---

* Theal, G. M., *Records of South Eastern Africa*, 1898, vi, p. 223.

was brought down to Sofala, and believed that it came from the Nile, a month's journey inland, " but it cannot be visited by any white man because they would kill him before he got there."*

PORTUGUESE.

The first white man to leave an account of his travel into the interior was Antonio Fernandes. The Portuguese had long been attracted by the wealth of the East Indian trade and Vasco da Gama's voyage of exploration to visit the Arab settlements in East Africa (1497-9) was quickly followed by their conquest. By 1509, almost all the coast from Malindi to Sofala was in the hands of the Portuguese. Their chief settlement was at Mozambique, the safest port then known to them, and they had forts at Kilwa and Malindi to the north. But Portuguese eyes were greedily fixed on the " Land of Monomotapa " behind Sofala, reputed to be the Ophir whence came the Queen of Sheba's gold. Here, it was believed, it could not only be picked up in nuggets on the ground, but even gathered from the trees. A fort was built at Sofala, and from here, in 1514, Fernandes set out to explore the interior, with his stock of trading goods, muskets, cloth, beads and slaves.

FERNANDES.

The greatest explorer of this period was Antonio Fernandes, who not only discovered the land of the Monomotapa but (as the Governor of Sofala wrote to the King of Portugal in 1516) " has so much credit in all those lands that they worship him like a god."† He was a *degredado*, i.e., a convict, who according to the custom of the time, was given his freedom and landed on the coast of Africa to explore the interior for the honour, glory and profit of Portugal.

His first journey was along the Buzi River, which then reached the sea at Sofala, then up the Sabi Valley. Near the site of Birchenough Bridge was a great fair every Monday to which Moors and Kaffirs brought their goods. " That fair is said to be as big as you can see anywhere. And there is no other money than gold by weight." Continuing north he reached Manica (Penhalonga) and reports for the first time the presence of gold. Near the Pungwe River he saw the natives extracting it " in bars as large as a finger and in bulky grains." He continued northwards towards the Zambesi, then turned west, crossing the Mazoe River and so reached the Empire of the Monomotapa, " the greatest source of gold in the whole land." He made excursions of ten days to Butua (the modern Hartley ?) and of seven days to the kingdom of Mobara (in the neighbourhood of Sinoia) where copper was exported

---

* Ibn Batuta, *Travels in Asia and Africa*, translated by H. A. R. Gibb, 1929, p. 112.
† Eric Axelson, *South-east Africa*, 1488-1530, 1940.
   Hugh Tracey, *Antonio Fernandes, Descobridor do Monomotapa*, 1514-1515, 1940.

" in ingots like ours." Fernandes describes the " silent trade "
here, the natives paddling their goods across the river (Hunyani)
and the " Moors or Kaffirs " placing their cloth and other goods
on the bank in exchange. Having exhausted all his " presents "
Fernandes returned to Sofala.

He made a second journey to Monomotapa in the following
year and when some 100 leagues from Sofala came to a " city
hard by a great river (Zambezi). With pilots one could sail down
this river to the sea—in this city is sold all the merchandise that is
stolen from our vessels by the Moors of Kilwa and Malindi." On
his return journey he worked southwards through the Salisbury,
Gwelo and Que Que districts to the Tokwe River where " Fernandes
Island " is marked on old maps. Here it was proposed to set up
a factory to receive the gold and ivory from Monomotapa and the
surrounding districts and with the aid of a frigate to cut off the
Arab trade, keeping the river clear of their boats, which flooded
the markets with their goods.

Both the advice and the report of Fernandes appear to have been
ignored. The southern route into the interior was neglected,
the fort of Sofala abandoned, while the Portuguese strengthened
the Zambezi route with forts at its mouth, at Sena and at Tete,
with factories for storing trade goods. Missionaries made their
painful way inland to the " Simbaoe " (Zimbabwe) of the Maka-
ranga Chief, ennobled with the title of King Pedro, Emperor of
Monomotapa and he, together with his mother and son, was converted to Christianity (in twenty-five days) by the Jesuit Father
Silveira. But the Arabs saw their rich trade gravely menaced by
the Portuguese infiltration and their accusations of witchcraft
led to Silveira's murder in 1560. A few years later an ambitious
expedition was organised to punish the murder, to subdue the
country, and establish Portuguese supremacy over the whole
East Coast from Cape Guardafui to Cape Corrientes. It was
expected that by monopolising the gold trade, wealth to rival
that of the Indies would pour into Portugal.

BARRETO.

Francisco Barreto, Viceroy of India, was in charge of the
expedition consisting of 1,000 men, drawn largely from the nobility
and gentry, eager adventurers, " the noise of gold drowning the
thoughts of danger." They started from Sena in November,
1572, with twenty boats laden with provisions, twenty-five wagons
drawn by native oxen, and 2,000 slaves with baggage, Barreto
riding ahead clad in a heavy coat of mail. They had to fight
their way, killing natives by the thousand, but sickness was a more
deadly enemy. Deaths occurred daily, reducing their strength
until there were not porters left to carry the sick and the miserable
remnant had to crawl back to Sena where Barreto died.

[149]

HONEM.

Fernandes Honem, who took charge after Barreto's death chose the easier route from Sofala ; he succeeded in reaching the "Simbaoe" of the Monomotapa by way of the Revue River and had a friendly reception from King Pedro. But there were no gold nuggets to be picked up by the handful. The gold-mining was a "poor and miserable business," and he and his men, suffering from famine and sickness, returned disillusioned to Sofala.

These early pioneers found that money was no use in trading with the natives. Vasco da Gama had made use of "glasses and small bells," in exchange for ivory and provisions. Barreto relied mainly on cloth, both to pay his soldiers and to buy food. Indian cloth bought at Mozambique for six to seven *crusados* was worth fifteen at Sena. The usual trade goods were blue or striped cloth, ten pieces of which in a bundle made a slave's load, together with small beads strung in necklace lengths. Especially rich cloths were presented by Barreto to the conquered chief of Quiteve, who, in return, gave him a string of gold beads "like a rosary," and as a very special honour, eight bracelets of fine gold wire, such as were worn only by chiefs.

Portuguese expectations of enormous wealth to be obtained from the gold of Monomotapaland had been shattered by Honem's report. Expectations of profits from silver mines lasted longer but had to be abandoned. The "Empire of Monomotapa" was broken up on the death of King Pedro and petty chiefs fought for dominance. Disorder and insubordination increased not only among the natives but among the Portuguese both lay and religious. They were governed from Goa by the Viceroy of India, whose orders took months to reach their destination, and royal commands and cancellations from Portugal took longer still. Such trade as there was in ivory and small quantities of gold in return for cloth did not even support the settlements or keep the forts in repair.

LACERDA.

But a better source of income was developing on the East Coast as well as on the West, for the increasing demand from the Americas made slaves more valuable than gold or silver. By the middle of the seventeenth century the supply of slaves from Angola was running short and there were royal demands from Portugal for shipments from Mozambique. At the same time English merchant ships from the Cape were arriving at East Coast ports and threatening the Portuguese monopoly. It was to safeguard the slave trade by linking up the Portuguese colonies to east and west as a barrier to interference from the south, that Ferreira de Lacerda started on his expedition in 1798, hoping to be the first white man to cross Central Africa through the country of the Cazembe.

Captain Burton edited Lacerda's journal* and mapped the route taken by his expedition across Northern Rhodesia. Entering at the extreme eastern corner, south of Fort Jameson he crossed the Luangwa (which he called the Aruangoa) climbed over the Muchinga escarpment, " high, great and rough," and crossed the Chambezi south of Kasama. The usual discouragements were met with ; thick bush, marshes and swamps, flies, ague and fever, shortage of food and water, attacks or threatened attacks from natives, quarrels and inefficiency among the Portuguese and desertions of native porters, and Lacerda died, utterly worn out, shortly before reaching the capital.

PINTO.

The expedition proceeded under the nominal leadership of the chaplain, Father Pinto, and was received by the Cazembe at his " city " at Lunda, south of Lake Mweru, in November, 1798. Cloth and beads were the first gifts sent on ahead to obtain " the King's beneplacet," and two ivories and two slaves were sent in return, followed later by a present of " some blue drinking glasses " (imported doubtless from the West Coast). When the king was feeling generous his usual gifts were slaves, ivory and copper bars. Greenstone (malachite) was also given in presents, but (says Pinto) was not indigenous. Both copper and malachite came from Katanga. Father Pinto records many articles of trade, " but it is now confined to two, ivory and slaves. Copper bars are sold for four common cloths or forty to fifty couros " (beads). A cloth was valued at about sixpence. Cowries were abundant as decorations. On gala occasions the royal feet were " covered with strung cowries, large opaque stoneware beads (pedras de cores) [see Exhibit in Museum] and white or red porcelains (velorios)." Cloth and beads were freely expended in attempts to win permission for the expedition to continue to the west, but all efforts were obstructed, mainly because the Cazembe wished to keep all profits of trade for himself. The unfortunate party was forced to return whence it came, and in disorder, robbed and maltreated, footsore, hungry and in rags, reached Tete in November, 1799.

BAPTISTA.

P. J. Baptista, a native trader (pombeiro), visiting the court a few years later (1806-10), found it well supplied with trade goods brought from both eastern and western coasts, together with the relics of Lacerda's expedition. " King Cazembe has tea-pots, cups, pans, demi-johns, silver spoons and forks, plates of Lisbon earthenware, good hats, shoe buckles and gold money, doubloons and half doubloons." The tea and coffee equipages were for display, as only millet beer and palm wine were drunk, and the doubloons were curiosities, as the use of coins as money was un-

* The Lands of the Cazembe, 1873.

PLATE I

*Three views of a conus shell showing stages in the manu-
facture of the " mpande bead." It was the flat end of the
shell that was used and extensively traded throughout
South Central Africa.*

PLATE II
A special type of basket containing salt currency formerly traded by the Ba Ila tribe in the Kafue Flats.

Photograph by the Information Dept., Lusaka.

PLATE III

Showing some of the types of beads that were imported by Arabs and Portuguese traders into southern Africa between the seventeenth and nineteenth centuries.

Photograph by the Information Dept., Lusaka.

PLATE IV

A copper currency bar in the shape of a St. Andrew's Cross. These were manufactured in large numbers in the Katanga and on the Northern Rhodesia Copperbelt and traded as far as Zanzibar.

Photograph by Dr. A. I. Richards.

PLATE V
Bemba women carrying baskets of salt as tribute to the chief.

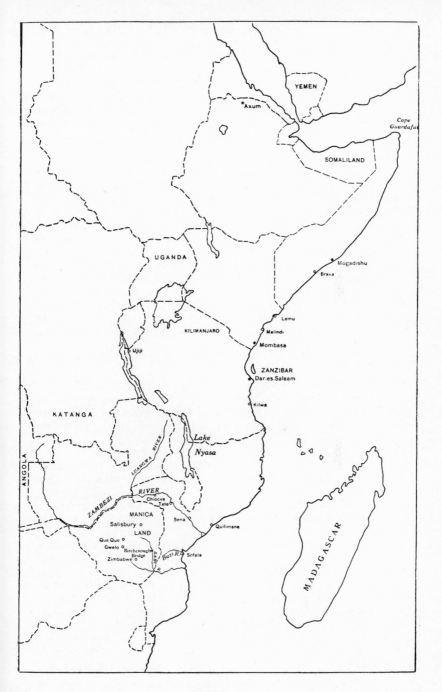

PLATE VI

known. Baptista had reached the country through Angola passing through Katanga where he saw the copper being made into bars. These bars he said, were paid in tribute, together with native salt, and were also used in barter, "They exchange [the salt] for what they consider wealth, i.e., cloth, Indian tissues, beads and strawcloths. The smiths also exchange their bars for flour and other provisions." Salt from the coasts, both east and west, reached Cazembeland, where it was highly prized, and ivory was carried down by slaves to the coastal trading ports in return.

GUILLAIN.

Between 1846 and 1848 Captain Guillain of the *Ducouëdic* was sent to explore and report on the trade of the East Coast with a view to making the island of Maiotte, north of Mozambique, the *entrepôt* of French trade to rival that of Zanzibar. He describes the sailing of the Arab dhows from Oman or the Persian Gulf, and the Indian flotilla from Bombay or Cutch, the goods amassed at Zanzibar, Lamu or Mombasa, and the paths trodden out by the caravans making their sinuous way into the interior. Trade was by haggling, goods being exchanged for goods, though they were estimated in grain, dollars or piastres. Slaves were worth five to seven dollars' worth of goods at the source averaging some twenty dollars at Zanzibar. Captain Guillain found it impossible to travel far into the interior and he was recalled before his mission was accomplished.*

LIVINGSTONE.

The first white traveller to link up the East Coast with the interior and to leave an accurate account of his journey was David Livingstone. In 1853 he had started north from Linyanti on the Chobe, travelling up the Zambezi and the Liba, reaching Loanda on the West Coast in 1854. Returning to Linyanti he set out for the East Coast the following year, discovering the Victoria Falls on the way, and reached Tete in March, 1856. He found Arab traders from Zanzibar and Kilwa and half-caste Portuguese traders from Angola in the very heart of Africa, bringing trade goods, especially cloth and beads, tobacco, guns and powder to exchange for slaves and ivory. He was presented with an ornament made from the end of a conus shell, which, in native estimation, was almost as highly prized as slaves and ivory (illustrated, *Missionary Travels*, 1899, p. 205, and at *Plate I* in this present work). This was formerly a royal badge among the Ba-Ila and was used, like other valuables in exchanges. Two would buy a slave and five a £10 tusk (*see* below, and cf. Exhibit 803). Livingstone noted that money was of no use, barter being the only means by which a missionary could pay his way. The natives saw the white man's lust for gold and tried to conceal its existence, but knew nothing of the value of silver and could not distinguish it from tin. They were all fond of trading and bargaining but had

* Guillain, Ch. *Documents sur l'histoire, la géographie et le commerce de l'Afrique Orientale*, Paris, 1856.

[158]

no ideas beyond ivory and slaves. Livingstone found to his great distress that his opening of the way into Central Africa led not to the destruction of the slave trade, as he had hoped, but to its extension. Everywhere the slave traders maintained a network of trading camps connected by zigzag paths from the East Coast to the interior. T. Wakefield* mapped some of these from information given him by a Zanzibar Arab. The main routes were from Tanga, through Arusha and Naivasha to Victoria Nyanza, and back with deviations; and from Mombasa, passing to the east of Kilimanjaro, to Dhaicho, north-east of Mount Kenya, and back to Tana. There were also routes from Samburu to the north and from Lake Nyassa to Lake Baringo. The ports were all connected by inland routes as well as by coasting craft. J. Stevenson, Chairman of the African Lakes Company,† traced on a map the slave routes from Mogadishu, Mombasa, Zanzibar, Kilwa, Lindi and Ibo into Central Africa, where they met the routes from the Congo and the West Coast. Guns, powder and spirits were the best sellers up-country. Slaves and ivory, the main exports since the days of the *Periplus*, made their way down to the coast. It was not until towards the end of the nineteenth century that Livingstone's work bore fruit. He had cut " the jugular vein of the Slave Trade " at Lake Nyassa, and opened the way for Christian Missions and legitimate traders, and 1898 saw the capture of the last slave caravan in East Africa.

BARTER.

With the advent of traders and missionaries and especially with the building of the railways, the introduction of coins altered native trading methods and ousted native currencies.

Down to the twentieth century trade consisted in primitive barter, the exchange of goods for goods, without the use of money. Varieties in natural or in human products lead everywhere to exchanges between the " haves " and the " have-nots," and throughout Africa in one part or another can still be found the universal barter of game and skins, river or sea fish, etc., for vegetables and grain, while iron workers and potters, basket makers and weavers exchange their goods with their neighbours, and salt from the coast or from inland deposits is traded far and wide.

SILENT TRADE.

Relics of " silent trade," such as was noted by Herodotus on the West Coast in the fourth century B.C., or by Cosmas in Abyssinia in the sixth century A.D., was described by Fernandes on the Hunyani in the sixteenth century and by Moubray in Northern Rhodesia in recent years.‡ On these occasions buyers and sellers never meet. Goods are laid down and the owners retire to a safe

* *Routes of Native Caravans from the Coast, J. R. G. S., Vol. XL,* 1870.
† *The Arabs in Central Africa and Lake Nyassa,* 1889.
‡ Moubray, *In South Central Africa,* 1912, p. 58.

distance, returning later to collect the goods left in exchange. Silent trade is found sporadically all over the world, probably due to mutual distrust or lack of a common language.

MARKETS.

Over most of Africa trading has its recognised meeting places, and markets, held once, twice or more times a week, provide the chief entertainment for the neighbourhood. Off the main trade-routes business is still often done without money, goods being exchanged for goods, and this haggling may continue in the markets even when coined money is otherwise in use.

NATIVE CURRENCIES.

In the absence of money there are certain articles in general demand that are accepted as a form of currency or medium of exchange. These are either local goods, such as salt, native cloth, and metal (in the form of ingots, bars, tools, weapons or ornaments), or imported goods, such as shells and beads, or more recently, cloth and tobacco.

SALT.

Salt is scarce in many parts of Africa, yet it is essential in a vegetable diet, so it passes for money over wide areas. In the west the salt trade across the deserts and its influence on trade routes and the slave trade are well known. In Nigeria a pot of salt still forms part of the " bride-price." In the Congo payment in salt is often preferred to money ; the roadmakers round Lulua-berg are paid in salt by the bucketful and spend it, in teaspoonfuls in the bazaar.* Further east Sir Samuel Baker described the street cries in Nyoro (Uganda), " Milk to sell for salt ! Salt to exchange for lance-heads ! " etc. The most important centre for the salt trade in the east was Ujiji on Lake Tanganyika, from where, in the last century, slabs were exported weighing between 20 to 30 lbs., each valued at two yards of calico, or 100 strings of blue beads.† The salt currency of Abyssinia with blocks of definite weights and values passed for money across Africa from east to west in the sixteenth century though ousted since by the Maria Theresa dollar. At the beginning of the nineteenth century P. J. Baptista noted the trade in native salt in the Katanga region, where it was exchanged for imported cloth and beads. Sea salt, brought from both eastern and western coasts, reached Cazembe-land, and in return ivory and slaves travelled down to the coasts. A basket of native salt was a unit of currency among the Ila of Northern Rhodesia (*see* Exhibit 804 and *Plate II*) ; five were the price of a male calf and twenty of a heifer.‡

---

* Norden, *Fresh Tracks in Belgian Congo*, 1924, p. 173.
† Hose, J. A. I., 1882
‡ E. W. Smith and A. M. Dale, *The Ila-Speaking Peoples of Northern Rhodesia*, 1920, p. 148.

TOBACCO.

Tobacco, like salt, is in universal demand and it has taken the place of more picturesque forms of currency in Africa as in almost all parts of the world. (*See* Exhibit 805.)

CLOTH.

The currencies in native cloth, which were so common in West Africa, are seldom met with in the East, though pieces may still play a part in "bride-price." The *machiras* of the Bororo to the east of Sena had a wider distribution in the sixteenth century. These were strips of cotton cloth made of the native cotton, and they provided a flourishing trade across the Zambezi. Two *machiras* could be bought for a bunch of beads, and by the expenditure of 100 *crusados* make a profit of 3,000. Imported cloth soon supplanted native products and, eked out with beads, became the basis of all trade along the coast. It was a Government monopoly so that a trader or friar, denied a permit to buy cloth, was reduced to destitution and had to leave the country. Cloth has maintained its position as a standard of value in Northern Rhodesia down to present times. "For most purposes it takes the place of hard cash. Men draw their rations in calico—marriage portions are paid in calico."*

Captain Burton, who set out in 1856 to discover the source of the Nile, was commissioned to determine the exportable products of the interior and he gives a valuable and detailed description of the beads, cloth and brass wire that took the place of copper, silver and gold in native trading. "Mercani" (American) unbleached shirting, four cubits or six feet long, formed the *shukkah* (loin wrapper), "the shilling or florin of East Africa and assuredly the worst circulating medium ever invented by mankind."† The *shukkah* could be divided into cubits, and the cubits into bits as small as the *fitr*, measured from the tip of the index finger to the thumb. "Kaniki," of lower value, was Indian cloth dyed indigo. "Cloths with names," were the showy checks demanded by chiefs.

IRON.

Iron, like salt, is not found everywhere, and iron-working is a special craft, hedged round with taboos, so the metal, being in universal demand, is accepted in place of money throughout much of Africa. Here no clear distinction can be drawn between what is money and what is not. A man will take a lump of iron, a rod or a bar, to the smith, to be made into tool, weapon or ornaments, and the tool, weapon or ornaments will have the value, save for the smith's deduction, of the original metal. In West Africa,

---

* C. Gouldsbury and H. Sheane, *The Great Plateau of Northern Rhodesia*, 1911, p. 10.
† Burton, R. F., *The Lake Region of Central Africa*, 1860, pp. 387-419

currency bars, *manillas, mitakos* and " Kissi pennies," are familiar. To the east, iron currencies are scarce, though in agricultural areas the iron was worked up into hoes, which were exchanged for goods. Large hoes were especially made for " bride-price " in Uganda, and hoes took the place of cattle in similar bargaining among the poorer folk of Bechuanaland. Livingstone, on his way to Lake Nyassa, noted the large hoes used in barter by the Manyanya, one weighing 2 lb. being exchanged for calico worth about fourpence.* A special form of iron currency came into use along the coast in the sixteenth century, consisting of nails and bits of metal from wrecks. The survivors bought provisions from the natives with these, and in unexplored regions marvellous bargains were made. In 1552 the *S. João* was wrecked near Delagoa Bay and some canoes were bought " at the price of a few nails." The survivors of the Santo Alberto (1593) bought four cows for four pieces of copper worth as many pence. A cow that cost a piece of a broken astrolabe, two kettle handles and six bits of copper was considered very dear. It was part of a deliberate policy to burn the wrecked ship for the sake of the metal and nails, and to destroy what could not be carried away, to preserve the monopoly. But the idea of money and its uses was already penetrating these parts of the coast, frequented by traders, and in 1585, at the mouth of the Zambezi the natives hunted eagerly for reals, " which they now value more than the old nails which they prized so much a short time ago."†

COPPER.

Copper has an ornamental value denied to iron, making it still more acceptable, and " Katanga crosses " (Exhibits 326, 656), have been found from the Cape to Cairo and from Mombasa to Boma. These copper ingots took various shapes, sometimes rather like a capital H, but commonly more like a Greek or St. Andrews' cross (*Plate IV*) and they were made in different sizes or weights, from large ones, sixteen inches (forty cm.) across, to tiny ones with knobby ends measuring only an inch or so. Their dating is difficult, and it is generally believed that copper working goes back only a few centuries. Both ingots and the soap-stone moulds in which they were made have been found at Zimbabwe, but in undatable deposits. They are mentioned by Father Barreto in 1667 and called *massoutas* (? *massontas*) " which are two St. Andrews crosses joined by a bar in the middle used as money by the Kaffirs."‡ Crosses are not mentioned by Livingstone, who was more impressed by the large bars in the shape of a capital I, weighing from 75 lb. to a cwt. (Letter written from near Bangweulu to Oswell, 1868, cf. Exhibit 687.) The small H-shaped coppers (Exhibit 568) are said to have been used by Arab slave dealers. The value of the crosses

---

* Livingstone, D., *The Zambezi and its Tributaries*, 1865, p. 113.
† Theal, G.M., *Records of South Eastern Africa*, 1898 i, p. 345.
‡ *ib.*, iii, p. 505.

was very variable. Mahieu* says that in the Congo region a small one of about 600 gr. (nearly 1½ lb.) would buy a kilo of native flour, five would buy a fathom of cloth or four fowls, and ten a gun (p. 124). The market price in the Basonga area was calculated at between two and four francs, and the " bride-price " for the great ones in the land might run to 100 slaves, 200 goats and 300 crosses (p. 35). They are still used for " bride-price " in Northern Rhodesia. A local magistrate finding on his table a pair of suspenders, some pieces of rapphia cloth and a pile of copper crosses recognises the signs at once, " Hullo, a dowry returned. Another divorce."† The crosses were a convenient trading medium, though no satisfactory reason has been given for their specialised shape. They were used in making tools, weapons and ornaments, especially the latter. Boccaro, who in 1616 took the silver found at Chicova across from Tete to Kilwa, provided his party of ten to twelve slaves with 1,000 bracelets of copper wire made by the Bororo,‡ as " these bracelets serve as money for small expenses throughout all these roads of Kaffraria." Livingstone mentions the copper rings, two of which would buy an elephant tusk among the Babisa.§

Before leaving metal currencies mention may be made of Father Barreto's description of a currency in pewter on the Zambezi in 1667. " Pewter they use in bartering like square money with a point in the form of a diamond on one side, which is done in the melting.**

COWRIES.††

Of imported currencies which may claim to be called " money," cowries (*Cypraea moneta* or *C. annulus*) and beads, take the most

* *Numismatique du Congo.*
† Norden, 1924, p. 177.
‡ Theal, *Records*, iii, p. 416.
§ *Last Journals*, 1874, ii, p. 120.
** Theal, *Records*, iii, p. 505.
†† Curator's note. The base of a Conus shell—a marine gastropod from the Indian Ocean—was noted by Livingstone (*see* above), and until quite recently, widely used as a means of barter. The shell was filed off at the base, which was the part used.• It had also great value as an ornament and was worn on the forehead or arm, its use often being confined to chiefs. It is known in Northern Rhodesia as the *mpande* shell. In Southern Rhodesia it is known as *ndoro*, and was usually worn as a pectoral suspended from the neck. (The name *ndoro* may be derived, through the Chinyanja word for " money ", *ndarama*, Arabic dirhema from the Greek *drachma*. The shells were known in Portuguese times as " andoro," and Gaspar Bocarro in 1612*** speaks of them as " round ornaments worn on the foreheads of chiefs," and one was made in gold " set with false stones, but very beautiful," as a present for the Monomatapa from Diôgo Simoes, in return for the gift of Chicova.

Porcelain or earthernware substitutes for the *mpande* are common in Southern Rhodesia at the present time.

The illustration shows the Conus shell both (*a*) before and (*b*) after filing, the round base (*c*) being the *mpande*. *Plate I*.
*** Theal, *Records of South Eastern Africa*, iii, p. 405.

[163]

important place. Cowries, derived either from the Red Sea or from the Indian Ocean, which was the main source in later centuries, are found in pre-dynastic graves in Egypt, and they may have taken part in trade down the East Coast at the beginning of our era (though the reference in the *Periplus* is doubtful). In later years the Arabs brought them in their dhows to their coastal settlements and they spread along the trade routes across Africa. Some idea of the profits they made can be found in Ibn Batuta's report that they could be bought in the Maldive Islands for 400,000, sometimes over 1,000,000 to the gold *dinar*, and he had himself seen them sold (in what is now Nigeria) for 1,150 to the *dinar*.* When they were first seen in Uganda they were extravagantly valued and two shells would buy a woman, but they soon depreciated until (about 1860) 2,500 would only buy a cow and a woman was worth four or five cows.† The depreciation was due not only to the quantities shipped to the coast, but also to the fact that the " ring cowry " (*C. annalus*), a similar shell to the Indian " money cowry," can be picked up on the East African shores. Captain Burton describes how these were collected between Ras. Hafun and Mozambique by Moslem hucksters and exchanged for grain. They were carried up-country by returning African porters, and used as currency. Thousands of sackfuls were shipped round to the West Coast by Hamburg merchants, selling at £80 a ton and making a profit of 500 per cent. Supplies being unrestricted, values soon fell. Cowries may still be used for small purchases in out of the way parts of Nigeria and the Gold Coast. They were currency in Uganda until importation was forbidden in 1901. One shell would buy a portion of salt, a stick of sugar cane or a few vegetables. Hut tax was 1,900 shells. In 1897 75,000 cowries, taking seven men to carry the bundles, were worth £5. But the exchange fluctuated widely, sometimes 200, sometimes 1,000 to the rupee, and with the introduction of cents and half cents, cowries went out of circulation.‡

BEADS.

Trade beads (*Plate III*), like cowries, have a long and undatable history behind them. Beads of glass, faience or porcelain were well known in ancient Egypt, they are found in seventeenth and nineteenth dynasty graves, and wall paintings in tombs illustrate strings of beads being used in barter in the market place. Knowledge of the manufacture spread in the early centuries of our era, the most prolific centres of distribution being Venice for the Mediterranean and Cambay for the Indian Ocean. They were traded far and wide, and similar beads, some of them over 1,000 years old, have been found as far apart as Zimbabwe and the Malay Peninsular. The East Coast has nothing to equal the mysterious " aggries " of the West Coast, but here also are legends of supernatural origin.

---

* Ibn Batuta, *Travels in Asia and Africa*, tr. H. A. R. Gibb, 1929.
† J. Roscoe, *The Baganda*, 1911, p. 456.
‡ A. R. Cook, *Uganda Memories*, 1945.

They were believed to be dug out of the earth in Monomotapaland, and their rarity was attributed to the caving in of the earth so that no more could be found. From the sixteenth century onwards travellers tell of Cambayan beads which, together with Indian silks, stuffs, muslins, etc., were traded down the coast by Arabs who bartered them for Rhodesian gold. Largish beads, especially yellow ones, and the dark blue beads familiar throughout Africa, were called *talama*, a word which has been traced to the Arabic *dirhem*, meaning money, and ultimately to *drachma*, a weight, originally a handful. Beads are still measured by the handful in East Africa. Captain Burton described 400 varieties of beads used in trading in the middle of last century. The cheapest strings (*hafizi*, *khanyera* or *ushanga waupe*) were the white porcelain "staple of commerce," bought in Zanzibar for about 10*d.* a lb. They were measured by the *bitil*, from the tip of the index finger to the wrist worth roughly a farthing to a penny. Four *bitils* made the *khete* or string, twice round the neck, roughly equal to threepence, the normal payment for the African's daily ration. The most valuable were the small coral beads (in fifteen different sizes) worth nearly 10*s.* a lb., called "town-breakers" because women would ruin themselves and their husbands for them. Among the beads exhibited in the Museum are the short white porcelain ones (probably the kind mentioned in Lacerda's expedition in 1798) used as currency in Mozambique ; the chalcedony beads brought by Swahili and Chikunda slaving parties, a girdle being the price of a slave, and a necklace added to cloth for ivory ; and the plum-coloured glass beads with white cores also used in the slave trade. Yellow glass beads are known to have been introduced by Carl Weise's expedition in 1890-1891 and used for buying food, while the African Lakes Corporation used the blue opaque glass beads for buying firewood a bead for a log.

Fuller descriptions of the beads in the Museum, their ritual and currency uses will be found in the section BEADS, in the technological handbook to the Museum collections.

6

LIFE AMONG THE CATTLE-OWNING PLATEAU TONGA

THE MATERIAL CULTURE OF A NORTHERN RHODESIA NATIVE TRIBE

E. COLSON

1949

INTRODUCTION [1]

In 1855, Livingstone found the Tonga living in their present home. Apparently they are ancient residents of the area, and have long since lost any tradition of an earlier home or former migrations.

Never, in historic times, have they had any large scale political organization which established boundaries dividing them from other peoples. Instead they lived in little village communities, which were at frequent odds with each other. Small districts, rarely of more than five or six villages in extent, seem to have strained their powers of organization to the limit. The matrilineal clans were dispersed throughout the country, and did not form the nuclei of political or local organization. The name " Tonga " therefore seems to apply at most to a people who shared on the whole a common culture and a common language. They were spread from the southern bank of the Kafue to the Zambezi and to the Wankie district in Southern Rhodesia.* Within this area there are numerous variations in language and culture, and from time to time various groups have been given or have called themselves by distinctive names.† The Tonga are also related both culturally and linguistically with the Ila, the Sala, and the Lenje. It is well nigh impossible, indeed, to fix the boundary between Tonga and Ila on the one hand and Tonga and Sala on the other.‡

Early in the nineteenth century, the Tonga seem to have been a peaceful agricultural people living in small hamlets scattered across the plateau. They had herds of the small Ila cattle§ and large fields of maize, millet, kaffir corn, and ground nuts. About

---

1 The material for this paper was collected during my appointment as a research officer of the Rhodes-Livingstone Institute, and was obtained during 1946-47 and 1948.

* Two other Tonga groups in Southern Rhodesia, the Tonga of the Ruenya Valley and the Tonga of the Sabi-Devuli delta, appear to be unrelated to the Northern Rhodesian Tonga. Cf. Posselt, n.d., pp. 127-128. The Tonga of Nyasaland are still a further unrelated group. Posselt says that the name " is generally applied as the designation of a tributary people, also to those where the clan system is in vogue without a recognized paramount chief. . . ."

† E.g., the We of the Zambezi Valley, the Lundwi of what are to-day the Choongo, Simuyobe, and part of the Monze chieftancies, the Leya near the Victoria Falls, and the Toka of the plateau south of Kalomo. This paper deals specifically with those Tonga who live on the plateau north of Muzoka.

‡ Cf. Brelsford, 1935, 205-209 ; and Smith and Dale, 1920, Chapter I.

§ Livingstone tells us only that the Tonga had cattle early in the nineteenth century. Selous, 1893, 212, report that in the 1880's he found small cattle along the Magoye, and one or two other early visitors to the area say that the cattle were small.

1820 they suffered under a raid from the north led by a man known as Pingola. The raiders killed the cattle and scattered the people before they disappeared again into the obscurity from which they came. To-day the Tonga have no tradition of this raid. It has been swallowed up in the general misery of the latter years of the 19th century. It was soon followed by the invasion of the Makololo about 1832. For a time the Makololo attempted to settle in the Kalomo region, but they were forced on by the pressure of the Matebele. The Tonga were left with their country the common raiding ground of both Makololo and Matebele. When the Makololo fell, their place was taken by the Lozi who continued to send their raiding parties against the Tonga. By the middle of the nineteenth century they had lost most of their cattle. Livingstone observed only a few goats and chickens. He also noted the scattered nature of their tiny hamlets and the ruinous condition of their huts.*

The raids continued almost to the end of the nineteenth century, ending indeed only with the pacification of the Matebele. By that time the Tonga seem to have been reduced to small groups hiding out in the hills. In the north-western districts they may always have retained the nuclei of their herds, but over most of the country cattle were rare. Old men on the edge of the escarpment swear that in their youth it was a rare man who owned even one beast, and he was considered wealthy. Bride wealth in that period was paid in hoes or in goats or sheep or beads. Many of the people had been taken slaves by the Matabele or the Lozi ; others had been killed outright. After the 1860's, Portuguese and half-caste slave traders began to penetrate up the Zambezi and into the Plateau, in search of slaves and ivory.

In the years since the raids ended and European administration brought peace, the Tonga have prospered. There has probably been a rapid increase in population. To-day the Mazabuka district, in which most of the Tonga live, is estimated to have a population of between 80,000 and 120,000 Africans. In 1947 the district supported over 200,000 head of cattle owned by Africans, as well as numerous goats and pigs. Part of the land has been alienated for European development, but the Tonga have shared in the opportunities offered by the presence of the railway and the possession of fertile soil to develop into maize farmers. Even those who still remain nearly at a subsistence level sell enough maize in a normal year to pay their taxes and meet their other cash requirements. Some have not been content with this and have turned to farming on a larger scale, which nets them incomes of several hundred pounds a year. The sale of pigs, poultry and eggs are profitable sidelines, and there is some sale even of the prized cattle. In recent years a few men have invested in lorries. The plough is everywhere.

* Livingstone, 1857, 551–558.

Life Among the Cattle-Owning Plateau Tonga

LIVELIHOOD.

Agriculture.

Originally the Tonga practised a simple hoe culture based on a soil selection system.* Their staple crops were maize, millet and sorghum, with ground nuts, beans and peas, and melons, pumpkins and various types of gourds planted as important subsidiaries. They also grew a sweet stemmed sorghum, which is chewed to extract the sweetness. Sweet potatoes and cassava were grown by a small minority. The variety of crops remains much the same to-day, save that maize has become all important, and millet has almost disappeared. Many are growing increasing quantities of beans, and a few have begun the cultivation of vegetables such as cabbages, tomatoes, and onions. About the villages more progressive people have begun to plant mangoes and other fruit trees.

When a new field is prepared, the family usually brews beer and calls the men of the neighbourhood to help cut the trees on the site. Unlike the Bemba and others who practice *chitimene*, the Tonga cut only the trees on the actual acreage which they plan to cultivate. Smaller trees are chopped down, their branches lopped, and the logs scattered over the surface of the field. The whole area is burned and the ash left to settle into the ground. Under the old system, when it came time for planting, the field was hoed and at the same time the seed was planted. The field remained in cultivation for a number of years, but each year the family cut its way into the bush alongside to add extensions to the garden. Finally when the soil had been worked out, the field was abandoned and a new one begun somewhere else.

This method was early disrupted as the Tonga learned from the missions or from European farmers in the area the use of plough and draught oxen. To-day they depend almost entirely on the plough, and only a few old men and women still hoe their fields. The fields are still cleared in the same manner, but many to-day hire labour for the clearing rather than depend on the more happy-go-lucky methods of the work party. This is especially true on the western borders, where the influx of Balovale provides labour which can be exploited and often cheated by the Tonga. Less clearing is necessary under the new conditions, since land is no longer plentiful enough to allow of shifting cultivation to the same degree.

* For a discussion of Tonga agriculture, *cf.* : Allan, Gluckman, Peters, and Trapnell, 1948 ; and Trapnell and Clothier, 1937, 48-52.

Fields must be kept in cultivation over the years. Under the direction of the Agricultural Department the Tonga are turning to the use of manure and the practice of crop rotation to achieve this end.

Planting is done usually in late November or early December, after the first rains. Men and boys guide the plough while the women follow behind dropping the seed in the furrows. In January the women are again in the fields planting beans and ground nuts. Much of this planting is still done with the hoe. Soon after the crops are up, weeding begins. Women do the major portion of this work, chopping out the weeds with their short handled hoes. Most people, however, find that the weeds are outstripping them. Progressive people hire labour ; conservatives call a work party to hoe the entire field in one burst of energy. The owner makes beer and announces through the neighbouring villages that her field is ready to be hoed. The response depends partly on the number of work parties called for the day, and partly by reports circulated concerning the quantity of beer. Early in the morning, men and women begin to trickle down to the field. The owner sends down two pots of beer, one for the men and one for the women. The workers form themselves into long lines and begin hoeing vigorously under the impromptu direction of some man who cheers them on with jokes and shouts. By mid-morning, they call for rest and beer. The men and women divide themselves into separate groups around their pots, and then as the beer vanishes join again for rough horse play. The men joke with the women and snatch at their breasts. Suddenly a group of women make a concerted attack and tumble some man to the ground and rub his face along the dust. Then some conscientious soul suggests a return to work. Most straggle back, but a few depart for the shade of a tree by the side of the field to sleep off the morning's work. Shortly after noon, all abandon work to return to the village and finish the beer that is left.

Those who are unfortunate enough to find that their neighbours have scheduled a work party on the same day may find their workers by another scheme. If there is a school nearby, and the teacher is agreeable, a woman may send a pot of beer to the school teacher who then assigns his students the task of weeding her field, while he sits at home and drinks the beer. Others prefer to pay their work parties with salt or sugar. The wealthy farmers, whose farming methods have been assimilated more or less closely to those of their European neighbours, have cultivators and are unlikely to find a work party necessary.

At harvest time people return again to the fields. Women and children pull the maize from the stalks and pile it in great heaps. The men come with oxen and sledges to drag it to the drying platforms and then to the granaries. When the maize harvest is finished, there still remain long hours of work for the women who

[171]

must dig their ground-nuts, a job which involves turning over every inch of the field with the hoe. Women complain more of this labour than they do of all the rest of their toil.

Stock-Raising.

Care of the cattle is left to the men and boys. The cattle are herded from the beginning of the planting season until the end of the harvest, to keep them from the fields. Young boys are the herds, who guide the cattle through the day and bring them back to the kraals at night. During the rest of the year, the cattle are left free to roam where they will. Often they wander miles from the village, and the owners spend frantic weeks just before the rains wandering the country side in search of strayed beasts.

In the western areas, it is necessary to drive the cattle to dry season pastures, and the free roaming does not occur. The men and boys go down to the Kafue and build a kraal for the cattle and rough shelters for themselves. Here they keep the cattle until the rains have once more restored the pastures and the water holes of their own areas. Once such moves were common over much wider areas, but the building of dams has made them no longer necessary.

Cattle are highly prized for their ritual and symbolic significance, but it would be a mistake to think that the Tonga do not appreciate their practical value. Cattle are killed for funerals and for girls' puberty ceremonies, they change hands in bride wealth and as fines and awards for damages. But they are also prized as plough and general draught animals. In increasing numbers they are sold to the traders on the railway line. During certain seasons of the year, the milk is an important part of the daily diet.

Small stock are also common. In many villages there are great numbers of goats, pigs and chickens. Goat and chicken share some of the ritual importance of cattle. Both are killed for rain rites, mourning, or for any occasion when an offering is required. They are also killed to provide food for important guests or returned wanderers. Chickens and eggs have a large sale to the railway line, and the Tonga of recent years have acquired fowls from European sources and bred up their flocks. Pigs, on the other hand, are regarded with general disgust as dirty beasts, and are kept purely for sale to the Europeans. Many Tonga claim that they will not eat pig meat, though when a pig is killed for some reason, most forget these scruples. A few families keep pigeons, and eat the young. Recently they have begun to raise ducks.

Hunting, Fishing and Gathering.

Early travellers reported the Tonga country a game paradise and the Tonga as excellent hunters. In a few spots along the Kafue one can still see game, but over most of the country only a few small buck and an occasional stray from some more protected spot are to be found. The Tonga still have game drives behind grass fires in September and October, but the results are usually meagre save where they have access to the Kafue. The men hunt with spears and dogs ; a few fortunate ones have guns. To-day they have abandoned the use of deadfalls and pitfalls, but occasionally a gun trap is still set for the rare leopard or lion that attacks the herds. Boys set snares for rats and birds and also hunt with bows and arrows and with catapults.

Fishing is important only on the lower Magoye and in a few other spots. The Kafue fishing is largely in the hands of foreigners and always has been. Some use is made of fish weirs and traps, and at the end of the rains the men from a number of villages may come with their spears to join in a big fish drive. During slack seasons, women go daily with big fishing baskets to drag the pools left standing as the rivers dry. Usually they catch only small fish a few inches long. Sometimes they are joined by a lone man who stands a bit aloof from the shouting, splashing mass of women and children while he waits with his spear poised for a thrust. Small boys show some persistence with lines and bent pins or with small fish nets, but rarely seem to have any success.

Of far more importance is the gathering of bush products which goes on throughout the year. Roots and wild greens loom large in the daily diet, and often provide the only relish. At certain seasons, the Tonga also gather quantities of wild fruit. At the beginning of the rains, there are both termites and mushrooms to be had. On the whole the Tonga have little success in collecting honey, unless they have come under the influence of Balovale who have introduced the use of hives in some areas. Elsewhere, if they are lucky enough to stumble upon a hive full of honey, they cheerfully ignore stings to get the comb. This is not a frequent event, and most people have an unsatiated craving for sweet things.

VILLAGES.

In the middle of the nineteenth century the Tonga lived in small widely scattered villages. Perhaps this was a recent change, since Livingstone was told that once the Tonga had large villages but the danger of frequent raids had led them to scatter into small communities which could give an alarm in case of attack.* Miles might intervene between a village and the huts of its nearest neighbour. To the north-west, however, the Mwanachingwala (Munenga) area seems to have been more heavily populated, and the small villages were thickset along the Magoye and the Ngwezi.†

The earliest travellers give no details of the appearance of the villages (*munzi*). Presumably, however, they looked much the same as those described shortly after 1900. " Among the Batongas,

---

* Livingstone, 1855, p. 555.
† Selous, 1893, 216.

the villages are either circular or elliptical in form. All the huts comprising a village are arranged around the outside of the circle, with the doors opening into the inner courtyard ; there are no outside doors. For protection from the wild animals, which are common in the country, each village is surrounded by a high stockade of poles.

" On the opposite side of the village from the main entrance, and facing this entrance, is the house of the chief, or headman. On either side of his house are the huts occupied by his wives.

" The whole inner courtyard forms the cattle corral. Sometimes it is separated from the huts by a fence, but often there is no barrier between the cattle and the dwellings of the people. The size of this inner courtyard varies with the size of the village. Sometimes there is room for only forty or fifty head of cattle ; and sometimes the court is large enough to accommodate two thousand."* Present day Tonga can add to this description only that unmarried men and boys had their huts placed at the entrance to the village in the most exposed position, since they were expected to bear the brunt of any attack.

The circular stockaded village has disappeared along with the need for defence. A few villages are built on a curving line, or with the huts forming several lines, but the typical village is a scattering of huts in clusters of two or three—or perhaps as many as ten or so—without any order or arrangement. In some parts of the country the huts of one village are scattered in amidst those of the next, and membership in a given village can be ascertained only by asking at each hut for the name of the headman under whom its owner is registered. The huts of the headman have no assigned position amidst the clutter, nor do they have distinguishing marks whereby they may be identified. The headman may live by himself with one or two adherents, or he may live within some larger cluster. The huts of the unmarried boys are also set at random. Since the boys no longer have to undertake the defence of the village and the cattle, they place their huts where they will.

As the village disintegrated into scattered huts, the central cattle kraal disappeared. To-day each little cluster of huts may have a cattle kraal (*cimpati*) nearby, usually placed a short distance to the west of the dwellings, where the breeze, if it blows, will carry the flies away into the bush. Closer to the huts are set drying platforms, granaries, and perhaps a pigeon cot. The outer stockade has also vanished. Some people plant hedges of euphorbia or other quick growing plants to mark the limits of their dooryards and give some semblance of privacy, but most Tonga—unlike the Lozi and many other Northern Rhodesian people—seem to feel no desire for the privacy offered by a surrounding wall.

* Anderson, n. d., 292.

The ordered structure of the old village was accompanied by a greater formality of life. When a new village was to be built and a site had been chosen, all the people joined together to build first the houses of the headman. After that they built the houses of the other members of the village in order of their seniority. Meantime they continued to live at their old village. When the huts in the new village were completed, boys below the age of puberty were sent to sleep in them. The boys had to be those " who weren't yet thinking about sleeping with girls." A few days later, all the people with their possessions moved to the new site, leaving their old huts standing and the fires burning. At the new village they started new fires with fire sticks (*kapisyo*).

At the present time a village rarely moves as a unit. Instead sections move, or sometimes a single family sets out to a new site. Before they move, however, they usually make beer, and again once they are settled into their new site, each family celebrates the move with another beer and an offering to the ancestors. Even this remnant of village ritual is no longer observed among the people who are Christians.

Dwellings.

Styles of architecture have changed less drastically than the arrangement of the village. There are many Tonga who have adopted new types of housing, but many cling to the old even close to the railway line where changes are most common.

The older type of hut (*inganda*) is circular and built of poles firmly plastered with mud. It is topped with a conical thatched roof. A large pole (*musemu*) placed in the centre of the hut supports the roof poles which radiate out to rest on the walls and ultimately on the verandah poles. The latter circle the hut at a distance of two or three feet from the wall, and the thatched roof extends down over the verandah. The verandah poles may be set close together, and the space between built in with mud, to form an enclosed outer room, which provides storage space for the big beer pots or a sleeping place for the goats and chickens or perhaps for a stray guest. The doorway of the hut is framed with roughly hewn logs, and blocked at night with mats or poles, secured by a pole inserted crosswise. Light filters in through the open doorway or through the cracks that develop as the mud cracks and the poles disintegrate under the onslaughts of termites and wood borers.

In earlier times, many huts had near the apex of the roof " a little platform about three feet square, suspended from the rafters, to which people resort for safety."* This has vanished, but in other respects many of the huts which are built to-day seem to be similar to those built fifty years and more ago.

---

* Anderson, n.d., 256.

Other people follow more recent fashions. Two basic changes have occurred : a change in material and a change in shape. The square or rectangular hut is found everywhere to-day and so is the hut of unbaked bricks. The two changes, however, are not necessarily associated. Many build round huts of bricks, and others build square huts of pole and dagga. In any case, the roof is still of thatch. The Tonga object to tin roofs on the ground that they are expensive, hot, and noisy in the rain. They have no ambition to possess such luxuries.

Most men make their own huts, or at least do the major portion of the work themselves. They collect the poles or make the bricks, with the assistance of any boys they can press into service. Once this is done a man should be able to build the walls of a hut within a day or two if he has undertaken a modest sized structure. He usually builds during the cold season, and then for months he rests while his house remains open to the sky. It may be in use, but there is no reason to worry about a covering until the first rains are near. Meantime he gradually cuts his roof poles while his wife cuts the thatching grass.

The poles are brought in and left till it is convenient to start the roof. Then the builder usually calls in other men to help him in a work party which he repays by a meal of chicken and porridge, or a beer drink. Perhaps four to eight men co-operate in lifting the roof timbers into place, balancing them against each other, and lashing them firmly in place with bark rope. The builder may also call in assistance for thatching, though one or two men can do the job themselves. The thatch is tossed to the roof in bundles and spread thickly along the roof poles. The thatchers work from the eaves upward. At the apex, a stake is driven in amongst the roof poles. To this a bundle of grass is fastened in a small cylinder perhaps eight inches high and two or three inches in diameter. It is decorated in various ways, with ornamental lashings, with circlets of grass, or in any way that strikes the owner's fancy. Some perch a wooden bird on the peak, as a final finishing flourish.

The hut is then finished off with a plastering of mud. This may be done so as to cover completely the pole or brick structure, and leave only a firm plastered wall on both inner and outer surfaces. This part of the work is turned over to the housewife, for it is a woman's job. Younger people often apply the knowledge they have learned at school by painting the daubed walls with flowers or figures, which soon are dulled by the layer of smokey grime that quickly coats the walls.

Often the walls are pierced with small slits to let in additional light and air or to let out some of the smoke. Some, though only a few, have proper windows and even glass panes. Doorways to-day are often of planed lumber, fitted into the wall, and provided with a plank door fitted with an iron staple and a padlock. These are often made by carpenters trained at the missions, who sell their skill to their less knowledgeable neighbours. In this case, the frame and door are kept for years and moved each time the owner rebuilds.

These are the typical dwellings of the Tonga to-day, but close to the railway line or among the class of wealthy farmers, more ambitious houses are built, and many experiments are made as men try one style after another. Some build houses of many rooms, perhaps of baked bricks and with cement floors. Some employ professional builders and thatchers, and the resulting houses compare favourably with the better houses built in the new African townships. Most of the Tonga, however, remain untouched by such developments.

Interiors and Furnishings.

Inside the hut, if of any size, is commonly divided into two rooms by a mud or brick wall which stretches from the entrance two-thirds of the way to the opposite wall and reaches nearly to the height of the outer wall. This is both a matter of tradition and of present day practice. The compartment to the right as one enters the hut is set aside for sleeping and for the storage of pots and other valuables. The general living quarters are in the compartment to the left. Here is the fireplace, set approximately in the centre of the left hand wall.

The fireplace (*ciko*) usually consists of three stones or three conical clay blocks (*majua*). Some housewives, however, build up the fireplace with clay so that it stands some inches above the floor, and it may have a special stand for holding the clay pots.

The furniture among the more conservative, or perhaps among the more poverty stricken, consists of a rough bed made by laying poles across six forked stakes, some small wooden stools and headrests, pots, calabashes and baskets, such miscellaneous equipment as hoes, spears, axes, and other tools, and very little else. From the ceiling is often suspended a small shelf, where goods may be stored from the rats.

To-day the beds are usually raised only a foot or so above the ground. Once they were high racks with space beneath for the penning of calves or goats. During the cold season, a fire was often built in this space and left to smoulder so that the smoke and heat rose to provide a blanket for the sleepers on the rack above. This arrangement was usual in the boys' house, for the boys were even less likely than their elders to possess the luxury of a blanket and therefore lay huddled together protected only by their blanket of smoke.

The old style bed has been abandoned by some who have adopted instead a wooden frame strung with thongs. On top are spread mats and blankets. Still others have bought themselves metal springs with or without a stuffed mattress, and a growing number aspire to own these luxuries.

[177]

Husband and wife sleep in the sleeping compartment, along with the baby of the family, who may be five or six years old. Other children are relegated to the floor or sent to sleep with a grandmother or some other relative, or sent out to the family kitchen. The children nestle close together, lying close to the fire, protecting themselves with such scraps of clothing as they may have. So close do they hug the fire in the effort to keep warm that even these scraps are often ruined by contact with the coals. As the boys grow older, they build themselves houses or move in with some friend. Older girls are given a bed of their own in the main hut, since Tonga parents do not approve of girls escaping from family supervision. This is true even if the daughter has been married and divorced, or if she has already had several children by a lover. Her bed is usually placed opposite the door inside the living compartment, which observes the proprieties and yet gives her lover opportunities to visit her.

Among the people who have been to school or who live close to the railway line there is some attempt to imitate European standards. They build themselves cupboards or buy old wooden chests or bureaus. The few carpenters make wooden tables and straight backed chairs, or folding chairs. They sell these through the countryside to all who happen to have the money when the hawker appears. A few have deck chairs, usually with burlap covers. Most people still depend upon wooden stools (*cuuno*), but these have less prestige value than does a chair, even a very rickety one. A guest will always be offered a chair, though it may involve a difficult problem of balance and he looks longingly at the substantial stool which supports his host.

The stool however retains its symbolic importance. Formerly no young boy was allowed to sit on a stool in the presence of his elders until he had been through a rite which recognized his maturity, and during which he was seated on a stool by one of the older men. This custom is no longer observed, but young men usually sit on the ground in the presence of their elders, unless they come as visitors, and then often they are given the seat of their elderly host. In other ways the Tonga seem to regard the stool as a symbol of its owner. Thus, a man presents his wife with a stool soon after they are married (*cuuno ca bwinga*). Her brothers, real and classificatory, should not use it. A man's own stool is tabooed to those whom he calls "sister's son." But to-day this symbolism has largely faded.

Other Structures.

Men who have been caught by the advance of the season and still have no house constructed, will build a hut of thick bundles of thatching grass well mudded over. Or if they are moving some distance, they will build temporary shelters of thatch. Families which expect many guests for a mourning or for a girl's puberty ceremony, will put up at least windbreaks to shelter their guests.

More permanent is the *insaka*, a shade built by perching a thatched roof on supporting poles. A few men have these simply for lounging, but more commonly they are built by blacksmiths for their workshops.

Many Tonga build themselves a separate kitchen where all cooking is done when the weather does not permit the women to use the open fires in front of their huts. These are merely smaller editions of the dwelling house, without the inner division. Or often the kitchen is an old dwelling hut, so dilapidated that the family will no longer sleep within it.

Every family must have its drying platforms and granaries. The former are usually made in the fields, but additional platforms are often erected near the dwellings. They are rough platforms set high above the ground. The sides may be built up with brush until the platforms look like large untidy birds' nests. On these the grain is placed to dry before being stored in the granaries. Pumpkins, melons, calabashes, cakes of tobacco, and a general clutter of baskets, pots, or large fishing baskets are also thrown on to the platform (*isansa*) for safe keeping during the dry season.

There are several types of granary (*butala*), all constructed on stout platforms resting on forked poles. The commonest type is built of poles, set close together and bound in place with withes. Others are made of coils of thatching grass, and in the east the largest granaries are made of wickerwork. In some villages all types are to be seen standing side by side, and one man may build any or all types. The large granaries are used for storing maize. Smaller ones of the same shape and construction are given a plastering of mud and then used for the storage of ground nuts, beans, or kaffir corn.

Granaries are made during the dry season, as soon as the harvest is completed, and may last for a number of years. When the maize is dry, it is thrown into the granaries unhusked, as this is said to keep the grain more free of weavils. Then the granaries are left open until the approach of the rainy season and the first light showers suggest that some covering will be necessary. Usually there is a sudden shower accompanied by a rush of people hurrying home to throw bundles of thatching grass over the tops of the granaries to keep the contents from wetting. If the first rains are heavy, the women spend the next few days spreading maize and ground nuts in the sun to dry, as they mournfully look for signs of sprouting and estimate their losses, while the men and boys rush through the work of making the detachable thatched roofs. These are made on the ground and then lifted into place. Access to the smaller granaries can be obtained only by raising the roofs, but the larger ones have a doorway cut through so that the women can climb in and throw out the day's supply of maize. The chickens take advantage of these openings to nest in the granaries. Often they choose a neighbour's granary for this purpose, which may give rise to battles between embittered housewives and accusations that the granary owner is absconding with eggs and chickens rightly belonging to her neighbour. From the poles will hang rolls of bark rope, or medicine, or small skins kept to make bags. On top of the maize, the housewife stores pots of dried seeds or ground nuts or dried meat or greens and extra calabashes which will later be made into ladles or cups.

An additional means of storage is the *cikoko,* a large bark container. This is fairly common in the western districts but elsewhere is rare. A tree is girdled at two points, and a slit made down one side. Wedges are driven in and pushed home until the bark comes loose. The resulting cylinder is sewn down one side, and a round circle of bark is sewn into the bottom. The *cikoko* may be fastened to a sledge and used to bring home the harvest. Later it may be slung to the walls of the granary.

CRAFTS.

The craftsmanship of the Tonga consists of work in clay, wood, iron and basketry. They also prepare hides very roughly, and to-day the women spend their time stringing beads or occasionally turn to knitting or crocheting. The Tonga recognize their lack of craftsmanship, and say that they are farmers and not artisans.

Nevertheless a minimum of technique sufficient to provide for most of their needs is widespread throughout the community. Most men are capable of building their own huts and making their own tools, or at least doing a part of the necessary work. Many women are able to make baskets and pots. To-day, of course, there is a growing dependence on trade goods.

Craftsmanship is specialized to a small extent through the belief that only those chosen by the ancestors have the ability to make certain objects.* Those who make pipes, pots, baskets, wooden drums and mortars, and those who do the more difficult work in smithing, must acquire the skill from some ancestor who has previously carried on the craft. The ancestor causes them to dream ; after this they begin work. The making of pipes, for instance, is confined to men, but not all men can make pipes. " When a man who knows how to make pipes dies, his spirit comes to one of his relatives and in his sleep the man dreams, ' You must make pipes.' When he gets up in the morning, he starts to make a pipe, and he sees that he can mould it. He doesn't learn from watching somebody else make it. It is the spirit that shows him how. When he tries to fire the pipe, he sees that his pipes always break. He tries again and again. Then he thinks, ' I must go

---

* I have recorded this belief only in the eastern districts, but presumably :1is wide spread.

to the diviner to find out what is wrong.' The diviner says, ' Did you dream when you started to make the pipe ? ' ' Yes.' ' I think that a spirit has given you this job, but when you are ready to fire the pipe you should make beer and make an offering to him. He is thinking, ' This man must make an offering to me since I showed him how to make pipes.' Then the pipe maker should go home and put maize to sprout. When he removes the sprouted maize, he should take the water and sprinkle it on the unfired pipe while he says, ' Look, ancestral spirit, now I am able to make pipes, and this is the beer which I am making for you.' After that he should fire the pipe and they should brew beer and make an offering to the ancestor. On the day of the beer, he should kill a fowl and take the blood to mix with the clay he uses for making pipes. That finishes it, and he does not make a special offering again to the spirit who gave him the ability to make pipes, but when he makes beer for any of his ancestors, he will also remember this one."

Similar beliefs, with suitable variations, attach to the other crafts. The basket maker is made ill by the ancestral spirit, since, as the Tonga say, " the basket isn't fired and therefore the ancestor can't break it in firing and it must do something." When she becomes ill, the diviner informs her that one of her ancestors has given her the skill to make baskets and is now demanding an offering. Someone who has not received skill from an ancestor for a particular craft may still try his hand at it. That is not forbidden, but " If he has no spirit who comes to him and he just tries himself, his heart will become lazy and he won't be able to finish the work. Or, suppose he wants to make a drum, but no ancestor is helping him. Then the people will come to look at it and they will say, ' Ah, it doesn't look good.' So he stops making drums. But if the spirit has given him the skill, the drum will look good and the man will always make good drums."

The ancestor who knew the craft, and who in turn was given the craft by one of his ancestors, may choose any one of his descendants as a recipient of the craft. He does not have to follow matrilineal or patrilineal principles of descent. It is possible for a man to begin his work without the conscious prompting of a spirit, and then at a divination to be informed that some ancestor whom he now hears about for the first time has given him the craft. Crafts are therefore not tied to any one family line, and probably no one who has a real desire to embark on one is prevented from starting, since the assumption will always be, if he is successful, that some distant ancestor has only now decided to pass on his skill. The ancestor does not need to be in any hurry to do this. One man showed me a bellows used by his father, who died about 1915. They were keeping the bellows on the chance that someone in the family might be endowed with the craft. " He hasn't come to anybody to give them the skill since he died. We're still waiting."

[181]

Most of the younger Tonga would now laugh at the suggestion that they should wait upon the ancestors, as did the young woman who made a clay pipe, though she had received no skill and was quite blatantly trespassing in a man's domain.

Certain occupations, and not necessarily those which are specialized, are surrounded with ritual precautions. The occupations subject to taboos are pottery making, beer brewing, smithing, hunting and fishing. The same two taboos apply in each case. No one may wash on the morning that he undertakes any of these enterprises, save for the fishermen whose work takes him into the water anyway. The other taboo enjoins continence on the night before the undertaking is begun. A potter must observe the taboo on three occasions, before she digs her clay, before she makes her pots, and before she fires them. The brewer is required to be continent on the night before she puts her grain to sprout, and again from the night before she starts to make beer until the evening of the day on which the brewing is completed. The smith, hunter and fisherman must be continent on the night before they begin the enterprise. The prohibitions are backed with a sanction. Those who transgress run the risk of failure. The woman's beer will not mature properly and the taste will betray her ; the potter's pots will crack in the firing ; the hunter will either have no success or he will meet some dangerous beast in the bush ; the fishermen either catches no fish or when he brings his spear down to impale a fish, he is likely to find himself impaled instead. The blacksmith finds that the metal on which he is working will break and not fuse properly. Men making bullets will also observe the taboos to prevent their guns from backfiring.*

---

* The man who has the right to name the day on which a particular part of the country will be hunted has certain ritual to perform to make the hunt a success. On the day when he announces the hunt, he should go to the bush and bring back animal dung which he mixes with medicine and burns. On that day he observes the taboos, and also on the following day when the hunters are sharpening their spears. All the hunters must observe the taboos on the days when they are actually hunting.

There are other taboos in connection with hunting which apply to the people remaining at home in the villages. The women are forbidden to stamp meal or to do other heavy work, and they are not allowed to tie their cloths tightly as this will prevent their husbands from running fast if they come across dangerous game. The rules were still more stringent on the wives of elephant hunters, for the hunter could tell what his wife was doing during his absence by watching the actions of the elephants. If the wife stamped meal, the elephant would point his trunk straight into the air. If she joked with someone and playfully slapped at him, the elephant would attempt to rush her husband. If she committed adultery, the elephant would tear up a tree and throw it at her husband. The elephants would also betray her past affairs, for if several men hunted together and one was the lover of another's wife, the elephants would wait for the departure from camp to raid the place and break the pots. The hunters also watched the elephants to learn of misfortune at home. If the elephants tore leaves from the trees and dusted themselves, the men knew that someone at home had died and they returned to mourn. To-day, of course, since the Tonga no longer hunt elephants, the old beliefs are merely the talk of the old men.

Smithing.

A few Tonga may once have been able to smelt iron,* but to-day none of this skill remains and informants insist that smelting was never undertaken. Instead they bought hoes from the Lozi, and used the worn out blades to make spears and axes. To-day the blacksmith depends still on trade iron—old hoe blades, broken ploughs, and other scrap metal.

He is at best a slightly more skilful technician than other men, all of whom seem to be able to do minor repairs. His equipment consists of an anvil, often of stone, but sometimes of an old railway tie, a couple of hammers, and a bellows. This last is similar in shape to the Ila bellows, and indeed seems typical of Central Africa as a whole. In the Mwanachingwala district, bellows (*mavuba*) may be made of clay mixed with sorghum grain. Elsewhere the bellows are of wood, but old men in the Escarpment borders say that once they used clay bellows and turned to wood when they found the clay bellows breaking too readily. Many blacksmiths to-day have tongs for holding the hot metal, but some still depend on a couple of sticks.

Usually his clients bring their metal with them and sit around while he reprocesses it into the objects they order. Often they do the majority of the work, and he gives a hand only on the more difficult technical points. His payment is usually a share of the client's metal, which he then uses to make spears. When someone happens along who wants a spear blade, he sells one and makes his profit at that time. Occasionally he may make a number of blades and then wander off across the country to peddle his stock. Usually he stays home at his forge. He works only in his spare moments, and spends most of his time in his fields or with his cattle. One or two are said to be skilled enough to undertake repairs on scotch carts or wagons. Most are much less ambitious. They make axes (*keembe*), and a few make ornamental axes (*kabanga*). They make adzes (*imbezi*), and spear blades (*isumu*) of six or seven different varieties, some barbed. Occasionally one undertakes to make a cow bell. Hoes must be bought from the stores, as well as most of the other metal objects the Tonga desire.

Wood Workers.

Wood working like smithing is restricted to men. Most men make the handles for their hoes, axes, adzes and spears, and wooden spoons and porridge stirrers for their wives. Some prefer, however, even to buy these necessities, and a few men turn out quantities of handles or spoons in their spare time and retail them to their neighbours for 3*d.* or 6*d.* Since they have begun to use draught oxen, wooden sledges have become common. Most men make these for themselves, since it requires little skill, and they also make most of the ox yoke. For ox chains, of course, they are dependent on the trading store.

---

* A. Casset, " The Chikuni Mission," *Zambezi Mission Record*, 4, p. 92, 1910. He refers to a Tonga smith who got ore from hills somewhere south of the mission and smelted it.

Specialists make drums, mortars, stamping poles, wooden dishes and stools. Their tools are usually restricted to axe, adze and a chisel. Some, however, have purchased saws, planes, and augers. The technique is usually the same for all articles. The carver selects a piece of wood of the approximate size and attempts to choose a wood fitted for the particular article he is making. Then he roughs it into the desired size and shape with his axe. From there on he continues the shaping and finishing with the adze. For drums or mortars he requires a chisel for chipping away at the centre of the block of wood until it is hollowed out. He may smooth the object by scraping it with a spear blade or knife, or he may leave such finishing touches to his customers. Some ornament their work by burning designs into the wood with hot metal, but many do not bother.

The carvers make drums of three types : the *mudima*, the *ingoma* and the *namalwa*. The first is used chiefly at rain ceremonies, but is occasionally used during the rest of the year for ordinary dancing. The *ingoma*, however, is the ordinary drum used for dancing and at beer drinks. Both are beaten with the hands. The *namalwa*, a friction drum, is used at mournings to accompany the wailing or singing, but it is sometimes used in the fields to scare away the birds from ripening grain. The stool (*cuuno*) is made in two shapes, round and elliptical. Some are substantial well made objects, which may be ornamented with copper studs or with carved bands, or with burned wood bands. Many are small, and may be used also as headrests though a few old men have headrests for this purpose and too small to serve as a stool.

In recent years, a few professional carpenters have set up shop in the reserve, utilizing their mission training. Although their carpentry is but a sideline to farming, they still operate on a fairly large scale and are already having difficulties in getting suitable wood in the quantities they need.

Pottery.

Pottery, save for pipes and clay bellows, is a woman's craft. The potter digs her clay at the nearest available bed, and brings it home to stamp in her mortar or work on the grind stone to reduce it to a uniform mass. Then she proceeds to make a paste with water. In the Mwanachingwala area, the potter uses a temper of ground pot sherds. Elsewhere they claim to add nothing to the clay. Pipe makers do use a temper of pot sherd in the east, so the principle is known.

The clay is shaped with the fingers into a long roll, and this is twisted into several coils. The potter then proceeds to pull this upward and outward to form the body of the pot, working with her fingers and perhaps a maize cob or a large shell. At the neck another coil is added and shaped to form the top. If the pot is a small one, it is now finished. If the potter makes a large pot, she starts it about a quarter way up, and completes the top. Then she turns it upside down and leaves it to dry for several days. Additional clay is then added and the bottom shaped. Pots are left to dry inside the house, resting on their rims on the floor. After several days they are brought out and left in the open air for several hours. Towards evening they are fired. Where a large ant hill is available, this may be hollowed out as a kiln. Elsewhere pots are placed in a shallow pit. A tipi-like structure of bark and thatching grass is built up around them. Towards sunset the fire is lit. When the fire dies down, as it does in a couple of hours, the pots are glowing red. The potter has meantime brewed a decoction of *mwihinga* bark which she sprinkles over the pots as she removes them from the fire. The decoction is said to strengthen them and keep them from breaking.

There are a variety of pots : the big *citalo* which may hold eight gallons and is used for cooking beer ; the *muleu*, a wide-mouthed pot used chiefly for storage of beer or water ; the *inongo*, used for carrying water or for storage ; the *imbede*, a small pot used for drinking ; the *cibia*, in various sizes used for cooking porridge and relish ; the *sikaleleke*, which looks from a distance as though the potter had made an *imbede* and then added another on top and is used for storing beer ; and the *inshabia*, a low bowl or dish used as an eating bowl. Not all the potters have the skill to make the various types. The *citalo* is notoriously difficult.

Ornamentation takes various forms. The *imbede* is often burnished with a pebble before firing, but this takes so long that seldom is a woman ambitious enough to undertake this with a larger pot. Most commonly the ornamentation consists of geometrical designs incised into the still moist clay with thumb nail, straw, or comb. Ash from the fire may be rubbed into the incisions after the firing.

Pipe makers often show considerable skill in modelling animal or human figures as rests for the pipe bowl. The bowl may be further ornamented with cross-hatchings or other designs. To it is added a reed stem often bound with brass. Children at play model clay oxen or people.

Baskets and Mats.

The two common baskets made by the Tonga are the *intumba* and the *cisuo*. The former is a small basket used as a food dish ; the latter is large and used for carrying, for winnowing, and for various other purposes. The technique is the same for both, save that the *intumba* is more finely twined. A number of narrow strips of split reed (*lutete*) are twilled to form a square bottom, and then the ends turned upright and caught by a threadlike strand of split vine (*lutende*). The strands extending from the base form the warps, and on these the basket maker twines the sides with two wefts of moistened vine. The sides expand until the basket assumes

A Spear Rest, with leaning gun and spears.   Skins and skulls are hung from the projecting branches of the rest.

*A Spirit Gate through which the spirits of the ancestors
enter the homestead.*

The rain shrine of Nangoma from the Chona Area.

The mudima drums which are used at the time of the rain ceremonies.

Men and boys unloading a sledge and throwing the maize and gourds on to a drying platform.

A typical Tonga hut of the old style.   Beside it rest the big tins used for brewing beer and a couple of the carrying baskets.   On the verandah of the house is the family wood pile and a half-made mat.

*An old woman clad in her finery of beaded necklet, brass
snuff knives, and ivory bracelets. She wears the typical
dress, a combination of skirt, over cloth, and blouse.*

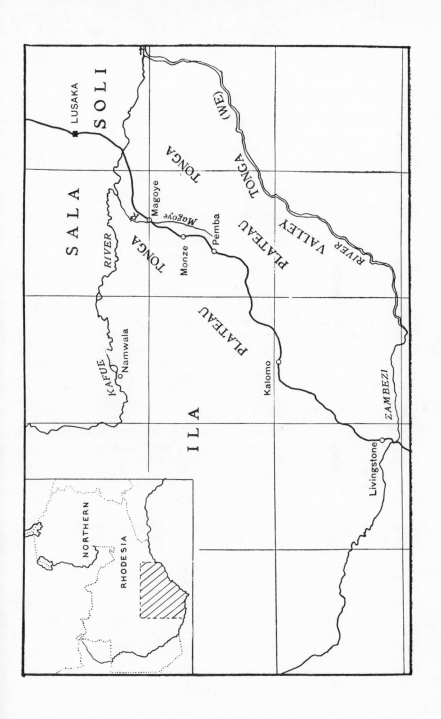

a circular shape, and the top is finished off by inserting a circular withe. Some slight attempt at a pattern is often made by inserting a weft, dyed black, but this is never elaborate. When the *cisuo* is finished, it is given a thin coating of manure well rubbed into the interstices to make it less permeable and to keep meal from sifting through.

Tonga women are not able to make another type of basket which is preferred to the *cisuo*. This is the *cibango*, a round flat basket plaited in check or twilled work. Most women seem to have the *cibango* to-day, but they purchase it from the trading stores or from hawkers who wander through the reserves.

Near fishing sites two other types of baskets are made. Most women make their own *moono*, a large basket of unsplit reeds twined together by bark cord at intervals of about eight inches. With these they sweep the pools for small fish. Along the lower Magoye, fish traps similar to the Ila *ivhumbo* are set in rough weirs. These are said to be made by men.

Women make two varieties of rough mats. One is made from split reeds and woven in a simple check or twill plait. The finished mat is lightly smeared with cow dung, since it is to be used for spreading meal to dry. This is the *citati*. The other mat, the *cisasa*, is made in much the same fashion as the *moono* fishing basket, and is used for a sleeping mat, or sometimes as a door covering.

Miscellaneous.

The Tonga seem to have no knowledge of any tanning process, and indeed do a minimum of work with skins. Men skin an animal, peg out the skin and scrape the underside until it is free of adhering flesh, and leave it to dry in the sun. The stiff skin is then used as a mat. A few old women still wear skin skirts, and for this purpose the dried skin is worked between the hands until it is supple again. The Tonga do not attempt to sew skins together, and the few karosses that they own have been obtained from Lozi or other western peoples.

In spare moments, both men and women make thread, usually from the aloe, by rolling fibres on the thigh. Women use the thread for beadwork. Boys and men double or braid the thread and use it for snares or for making fishing nets. Bark cords and rope are twisted from the bark of the *mubombo* tree. Some work is done with gourds of various sizes and shapes. They are hollowed out for water pitchers, churns, drinking cups, ladles, and snuff containers, depending on their size. Often a drinking cup or a snuff container is given a high polish, but no other attempt is made at decoration.

[194]

Informants deny that they ever made bark cloth or had any form of weaving. Nor did they attempt ivory work. Instead they traded their ivory in the distant past to the Ila, and later on to the European traders.

UTENSILS, FOOD AND DRINK.

Besides growing much of the family food and collecting wild greens for relish, the Tonga housewife is responsible for bringing the water, gathering the firewood, and cooking the daily meals.

In the north-west where wood is scarce, or elsewhere in the open plains along the Magoye, some of the burden is taken from the women. The women go out, perhaps a day's journey away, and gather great piles of firewood. The men then go out with scotch carts or sledges and bring the wood home. This is usually done before the rains start and the planting begins, since the men know that the women cannot spend time searching for fuel when they are working through the day in the fields. In the wooded portions, a woman is expected to bring in the firewood by herself, and daily as she returns from the fields or from her search for relish, she adds a pile of wood to the other burdens which load her head. The men come to her assistance only when she is making beer. They will then use sledge and oxen to haul home the pile she has collected somewhere in the brush. The men also assist to bring water for brewing, since great quantities are necessary. Almost every village to-day has a water drum—an old petrol drum—which the men haul down to the water hole with sledge and oxen. The woman and her friends go down and fill the drum, and then once more the men come with oxen to haul the heavy drum back to the homestead. At other times the woman is left to transport all the water used for cooking, drinking, and washing, though the nearest source of water may be over a mile away. The clay *inongo* is still commonly used for bringing and storing water, but many families prefer to buy buckets, and there is a firm affection for 4-gallon paraffin tins, which even the warning that the container is poisonous will not shake. The women prefer them because they are lighter than the clay pots, and strong as the Tonga woman is she appreciates a lighter burden as she toils up the path. Those who cannot obtain metal containers, make themselves a light substitute from a large calabash. But the calabash is brittle and easily broken, and the chances are that it will be smashed long before another growing season has passed and the new gourds have hardened in the fields.

For preparing meals, the housewife needs only a small amount of equipment. The indispensible items include a mortar (*incili*), pounding stick (*munsi*), sieve (*insefwa*), basket (*cisuo* or *cibango*), porridge stirrer (*muungo*), several cooking pots (*cibia*), several dishes (*mutiba*), and some spoons (*muungo*). Not every woman is fortunate enough to own all that she requires, and as meal time

[195]

approaches there is a scurrying back and forth of children sent to borrow a sieve here or a basket there. Often one sees several small girls alternately tugging and pushing a big mortar from one hut to another. For a really big job, every woman needs to borrow from her neighbours. If she is brewing much beer, she collects baskets, pots, stamping blocks and pounders, and little girls to help her stamp wherever she can lay hands on them. If several women are brewing at the same time each tries to send her messengers out to borrow the equipment first, and the laggards may have to send to relatives in the next village.

To-day few families bother to acquire a grind stone (*iziyo*), since most Tonga prefer the finer meal which can be made by stamping and then sifting. The women commonly use the grind stone only in a bad year when maize is scarce and they fear to waste the husk. At such times they wander up to a friend's house and use the grind stone resting on her verandah. The grind stone is any convenient stone which has been found and brought home, though use gradually makes a slight hollow. It may merely sit on the verandah with the small hand stone (*inkando*) nearby, or it may be set into a clay base which holds the stone tilted at a slight angle. At the lower end a large potsherd embedded in the clay receives the crushed meal.

A Tonga bride usually starts her married life with only the pot and basket which her family send with her. On her wedding day her husband gives her a spear (*cibemba*), which serves her for a knife. At first she needs no more, since she and her husband are attached to some established family for the first few years of their marriage. The young wife assists the older woman with the cooking, using her equipment, and she eats with the other women of the family while her husband joins the men around their separate set of dishes. Gradually over a period of years, the young couple establishes its independence, and the wife complains that she wants her own utensils. When it is decided that it is time for her to cook by herself, one of her relatives comes to place the three stones for her fireplace. Gradually she accumulates her utensils. If the couple can find the money, they will buy three legged iron pots, and tin or enamel dishes from the trading store. More often they must depend on the products of the native craftsmen.

The staple food is porridge (*insima*) made from stamped maize. The meal is sifted through a fine meshed wire sieve, which must be bought from the traders. Those who are unable to obtain these, sometimes use a basketry sieve traded in from other tribes, or they fall back on an older method of separating chaff from meal. The stamped meal is placed in a large basket which is rotated until the coarse husk comes to the surface. It is scooped off with the fingers and the process repeated until only the fine meal is left. This method is still generally used in preparing the meal used in making the light beer (*cibwantu*). For porridge, however, the

[196]

meal is sifted two or three times, and each time the coarse residue, is thrown back into the mortar to be repounded and sifted again. The coarse bran of the husk is finally thrown out to the goats and pigs and chickens which roam around the stamping place, dashing in to pick up any meal that falls from the mortar. Usually the women stamp before each meal, but sometimes they rise at the first cock's crow to finish their stamping before they are off to the fields with the first light. At other times they decide to stamp their meal for several days in advance. The meal is then spread on mats and placed in the sun to dry, perhaps on the side of the roof where goats and chickens have no chance to ruin the work, perhaps on the ground under the vigilance of a forgetful child.

After the woman stamps her maize, she has still to stamp and sift ground nuts to obtain a meal (*buntele*) which is added to almost every relish that the housewife makes. If no relish is available, it is added directly to the porridge as it cooks, to give it flavour. Wild greens are cleaned and shredded and stewed with ground nuts and salt. Sometimes dried meat or fish is available, and very occasionally fresh meat. When the relish is cooked, the housewife brings water to the boil in another pot, and then throws in handfuls of meal, stirring it constantly. When the porridge is so thick that the stirring stick stands upright, it is ready, and the family can be called to eat.

Sometimes, however, a woman is tired of stamping, or her hands are blistered from hoeing in the fields. She then merely soaks the maize kernels and then boils them, either with beans or with ground nuts, or sometimes with only ground nut meal, in a dish known as *musozya*. At some seasons of the year, the family subsists largely on roast or boiled green mealies and pumpkin and cucumber. Pumpkin and cucumber are also dried and later cooked in a stew to eat with porridge. Sweet potatoes are fairly rare, and cassava is little grown. Through the day the children take constant snacks on roasted ground nuts, or boiled maize, or wild fruit. Through most of the year, even a family wealthy in cattle has little chance to drink milk, as there is barely enough to feed the calves. In the rains, however, there is usually plenty. Much of it is made into the sour milk (*mabisi*). Occasionally a little butter is made. Milk is poured into a calabash churn (*insuwa*). A stopper of maize cob is pushed in, and as people sit around through the day they take turns at the job of shaking. Even a chief thinks it not below his dignity to take a hand in the churning. The butter may be mixed with porridge, but most of it is commonly used for covering the body with a protective coat of grease.

When the food is ready the housewife serves it out. She shapes the porridge into mounded hills in the dishes, using her stirrer for this purpose. To-day the bowls may be enamel or tin dishes, and often are. Or they are baskets, or clay bowls, or wooden dishes rather like small wooden salad bowls. In the north-western districts, the Tonga claim that these last are recent importations from the Lozi and that formerly only clay and basketry dishes were used. In the eastern districts in thickly wooded country, wooden dishes are said to have been made and used as long as anyone can remember.

The food is divided into two sets of dishes, one for the men and boys, one for the women and children. The groups gather for the meal, and squat around the dishes. Children are ordered to bring water for washing hands. Then the diners dip their fingers into the stiff porridge, form it into a ball, and dip this into the relish. For such a meal, no spoons are necessary. But if the meal consists of some dribbly dish, spoons are used instead of fingers. Some families have a tin spoon or two. Others use wooden spoons, which have two shapes : one very like the wooden mixing spoons seen in European kitchens and the other a deep ladle which holds almost as much as a small bowl. Some families use substitutes such as large clam shells or broken bits of gourd. Besides their own set of dishes, the women usually keep the cooking pots beside them, and while they eat they scrape the sides of the pot, and the cook may carefully finger from the stirring stick the last bits of porridge. Whatever is left is usually put aside for the children to eat whenever they grow hungry, but the porridge may be broken into bits and some relish added and the lot set down in a dish for the dogs, who meantime have been hanging hungrily on the edges of the eating groups, wolfing a mouthful from the pots or dishes whenever vigilance is relaxed and they can dart in unnoticed.

Water is not drunk with the meals. Whoever is thirsty goes to the water pot kept stored in the depth of the house where its contents grows somewhat cool except in the hottest weather. Men, of course, usually shout to a child to bring the water to them. Beside the pot is kept a calabash ladle used either for drinking or for pouring water into a drinking cup. The traditional drinking cup is either the *imbede* of clay or the gourd cup. Some men give their drinking gourds a high polish and fit them with a rope sling. With this they travel around to the beer drinks, assured that they shall never lack a container for any beer they may happen to find. Others in this age have tin pails or enamel or tin cups, and many have fashioned their own cups from discarded tin cans. Usually a family will have only two or three drinking cups in its possession, but sometimes a small boy has his own little drinking pot, made for him by a grandmother.

Besides water and sour milk the Tonga drink *cibwantu* and *bukoko*. The former is made from maize to which a root (*munkoyo* or *masabe*) is added. It is non-intoxicating and is drunk in great quantities. *Bukoko* is beer made from sprouted grain, meal and water. To-day almost all beer is made with maize, but the older people still maintain that the best beer is millet beer, and after that the next best is made from sorghum. After the grain is sprouted, the process of brewing takes about six days. To-day most villages have a couple of large metal vats, obtained by cutting a petrol drum in two. These travel from house to house, as the women brew. If a woman is unable to borrow one of these, she falls back on the largest iron pot available. It is only if none of these are available that she uses the *citalo*, the traditional beer pot. To-day these are fairly scarce, and even those which are found in the village are likely to be cracked and mended again with rope and new clay and therefore no longer can be trusted on the fire. On the final day of brewing, people begin to wander in early in the morning and wait until the beer has begun to cool. At this stage it is known as *mantabe*. To drink it at this stage is regarded by the older people as a deplorable practice recently acquired by the Tonga. They are most vehement, however, in lecturing the young against its evils when they themselves are somewhat excited from drinking *mantabe*. In the afternoon or evening of this day, the beer is poured into the *inonyo* pots for storage. The meal which has been gradually settling to the bottom of the pots is thrown out to the pigs and fowls, but even so most beer still contains a good deal of meal in suspension.

Beer making is not a specialized profession. Young girls quite often brew for sale to get money to buy clothes. But it is still held that once a woman is married she should not brew at her own house until her bride wealth has been paid. This usually occurs sometime after marriage. It is only after this that she can brew beer for offerings to the ancestors, and the privilege of making beer is regarded as the symbol of the final establishment of a new family.

CLOTHING.

Traditional.

The traditional clothing of the Tonga is rarely seen to-day. Indeed, from the accounts of Livingstone and Selous, one gathers that the traditional dress for men was a pristine state of nakedness. In some of the western districts, this was topped with the Ila-style of headdress. There are still old men whose scalps betray that they once wore the *impumbe*, but only a few on the far western borders still use it. Women dressed in skin skirts, which in the later years of contact might be decorated with elaborate bead work, and carried their babies caught to their backs in goat skins (*ingubo*). Only old women who have no relatives to rely on still wear the traditional skirt, and this is rarely ornamented, though sometimes one is seen with a cowrie shell or two sewn to the edge. The goat skin *ingubo* is also rare, and the women demand carrying cloths from the stores. Young girls were once dressed in a skirt made from hanging bark strings (*bwaaya*). This has disappeared completely, though there are women in their early forties who claim to have worn it.

[199]

Present Day.

To-day the preferred and most common type of men's clothing is an adaptation of European dress : khakhi shorts and shirts or white vests. Some indeed have woollen suits, leather jackets and sweaters, but the majority must perforce be content with much poorer garb which is often reduced to rags long before the man feels he can part with the money to buy a new set. A few old men still dress in cotton loin clothes, and many who customarily wear European clothing wear the loin cloth as night clothes or don it when they are wandering around in the early morning.

Women wear a full skirt reaching well below the knees and a blouse, both of which should be of dark blue cotton. They have clung to this colour since the earliest traders began to work in the country, but to-day they are gradually accepting other colours and even new styles of dress. Many younger women attempt to follow European styles and prefer a dress to blouse and skirt. The latter, however, have many advantages to the hard working housewife who also has a young child, since the blouse can be easily slipped up to give the child access to the breast. Some of the younger women have met this problem by slitting their dresses over the breasts. A further essential part of the costume is a long cloth known as the *mulembo*, which is wrapped around the waist as an overcloth. Often the skirt is so tattered that the *mulembo* is a vital necessity, since the Tonga consider it most immodest for a woman not to be well covered below the waist. The blouse is removed when the woman is at work, and even young women feel no shame at baring their breasts at such times.

If possible, a woman wants two sets of clothing : one her ordinary working garb and the other a new set similar to the first which she will wear only for holiday occasions. Sometimes a woman will sit alone in an almost deserted village when the others have gone off to a neighbouring beer drink. When asked if she is not going, she will say, " I have nothing to wear and I'm ashamed to go like this in these old rags." And she sits determinedly at home until the family is once more in a position to buy her something to wear. Young women whose husbands have a reasonably good cash income will expect, in addition to skirt, blouse and overcloth, to be provided with a cap, a coat or jacket, and possibly shoes. They may demand three or four dresses or *milembo* before they are satisfied. An older woman with children will be content with much less and spends her time worrying how to keep her children decently clad and herself covered.

Small children are not lavishly dressed. Babies usually wear nothing but a string of beads or a cord strung with medicine and find their shelter in the *ingubo* binding them to their nurses' backs. Younger women, especially those who have had contact with the schools, want their babies dressed in European fashion. Even in distant villages, small babies may be seen dressed in sweater and sunbonnet and perhaps drawers, or a dress. A single cotton vest or shirt is still more common.

Small boys usually spend their first few years in a shirt, and they may be lucky to have that. Sometimes they have only a fragment of cloth with which to drape their loins, and many boys of eight and nine still run naked though usually after about the age of eight the family makes some attempt to keep them in trousers. After a boy is about eleven, his family will have to provide him with shorts and shirt or he will run away to work for the European farmers along the railway line. Boys in their teens are therefore usually well dressed. Some effort will be made to clothe a girl from the time she can walk freely. The essential clothing is a skirt or a loin cloth, though many to-day have thin cotton dresses or a skirt and a blouse. Girls of six or so may sometimes be seen playing naked, but their elders are apt to tell them sternly to cover themselves and that it is wrong for a girl to go naked. Whereupon a child next appears in the blouse or *mulembo* of its mother. There is a general feeling that girls should be more carefully clothed than boys, and women complain about the expense of having daughters who must be fully clothed whereas the boys can be left to go naked until a much later age without anyone save the boys themselves worrying over much. From puberty on, a girl is usually fairly well clothed until after she is married, and after that her wardrobe depends on her husband's industry and amiability.

For warmth, although many to-day have old army coats or jackets, most people depend upon cotton or woollen blankets. Each adult demands his own, and teen age boys and girls often are able to acquire cheap blankets for themselves. There may be an additional blanket in the family under which all the small children huddle. In the cold evenings as they sit around the fire, they nestle in under the blanket or *mulembo* of some older person.

Ornaments.

Beneath their skirts, the women drape their hips with many strings of small seed beads in different colours. Old women still wear brass armlets and anklets. Many women wear bracelets of ivory or beads and necklaces of seed beads to which a pendant of imitation impande shell is added. Short strands of beads dangle from pierced ears. Finger rings of seed beads or of brass are fairly common, and some have begun to wear wedding rings. Small children often have a waist band or wristlet of seed beads, and babies have wristlets of beads placed on each arm at the time of naming. Men wear rings and some wear bead wristlets, but the more sophisticated prefer a wristwatch though it may not run. A few old people still have a treasured impande shell or two, which are often worn on the forehead, held there by a cord passing around the head. Others still have a few old beads brought by early traders from Mozambique, but these are very rare.

Most people wear their hair closely cropped. As soon as it attains any length at all, it is shaved off close to the head. Some people, however, amuse themselves by shaving here and there and leaving short tufts in between, and the more sophisticated young people cut their hair short but do not shave it. Very occasionally someone appears who still wears the hair fairly long and caught into tufts with a good coating of red ochre, which was once the common woman's hairstyle but is now found mostly among the We.

Most women and many men have their faces tattooed, but the marks are not of any set pattern. Each person pleases himself, and the operation may be done at any time. Scarification is also common. Women are scarified along the thighs and abdomen, and the scars are considered to be erotic stimulants. Until recently, beautification was not considered complete until the six upper front teeth had been removed. This has been called the Tonga tribal mark, but it is a custom also shared with the Ila. The teeth are removed just before puberty, the children slipping away to someone known to perform the operation, and taking him the traditional payment of a basket of meal to which to-day a sixpence may be added. Near the railway line, the young girls have for some years abandoned the practice, and to-day the Native Authorities of the area are forbidding it and threatening to fine the operator, the girl, and her family, if anyone appears without her teeth. The boys have long since dispensed with the custom since they discovered that it brought them ridicule when they wandered out to work. So far has the reaction set in, that some men have paid to-day to have their teeth replaced and even send their wives to the dentist for new teeth.

Old men often carry walking sticks (*inkole*) or fly switches (*mucila*). If possible a man cuts a stick which has a peculiar twist at the end resembling some animal or bird, but otherwise he makes no attempt at ornamentation. Flyswitches are commonly cow tails, with the ends left unfinished, though in exceptional cases they may be bound with brass. In the western districts, a few have wildebeest tails which have been traded in from Ila country. Many have tobacco pouches of skin or small polished gourds for snuff cases. Many women have snuff boxes and dangling around their necks are two or more snuff knives (*lubeko*). A few elderly men still possess ornamental axes (*kabanga*) with a more fragile blade than the ordinary axe which often has a design hammered into the blade. The handles are bound in brass or other metal. Possession of such an axe has no ceremonial or status significance, save among the women. Women leaders of the *masabe* dance may have an ornamental axe ; others do not possess them.

PLAY.

Young children who spend most of their time at play have a genius for entertaining themselves without toys, though rough toys are not unknown. Some are made by the children themselves. Small boys model oxen and men and play with them by the hour. To-day they think the game incomplete unless they also make scotch carts or waggons, and with these they play that they are hauling manure from the kraals to spread on the fields, or bringing the harvest home, or going to the towns with bags of maize for sale, or coming back again with waggons loaded with all the things they have bought at the stores. Those who have no knack of making clay oxen, or who perhaps have tired of such toys, collect small green fruit and calling these their cattle build a dust wall to form a kraal. Other children have toy sledges, made for them by their fathers. They run up and down dragging the sledges, pretending they are oxen, while one who has a toy ox-whip lashes them on. Sometimes a man presents his child with a toy waggon made from a hollowed out calabash set on a pair of roughly hewn wooden wheels. These toys are made by or for boys, but little girls join in the games, usually in some subsidiary capacity.

Small girls wrap up maize cobs or gourds in scraps of cloth for dolls and proceed to carry these around on their backs in imitation of the older women. Even girls of eleven sometimes play with these toys. A few children, at least in the eastern districts, have wooden dolls, *mwana wa musamu*. When the family sees a little girl begin to pack around maize cobs or sticks of wood or stones on her back, they realize that she wants a doll and fearing that she will carry stones too heavy for her young back, her father or some other male relative carves her a doll. The dolls represent females, and both genitals and breasts are fully indicated. As the girl grows older she abandons her doll, usually about the age she has her teeth knocked out. The doll is then put aside to be given to some other child in the family, perhaps a younger sister, or it is kept for the eldest daughter of the original owner. Small girls also play at making pottery, modelling little cooking pots and dishes. They also begin to practice making baskets, but usually only older girls of ten or more undertake such projects.

Children are early initiated into the work of the older people. Small girls of four or five are often given little stamping poles, light enough for them to use easily. By the time a girl is four she can probably be trusted to stamp the ground nuts ; a few years later and she can be left to stamp the maize. She early begins to learn how to carry water and other burdens. When her mother or the older girls go down to the water hole, a child of two or three tags along with them and is given a small tin or a little clay pot. When the women return, she is there with her pot perched on top of her head and a little cluster of leaves on top to keep the water from sloshing out. As hoes wear down, they may be made into small hoes suited to a child's grasp, and when the little girl accompanies her mother to the fields, she takes her hoe and helps in the cultivation or is ordered off to collect greens for relish. Even a child of five or six can be depended upon to choose the proper leaves. On the return, the little girl follows her mother into the village, her small pile of firewood balanced precariously atop her head, a duplicate of the great load burdening her mother. By the time a girl is ten or eleven, she is probably competent to manage a house and to work in the fields. It is not all work, however. Often all the girls in the village will assemble their mortars under a shady tree, and stamp their maize together, singing special stamping songs or joking and teasing each other. A boy may wander over and take a hand in the stamping for a moment, while the girls pass contemptuous remarks about his lack of skill.

Besides the work done for her elders, which is more or less under their supervision, a small girl also plays at housekeeping. When the harvest is started, children build themselves playhouses (*mantombwa*). These usually look like rough bundles of thatching grass, hollowed out inside and often containing a miniature bed of sticks not large enough to support a good sized doll. House and bed are made by small boys, since this is men's work. The children raid the fields for ground nuts or maize, or bring food from their homes, and the girls cook over fires built in front of their playhouses. When they are finished, the boys descend upon them demanding food. The boys may bring with them small birds which they have shot or snared to be roasted over the fire. Children play like this from the time they can toddle after a play group until the girls find that their breasts have begun to form and the boys that they have outgrown such childishness.

The boys are also forced early into the family labours. Small boys of five and six are already in the fields leading the oxen during the ploughing season. As they grow older, they are assigned to herd the cattle, though at first they may have to be driven out of the village with blows and threats before they finally submit to herding duties. Into the bush with them they take bows and arrows or their catapults, made of forked stick and rubber from old bicycle tubes, with which they pester the lives of any small birds they may see, or they spend hours spinning thread for making snares. Any large bird or animal they might kill, they would take home to supply the family larder, but tiny birds and animals are promptly cooked and devoured on the spot. While they are herding, the older boys set the younger ones to fighting each other, with kicks and fisticuffs. Sometimes the fights become more serious and stones are hurled back and forth, but this is unlikely unless they meet herdboys from another village. Then a general battle is likely to ensue in the old custom of *basimisela* fighting, which may begin with an arranged battle between two bulls which develops into a general fight when the herders of the defeated bull attempt to regain their village honour, or it may start in arguments as to whether certain boys from the two villages are near enough of an age to call each other " age-mate."

Back in the village, the children have many set games which require no toys. The older girls and boys instruct the toddlers in the actions and the songs and rhymes which form the game, and the toddlers play by themselves when left alone in the daytime to amuse themselves.* Sometimes they play a variety of jack-stones with small pebbles. Older boys and girls may play *cisolo*, using counters of pebbles and scooping out twenty-four holes in the ground under some shady tree.† Occasionally a permanent " board " is made by pecking holes into a slab of stone. Adults as well as children play *cisolo*, but they play only sporadically.

At night during the dry season, the women gather the smaller children around the fires for story telling. These are the traditional tales of hare and tortoise and other animals, or of children blessed with cruel parents. The listeners join in at the end of every phrase with " ulangatu," to show that they are still awake. The stories are interspersed with songs or recitations. The teller recites a verse, and a chorus is then sung or spoken by the listeners. At the end of the tale, the teller spits to show that it is finished. Then someone begins a new tale, while the tiny children drift off to sleep and the older ones wander off in the darkness to begin some game or merely to chase each other back and forth with numerous shouts and giggles. The season and time for story telling is limited. If the tales are told before the grain is brought to the granaries or after the beginning of the planting season, insects and vermin will destroy the grain. It is equally disasterous to tell the tales during the day time, for a whirlwind will come to carry teller and listeners away. So instead the children amuse themselves with numerous riddles which may be told throughout the year.

Small children have other forms of entertainment, based on scaring themselves into a dither. After dark, one or two boys will sneak away from the group, and suddenly a fiery apparition is standing in the midst of the village, while other children set up the shout of " Fire man " (*Shamulilo*) and the small tots begin to scream with fright. The boys have placed lighted straws between toes and fingers and hold a long straw lighted at either end between their lips. As the light quickly fails, they suddenly cringe away to renew their fire and continue the game. A somewhat similar game is played in the daytime, but this time the aparition is *Shacinkwamu*, " The Mask." For this the children make themselves masks, usually of a large gourd into which they burn holes for nose, eyes and mouth. A more ambitious boy may also make eyebrows and

---

* These are similar to Ila games ; even the same rhymes are in use in the two areas. Cf. Smith and Dale, 1920, II, p. 246-261.

† The rules have been described for the Ila. Cf. Smith and Dale, 1920, II, p. 237.

beard from the hairs of a cow's tail and sticking these in place with masses of black gum make himself a still more horrible face. Others carve small masks from wood, but these are too small to cover the whole face. Over their bodies they drape a blanket, leaving space only to inset the mask, and go out to terrify the small children. The latter, however, quickly take up the game themselves, and within a few days will be throwing a shirt or a scrap of paper or a blanket over their heads and setting out with the cry of *Shacinkwamu*. Their fellows of three and four find this as satisfactory as the regular mask and rush off with delighted shrieks which may turn suddenly into cries of genuine terror.

Many nights the children organize a dance in the village, especially when the moon is full. To-day the dance is always *makwaya* ("choir") which they say was introduced by children from the mission schools. The children dance always in a circle, usually graded more or less by size in their earnest endeavour not to be stepped upon by someone too much bigger than themselves. As they circle, they sing and clap their hands, shake rattles, or whistle on a tin whistle while the drummer stands in the middle. Small boys dash in and out and between boxing matches worm their way into the circle for a few rounds of dancing ; very small girls will be jigging ecstatically on the sidelines. Boys in their late teens join the dance as drummers or occasionally as dancers, but they seem to act mostly as spectators, while girls of their age are the leaders in the dance. *Makwaya* seems to have been introduced within the last ten years as a protest against the native dances. School teachers often took the children of several schools to some central point for a day of dancing. At first the dances were unaccompanied by a drum, but after the Tonga children observed that the Salvation Army, which has outposts in the area, uses a drum, they promptly decided that they too would drum again. The *makwaya* is now danced wherever children assemble ; at the dancing for a girl who is in her puberty seclusion, at the ceremony which ends the period of seclusion, at funerals where people are assembled for mourning, at the time of the rain ceremonies or at the harvest festivals. Some nod may be given to tradition by the older people, but within a few minutes the children have formed their circle and the familiar songs of the *makwaya* are drowning out everything else.

Boys entertain themselves as they wander back and forth or sit alone in their houses by playing on the *kalimbu*, made by fitting a gourd sounding-board to a wooden bow. The string is usually of wire to-day, but once gut or tendon was used. The player presses the sounding-board to his abdomen, and taps the string with a small stick or straw, while he shortens or lengthens the string by placing his thumb in different positions along it or by letting it vibrate freely. Boys and men also have the *kankobela*, hand piano, which consists of small strips of metal attached to a wooden base and a gourd sounding-board, but the *kankobela* is fairly scarce. In many

[206]

villages there are none. Women and girls deny any knowledge of either instrument, although occasionally one picks up a *kalimbu* and taps it experimentally while the boys sneer sarcastically behind her.

Adult Amusements.

The chief pleasure of the adults seems to lie in talk. When work is slack, they go on visits to relatives and friends, and the long gossip begins. While the women visitors remain, they take a hand in any activity that may be going on—shelling maize or ground nuts, stamping, working on a mat or basket, or even helping to wash or mend clothes. Men help in the building of a house, the repair of a plough, or the carving out of a sledge. But much time is spent merely talking, at least during the cold season and during the heat just before the rains.

Save in Seventh Day Adventist and other fundamentalist communities, a principal form of entertainment is the beer drink. Some people spend much of their lives wending their way from one beer drink to the next. Usually people begin to assemble early in the morning of a beer drink. When a crowd has gathered, the host brings out pots of beer and divides them among his guests. At a big drink, the division is made on the basis of villages and each village is given its pot. As the hostess brings out each pot, she should take a sip of the beer in the presence of the guests to prove that she has no intention of poisoning them. One man from each village then decants the beer into the drinking cups which are thrust before him. As each finishes the supply of beer in his own cup, he begs from his neighbour until all are finished and they settle down to wait for another distribution. Finally the hosts announce that the beer is finished. Usually, the housewife still has hidden away an *inongo* or a *sikaleleke* of beer. The latter is a pot made especially for this purpose and never brought out at beer drinks. It is the pot that the wife keeps for her husband's private consumption. Sometime during the drink, a drum is usually brought, and the singing and dancing begins. In turn each one rises to start a song. The others take it up, while the introducer dances. Sometimes two or three are needed to act out the dance, though many are solos, and suddenly the rhythm may catch the whole room and a dozen are trying to dance at once in the crowded space. Some dances imitate the actions of animals, often of the frog, and the dancer hops around the room in great bounds. Or someone may dance that a man has been wounded in a fight and is dying on his way home despite the help of his companions who try to carry him. Women often dance about going to work in the fields, or that they expect a bad harvest, or that they are having trouble with a co-wife. They may dance about going to work on the railway, or about the discomforts of the diseases one picks up along the railway. These dances are called *indikiti* or *hamatika*, and are said to have been introduced fairly recently. Before that

[207]

the Tonga danced the *cingande*, which is slightly more violent, and before that they danced a variety of dances including the *budima*, which have now disappeared. The dancing may continue far into the night, interspersed with a recitative, when a man rises to thump the drum and speaking very rapidly relates some adventure. This is known as the *kwaangula*.

Sometimes the entertainment is varied with a free for all fight, or many of the men may wander off to another hut to gamble at cards and lose what money they have. Card games, however, may be played at any time when there is no work on hand, though the practice seems to be restricted to men, who are probably the only ones with money to waste in this manner.

The more serious of the younger people, who have had some education, spend some of their time reading anything that comes into their hands. This is little enough. They read *Mutende* or religious books they have bought from the missions or stray volumes they have picked up apparently only because it was something written. Religious arguments are common, with many references back to biblical texts to prove the different points. Some sit quietly writing letters, which later to their misfortune may appear as evidence in a court case. Young men spend much time in washing, ironing, and mending their clothes, while many of the young women crochet caps or bags in bright colours, or embroider towels, or knit endless belts. Few have the skill to knit anything more elaborate, but some can make tiny jerseys for their babies.

For solace during the quieter hours, or for enjoyment during the riotous ones, there is tobacco, for which most Tonga have a sincere affection except for those who are prevented by their religion from indulging. Older men smoke it in big clay pipes (*imfuko*). They break chunks of coarse tobacco from big cakes prepared by themselves or traded in from the We, place coals on top, and draw the smoke up through long reeds. Some of the younger men have adopted the European pipe, and have even attempted to make rough and rather unsuccessful imitations. Women do not use the pipe, and most prefer to take their tobacco in the form of snuff. Both men and women smoke cigarettes, made by stuffing tobacco into a short end of reed or by rolling the tobacco in any bit of paper available. *Mutende* is a favourite for this purpose, and traders go through the country selling nothing but tobacco and copies of *Mutende*. Wealthier people buy cheap cigarettes from the store, and all prefer these to their own tobacco on the grounds that it is milder and less painful to their throats.

RITUAL OBJECTS.

The Tonga are not rich in ritual objects and what they do have are usually common every day articles which have been set aside for particular ritual use. They have no images or similar cult objects.

[208]

Ritual Structures.

There are, however, three structures which are primarily ritual : the *kaanda*, the *cilyango* and the *lwaanga*. The last is universal throughout Tonga country. The *cilyango* or " spirit gate " does not appear in the western area around Katimba, and informants claimed that they had never had it. Their eastern neighbours maintain that it was once universal and that the westerners have merely forgotten their own customs. The *kaanda* or " shrine " is common everywhere, though its use varies somewhat.

The *kaanda* is a tiny hut regarded as the domicile or symbol of powerful spirits, the *basangu*.* It usually stands only a couple of feet high and consists of a circle of poles topped with a thatched roof. In the country close to the escarpment several shrines have supports made from slabs of stone. Inside the shrines are a number of pots, turned upside down, and rarely anything more. The pots are the typical pottery of the area. When they break, the custodian of the shrine has the job of finding replacements, which he buys or begs from anyone who has a spare pot, and it does not become ritualized until placed within the shrine. Sometimes several shrines are placed together and usually about the shrine is a circle of trees.

The *basangu* are spirits who have control over the rains and the power to avert epidemics, locust plagues, and other disasters. The rain ceremonies are held at their shrines, and consist usually of the killing of a black fowl or beast, the pouring of a beer libation, and the singing of rain songs. As part of the ceremony, the people dance before the shrine and call upon the spirits to send them rain, good crops, and general prosperity. Sometimes a man or woman is possessed by one of the *basangu*, and then proceeds to announce its wishes to the people of the district. In the east and northwest, those possessed usually build a *kaanda* adjacent to their huts, to the right side of the door of the principle hut. This is not the custom in the western districts, where only the *kaanda* set away from the village is found.

The *kaanda* is a community shrine common to all the people of the district though it may be under the direct supervision of one particular matrilineal group. The *cilyango* or " spirit gate " is an individual thing, the symbol of the ancestors of its owner. He and his supporting relatives alone may make offerings at the spot. It consists of three clusters of poles placed in a straight line at intervals of perhaps two feet. A cross piece is lashed across the top, forming the whole into two doorways. Through these doors the spirits enter the homestead of the owner. The poles soon take root and send out new branches. At an abandoned village site,

---

* Cf., Colson, 1948, pp. 272-283 for a discussion of the role of the shrines. Smith and Dale, 1920, II, p. 171 describes similar shrines among the Ila. The name *basangu* is not used for these spirits in the north-western districts. " *Baami ba imvula*," " Lords of the rain," is substituted.

one may still make out the characteristic shape beneath a twisted tangle of trunks and branches. Two doorways are the standard number, but some men make them with one or three doors. This requires some readjustment in ritual, for the right hand doorway is the doorway for the spirits of the owner's father's line and the left hand doorway belongs to the spirits of his own matrilineal line.

Not every man has a " spirit gate." Those who have inherited the place of someone who was accustomed to build a *cilyango*, must perforce continue the practice or run the risk of illness. On the other hand, someone may suddenly find the practice thrust upon him. If he is ill and consults a diviner, he may hear that the ancestors have now decided that they want a *cilyango* built in their honour although no one in the family has previously had one. Thereafter the man or woman would try to build. Henceforth each time the man moves his homestead he should make a new *cilyango*, though he may delay for several years before taking the step which requires the brewing of quantities of beer.

On the day that the brewing ends, the builder calls the young men of nearby homesteads to go out and cut the poles, bring them in, set them in the trenches, and bind the crosspiece in place. A black fowl is killed before each doorway, by striking its neck against the poles. The blood trickles over the poles, while the builder announces to his ancestors that he is carrying out their wishes and that he now wants them to help him and see that no illness or misfortune afflicts his family. Wing feathers from the fowls are tucked into the spaces along the top poles to remain until wind and rain finally tear them down. The following morning when the light has come, the builder and some representative of his father's line go to the two doorways and pour a beer libation to the ancestors. After this, rites are very seldom carried out at the *cilyango* unless the diviners specifically tell the owner that he must make an offering there. For ordinary family ritual it can be ignored.

The *lwaanga* is the spear rest found in front of most houses.* Here men lean their spears and guns before and after a hunt. When a man kills with his gun for the first time, he brings a little circlet of beads and places it on the stock while he thanks the ancestors and asks them to help him in the future. Then he takes his gun to the spear rest and leans it there, while he kills a black chicken in the ritual manner. The blood from the neck is allowed to drip on to the gun and spear rest, and the wing feathers are stripped off and placed on the rest. When a hunter kills any large game, he places the skull on the spear rest.† To-day due no doubt to the absence of large game over most of the country, many perch a goat or ox skull on the rest. The spear rest is in itself merely a rough pole placed on the right side of the doorway.

---

* The Ila have what is called *lwanga*. It seems to include both *cilyango* and *lwaanga*. Cf. Smith and Dale, 1920 II, 172 ff.

† Some men place the skulls on the *cilyango*.

Other Ritual Places.

Most of the ritual which accompanies Tonga life is connected with the dwelling hut. The pubescent girl is secluded within the ordinary dwelling and when she comes out, most of the final ceremony takes place before the door of the hut.

The doorway is the proper place for the offerings to the ancestors made by the head of the family, the right hand post being associated with his father's line, the left with his mother's line. The gourd ladle used for the offering is kept tucked into the thatch of the roof. A woman, unless for the moment she is widowed or divorced, is not allowed to make offerings at the doorway on the grounds that she is not the owner of the house. Instead she makes her offering by the bed, pouring the beer along the bed posts. In the western districts, however, both men and women seem to make their offerings at the centre pole which supports the roof of the hut. Elsewhere people deny that the centre pole has any ritual significance, nor are offerings made at the fireplace. To-day, of course, many people are Christians or at least are dubious of the old customs. Few go to the *kaanda* for the rain ceremonies. Many refuse to build *cilyango* or *lwaanga*. Some refuse to carry out the offerings within the house, though here they are usually overborne by their elders. "School people" therefore usually allow some older member of the family to come and make the offerings while they absent themselves until the rite is finished. Thus the family is protected and they themselves are not culpable of taking part in a "pagan" rite.

To some extent the house is permeated throughout with a symbolic identification with the people who live within it, and there are a number of restrictions or observances which emphasize this. No one may climb on the roof except when it is in the process of construction or repair, for at the death of it's owner, a representative of his father's line must climb to the top and cut off the *insonje*, the little bundle of thatch which crowns the roof, which is then burned in the funeral fires. An adult who climbed on the roof at any other time would be suspected of witchcraft ; a child would be beaten soundly to teach it better manners. When a man dies, the right hand poles of the bed and of the door are torn out and burned and the right hand poles of the verandah may be destroyed as well. The left hand poles are burned when the wife dies.

The cattle kraal for some reason does not seem to be ritually important. The Tonga claim that they do no more than place charms near the entrance to protect the cattle. The only ceremony that takes place within the kraal is that of the naming of the cattle, but this is rarely observed nowadays.

The graves of ordinary people are not ritual spots, save in that they are more or less avoided. A man was often buried near the door of his house, and women were buried in the kraal. A young child was buried within the house, or right behind it. In many parts of the country one still finds tell-tale little heaps of stones directly behind the dwellings. If the children play in their vicinity they are called away, but nobody visits the spots or makes offerings there.

Charms and Divination.

Many people have their houses protected against the machinations of witches with little horns filled with medicine (*insengo*). The *insengo* is usually tucked into the thatch near the doorway, or may be attached to the wall above the door, where it will be able to intercept any evil medicine and prevent it from working harm. In the granaries and about the house are tucked bits of roots and other parts of plants or animals which also serve as charms (*musamu*).

In addition most people wear personal charms, which usually consist of bits of plant or small pieces of stone. These are strung and worn around the neck, waist or wrist. Others wrap the charm in a bit of snakeskin or cloth, often covered with beads. The charms protect against witchcraft, against the attacks of ghosts, or against ill luck in general. Many come to the courts armed with charms to confuse the judgment of counsellors and chief and to force a favourable decision. A number of native courts have a good collection of such charms seized when a man's behaviour was such as to lead to a determined search of his person to find the source of his confidence.

Many claim that they have gathered medicine and made their own charms ; others have received them from friends or bought them from those with specialized knowledge. Charms or medicine may be possessed by any one, and usually is, save for the more determined Christians or modernists.

Other ritual equipment is rarer. The diviner's outfit belongs only to the specialists. Traditionally the chief form of divination seems to have been the throwing of bones, the *inkankata*. Four dice are used and the answer determined by the way in which the dice fall. Another method of divination which also seems to be of some antiquity in the area, consists of the manipulation of a small gourd in which a tiny horn rests. The diviner holds the gourd in his hand while he puts his question, and the answer is determined by whether the horn rotates constantly or comes to rest. To-day, however, with the influx of foreign diviners, many new methods have been introduced. Perhaps most common is the *muchape* divination, which is done by gazing in an ordinary mirror, or into a fragment of one. But all practitioners, no matter what the method, are called *munganga*, " diviner," and all methods are called alike *kusonda*, " to divine." In former days they occasionally resorted to the *mwaze* poison ordeal in which the poison was fed to a chicken, or to an ordeal in which the arm was thrust into a pot of boiling medicated water. Informants claim that both methods have long since been abandoned. A few men are said to be able still to use a form of divination for determining the guilt of witchcraft. Such men possess a skin, usually of spotted cat. When the diviner is called to determine the guilty one among a group of people for such a crime as stopping the rain, he puts the skin on each in turn while asking if the man is guilty. When the skin is placed upon the guilty man it becomes a living animal. In 1946-47, when Tonga country was suffering under a drought, some wished to call in this diviner and his apparatus to learn who was bewitching the rain. They gave the witch a week's grace to remove his spells before the diviner should be summoned. Since the rains came that day, his skill was not tested.

7

THE DISCOVERY OF AFRICA

A HISTORY OF THE EXPLORATION OF AFRICA
AS REFLECTED IN THE MAPS
IN THE COLLECTION OF THE RHODES-LIVINGSTONE MUSEUM

E. H. LANE-POOL

1950

For nearly two thousand years the chief speculation of geographers of Africa was the source of the Nile. Herodotus (*circa* 484–425 B.C.), a great traveller and observer, expatiated upon the rumours and reports of the Nile current in his time,[1] and in the middle of the nineteenth century David Livingstone was still pursuing the elusive Herodotan myth.[2] The account of Herodotus, based on a story told him by a scribe, that the Nile had its source between the two conical peaks of Crophi and Mophi and flowed in two channels to the north and south had considerable influence on future geographers. It accounted for the undue prolongation of the Nile to the south and for the erroneous ascription of the same source to the Nile and the Zambezi. Although Ptolemy (*circa* A.D. 127–151) was in no sense a great map maker, and topography did not interest him, his first map of Africa presented in its essentials a striking resemblance to the real coast line, and his determination of the source of the Nile between 10°–12° south latitude remained unaltered until the famous French maps of the eighteenth century made the correction. He was a disciple of the school of Hipparchus (*circa* 140 B.C.) and was the first to draw maps to a stereographic system. In actual fact the error in his maps of Africa was about 7° in each meridian owing to a fallacious calculation of the earth's sphere, but his work was a great advance on that of any of his predecessors. He had a great vogue during his lifetime, but during the Middle Ages became almost forgotten until the Renaissance school of cartographers towards the end of the fifteenth century revived interest in him.

Born in Africa, he had access to all the records in the University of Alexandria, where he studied, before its dispersion. The information available to Ptolemy was first the description of Herodotus who had ascended the Nile as far as the first cataract, but believed it to have its source in the western part of the continent. Strabo (63 B.C.–A.D. 25) connected the inundations of the Nile with a source in a range of mountains, a theory which Herodotus had debated and discarded. The Elder Pliny (23–79 A.D.) originated the legend that the Nile, rising in Mauretania, flowed in a subterranean channel for the space of a journey of twenty days, emerging on the borders of what was then known as Ethiopia and Africa. Nero (A.D. 37–68) sent a military expedition to discover the Caput Nili, which returned without adding to our knowledge. But about A.D. 50 a Greek trader, Diogenes by name, announced that the Nile had its source in two lakes about twenty-five days march from the coast at Zanzibar, which were fed by streams rising in a range of snow-capped mountains. These two

---

[1] Herodotus II. 28–34.
[2] *Last Journals*, Vol. II, page 302.

lakes, first known as Paludes Nili, later as the Lakes of Crocodiles and Cataracts, finally as Lakes Zairi and Zaflan, emerged from the Montes Lunae or Mountains of the Moon and became perpetuated in all maps from Ptolemy until the end of the seventeenth century, when they were finally expunged by de Lisle. In these lakes were made to rise at different epochs, besides the Nile, the Congo (Ptolemy), the Niger (Il Idrisi) and the Zambezi, Limpopo and Sabi (Pigafetta). The source of the Blue Nile was discovered by Pedro Perez in 1616, but this information was not generally known until much later and the credit of the discovery is often wrongly attributed to Bruce about 1780. David Livingstone was still confident in writing that Ptolemy was probably right in ascribing the source of the Nile to between the 10° and 12° latitudes south of the Equator.[1] While he correctly believed the Chambezi to be the ultimate source of the Congo, he erroneously thought the Lualaba was the source of the Nile. Discovery progressed rapidly in the middle decades of the nineteenth century. Burton and Speke saw Lake Tanganyika in 1858 ; Lake Nyasa was rediscovered by David Livingstone in 1859 (see also map No. 37) ; Speke stood on the shores of Lake Victoria Nyanza in 1862 and so discovered the true source of the White Nile. Baker penetrated as far as Lake Albert Nyanza in 1864, and in 1867 and 1868 Livingstone discovered Lakes Mweru and Bangweulu. Finally in 1877, Stanley connected the Lualaba with the Congo and traced that river from its source to its estuary. There was not much left to be explored in Africa.

Of greater interest to Northern Rhodesia than the Nile is the discovery of the Zambezi. While the Nile attracted the attention of the Mediterranean empires and, in the last century, of the English explorers, the revelation of the Zambezi Basin was due almost entirely to Portuguese enterprise. Ptolemy was unaware of its existence but subsequent cartographers, on the authority of the Arabian geographer Il Idrisi (circa A.D. 1130), made the Zambezi rise from the same lake as the Nile and the Congo. The Muslim cities on the east coast of Africa as far south as Sofala and the mouth of the Zambezi were described in great detail in 1332 by the Moroccan traveller Ibn Batuta. In 1497, Vasco da Gama rounded the Cape of Good Hope, and made the first voyage to the East Indies. He contributed a careful chart of the coast, and filled in the interior with topographical features collected from the oral evidence of natives.

In the sixteenth century the Portuguese towns on the Zambezi were founded. In the seventeenth and eighteenth centuries the explorations of Bocarro and Lacerda gave us some knowledge of what is now Nyasaland and North-Eastern Rhodesia. But it was not until the middle of the nineteenth century that Livingstone discovered the source of the Zambezi and in 1855 the Victoria Falls. The various phases in the discovery of the source of the Zambezi will be alluded to under the description of the several maps.

1 Letter in Museum collection addressed to W. C. Oswell, dated 8th July, 1868, from near Bangweulu.

(1) 1478.—The Berlingerri Ptolemy.

The Florentine Berlingerri reproduction of Ptolemy's map depicts only the northern part of Africa as far south as the Mountains of the Moon. The Nile rises between 10° and 15° south latitude in the Monti della Lunae, thence passing by two channels through two lakes here called Paludes della Nilo. These features remained on all maps until they were expunged by de Lisle in 1700. The Mountains of the Moon have been the subject of legend from the earliest times. As placed by Ptolemy and many later map makers they correspond with the Muchinga escarpment in Northern Rhodesia which demarcates the Congo–Zambezi watershed and the mountainous country north of the middle course of the Zambezi. They are now usually identified with the Ruenzori range. A note inset in the centre observes that "in Africa are white elephants, rhinoceroses and tigers". The inhabitants are classified by their diet, *Anthropophagi* and *Ichtheophagi*. Inset in the top margin is a drawing of the University of Alexandria, an acknowledgment of the academy in which Ptolemy lived and died.

(2) 1486.—The Ulm Ptolemy.

The second Ptolemy is the well-known map from Ulm. It is in colour and the chief variation from the Berlingerri Ptolemy is that the Nile passes through three lakes instead of two. The third, almost immediately abandoned, is probably that which was later called Zachaf, from which, according to some subsequent cartographers, the Zambezi took its source.

As in most maps of the period, curious animals are dispersed about the continent. A strange animal which might be a dinosaur, or more probably the medieval conception of a giraffe, based on reports of natives, has its habitat in the Nile Basin. An alligator basks on the sands of the Upper Nile, and a beast which resembles a hybrid between a spaniel and a poodle is presumably a lion haunting the interior. On the west coast are depicted two negroes, attired in red costumes and a fantastic red headdress, mounted on what appear to be camels. They are confronted by two European adventurers on foot dressed in the picturesque costume of the fifteenth century. On the left margin is a picture of a negro drinking from a silver cup in front of an altar, illustrating the conversion of the natives of Africa to Christianity, which European governments in the Reformation period, and indeed until modern times, declared to be the chief object of African exploration and colonisation. At the base of the map is a sketch of two natives, armed with spears and bows and arrows, eating a ripe fruit from a forest tree. The Ptolemy map should be compared with the famous map of the world dated 1280 in Hereford Cathedral.

(3 and 4) 1540 and 1552.—SEBASTIAN MUNSTER.

In the collection are two maps by Sebastian Munster (1489–1552). Munster was a professor of Hebrew at Basle University and after publishing a grammar, a Bible and several Hebrew translations, devoted himself, in later life, to the study of astronomy and geography. He did more than anyone to revive popular interest in Ptolemy and his *Cosmographia Universalis* became a classic. The first of the two maps, ascribed to 1540, is in colour, and follows the familiar Ptolemy prototype in which Africa is disproportionately prolonged towards the west. Hamarich " Sedes Preste Johan " (*vide infra* Map (9)) is placed on the Nile below the confluence of the two feeders.

The result of Portuguese exploration is illustrated by the reference to Zaphala Aurifodina, the land from which Solomon was supposed to have exported " gold and silver, ivory and apes and peacocks " in ships of Tarshish.[1] The identification of Ophir with Sofala, which appears to have originated with Moorish merchants, has been debated by many scholars. Sofala is first mentioned by the Arabian traveller El-Mas'udi in the middle of the tenth century as the terminus of the voyages of merchants from the Persian Gulf and, he adds, the country produces " quantities of gold and other marvels ". In 1597, Vasco da Gama found here " Moorish ", i.e. Arab, traders employing natives to work gold mines and actually seized Arab dhows laden with freights of gold dust. There is evidence that gold washing and mining had been an industry here for many centuries and the claim of Sofala to be the source of Solomon's gold of Ophir is stronger than that of either India or Arabia. At a conservative estimate the value of gold derived from Sofala is placed by mining engineers at £75,000,000.

The discovery of the Cape of Good Hope by Bartholomew Diaz is recorded by C. bone Speri at the southernmost point of the continent.

The map is illustrated by pictures of animals and men, as was typical of maps of this period : a truculent elephant in the south, parti-coloured parrots, and a hideous sketch of an individual of the mythical race of one-eyed monoculi, to whom legend ascribed a home in the unexplored interior.

The inscription in German is not of interest.

The other Munster map, ascribed to the year 1552, is an illustrated page from his *Cosmographia*. The two Ptolemy lakes are still unnamed, and south of the Montes Lunae the country is said to be uninhabited. In the text Africa is said to be the home of " elephants, dragons, lions, bubuli, pards, goats and apes ".

---

[1] 2 Chronicles, ix 21, I Kings, ix, 28 ; 10, 11.

(5 AND 6) 1570.—JOHANNES LEO.

Africa, Tabula Nova, attributed to Johannes Leo dated 1570, and reproduced from the Atlas of Ortelius published in that year.

The second map, with the exception of a variation in the course of the River Niger is identical with the first.

Johannes Leo Africanus, who lived in the fifteenth century travelled in Northern and Central Africa, and his accounts were published in Rome in 1550. Ortelius (1527–1595), a native of Antwerp and geographer to Philip II of Spain, produced in 1570 his *Theatrum orbis terrarum,* the first great atlas of the world. This is the earliest map in the Museum series to give a more detailed conception of the interior of Africa, while retaining all the familiar features of Ptolemy.

On the Nile is marked, as in the Munster map, the capital of Presbyter John *hic longe imperitat magnus princeps Presbiter Joes totius Africae rex.* The Zuama (Zambezi) River is indicated for the first time and assumes the course which was perpetuated by all geographers, with rare exceptions, until the Sanson map of 1655. Rising from the south of the western lake of Ptolemy, as the Nile rises from the north, some miles south of the lake it diverges into two channels, the northern named Zuama, the southern the Rio Spirito Sancto, debouching into the Indian Ocean respectively north and south of the Tropic of Capricorn. They may be identified with the Zambezi and the Limpopo.

A new addition is Simbowe which can be recognised as what is now known as Zimbabwe. The word Zimbabwe is of Bantu etymology meaning " great stone " from the two elements *Zi* or *Chi* " great " and *mabwe,* plural of *ibwe* " stones ", and was applied to Monomatapa's town on the Limpopo, to Kazembe's fort on Lake Mweru and to many places on the Zambezi. According to the earliest Portuguese documents the Bantu themselves did not know who the builders were. The more widely held modern opinion holds that Zimbabwe is of Bantu origin, possibly erected by the Makalanga not more than 1,000 years ago. The ruins were re-discovered by Karl Mauch in 1871, who started speculations as to the original inhabitants and architects, about whom a con-siderable volume of literature has been amassed. A full description of Zimbabwe is given in Livius Sanuto's geography (*vide infra*).

The information furnished by the navigation charts of Vasco da Gama and his successors is now made known. Munster has already added to the map of Africa the Cape of Good Hope ; now Terra de Nadal (Natal) and several promontories along the coast appear. An interesting note in South-West Africa states that it was unknown to Persian and Arabian writers, the inference being that they were acquainted with the rest of the continent.

The map is beautifully drawn and, as usual, depicts forms of animals. A benevolent looking swordfish and a terrifying dolphin disport themselves in the Atlantic.

(7) 1572.—ABRAHAM ORTEL (ORTELIUS).

"*Presbeteri Johannes sive Abbissinorum imperii descripto*" on a frame surmounted by a head of Neptune. In the top left-hand corner is the crest of Prester John, a Lion Rampant supporting a Crucifix.

Inset is a panegyric to David, King of Goa, Caffates, etc., etc., whose pedigree is traced to Solomon. David, the conqueror of the Muslims, was believed to be the son of Prester John and was the name by which the Emperor Jenghis Khan (1162–1227), the conqueror of Mongolia, China and most of Asia, was known.

The Kingdom of Presbiter Johannes or Prester John, the fabulous Christian King in the eleventh century, fascinated European thinkers in the medieval and Renaissance periods. His person was associated with incredible and mythical legends. India, Arabia and China claimed him as well as Africa. According to Marco Polo, he lived in China and was a predecessor of Jenghiz Khan. Pope Alexander III in 1177 addressed a letter to him "*carrissimo in Christo filio Johanni illustrio et magnifico Indorum regi*". Over three centuries later, Vasco da Gama sent a communication to his descendant "Preste Johan" reigning in the interior to obtain a safe passage for his ships sailing up the East Coast. King John II of Portugal in 1495 courted the favour of Prester John of the Indies and his biography was published in 1501. Fra Mauro's map of 1459 (not in the collection) shows his kingdom and his capital at Habbish on the Nile.

The lakes from which the Nile rises, named for the first time Zairi and Zaflan, are said to be inhabited by Syrens and Tritons, a fable which is repeated in many maps. The names given to the lakes are clearly Arabic and are the result of Arabic exploration. A variation of the *regio Amazonorum*, as a description of what is now Northern Rhodesia is "the country unknown to the ancients".

The coast line is more detailed than in previous maps, showing the influence of Ibn-Batuta who had described the cities of Mombasa, Quiloa and Mozambique, now for the first time mentioned. The usual pictures of charging elephants, ostriches and birds are portrayed.

The map is beautifully drawn, and coloured and engraved with elephants, dolphins, and an Arab dhow firing a canon.

(8) 1588.—THE GEOGRAPHIA DI LIVIO SANUTO.

This is the first African atlas. It is divided into twelve books and was published at Venice in 1588 and was written in Italian.

The source of this atlas is mainly the description of Ptolemy. It contains twelve maps drawn after the Ptolemy model, of which the tenth and twelfth illustrate Central Africa. The account of Herodotus is faithfully reproduced, the Nile flowing north from a lake in the interior into the Mediterranean, whilst from the same lake the Rio Spirito Sancto (the early name for the Limpopo—*see map 15*) flows southwards. The comments on places of topographical interest are new and informative. Near the Nile, " It is written that in these mountains are many emeralds ". In the kingdom of the Christian Emperor, Presbyter Johannes, are shown the Nemus Ecclesiae, and the Mons Mortis, " From which condemned persons are thrown " and in the lakes " Marine men have been seen ".

The twelfth chapter (page 139 *et seq.*) concerns Ethiopia inferior and contains an early account of what was known of the country at that date. Of Zimbabwe it is written that " It is not the work of humans but the devil, and they affirm that this building is of much greater perfection than the fortress of the Portuguese by the sea ". " Over the door," Sanuto continues, " of this building is an inscription like an epitaph written in a language which cannot be recognised by any one of any nation." In Scefala " The Moors, speaking the Arabic language, have lived for a long time for the trade in gold which they carry on with the tribes of the interior." Of the customs of the natives it is written, " They believe in one God only, who is called by them Mozimu, and they have no idols nor anything that they worship."

(9) 1591.—FILIPO PIGAFETTA.

Relatione del reame di Congo et delle circonvicine contrade tratta dalli scritti e ragionamente di Odoardo Lopez, Portoghese, per Filipo Pigafetta, Rome, 7, August, 1591. This volume is of 82 pages and contains ten chapters and two maps. There is an English translation by Abraham Hartwell, dated 1597. It is prefaced by a foreword to the Archbishop of Canterbury.

Pigafetta, born in 1533, was an Italian historian and chamberlain to Pope Sixtus V. His information was derived from Odoardo Lopez, a Portuguese traveller who, between 1578 and 1587, made an extensive exploration of the Congo, and afterwards became Ambassador at the Court of Madrid. He related his experiences to Pigafetta in 1588.

His maps are supposed to demonstrate that he was aware of Lakes Tanganyika and Victoria Nyanza. What he really did was to transpose the lakes of Ptolemy from positions parallel to each other on the east and west, to positions vertically north and south of each other in the centre of the continent. It is no more true to assert that Pigafetta's southern lake is Lake Tanganyika than it is to identify Ptolemy's Lake Zaflan with Lake Tanganyika. But Pigafetta's northern lake, situated, according to his own description, on the Equator, corresponds in latitude, though not in longitude, with Lake Victoria Nyanza. This wide divergence from Sanuto's map, published three years earlier, is, however, noteworthy, but subsequent cartographers persisted in following Sanuto and it was not until the middle of the nineteenth century that Pigafetta's orientation of the lakes was adopted, as a result of English exploration.

Pigafetta unhesitatingly discarded Ptolemy's Mountains of the Moon, but no less arbitrarily substituted for them the wholly fictitious Sierras Caffates and elsewhere the Mountains of Silver, Chrystal and Saltpetre (*sal nitrum*).

Having demolished Ptolemy's theories of the source of the Nile, he precipitated himself into even more stupendous errors regarding the topography of the principal rivers. The Nile, the Congo, the Cuamo (Zambezi) and " monstrous rivers flowing south ", apparently the Sabi and the Limpopo, are all made to rise in the southern lake, which his eulogists have identified with Tanganyika.

Pigafetta is on much surer ground when describing the peoples and their customs. He relates divertingly how the King of the Congo (that personage whom later Portuguese writers styled " The Marquis ") was baptised a Christian to the satisfaction of the consciences of fifteenth century catholicism. Monomatapa in the east submitted to the same illusory ceremony. He debates the probability of Sofala being the source of King Solomon's gold, and after recording that " the Mahommedans trafficked there in small barkes from Arabia Felix ", dismisses the subject with the comment " A thing in truth not very unlikely ". He adds that there are " many buildings of great work and singular architecture of stone and of lime and of timber, the like whereof are not to be seen in all the provinces adjoining," a description which should be compared with Sanuto's conclusion about Zimbabwe that it was the work of the devil rather than of man.

His observations in Chapter XI on Natural History are usually most accurate and often amusing. He dilates at length on the elephant, whose life he computes to be 150 years. Among the many curious habits of this docile beast is that of " gathering the skin together and so nipping poor flies to death between the wrinkles ". Serpents are recorded which " carrie upon the tippe of their tails a certain little roundel like a bell, which ringeth as they go." There are also " creatures as big as rams, having wings like dragons, with long tails and long chappes and diverse rowes of teeth and feede on raw flesh. Their colour is blew and greene, their skinne bepaynted like skales, and two feete have they but no more ". But the largest bird is the Eastrich (ostrich), the plumes of which, intermingled with those of the peacock, are much coveted.

(10) Ascribed to 1592.—Probably Dutch School.

" *Ethiopia Superior vel interior vulgo Abyssinorum sive Presibiteri Johannis imperium.*"

The title piece is supported by the figures of a man and a woman in Abyssinian costume. On the top are two negroid babies. The map does not extend beyond the 15° of south latitude. It closely resembles the 1572 Ortelius but the coast line is shown in greater detail. The usual pictures of charging elephants, ostriches, and birds are portrayed.

(11) CIRCA 1627.—JOHN SPEED.

" Africa described, the manners of their habits and buildings newly done into English by I.S.", drawn by Abraham Goos, and sold by Tho. Basset in Fleet Street and Richard Chiswell in St. Paul's Churchyard. I.S. are the initials of John Speed, one of the greatest of the English map makers. In 1627, he published his " Prospect of the most famous Parts of the World ", the first printed general atlas by an Englishman. This is the first English map of Africa.

On the top margin are plans in perspective of the principal coastal fortresses, e.g., Ceuta, Alexandria, Mozambique, etc., and in the margins to left and right are ethnological figures of the different peoples inhabiting Africa. There are, for instance, the native woman from the Cape of Good Hope, apparently smoking a hookah, and the male from the Congo with a headdress of feathers, and belts of beads.

On the reverse is a description in English of the people. Abyssinia even in the seventeenth century was said to be ruled by " one of the mightiest Emperors in the world ", Presbyter John, whose kingdom extended south to the Mountains of the Moon. In Aethiopia inferior the Kingdom of Monomatapa is of most interest to Northern Rhodesia. " Of Monomatapa in which is reported to be three thousand mines of gold. Here there live a kind of Amazons, as valiant as men. Their King is served in great pomp and hath a guard of two hundred mastives." Of the natives in the basin of the Congo it is said, " the inhabitants are in some part Christians, but in other bye Provinces Anthropophagi, and have shambles of man's flesh as we have for meat. They kill their own children in the birth, to avoid the trouble of breeding them and preserve their nation with stolen brats from their neighbouring countries."

(12) 1630.—JODOCUS HONDIUS.

Nova Africae Tabula. The inscription is on a ship's bowsprit, and it is printed in Amsterdam.

During the early part of the seventeenth century Holland was pre-eminent for its map makers, and Antwerp and Amsterdam the chief centres of publication. This map of Jodocus Hondius is an admirable example of Dutch technique. Hondius had purchased the plates from his famous predecessor Mercator and produced his maps on Mercator's projection. The example in the Museum series is beautifully drawn and the pictures of marine monsters and a variety of sailing craft are delicately depicted. The source of the Nile in the Mountains of the Moon is now transferred further south, and it is probable that about this time they become confused with the great range of hills in Northern Rhodesia now known as the Muchinga escarpment, which in later maps are styled the backbone of the world. Near the point where the rivers Zuama and Rio Spirito converge is Castrum Portugal, which must have been the furthest point in the interior to which the Portuguese at this date had penetrated.

Monomatapa from this time finds a place on African maps. The name is popularly interpreted to mean " lord of the mines ", but the Portuguese understood it to mean merely king or ruler. Dos Santos writing in 1616 described him as merely " a Caffre chief living in a Caffre village ", but the Viceroy of India addressed him in 1719 as " the most illustrious among all the great princes of Africa ". In 1560, the Monomatapa of the period was baptised a Christian, and in 1569 completely annihilated (with the aid of malaria) the strong Portuguese army under Barreto. He was ruler over a vast kingdom extending from the Indian Ocean to the Kalahari.

A new contribution of Hondius is Zachaf Lake, where an unnamed river (obviously the Zambezi) has its source. Zachaf is another Arabic intrusion.

The Equator assumes its approximately correct latitude.

(13) 1633.—MERCATOR THE YOUNGER.

Africa ex magna orbis terre descriptione Gerardi Mercatoris desumpta studio et industria. G.M. junioris. Ascribed to the year 1633, it is a copy of an earlier map by his more famous father. Above the panel are the figures of two satyrs.

This is the son of the famous Mercator (1512–1594) whose real name was Kreemer. He is best known for his invention of what is commonly known as Mercator's projection or the projection of meridians as equidistant and parallel lines, so that latitudinal and longitudinal lines are rectangular. Mercator had attempted this projection in 1556, but navigators declined to make use of it. It was not until Edward Wright compiled tables for the construction of the projection that it became popular. Writing of this projection in 1610, he said, " Some will have Mercator to be the first author, who though he hath well deserved of geographie, yet should not Ptolimee be wronged herein, who in the I Chapter of the 2 booke of his geographie teacheth us that we may make maps with aequidistant meridians and straight parallels . . ."[1]

Mercator was born in Flanders but spent most of his life in the Spanish Court under the patronage of the Emperor Charles V, where his son succeeded him. The lucidity which he gave to his maps made him immensely popular, and the projection named after him, though now generally discarded, has not to this day been improved upon. In this map, however, a different projection is employed.

There are few novelties in topography and the map follows in the main the usual Ptolemy features, but no names are given to his lakes. The source of the Nile is extended, following the calculation of Herodotus to latitude 30° south, and rising in what is now the Drakensberg flows through the lakes Zachaf and Zairi to its delta in the Mediterranean.

---

1 Bodleian Quarterly Record, Vol. VIII, No. 92.

(14) 1655.—NICHOLAS SANSON.

Basse Aethiopiae qui comprend les royaumes du Congo Costo et pays des cafres Empires du Monomatapa et Monoemugi, by Nicholas Sanson, Geographer in Ordinary to the King, dated 1655. The Sanson map of 1655 inaugurated the epoch of the great French geographers. The French school for the next century achieved a continental reputation which was enhanced by the courageous policy and punctilious accuracy of de Lisle and the d'Anville School. Sanson (1600–1667), born in Abbeville, was tutor in geography successively to Louis XIII and Louis XIV and was associated in his business with his two sons Guillaume and Adrien. There are no meridianal lines or parallels of latitude. A reversion is here made to the main Ptolemy characteristics : the source of the Nile in the Drakensberg Mountains introduced by Mercator is now discarded in favour of its fountain in the old Ptolemy lakes and the Montes Lunae. The Monoemugi have been identified with the Anyamwezi who live round the shores of Lake Tanganyika and the country west of Zanzibar. Here they are shown in the mountainous country south of the Nile Lakes. The boundaries of Monomatapa's kingdom are shown as extending south of the Orange River and as including the basin of the Upper Zambezi.

(15) 1666.—PHILIP CHETWIND.

Africae descriptio nova by Philip Chetwind, 1666. An uncoloured map full of intricate detail. Its new feature is the separation of the Cuama (Zambezi) from the Rio de Spirito Sancto (Limpopo) which are now shown as distinct rivers. Reverting to Ptolemy the source of the Zambezi is now in the Mountains of the Moon instead of Lake Zachaf. Elephants, monstrous birds, a lion and a hyaena are depicted in the continent and a variety of curious aquatic monsters in the ocean.

(16 AND 17) 1669.—RICHARD BLOME.

There are two maps, both in colour, by Richard Blome (*fl.* 1660–1705). both being transcriptions of Sanson maps. Blome achieved note as a geographer at this period. In 1670, he published a geographical description of the "Four parts of the World", and in 1673 "Britannia". The larger of the two maps is entitled "*A new Map of Africa designed by Mons. Sanson, geographer to the French King rendered into English and illustrated with figures by Richard Blome by the King's special command,* 1699 ". It is dedicated to Henry, Duke of Dorchester, whose coat of arms is depicted in the lower left-hand corner. It is a close copy of the Sanson map of 1655 and contains no improvements on it.

The second Blome map is drawn to a smaller scale. It is entitled "*A Map of the Higher and Lower Aethiopia comprehending ye several Kingdoms . . .*" Like the preceding map, it is a reproduction of a Sanson map, and is dedicated to the Hon. Sir Robert Viner of London, Alderman, Knight and Baronet. Like the preceding example it follows the topography introduced by Sanson.

(18) 1669.—NICHOLAS SANSON.

L'Afrique by Sanson, dated 1669, is not a good shape of Africa. It introduces a new feature which was copied by geographers for the next thirty years : between the Zambezi which is here called the River Indires and the Rio de Spirito Sancto or Limpopo is introduced the Zembere River. The Zembere and the Rio de Spirito Sancto become united below their source in Lake Zachaf, as formerly did the Cuama and the Rio de Spirito Sancto.

(19) 1680.—WILLIAM BERRY.

"*Africa divided according to the extent of its principal parts in which are distinguished one from the other the Empires, Monarchies, Kingdoms, states and peoples which at this time inhabit Africa.*"

It is dedicated to Charles II by William Berry. The title is decorated with figures of Neptune, with mermaids, animals and cornucopiae. It was on sale by William Berry at the Sign of the Globe between Charing Cross and Whitehall and is dated 1680. It is stated to be after Sanson with improvements, but there is no Sanson map in the collection even approximating to this for its up-to-date information. This is a beautiful map, well drawn, clearly printed, and distinctly coloured. There is an absence of that superabundance of place names in the interior, which had no foundation in fact beyond the inaccurate reports of Arab traders. While it retains the usual Ptolemy features of Lakes Zairi and Zaflan, it follows the departure, initiated by Chetwind, of separating the Rivers Limpopo and Zambezi. But its great claim to distinction is that the Portuguese discoveries on the Zambezi in the later sixteenth and seventeenth centuries are for the first time incorporated in a map of Africa. The mountain range which from mythical times had been called the Mountains of the Moon is now unnamed, but a spur, as a result of Portuguese discoveries, is now called Serras d'Lupata (below the Kebrabasa Rapids). Zambezi supersedes Cuama as the name of the great river and it has its source approximately where Livingstone stands to-day, that is to say at the base of the curve before it turns northwards into Barotseland, a country which at this time was still unknown and unnamed. In the country of Sacumbe (Chief Chikumbi), Chicova, the site of the silver mines which the Portuguese fought hard to discover, is marked, and below it the Zambezi expands into a lake. The silver mines of Chicova are one of the world's mysteries. That silver ore and silver objects were produced by natives is undeniable ; Bocarro speaks of 1,000 lb. weight of ore, and of every house in Tete being furnished with silver plate. From 1607 onwards expeditions to discover the mines were frequent, but to this day they have eluded prospectors. Sena, built about 1540, and Tete, founded in 1590, are now, nearly a century later, recorded on the map.

PLATE I WOODCUT-MAP OF AFRICA—BY SEBASTIAN MUNSTER,
1540.

PLATE II AFRICA—FROM THE ATLAS OF ORTELIUS, 1570—
ATTRIBUTED TO JOHANNES LEO.

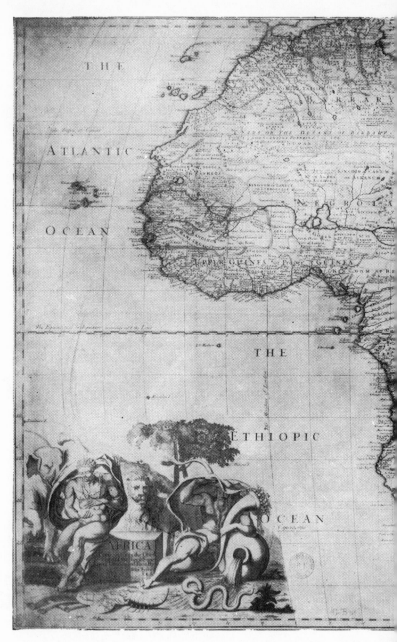

PLATE III AFRICA—B

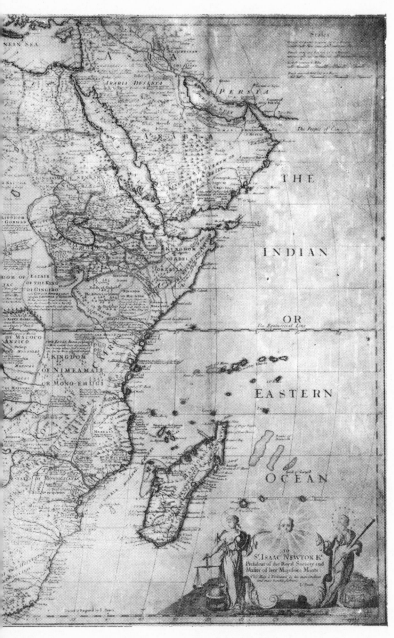

NEAN SEA

A...

ARABIA DESERTA

PERSIA

The Tropic of Cancer

THE

INDIAN

OR

The Equinoctial Line

EASTERN

OCEAN

KINGDOM
OF GONDAR

DOM OF ESTATE
OF THE KING
OF SINGIRO

DE MACOCO
ANZICO

KINGDOM
OF NIMEAMAIE
OR MONO-EMUGI

St ISAAC NEWTON Kt
President of the Royal Society and
Master of her Majestys Mints

Scales

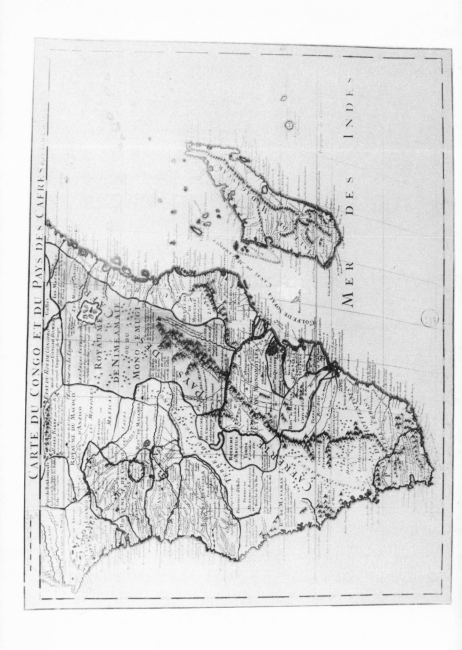

PLATE IV SOUTHERN AFRICA—BY G. DE LISLE, 1708.

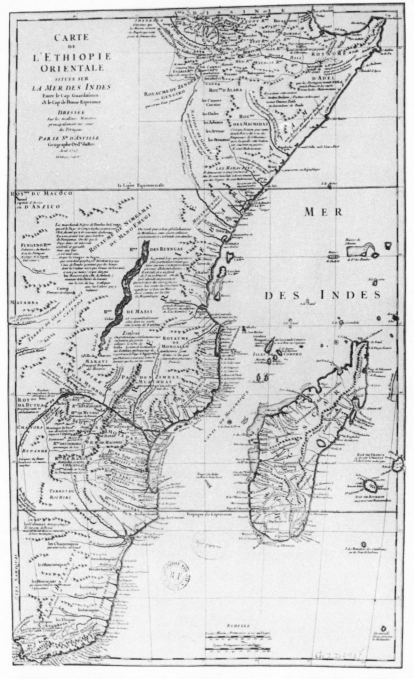

PLATE V EAST AND SOUTH EAST AFRICA—BY D'ANVILLE, 1727.

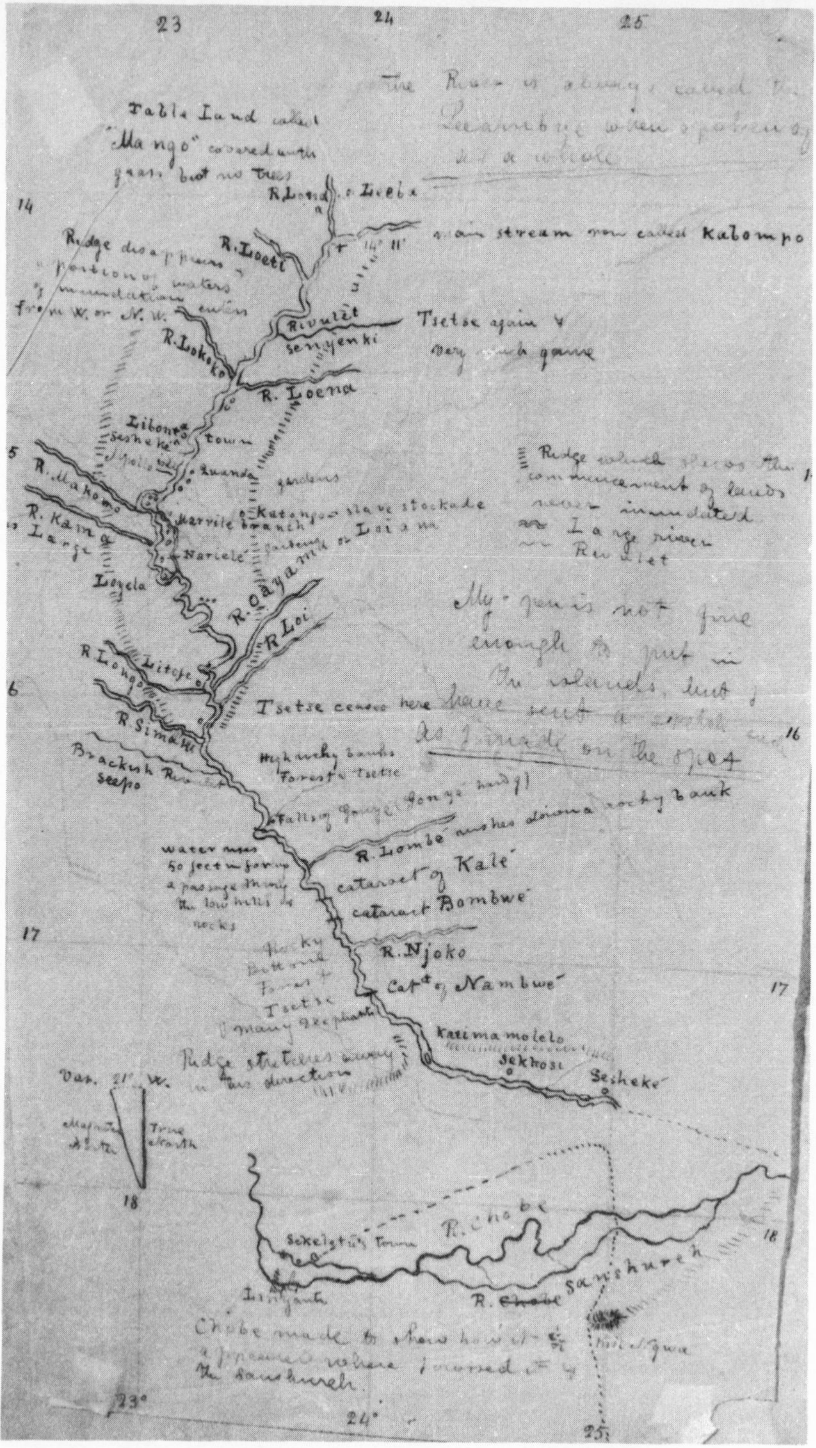

PLATE VI HOLOGRAPH MAP OF PART OF THE UPPER ZAMBEZI
VALLEY—BY DAVID LIVINGSTONE, 1853.

(20) 1682.—JOHN OGILBY.

"*An Accurate Description and complete history of Africa, containing an account of the origin of the various nations inhabiting that extensive portion of the globe, their peculiar habits, manners and religious customs and ceremonies. Forming a curious and entertaining collection of adventures and discoveries made by Ancient and Modern Navigators who have visited those barbarous shores,*" by John Ogilby, London. Printed for Thomas Jackson at the sign of the Golden Key in Fleet Street, over against Saint Dunstan's Church, 1682. This is the fourth edition, the first having been published in 1670.

John Ogilby (1600–1676) had an extremely versatile career, being a bookseller, translator, printer, dancing master, theatre owner, Master of the King's Revels, and finally a geographer. His contribution to cartography was a valuable one and he revolutionised the printed map. His historical and geographical account of Africa was handsomely printed in folio size with numerous maps and plates, well engraved and extremely decorative.[1]

The book contains one general map of Africa, while each of the main areas is shown on a separate map : there are eleven such maps which are of the seventeenth century Dutch school. Ogilby took his description mainly from the classical writers and from Sanuto and Pigafetta, as well as from the Portuguese historians dos Santos, de Barros and others. It seems unlikely, however, that he was conversant with Andrew Battell's account of Angola published by Purchas in 1613, and his description of this part of the continent closely follows Pigafetta, even to the inclusion of the fictitious Lake Aquilunda. Included in the section on West and South Africa are descriptions and engravings of natives panning for gold, of the *mwave* poison test for witchcraft, of musical instruments, bark cloth, methods of transport by *machila* and various other details concerning the Bantu inhabitants of those parts of the continent. Of the inhabitants of the Congo and Angola it is said, "Although some of them be surly and proud, yet in general they carry themselves very friendly towards strangers, being of a mild conversation, courteous, affable and easie to be overcome with reasons ; yet inclined to drink, especially Spanish wine and brandy." Speaking of the climate of Angola, he says, "The unwholesomeness of the air breeds divers sicknesses, especially violent and burning fevers, which kill in a few hours, unless prevented by frequent Phlebotomy." That the slave trade was already established on the west coast is seen in a reference which says, "The chiefest trade of Portuguese and other whites consists in slaves, carried from thence by shipping to several places in the West Indies."

Below Banguella is "Kaffrarie, or the country of the Kaffirs, otherwise called Hottentots", and the names of such Hottentot tribes as the Namaquas and Gorachonquas are recorded.

---

1 Tooley, R. V., *Maps and Map-makers*, London, 1949, pp. 53 and 54.

In his description of Zimbabwe Ogilby repeats Sanuto, who in turn obtained his information from Portuguese sources. There is continual reference to the East Coast trade in gold, silver, copper and ivory which were exchanged mainly for cloth and beads of various kinds.

Ogilby also has a reference, which is repeated on the d'Anville map of 1727, to a great lake lying between the east and west coasts, about the 7° or 8° south latitude, at which traders from both coasts met—it is possible that this may be identified with Lake Tanganyika. The lake is said to lie to the south-east of the Kingdom of Makoko, which is placed on the map to the north of the Congo River in the approximate position of Stanleypool, and the kingdom of Monoemugi (Nyamwezi). Black merchants from Makoko traded with the Portuguese settlements on the east coast. The lake is said to be more than sixty days' going from the coast. On the islands on the west side lived "blacks", but from the east side "sometimes in boats there came Tauny-men, and by chance Blacks, yet the sides of the lake are possessed by persons yellowish, with lank or uncurled hair hanging down at length, who daily come to trade with the aforementioned islands." The country between the lake and the east coast is said to be "exceeding fruitful" but no "Christian hath ever penetrated thus far, nor indeed are willing, partly because of the desolate and untrodden ways thereof, and partly for the intemperance of the air ; but principaly for fear of the Jages the cruellest and most inhumane people, which keep there in great multitudes."

Ogilby's maps are on the whole disappointing, as he has made little or no attempt to bring them up to date in accordance with his information.

(21) CIRCA 1680.—FREDERICK DE WITT.

Novissima et perfectissima Africae descriptio by Frederick de Witt of Amsterdam, coloured but not dated.

The inscription is framed by pictures of Arabs on the left and of negroes on the right, bearing tusks of ivory. A boy holding a parasol over his head is depicted riding an elephant, from which it may be inferred that the domestication of the African elephant was, as Pigafetta mentions, practised at this time. The map is similar to most maps of the period, and does not diverge from the orthodox type of Ptolemy.

(22) BETWEEN 1680 AND 1689.—JOHN OVERTON.

A new map of Africa divided into Kingdoms and Provinces, sold by I. Overton at the White Horse without Newgate and by Philip Lea at the Atlas and Hercules, in the Poultry near Cheapside.

The decorative title-piece and the geography are an exact replica of the above map. It was probably drawn by de Witt for the English market and sold at Overton's publishing house.

(23) 1690.—Nikolaus Visscher.

Africae accurata tabula ex officina Nic. Visscher. The inscription is enclosed in a decorative frame, formed by two negro slaves, one holding a scorpion, the other a cornucopia, standing on the prostrate bodies of two women. It is dedicated to Gerard Schaep. The pictures of Neptune and the mermaids show it to have originated in Amsterdam. The Visschers were an important Dutch family of map publishers who worked all through the seventeenth century.

The map, which is ascribed to 1690, appears to be based on one of Sanson's prints and is, apart from its colouring and decorative title, of no particular merit.

(24) Circa 1690.—Jacobus Meursius.

Africae accurata tabula ex officina Jacobum Meursium. Undated, but reproduced from Ogilby's Atlas. The decorative engraving round the title-piece showing negroes standing on prostrate women is similar to that of the Visscher map, of which it is an uncoloured copy. Both are possibly of an earlier date than that attributed to them. It is full of detail, much of which is valueless.

(25 and 26) 1690 and 1692.—Hubert Jaillot.

L'Afrique by Sanson, dedicated to the King (Louis XIV) by Hubert Jaillot, dated 1690. The topography follows the stereotyped examples of recent geographers. This is the second map in the collection to show the position of the Portuguese settlements on the Zambezi.

1692. *L'Afrique by Sanson*, presented to the Dauphin by Jaillot—a similar map in colour, dated 1692.

(27) 1700.—de Lisle.

L'Afrique dressé sur les observations de Messrs. de l'Académie Royale des Sciences by de Lisle (1675–1725) who was employed with d'Anville (1697–1782). De Lisle was geographer successively to Louis XIV and Louis XV and is known to have produced no less than 134 maps. He has been called the father of modern geography and made the greatest improvements to the map of African since Ptolemy. He was scientific in his methods, and availed himself of all the latest information. He was the first to depart from the orthodox features of Ptolemy, and for the first time the Lakes Zairi and Zaflan are expunged from the map. The Nile is now made to rise in Abyssinia, as Perez had reported in 1616, being acquainted only with the Blue Nile. The Zambezi or Empondo still rises in the south among the gold mines, as depicted by geographers for the last twenty years. The Congo, which up to this date had its source in Lake Zairi, now rises in the centre of the continent.

[237]

The Portuguese towns on the Zambezi, Sena, Tete and Chicova which appeared in the maps of Berry and Sanson in 1680 now received a permanent place. North of the river there is far more detail. Mount Chiri and the Lupata Mountains and the Mangania River (the river of the Manganja people), now known as Shire, find a place on the map. In the country east of the Luangwa River are the Mumbos and Zimbas, that horde of cannibals who towards the end of the sixteenth century appeared north of the Zambezi, annihilated the Portuguese forces at Tete, forced Sena to capitulate, opposed the garrison at Mozambique and devastated the coast as far as Mombasa. According to Da Conto's (1543–1616) monumental work " Da Asia ", " large armies of Caffirs descended in the year 1570 from the Rivers Cuama, Zairi and the Nile, and were joined on the way by Ambois and Macabires ". In the country now known as Barotseland are the Jagas or Giachas, and the Monemugi are still placed in the region of the Zambezi, following the error of previous geographers.

(28 AND 29) ASCRIBED TO 1704.—EDGAR WELLS.

A new map of Libya or Old Afrik showing its general divisions, most remarkable countries or people, cities, towns, rivers, mountains, etc., dedicated to His Highness William Duke of Gloucester and engraved by Spofforth. The authorship of the map is not stated but it is attributed to Wells and ascribed to 1704.

In shape and topographical detail this appears to be a reproduction of a sixteenth century Munster map. In spite of its comprehensive title it is singularly deficient in detail. Rivers and mountains are unnamed and there is only one town, Rapta, marked south of the Equator. The southern part of Africa is denoted " Unknown to the Ancients " and the regional divisions such as " Troglodytae " or " Cinamomifera regio " are reminiscent of a remote cartographical era.

About 1704 were produced two maps in one frame, copies of the above but uncoloured, and entitled " *A new Map of Libya or Old Afrik* ". The second map shows the boundaries of the Kingdom of Monomatapa and has a more deeply hatched outline.

(30 AND 31) DE LISLE.

Carte de l'Egypte de la Nubie et de l'Abyssinie by de Lisle, dated November, 1707. This is a map of Abyssinia and does not extend south of the Equator. The source of the Nile is placed in a lake about the twelfth parallel of north latitude, which though unnamed is clearly Tsana from which the Blue Nile rises, as was discovered by Perez and confirmed by Lopo at the beginning of the seventeenth century. The source of the White Nile is entirely ignored.

The *Carte du Congo et du Pays des Caffres*, by de Lisle dated January, 1708, is a continuation of the above, projected south of the Equator. A new feature in this map is the omission of the two rivers Zembere and Rio de Spirito Sancto which had a common source according to previous geographers. A new river, the Rio de Lorenco Marques is substituted, which is identifiable with the Limpopo.

The Mountains of the Moon are replaced by a range orientated in a north-easterly direction and intersecting the Zambezi, called the Lupata or l'Epine du Monde. This range corresponds in position with the Muchinga escarpment which, dividing the Congo from the Zambesi Basin, might appropriately be called by natives " The backbone of the World ".

The Zambezi, Empondo or Cuama, as it is described, has its source in the south among the gold fields of Butua. There are conflicting opinions as to what the word " cataract " denotes. It has been argued that this is the first record of the Victoria Falls, the discovery of which is generally attributed to David Livingstone in 1855. On the other hand its topographical position, situated between the Portuguese settlements of Tete and Chicova, suggests the Kebrabasa Rapids, which for many miles impeded the navigation of the Zambezi between these places.

(32) 1710.—H. Moll.

This *Map of Africa according to the newest and most exact observations* by H. Moll, geographer, was printed for Thos. Bowles by Philip Overton and John King. It is dedicated to Charles, Earl of Peterborrow and Monmouth (1662–1735), the general of the audacious campaigns in Spain during the wars of the Austrian succession, " the last of the Knight Errants ", as he was called by Macaulay. Encircling the inscription are engravings of a horseman pursuing an ostrich, a negro capturing a crocodile, an elephant, and a languid native chief. Inset are plans of the forts at Cape Coast Castle, St. Helena and the Cape of Goode Hope. In the last are shown Table Mountain, Sugar Loaf and Lyons Rump, under those names, and a plan of the slaughter house, lodging house, hospital, etc., in a nascent but recognisable Cape Town. A novelty in this map are sailing directions, the course of the current, and the monsoons. The reluctance of geographers to depart from what were believed to be the inviolable principles of Ptolemy is illustrated by the retention of " The Bogs or Morasses " of Zaflan and Zairi, which more enterprising geographers had discarded ten years previously. Moll has adopted de Lisle's example of excising the White Nile.

(33) 1714.—van der Aa.

L'Afrique selon les nouvelles observations de Messrs de l'Academie des Sciences. A Liède, Chez van der Aa. The title-piece is decorated by a negro woman on the left slenderly clothed, from whose lap an elephant is eating corn, and on the right by pictures of a lion, elephant, snakes, etc.

[239]

The author has followed de Lisle in ascribing the source of the Nile to Abyssinia, and disconnecting it from the Ptolemy Lakes which, however, are still shown in their pristine positions of the sixteenth century. The Indires, which in Seutter's map of *circa* 1740 is a tributary to the southern bank of the Zambezi, first occurs here as an alternative name for the Zambezi itself, and to the town of Sena is given the second name of Fort Martial. The Zimbas are now placed south instead of north of the Zambezi, an illuminating historical note of the progress of the migration of this tribe to their ultimate destination of Northern Natal. The author prudently remarks of the interior of Africa, " I would rather show this part of Africa as unknown and unhabited than supply my own imagination ". Other geographers might with advantage have followed his advice.

The map is accompanied by a text by Ferrarius written in Latin.

(34 AND 35) ASCRIBED TO 1720.—JOHN SENEX.

Africa corrected from the observations of the Royal Society of London and Paris by John Senex, F.R.S., dedicated to Sir Isaac Newton, K.E., President of the Society and Master of Her Majesty's Mint, undated, but ascribed to 1720. Isaac Newton (1642–1727) was president of the Royal Society in 1703 and re-elected every year until his death. He was knighted in 1705 and created Master of the Mint in 1695, an office which he held for the rest of his life. The dedication suggests that he was holding this post under Queen Anne, at the time the map was produced. The topography is based on the later de Lisle maps : the tradition of Ptolemy is abandoned, and the Portuguese discoveries inserted, but there is little advance on the more recent continental maps. As usual much curious information is derived from the commentaries appended to the place names. Of the Hensaquas, a people inhabiting the country of the Griquas, it is said, " This nation makes use of Lyons in fighting ". At the source of the Buffalo River is the note " This river is said to have no end." The Zimbas in what is now Nyasaland are " Anthropophagi or men-eaters who pay divine worship to their King ", and Mount Chiri (near the Shire River) is aptly described as " very fertile and populous ". John Cassangi becomes established at the headwaters of the Cuneni River about this period. His town was a famous market for traders in transit from the interior, and was the limit of Portuguese exploration from the West Coast. Seventy years later Cassangi was an embarrassment to the Portuguese on account of the embargo he placed upon trade between Mwatayamvu and the west coast. There is also a second map by John Senex, of the same date and a duplicate of the one described.

(36) ASCRIBED TO 1720.—THE WIDOW OF NICKOLAUS VISSCHER.

Carte de l'Afrique méridional ou pays entre la ligne et le cap de bonne espérance et l'Isle de Madégascar, by the widow of Nickolaus Visscher, who drew the map of 1690 (*q.v.*).

[240]

The map itself is a copy of the de Lisle map of 1707 but the outline and boundaries are depicted in colours. It is distinguished from that map only by the inset plans of Table Bay, False Bay and the Cape of Good Hope.

(37) 1722.—DE LISLE.

Carte d'Afrique by de Lisle dated 1722. This is the first dated map to show Lake Maravi afterwards known as Lake Nyasa. In his map of 1700 de Lisle had recorded the Mangania River, the outlet from Lake Maravi and the home of the Manganja (Maravi) people. As with most innovations of this period, the credit of introducing this lake into the n ,p of Africa belongs to de Lisle. It had been discovered a century earlier by Gaspar Bocarro, in 1616, who by making the overland journey from Tete to Mozambique accomplished something new in the annals of exploration, and made the first historical record of Lake Nyasa. The adjoining country is shown as the Kingdom of Massay (Mwase, the Chewa Chief) of whom a fuller description has been given by Manoel Boretta in 1667. The descendants of " Massay " are still rulers of the same country to-day. The map, therefore, is the first to exhibit a distribution of native tribes bearing some relation to that of modern times.

(38) 1727.—JEAN BAPTISTE BOURGUIGNON D'ANVILLE.

" *Carte de l'Ethiope Orientale Située sur la mer des Indes entre le cap Guardafouis et le cap de Bonne Espèrance dressée sur les meilleurs mémoirs principalement sur ceux des Portugais.*" Perhaps the greatest geographical author of the eighteenth century, one of d'Anville's main objects was to reform geography by putting an end to the blind copying of older maps by testing the commonly accepted position of places through a rigorous examination of all the descriptive authorities and by excluding from cartography every name inadequately supported. Vast spaces which had before been covered with countries and cities were thus suddenly reduced almost to a blank.

This is a very important map and is the most accurate of any prior to the nineteenth century. It is based on the de Lisle but included a number of notes not found in the earlier map. Lake Nyasa " *le lac du Maravi* " is shown in greater detail than before, and identified with the hitherto hypothetical lake Zembere. Of the Zimbas it is said that " *on prétend que c'est la même race ou nation qui porte ailleurs le nom de Gallas* "—a suggestion perhaps that they were predominantly of Hamitic rather than Negro extraction. The " *Pays des Mumbos* " (Mambo being the hereditary title of the Rozwi Chiefs) is shown to the north-east of the Kebrabasa Rapids, though in 1693 this tribe under their chief Changawire swept over what is now Southern Rhodesia, destroying the Portuguese settlements on the Zambezi as far as Sena, on the west.

The capital of the " Giagas " (to be identified to-day with the Bayaka) is shown as " Casangi ". Although no lake is shown on the map an important note strongly suggests a record of the

[241]

conjectured existence of Lake Tanganyika and of the trade with the East Coast. This lake is placed somewhere to the east of the Kingdom of Nimeamai or Mona-Mugi to the north-west of Lake Nyasa. The note says "*Les marchands nègres de Pombo de Congo qui est le Pays de Congo le plus avancé vers l'est, disent qu'à 60 journées de chez eux il y a un grand lac qui est a l'est de Nimeami. On dit que le pays dans cet intervale est fertile et agréable, mais, que l'air y est mal sain, et que les Giagas ou Jagas qui sont Anthropophages désolent le pays. Ceux de Pombo ajoutent que des hommes dont la couleur n'est que brune ou bazanée et non pas noire (ce qui désigne les Maures de la côte de Mélinde) viennent de la partie du Levant sur le rive du lac trafiquer avec les cafres qui y habitent.*"

Of "*le lac de Maravi*" it is said that it is full of islands which are inhabited, that the water is salt and very shallow. This description can hardly be applied to Lake Nyasa, except perhaps at its southern end, but a reference to the strong westerly winds which blow there during March and April, and to the abundance of fish and food is certainly true. The Zambezi is accurately shown as far as Chicova. Of this river it is said "*L'origine du fleuve Zambèze est encore inconnue*".

(39) ASCRIBED TO 1730.—HENRY OVERTON.

To her Sacred Majesty Caroline, Queen of Great Britain, France and Ireland, this map of Africa after the latest and best observations is most humbly dedicated by Your Majesty's most obedient servant Henry Overton. It was sold by Overton at the White Horse without Newgate. This map has been ascribed to 1750, but since Caroline was the Queen of George II only from 1727 to her death in 1737, it may more accurately be attributed to about 1730. This uninspired map so far from incorporating the latest and best observations, reproduces all the fallacies common to the maps of the early seventeenth century. The conservatism of English geographers at this time is exemplified by the retention of the old Ptolemy lakes deleted by de Lisle, and of the fantastic Arabic names Zembre, Zaflan and Zachaf still appended to imaginary spaces of water. The Portuguese explorations of the previous two hundred years are omitted, and even the shape of the continent is a discredit to English map-making. The engraver, however, has concentrated all his art on the pictures in the margin. On the left hand are depicted episodes of native life from the pyramids to the Cape, and on the right hand plans of the principal fortresses of Africa of which two are dated 1727.

(40) CIRCA 1730.—DE LISLE.

Carte d'Afrique by Guillaume de Lisle published in Amsterdam by Covens and C. Mortier.

Its caption is *Africa accurate in imperia regna status et populos divisa ad usum Lodovici XV, Galliarum regis*, undated. This is a posthumous reproduction of an earlier de Lisle map of Africa, printed by an Amsterdam firm, and ascribed to the year 1730. It is a close copy of the 1722 de Lisle map and shows the Lake Maravi.

(41) 1737.—JOHN MATTHEW HAS.

Africa secundum legitimas projectionis stereographicae regulas by John Matthias Hassius, after Johannes Leo, the Nubian geographer and other ancient writers. The map is coloured, probably German, and ascribed to the early part of the eighteenth century.

The continent is defined in areas according to religions. It includes the Lacus Grandis Maravi, the Maravi Urbs and regnum Maravi, and the information may have been obtained from a de Lisle map, probably that of 1722. Notes are made on different places marked on the map. The country of the Butua bears the legend *"Quod auriferum dicitur"*. The Zambezi *"Cujus fons ignorat"* rises in the south instead of the north and to Chicova is appended the epithet *" Argenti ferax "*.

(42) CIRCA 1740.—MATTHEW SEUTTER.

Africa juxta navigationes et observationes recentissimas aucta, correcta et in sua regna et status divisa in lucem edita a Matthaeo Seuttero. A German map, undated, but ascribed to 1740. The title is adorned with palms and pyramids, crocodiles, lions and snakes, surmounted by a fire-breathing dragon. The Nile is made by Seutter to rise in the south, whence it circumambulates by a tortuous course to Lake Zachaf. The Zembere and Rio de Spirito Sancto form the junction effected for them by previous geographers, but north of the Zembere River is the River Sacumbe, so called after the Chief through whose country it flowed, and identifiable with the Zambezi. From the south enter two tributaries, Cuama and Indires. On it are situated the Portuguese towns of Fort Chicova, Teutta (Tete) and Sena. Below Chicova is a lake named Lacus Ananegacano, a name which is not repeated by later geographers. The whole of this part of the Zambezi is comprised in the kingdom of the Monemugi, in which is an immense forest, situated about the centre of what is now North-East Rhodesia, named Tirut.

(43) 1745.—EMAN BOWEN.

A new and accurate map of the southern parts of Africa by Eman Bowen, more especially concerns the countries of Monomatapa and Zanzibar and the Island of Madagascar. In topography it much resembles the map of John Senex, but there are notable departures. For instance, the lake near Chicova is expunged.

(44 AND 45) 1761-62.—ROBERT DE VAUGONDY.

L'Afrique by Robert de Vaugondy, dated 1761. De Vaugondy was grandson of Nicholas Sanson, who achieved fame as a map maker in the previous century. This map, like the following, is drawn to a small scale and contains little that is new.

[243]

Congo Cafrarie by Robert de Vaugondy, dated 1762. Similar to the 1761 map comprising that part of Africa south of the Equator only.

(46) 1763.—ISAAC TIRION.

Nieuwe Kaart van Africa, by Isaac Tirion, printed in Amsterdam. An acknowledgment in the left-hand bottom corner is made to the original by de Lisle, of which this is a copy, as indeed were most maps of this period. While there are no novel features in this map, it is delicately drawn and coloured, on a small scale.

(47, 48 AND 49) 1770, 1772 AND 1787.—ROBERT SAYER.

A new map of Africa wherein are particularly expressed the European forts and settlements drawn from the most approved geographers with great improvements from the Sieurs d'Anville and Robert, printed by Robert Sayer, undated but ascribed to 1770. The map resembles all others of this period, the only change is an avoidance of over-crowding the interior with place names. The direction of currents and monsoons is adapted from the Moll map of 1770. An affluent to the west bank of the Blue Nile has this commentary, " It is said that in this country are to be seen ruins of many Christian churches ". North of the Coast of Guinea is the note " That the country is inhabited by white men or at least a different kind of people from the blacks " a reference to the lighter skin of the Semitic intrusion.

The second map printed for Robert Sayer, on the 2nd March, 1772, is entitled " *Africa divided into its several regions and laid according to the most exact observations* ".

While adding little that is new, this map is well drawn and finely engraved. In the region of the Nile, one branch " The father water ", rises in Lake Dembea (Tsana), as had now been well established by previous geographers. The " Nile of the Arab Geogra " rises in the Mountains of the Moon and flows through two lakes reminiscent of Ptolemy, but transferred now to 5° north of the Equator. A third branch, "The Nile of the Negroes", has its source in the same range of mountains, but slightly to the west, while yet a fourth affluent, named Gazel River, rises on the borders of Nigritia to the north of the River Senegal. Below their junction the Nile is named the White and Blue River.

In the basin of the Zambezi there is no change beyond the deletion of many fictitious names. A merit of this map is its lucidity, and the absence of numerous unidentifiable and conjectural place names. Lake Aquilonda in the Congo, first mentioned by Pigafetta about 1588, unexpectedly reappears.

" *Africa with all its states, kingdoms, republics, regions, islands, etc., improved and enlarged from d'Anville's map . . .*" by S. Boulton, was printed for Robert Sayer in January, 1787.

[244]

The map comprises only that part of Africa north of the Equator. The course of the Nile follows the previous map, and being on a large scale repays study. The " White River " is said to be larger than that which comes from Abyssinia. The Nile of the Negroes is described " According to Edrisi, named Gir by Ptolemy ", while the western branch is named " Bahr al Gezal or Antelopes River ". In the left margin is a written description of the several regions of Africa.

(50) 1800.—ROBERT WILKINSON.

A new map of Africa including Arabia, the Mediterranean and part of the coast of South America, compiled from the observation of the latest travellers, published 1st January, 1800, by Robert Wilkinson, Cornhill.

Wilkinson's map inaugurated the great era of English map makers, and introduces the greatest improvements since the memorable de Lisle map of 1700. It is published in two sheets each comprising Africa, north and south of the Equator. Wilkinson had availed himself of the explorations of the most recent travellers, e.g., Bruce in Abyssinia, Mungo Park in the Niger regions, Le Vaillant in the Cape of Good Hope and others whose routes are surveyed on the map.

The traverses of James Bruce (1730–1794) left little for further explorers to do in the basin of the Blue Nile, and this part for the first time resembles a modern map of Abyssinia. His claim to have discovered the source of the Nile in Lake Dembea (Tsana) in 1770, while ignoring the discovery of Perez in 1616, was none the less received with complete scepticism by the English public. The explorations of his successor Browne between 1793 and 1796 in Darfur did much to supply some information about what had hitherto been a lacuna in the map of Africa. Wilkinson is only able to record the first journey of Mungo Park (1771–1806) when he was sent in 1795 by the African Association to explore the course of the Niger, and this river as far as Sego is carefully mapped.

On the second sheet Le Vaillant's route of his exploration between 1781–1785 is shown, with the result that the topography of Africa south of the Drakensberg Mountains assumes a more accurate and a more modern aspect.

There is no innovation in the region of the Zambezi.

(51 AND 52) 1802 AND 1811.—AARON ARROWSMITH.

To the Committee and Members of the British Association for discovering the interior parts of Africa this map (51) *is inscribed :* A. Arrowsmith, Rathbone Place, November 1st, 1802.

This map is in colour and, like that of Wilkinson's, on two sheets. It comprised all the recent discoveries and surveys of Bruce,

Mungo Park, Davies, Le Vaillant and others, and a diligent study has been made of the volumes in which the explorations of these travellers are described. As is often the case, his notes are as interesting and illuminating. as his topography. South-east of Abyssinia is the remark " Here the Portuguese found King David (a successor of Prester John) encamped in 1520 ". The source of the Blue Nile in the Mountain of Gogam south of Lake Dembea or Tzana, Bruce " inferred from his barometer was more than two miles above sea level," while at its confluence with the White Nile the river is said to be " quarter of a mile wide at the passage in September and a half a mile in the rainy season ".

The second map containing South and Central Africa is more devoid of conjectural detail than any map since Ptolemy. The charted coast, the Cape of Good Hope, explored by the Dutch and by Le Vaillant, the Zambezi as far as it was known from Portuguese records, are depicted, but the multitude of place names in unintelligible dialects is wisely discarded in favour of accuracy.

The second Arrowsmith map is dated to 1811. *To the Committee and Members of the British Association for discovering the interior parts of Africa this map is inscribed.* A. Arrowsmith, Topographer to H.R.H. The Prince of Wales, dated 1802 with additions to 1811, Soho Square.

This map is in four sheets, and is very similar to the one previously described. Even at this date it was possible for a conscientious and accurate geographer to write in the centre of Africa " The general opinion in the interior of Africa is that the Niger and the Nile of Egypt are one and the same river ". The results of the second journey of Mungo Park in 1805 are now for the first time made known. A note against the town of Timbuctoo is " It is said that about 1670 the Moor first settled here ". In the upper course of the Niger is recorded " A Territory of white people, according to the Arabs, who are Christians ". The caravan routes from Egypt, Tripoli, Ceuta and the West Coast are marked.

South of the Equator there appears less new information. The Zambezi region, the Mountains of Lupata or the Spine of the World are marked as covered with perpetual snow, evidently a confusion with the Ruwenzori and Kenya ranges. In South Africa, for the first time, there is evidence of the Bantu immigration. Hitherto it has been populated by the Hottentots, Griquas, etc., now, names like Tambookies, Booshuanas (Bechwana) are recorded. But the careful survey of the Lacerda expedition to Kazembe and Lake Mweru in 1789 has not yet found a place on the map.

(53) 1812.—MALTE-BRUN, AFRIQUE MERIDIONALE.

The results of Manuel Pereira's journey in 1796 and of de Lacerda's expedition in 1798 to Cazembe, the Lunda Chief's capital near the south-east shore of Lake Mweru, and of the journey of the "Pombeiros" across the continent from Angola through Cazembe's to Tette on the Lower Zambezi in 1806–1810 are first seen in the French map by M. Malte-Brun dated 1812. On this map is marked "Route des Portugais". The route is incorrectly shown as ending at Chicova instead of at Tette, and it is marked considerably south of the route actually taken. This and the two following maps are represented in the Museum collections by photostat copies only.

(54) 1822.—C. RITTER, KARTE VON AFRIKA.

This map and that of 1826 by Berghaus report the latest knowledge of the Zambezi and the Central African Plateau obtained before the journeys of David Livingstone. The Portuguese fort at Zumbo (founded 1720 ?) at the confluence of the Zambezi and Luangwa is marked, as is also the country of the "Muvisas" (Bisa), the Zambezi (Chambezi), the "Hauptstadt der Cazember" on the "Muruswa" and the Ruapura (Luapula) River. The transcontinental route from Angola is again marked and is shown ending at Zumbo.

(55) 1826.—HEINRICH BERGHAUS, KARTE VON AFRICA.

This map contains little that is not found in the Ritter map. The authority for the topography of that part of the Central Plateau which is now Northern Rhodesia is given as "Pereira" and reference is made to the East Coast trade with the interior. The last Portuguese expedition to Cazembe, led by Majors Monteiro and Gamitto in 1831, seems to have been too close to Livingstone to have found a place on the maps,

(56) DAVID LIVINGSTONE (1813–1873).

The importance of Dr. David Livingstone's travels in Central Africa cannot be over-estimated. It is of interest to compare the Wilkinson and the Arrowsmith map of the beginning of the century with the maps incorporating the result of Livingstone's explorations which initiated the modern era of map making. Livingstone found this part of the continent entirely unknown country, and although he was not the first European to cross the continent, having been preceded by the Pombeiros (1806–10) and Silva Porto (1850–52), he was the first man to make accurate maps and bring back detailed accounts of the country and peoples through which he passed.

The Museum owns two originals and six most carefully executed reproductions of David Livingstone's own maps. The original maps are :

(i) A small fragment showing part of the Upper Zambezi in Barotseland between the Katima Mulilo and Kale Rapids, marking the rapids and islands in this part of the river. Found in an envelope addressed to "Sir William Hooker, Kew Gardens," the envelope dated 1857.

(ii) Map of the Upper Zambezi between Sesheke and the junction of the Kabompo with the Zambezi, showing the portion of the river explored in 1853.

The map records Livingstone's journey up the Zambezi from Sesheke to the confluence of the Kabompo and Liba. The expedition set out at the end of June, 1853, with the object of finding a suitable place for a new mission station, but as the tsetse fly prevailed throughout the region—a fact duly noted on the map—nothing came of this journey. Livingstone returned to Linyanti and shortly after set out on his journey to Loanda on the west coast.

The reproductions, the originals of which are in the Royal Geographical Society's Museum, are of the following maps :

(1) Map made of the route from Kazungula at the mouth of the Chobe or Linyanti River to Loanda. Information received from natives is marked in red, this includes the Victoria Falls marked as " Cataracts ", 1854.

(2) Detailed map of the Upper Zambezi from Sesheke northwards. 1854–55.

(3) Map of the Zambezi from Tette to Barotseland and of the Kafue River. 1855.

(4) Map of a large area of Central Africa including Lake Ngami, the Zambezi and all tributaries. The map was drawn by Shakolo, a Balochaze boy, from the original and is certified by Robert Moffat, Junior, Livingstone's brother-in-law. Correcting the map of 1855.

(5) Small map of the Upper Kasai and tributaries. 1855.

(6) Map of Lake Nyasa and the surrounding country. 1863.

The museum collection is completed by several maps of Africa, bringing the series up to modern times. Four of these are Arrowsmith maps and one a Bartholomew map which have David Livingstone's routes marked on them. Finally there are many maps, some of them dating from the nineteenth century, of Northern Rhodesia alone.

8

SOME PIONEER MISSIONS
OF NORTHERN RHODESIA AND NYASALAND

C. W. MACKINTOSH

1950

NORTH-WESTERN RHODESIA.

" The end of the geographical feat is the beginning of the
missionary enterprise."

" The door of Africa is now open. Do you carry on the work
which I have begun. I leave it with you."

" All I can say in my loneliness is, ' May Heaven's richest
blessing come down on everyone. American, Englishman, Turk,
who will help to heal this open sore of the world (the Arab slave
trade)'."

These three utterances of David Livingstone's have become
historic. To them and to the impulses they stirred in the young
generation to whom he addressed them, the peaceful development
of this part of Northern Rhodesia is largely due. For most of this
region, unlike many other parts of Africa has never been a conquered
country, for the people of the Lozi–Mbunda Empire united their
lot with Great Britain by a Treaty of Alliance signed and sealed on
27th June, 1890, between Lewanika, as king of this vast territory,
and Queen Victoria, as represented, by the British South Africa
Company. But long before this memorable date, Christian Missions
had sought to penetrate the recesses of the country. These were the
Pioneer Missions, some of which form the subject of the present
paper.

The Lozi–Mbunda, or Marotse–Ma–Mbunda Empire (as it was
known to the Portuguese), corresponded more or less to what we
know as North-western Rhodesia.   Its Paramount Chiefs had for
two or three centuries claimed tribute from some twenty or thirty
subjugated tribes whose habitation extended from the great bend
of the Zambezi on the south almost to the high watershed on the
north between the Zambezi and the Congo basins ; eastward to the
Kafue River, beyond which lies North-eastern Rhodesia, and
westward of the Zambezi to about the 20th meridian.

The pioneer epoch of Protestant Evangelical Missions north
of the Zambezi may be said to have begun in June, 1851, when
David Livingstone with his companion William Cotton Oswell
reached Sesheke on the mid-Zambezi ; and to have ended in June,
1904, when the Cape to Cairo Railway bridged the Zambezi at the
Victoria Falls. It finally closed with the King of Italy's Arbitration
Award (published in July, 1905) which fixed the western boundary
of King Lewanika's dominions at the 22nd meridian, and made it
possible on the one hand to put an end to the traffic of the Mambari

slave traders from Angola and on the other to abolish the legal status of slavery within the Barotse Empire (16th July, 1906). These achievements were the work of civilised British administration, but it is not too much to say that the pioneer Christian missions had paved the way by creating an atmosphere favourable to these and to other reforms in the minds of the leading Barotse rulers, namely King Lewanika himself and his prime minister, Mukamba, both declared Christians, and Lewanika's son, Litia, the Prefect of the Southern Province and, later on, his successor under the name of Yeta III.

For some three hundred years (or perhaps more) the Barotse tribe under their royal chiefs seem to have controlled their great country with varying success. Early in the last century, however, they and their twenty or thirty subject tribes were divided amongst themselves and against their rulers who hideously abused their power, and they thus fell an easy prey to the Basuto chief, Sebituane, whom Livingstone on his first journey found in authority at Linyanti, south-west of the confluence of the Zambezi and the Chobe.

Sebituane imposed the Sesuto language on his new subjects, but otherwise they found his yoke milder than that of their own kings, and the Makololo, as his fighting followers were called, were not resisted. He made a most favourable impression upon Livingstone, but unfortunately he died during the Doctor's visit and when the latter reached Linyanti for the second time he found Sebituane's son, Sekeletu, in authority. Together they went up the Zambezi to Naliele (then the capital of the Upper River, but now almost abandoned), Livingstone's object being to find a suitable spot for a mission station. In this he himself says he was unsuccessful but Sekeletu seemed very willing to receive missionaries and to assign a place to them, so that in response to the urgent appeal made by the great explorer on his return to England in 1856, his own society —the London Missionary Society—agreed to arrange for an expedition to be sent to the Zambezi.

THE FIRST PIONEER MISSION.

The London Missionary Society.

In 1860 Livingstone's father-in-law, the great Dr. Moffat, sent out a party from the Bechuana Mission northwards to the Makololo. This expedition was placed in charge of the Reverend Helmore and the Reverend Rodger Price who took with them their families and several native helpers. Helmore's party made its way by ox wagon across the Kalahari Desert and reached Linyanti in February, 1860. It had been understood that Sekeletu had invited them into his country but dark disaster awaited them. Sekeletu played them false and offered them no sort of a welcome. Encouraged by their witch doctors his people plundered the wagons and refused to sell food to the missionaries. All the party fell ill with fever, so badly that they even suspected that they had been poisoned, though this could, of course, never be proved. In a few weeks, out of eighteen persons, fifteen had died, and only three escaped with their lives, namely the Reverend R. Price and two of the Helmore children. Such was the fate of the first pioneer mission to the Zambezi.

Livingstone on his return to Linyanti from the west coast was distressed. He told the Makololo, "You have killed the servants of God whom you invited into your country and He will surely visit it on you". Four years later the Barotse rose against their Makololo conquerors and exterminated them all except the women whom they kept as wives. Many years later, after M. Coillard's preaching, a man said to him, "That is what Nyaka (the doctor) told the Makololo, but they would not listen to it, and now where are they ? "

After the tragedy of the Helmore and Price expedition, no further attempts were made to evangelise the Zambezi tribes for nearly twenty years, during which the Barotse country was given up to tribal warfare between different claimants to the throne. Traders continued to come and go, not only the Mambari slave traders from the west, but Europeans from the south in search of ivory, cattle and other produce of the country. None, however, were permitted to cross the Zambezi except one, George Westbeech, a fine man who contrived to gain the confidence of the chiefs and who used his opportunities to the best advantage. It was largely due to his influence with Lewanika (then called Robosi or Lobossi) that the expedition of 1878 led by the Reverend François Coillard, obtained access to the country.

THE SECOND PIONEER MISSION.

Société des Missions Evangéliques.

Meanwhile, Livingstone's appeals for missionaries were still echoing and re-echoing throughout Europe and North America, and amongst those who were most moved thereby were the French Protestant Missionaries of Basutoland, and especially the two friends, François Coillard and Adolphe Mabille, who ardently desired to see work started beyond the Zambezi amongst those Africans, who, as they were told, now spoke the same language as the Basuto. For a long time this seemed impracticable but unforeseen events providentially led up to it.

The Basuto Christians, by this time numerous, and zealous evangelists, wished to carry the Gospel to the Banyai tribe of Mashonaland. Asser, a very intelligent catechist, visited this tribe with several companions and his report to the Basuto churches was that three great chiefs would gladly welcome the coming of missionaries and had even chosen sites for the stations. "Ah, why could I not cut off my own arms and legs," he cried at one memorable meeting, "and make every limb of mine a missionary to these poor Banyai"? An old man rose at the back of the church, "Enough of talking," he said, "let us do something", and going up to the communion table he put down half a crown. The whole congregation followed his example, and within a few months the Basuto churches had themselves raised enough money to fit out an expedition with several native evangelists.

Their point of departure was the very spot where Sebitoane had started with his followers on the warpath, to found his Makololo Empire beyond the Zambezi. Survivors of those days were present, some converted, some still heathen, to see their fellow countrymen going forth on a mission of peace and goodwill. François Coillard described it as " a striking object lesson ".

After some initial set-backs the leadership of the expedition was finally entrusted to the Reverend François Coillard, and his Scottish wife. They set out on 16th April, 1877, and did not return until July, 1879. Following the indications given by Asser in his journal and with the help of the sketch map of the explorer Thomas Baines, they pursued an almost untrodden path to their goal, toiling through deserts, swamps, rivers and forests, guided largely by the compass. Arrived in the Banyai country, however, they discovered that the chiefs' only idea of white " teachers " was as an inexhaustible source of guns, powder and blankets, and they had no further use for the missionaries when these things were not forth-coming. One treacherous chief, Masonda by name, invited the party to visit him in his mountain fortress, received them with abundant protestations of friendship and accepted a fine blanket. But it was all a plot to throw them down a precipice—a fate they narrowly escaped—and then to plunder their wagons. Hastily regaining their camp they were followed by a messenger and the next day by the chief himself. " He does not like the blanket, he wants powder and caps." This being again refused and an ox of his own selection offered instead, " I have something in my heart ", he said, " I shall come back to-morrow ". The mission leaders decided not to wait for his visit and the wagons were inspanned at dawn, but directly they began to move the first wagon sank deep in a muddy stream, and bands of armed men ran down from all the neigh-bouring heights and surrounded them. The chief standing on a rock and foaming with fury ordered his men to take away the oxen and dictated his terms : " So many sacks of powder, so many caps, so many blankets, or you shall not go." This went on all day, the crowd, led by a " seer ", shrieked wildly : " We will have your blood and everything you possess and we shall see if your God will deliver you ". Madame Coillard's journal says, " All this time Frank was perfectly calm, and moving about as if nothing particular was happening ", whilst he himself recorded : " Christina could not rest seeing me thus exposed, she flew to me like an angel, with a message. ' Think ', she said at the worst moment of the struggle ' that this is a great day in Heaven '. When once the bullocks were inspanned we thought the cry of ' Trek ' would be the signal for a hail of assegais, but no ; it only provoked the yells of the infuriated mob, and the bullocks were so excited thereby that they gave a vigorous pull at

[253]

the yoke and dragged the wagon out " ; and the astonished tribes-men fell back to let them pass.

At the next halt they were at least unmolested by the chief —Maliankombe. Before long however they learnt that the Banyai paid tribute to Lobengula, the Matabele king, who was furious at the Coillards having entered his territory " by a back door " and sent an *impi* (regiment) to bring them to his capital at Bulawayo.

After compelling Masonda to give back everything he had stolen (including the seventeen oxen he had seized), the *impi* ordered the missionaries to strike their camp, and in fact made them prisoners. Three weeks of forced marches under a burning sun brought them to Bulawayo. Here, Lobengula kept the party in captivity for four months, treating them not unkindly but always deferring any reply to their request for permission to settle among the Banyai, " his dogs ". At length after a great national festival entailing the sacrifice of fifteen human lives, the great ones of the nation assembled. Mr. Sykes, Lobengula's missionary, was called to attend and the reply was given—an irrevocable refusal as the chiefs were fiercely opposed to it. The Matabele were of Zulu extraction and the Basuto catechists were the principal objects of their objurgations. " Allow *you* to settle in our land ? Never ; never ; there is the road that leads out of our country !—begone ! "

The road thus rudely pointed out was the main wagon track to Bechuanaland. Arrived there, like mariners escaped from ship-wreck, they received a warm and touching welcome from the Christian Chief Khama and his people, the Bamangwato. But the Basuto catechists who had regarded the expedition as their own enterprise would not hear of returning to Basutoland defeated in their purpose. Nor were their leaders M. and Mme. Coillard willing to do so either. Moreover at Bulawayo they had met refugees from beyond the Zambezi who spoke Sesuto. " Why do you wish to go to the Banyai whose tongue is strange to you," they asked, " when you know ours already ? Ours is a country of blood " (referring to the civil wars that had raged ever since the massacre of the Makololo) " why not go there and bring us peace ? " After mature consideration it was decided to trek to the Zambezi and explore the possibilities of founding a mission in Barotseland. Thus the vision of years past began to be realised.

Khama took up the project warmly, and assisted the Coillards to carry it out, by procuring guides for them and above all, sending a high-ranking chief (Makoatsa) with an escort ahead of them to introduce them to the Barotse ruler. This was important, since one of the accusations of the Matabele at their national assembly had been that the missionaries and their Basuto colleagues had come without anyone to vouch for them.

Somewhat discouraging was their arrival at the trading station of Leshoma on the Zambezi after a dreary six weeks' trek through bare sandy flats with their dilapidated wagons and worn out oxen. Here Khama's envoy, Makoatsa, met them with the news that the ostensible ruler Lewanika (then known as Robosi or Lobossi) had removed his capital from Linyanti to Naliele three hundred miles further north. Thereupon M. Coillard sent Makoatsa on with a fresh message and present to Robosi, requesting the chiefs at Sesheke to forward these without delay.

Whilst awaiting the return of the messenger, they made a brief excursion to the Victoria Falls in order to give their Basuto helpers a holiday and to raise their spirits after their long weary trek. It was on 6th August, 1878, that they reached the Falls which Madame Coillard was thus the first white woman to see. Their reception by the tribesmen living round the banks of the Zambezi was in happy contrast to their experience amongst the Matabele. The Barotse remembered their Makololo conquerors with respect, in spite of having exterminated them : and they welcomed the Basutos with every possible courtesy. The end of the sojourn however was not so fortunate as the beginning. Owing to the faction-fighting in the country, it was many months before the chiefs at Sesheke could be induced to forward M. Coillard's request for an interview to the king, and then it was sent by a slave as though quite unimportant. During this long stay in fever-stricken surroundings M. Coillard fell dangerously ill and three of the Basuto Christians died.

It was not till November that a polite message was received from the king that he was building a new town at Lealui, but that if the missionaries would come back next year after the harvest, he would be happy to receive them. On the strength of this assurance, the mission party then withdrew from Leshoma on 13th November, 1879. But it was not until 26th July, 1884, that they were able to camp there again.

In spite of this check to their purpose the mission party were not discouraged. " God be praised, the door is open. My tomb will be the finger-post of the new mission." Such were the dying words of the evangelist Eleazar when he heard the king's second message.

Their experiences had convinced the party of a providential call to bring the Gospel to Barotseland, and this conviction upheld them during the five years that elapsed before they could carry out what had now become a settled purpose.

Two years were spent by M. and Mme. Coillard in winning helpers and financial support for the new enterprise which the Société des Missions Evangéliques was persuaded after some hesitation to sanction. The Paris Committee, however, whilst granting its moral support to the undertaking, did not feel justified in diverting any funds to it ; the £5,000 required must be raised by the Coillards themselves. An English friend started it with £1,000. Others, both in France and Great Britain, rallied to their help, especially in Scotland, and in August, 1882, the Coillards returned to Basutoland, hoping to organise the expedition at once. This however proved impossible for the time being, as Basutoland was still in the throes of the strife which had arisen from the Gun-war of 1881, and even the Christian natives had lost their enthusiasm for what they had so proudly called their *own* mission. But fixity of purpose finally triumphed and the new expedition was launched on 2nd January, 1884. It consisted of, besides two Basuto cate-chists (trained schoolmasters), the Reverend F. Coillard and his wife, his niece, Elise Coillard, and a young Swiss missionary, the Reverend D. Jeanmairet, together with William Waddell, a Scottish cabinet maker, whose services to the mission proved to be beyond price ; and another lay-helper who unhappily left later on.

During these years of waiting for the hoped-for missionary, Lewanika's interest had been maintained somewhat unexpectedly by the presence of a young Scotsman, aged about twenty-four, who arrived in August, 1882, Frederick Stanley Arnot. Without being attached to any recognised society, he too owed his call to the influence of Livingstone. His own family and the children of Livingstone had been neighbours in Hamilton, and when quite a child he had heard the doctor speak at a prizegiving. When one of Livingstone's daughters read a letter from her father about the horrors of the slave trade, he then and there determined that " he would go and help that great man in his work " and if no one gave him the money to go there he would swim. This childish resolve never faltered, and although his first sojourn in Barotseland lasted barely two years, it was not without influence on the future of that country and its rulers.

Mr. Arnot was exploring with a view to founding a mission among the Batoka. As this tribe paid tribute to Lewanika, his permission was necessary, and he insisted that in order to obtain it Mr. Arnot should visit him at Lealui. The permission was never granted, so that Arnot had simply to live from day to day in the midst of the people, enduring great privations, and daily witnessing the terrible practices of the chief and people at the instigation of their witchdoctors.

The condition of the country at this time was woeful and had been so ever since the death of Sekeletu and the extermination of the Makololo. Various tribes put forward their own nominees for the chieftainship, and the choice had finally settled on Lewanika (Robosi). At first he was able to maintain not only order but considerable state and dignity, as is recorded by the Portuguese explorer, Major Serpa Pinto, who visited him in 1878. But he found himself surrounded by enemies without and within. His cousin, the ex-king Nguanawina (deposed for his cruelties), was hatching plots against him in the east ; and in the south the chiefs of Sesheke were divided for and against him. He also feared the Matabele hordes. Mr. Arnot's journals give a vivid picture of his experiences,

Arriving up river half dead with fever, he says : " The king could give me no dry hut, so I just had to lie to, day after day, in that filthy round hut with my goods (drenched on the canoe journey) rotting by my side and a perfect swarm of rats devouring everything and running over me at night.

" By this time I was on fairly good terms with Lewanika. He and his headmen had decided to wait for M. and Mme. Coillard on the one condition that I would remain with him until they arrived. I shall be the first Scotsman and the second British subject who has gone beyond Sesheke since Livingstone : the other is Mr. West-beech.

" Covetousness is the ruling passion of these natives. A man will kill another for his coat . . . Nothing of importance can be sanctified without a human sacrifice—in most cases a child. First the fingers and toes are cut off and the blood sprinkled on the boat, drum, house, or whatever may be the object in view. The victim is then killed, ripped up and then thrown into the river. A common occurrence is tying the victim hand and foot, and laying him near a nest of black ants, which in a few days pick his bones clean. The details of scenes which I have been forced to witness are too horrible to put on paper. A few yards from my hut lies a perfect Golgotha of skulls and human bones.

" During the time I was in Barotse, the Chief of the Matabele (Lobengula) sent a powerful embassy to Lewanika bringing presents of spears and shields and inviting Lewanika to become his blood brother and join with the Matabele in resisting the invading white man. I was able to persuade him that . . . Khama was a better man to make friends with than Lobengula.

" Lobengula's men were treated with great hospitality and sent away with many presents, but Lewanika immediately decided to write to Khama asking for his friendship, his daughter to be Lewanika's queen, and a black hunting dog. I wrote the letter for him . . . Lewanika added a postscript that Khama was to do all in his power to help M. and Mme. Coillard forward. It happened that this letter arrived in time to meet the Coillards (at Khama's town of Mangwato). Khama replied by sending a horse instead of his daughter, giving him to understand at the same time that he must join with him not against the white man but against the white man's drink if he wished to be Khama's friend."

As soon as he had acquired enough of the language Mr. Arnot started a school ; his first pupils being Lewanika's son and future successor, Litia, and Litia's friend, Mukamba, later on the first Christian prime minister of the country. It was very necessary, however, that the king himself should be influenced for good if Christianity was to make any headway amongst his people, because of the universal slavery, and the conviction of the subject classes that anything good existed not for them but for their masters only.

[257]

But to exercise such influence was not easy. "The king cross-questioned me as to what I had come to teach. I spoke to him of the death and judgment and of God's love in the gift of his Son. 'This', I said, 'was my first and chief message, besides which I wanted to teach the children to read and write, also about the world they live in.' The king then said 'Yes, yes, that is good : to read and write and know numbers. But don't, don't teach them the Word of God. We know quite enough about God, and we are not going to die yet.' But one day, he added 'Was there anything in my Book suitable for kings to listen to ? ' I assured him that there was more in the Bible for kings and about kings than any other class of people. 'Well', he said, 'if that is so, come and I will gather all my nobles and we will listen to the message that your Book has for a king.'

"On the appointed day I went to the *khothla*, and translated the story of the great eastern potentate, Nebuchadnezzar . . . At last he burst forth with 'I am the great Nebuchadnezzar of Central Africa '. But when I came to the downfall of the great monarch, the king's face fell somewhat. He sprang from his chair, and left the enclosure with the strange remark ' I am not going to die to-day '. For two months I was left severely alone by both chief and councillors ; then I heard that the chief was ill and sent for Mr. Arnot. As soon as he was assured that there was no one near to hear, he began to tell me how he abhorred burning witches, and selling slaves, and making war on the poor tribes around, but he was helpless, he said ; still he wished to keep ' My Sunday ' . . . and as I left him he said, 'Come every morning and teach me'. Troublesome times, however, were awaiting Lewanika, and the shadow of a serious revolution was already upon him."

Mr. Arnot was advised to leave whilst it was still possible to do so, he therefore went northwards to Benguella, and eventually found an opening for his work in Katanga (now part of the Belgian Congo), and was able to initiate a mission which has since become large and important, and is now carried on under the title of " Christian Missions in Many Lands ". It was begun in completely pioneer conditions and now extends in a chain of stations from Bihe in Angola to Katanga. From 1897 onwards it was extended southwards into Barotse regions (Northern Rhodesia) as far as Chitokoloki where the Reverend Suckling and others have worked amongst the Balunda and Balovale who were at that time tributary to Lewanika. The work of the " Christian Missions in Many Lands " was carried on also at Kalene Hill, in Northern Rhodesia, by Dr. Walter Fisher, who began his medical and educational work there in 1905. His experience seems to have been happier than that of many other pioneers. " Before the Government was properly installed he had a great deal of influence with the chiefs, who treated him as if he were himself a native chief superior to them. He had to dissuade them in the earlier days from bringing him regular tribute. They often brought him their inter-tribal problems, until the Government took over, and then when the tribesmen were very suspicious he did much to help them to understand how the Government was to be trusted. Dr. Fisher also made the first translation of St. John's Gospel into Lwena, besides setting-up schools for native children. He founded a school for European children and cared for a large number of orphans. His medical work was renowned, especially his operations for cataract." The people were very suspicious of his hospital at first, but after one or two remarkable cures, they all wanted to be cut open " so that the devils could be let out ".

At the same time as Arnot left Lealui, the Jesuit missionaries who had been endeavouring to found a mission nearby also left.*

It was during these troubled times that the second expedition of the Coillards and their Basuto evangelists set out from Basutoland, in January, 1884. They reached Leshoma near the right bank of the Zambezi on 26th July, and here they were halted—as it proved for many months. The great bend of the river formed a natural frontier to the Barotse Kingdom (although tributary tribes lay to the west of it) and no one was allowed to cross except at the well guarded ford of Kazungula. (This place later on lost its importance and the town has since disappeared.) The expedition was confronted with an unexpected state of affairs. There was no one at the capital who could read or reply to M. Coillard's letter to the king announcing their arrival, moreover, the chiefs at Sesheke, as on the former occasion (1878), sent it up river only by a slave on foot, as if it were a matter of no importance. Sesheke was the residence of twelve or fifteen chiefs, Barotse by birth, governors of tributary tribes and forming a council under a president, the Morantsiane. All communications were in their hands and, as it afterwards appeared, in those of the witchdoctors, who were administering the *mwati* poison to fowls to see whether the newcomers should be admitted. As the results of the *mwati* were uncertain, M. Coillard and M. Jeanmairet were brought to Sesheke and received with courtesy in the council (*khothla*). A messenger arrived from the king to say that if the letter was from M. Coillard he was to be conducted to the capital at once.

The Sesheke chiefs, however, aware doubtless of the impending trouble, delayed to comply, and it was not until M. Coillard declared he would go to Lealui on foot, that two canoes, old and leaky, were put at their service. Soon they had to land and repair them, and whilst this was being done, urgent orders were sent for them to return to Sesheke immediately. What could have happened ? A revolution had broken out in the Valley (the upper river) and the king had fled. This was serious news. " How could we make such a long journey in a country where anarchy prevailed ? Who were

---

* In 1880 an attempt had been made by two Roman Catholic Fathers to found a mission in Barotseland. The idea was abandoned, however, after one of the two had been drowned when the canoe in which they were travelling capsized in the Zambezi. J. D. C.

the leaders of the revolution ? . . . and so we had to follow the councils of prudence and *wait*. What a hard lesson that is ! " It was not till eleven months later (August, 1885) that the wagons were able to cross the Zambezi at the ford.

The first station was founded at Sesheke on 24th September, 1885, and placed in the charge of M. Jeanmairet to whom Elise Coillard was married soon afterwards. During the preceding months of suspense, the party had installed themselves at Leshoma : huts had been built, a school opened, Sunday services and the usual routine of a mission station carried on ; and this was continued at Sesheke.

The very first night they crossed the river, some fugitive women rushed into their camp and implored Madame Coillard, who was alone at the moment, to save them, as the king's people had arrived to execute their menfolk (as rebels) and they expected to be killed too. As not even a fence had been put up as yet, there were no means of protecting the poor creatures, who, before dawn, had all been massacred. M. Coillard wrote : " Amid this appalling outbreak of passion, we ourselves have had, and still have to suffer . . . Without protection, without any defence as we are, it is truly a miracle of God's goodness that we have not been completely stripped. The slaves steal audaciously for their masters. It is hard to see our sheep and cattle stolen and killed in broad daylight, and to recognise our own shirts and stuffs on the greasy backs of chiefs of the second and third degree ; what could we do ? Pray that God may enable us to take joyfully the spoiling of our goods and means while our Master will never let us lack for necessaries." In such surroundings M. Coillard had to leave his wife and niece with his young and inexperienced colleague, M. Jeanmairet, and their greatly valued lay-helper, William Waddell, whilst he went up river to Lealui, not knowing whether the chief might not have determined to drown him on the way. The puppet king, Akufuna, whom the revolutionaries had installed, sent for M. Coillard, hoping, he said, that he might be able to give him good advice. Coillard, therefore set out with the evangelist, Levi. At Lealui, Akufuna and the assembled chiefs gave them a cordial reception and their future mission station was pointed out to them.

"You are welcome, servants of God ", said the prime minister, Mathaha. " The nation is weary, it sighs for peace. We do not ask for presents ; we do not seek your goods if you have any. What we ask for is your teaching : what we wish for is peace." The other chiefs spoke in the same strain, but this Mathaha had been the instigator of the revolution and his one object had been to get all power into his own hands. Akufuna was a beardless boy, and by the end of 1885, a counter revolution had broken out. After severe fighting, Lewanika (Robosi) regained the throne. A fearful slaughter of his opponents followed, neither women nor children were spared. At Sesheke, the chiefs were divided in their allegiance, and " Thereupon ", says M. Coillard, " a small civil war became imminent, then began a system of brawls, and panics such as are only known in Africa, but all our efforts towards a reconciliation proved abortive ". " Your intentions are good ", said the chiefs, " you are servants of God—men of peace ; but we are men of blood, we murder each other, drinking, talking and laughing together." Even when Lewanika's position at Lealui seemed secure the chiefs at Sesheke kept on delaying to comply with his orders to bring the missionary up to the capital. They were afraid that his escort would be killed on the way.

At last, however, they started, and on the 22nd March, 1886, M. Coillard met Lewanika on the river, where, with all his chiefs he was paying his annual visit to the graves of his ancestors, a form of animism which was the real religion of the Barotse.

The official reception took place the following morning at the *khothla* : Mr. Westbeech introducing the newcomers.

They found the capital desolate, and Lewanika in poverty. Every day he shut himself up with his new friend, and consulted him on every possible subject. Their recorded conversations show more maturity of mind on Lewanika's part than in Mr. Arnot's journals ; doubtless his bitter experience in exile had taught him much.

" Moruti, give me counsel how I shall rule my country."

" First put away your assegai and let it sleep, and renounce vengeance once for all. Set yourself to win the confidence of your people and inspire the smallest with a feeling of perfect security. Punish theft and, above all, accept the Gospel for yourself and your nation."

" What are the riches of a country ? The riches of mine is ivory. But there is less ivory every year, and when all the elephants are killed, what shall I do ? "

" I pointed out to him the fertility of his country, and that if the chiefs would give themselves to the cultivation of cotton, tobacco, coffee, sugarcane, etc., they would soon find that it would be an inexhaustible source of wealth to them. He then questioned me about Lobengula. ' Had he missionaries ? Was he a believer like Khama ? ' He seemed to have a great desire to resemble Khama."

Lewanika assigned to them the site of their future station of Sefula. M. Coillard and the Basuto catechist returned to Sesheke (where Madame Coillard had remained with the Jeanmairets) and prepared to bring the wagons overland to their new home before the annual flood should render such transport impossible. After a difficult journey, Sefula was reached once more.

" It took four days for twelve men to open a passage for us through the forest of Kanyonyo." Four or five rivers had to be crossed, and at one of them, the Njoko, the wagons were upset and everything, food, barter goods, bedding and scientific instruments, half or wholly ruined.

Waddell and his lay-helper put up a little two-roomed hut for Mme. Coillard, who arrived on 12th January, 1887. The king appeared ten days later to install them, and the work began which was to have such momentous results for the country.

The first *pitso* which they attended at Lealui, after their arrival, lasted three hours, and the speeches of the chiefs disclosed a latent element of opposition. But one who had sojourned at Khama's court testified eloquently to the benefits " teachers " had brought to Bechuanaland, and his plea carried the day in favour of the new arrivals.

They were certified by the council as " Barotsi "—given the freedom of the city as we should say—and their work began to take shape.

Fortunately the missionaries thus brought to Barotseland were familiar from the start with the Sesuto language spoken by the people, and they were respected because they had come from the Makololos' own country. Great difficulties, however, had to be faced in other directions. Material troubles need not be dwelt upon —they were the same as had to be endured by all early travellers, traders, and later on by officials—the need for bringing up vast quantities of barter goods without which essential supplies could not be obtained, the obstacles to transport, whether by land or by river, the tsetse fly destroying the cattle, the deadly climate, which in the first twenty years of the mission cost the lives of thirty-three persons (including fifteen children), the discomforts in housing, and the privations in food (often no milk, fruit, vegetables or sugar could be obtained for months together).

Tribal custom held the king to be not only the ruler but the owner of everything and the employer of every person in the country. Property did not exist ; what a man owned or appeared to own was only his as dependent upon the king or his immediate superior chief who could (and often did) take it from him, or forbid him to sell it or give it away. Nor could he dispose freely of his labour. All means of transport were owned by the king, whether canoes for the river or oxen for the wagons, consequently the missionaries were dependent upon his favour for the means of locomotion as well as for the means of existence, and he did not hesitate to use his power if at any time they refused to comply with his wishes and particularly if they refused to buy at his own arbitrary price anything he might wish to dispose of. All human relationships, including marriage, appeared to the missionaries to be at the mercy of caprice ; there was no sense of contract in labour or barter ; and all civil administration and justice depended on the witch-doctor's " findings ". Quite often (as M. Coillard wrote) " the very existence of the mission hung on a thread, but the thread was in God's hand, so—courage ; we cling to the immutable promises of

God ". Mme. Coillard wrote on 27th May, 1887, " Oh, the quantities of people that have been burnt as witches and wizards since we came here. It is almost a daily occurrence." All misfortunes were attributed by the tribesmen to sorcery. The witchdoctors were the detectives. By casting " the bones " they pointed out the supposed authors of crime or sickness, who if not lynched on the spot were tried by ordeal, which consisted either of plunging their hands into boiling water or drinking the *mwati* poison. If they were innocent these tests were supposed to do them no harm, but of course this seldom occurred, and guiltless persons were daily put to cruel deaths as sorcerers.

The king himself was somewhat sceptical as to these matters, " Pooh, the bones say what I wish ", he told M. Coillard. This, however, was not invariably the case, as in 1892 the old prime minister was sent to Lewanika to inform him that the divining bones had pointed out him—their own king—as the sorcerer responsible for the nation's misfortunes. This was too much ! He had the witchfinders seized, and their instruments of divination destroyed and the following year he decreed the trial by ordeal and the practice of sorcery to be forbidden, and had a police force set up instead. A person accused of being a sorcerer did have one alternative to being lynched, namely to rush to the Natamoyo, the " Minister of Mercy ", and embrace his knees. After this he could demand trial by ordeal. M. Coillard claimed at once for himself and his colleagues the title of Natamoyo also.

Soon after Lewanika decreed Sunday observance and encouraged his people by word and example to attend the mission services. His own children and those of the leading chiefs were sent to live with the missionaries. No provision, however, was made for their board whilst being educated, the king merely remarking that the people living around the station were bound to maintain his sons and daughters, whose attendants requisitioned—in other words plundered—everything needed for or by their charges.

The missionary's work, however, could not be simply teaching, whether in the school or in the pulpit. Faithfulness involved unflinching denunciation of the bloodshed, spoliation and immorality going on unchecked around them. One is constantly amazed at the courage with which, defenceless as they were, the messengers of the Gospel stood up against all the forces of heathenism arrayed to starve, poison, or assassinate them. It was not long after their arrival before the first occasion to take a stand arose. During the period of civil war and anarchy, the cattle had almost all been destroyed, and the chiefs therefore planned a cattle raid against the Mashukulumbwe (or Ila) people on the east. In vain M. Coillard protested. The king's excuses were plausible, the Ila, he maintained, were a tribe subject to him. " They had ill-treated Dr. Holub, it is my duty to chastise them. Besides they are not human beings, they go quite naked and . . . we have no more cattle and . . .

we absolutely must have some." Five months later the expedition returned with thousands of cattle and hundreds of women and children who were distributed in the public square as slaves to the victorious warriors. The men who had not been killed in battle were nearly all massacred. Small herds of the captured cattle were offered to each of the missionaries who of course refused them. Lewanika's response was, " I understand ; but what do the Barotse possess except by plunder ? "

For the first six years of labour the missionaries' results seemed very meagre, but still the work extended. Before long, new missionaries joined the Coillards and amongst the first were the Jalla brothers whose work has left so deep a mark upon the country, and the number of the stations increased from two to five. As long as it remained a novelty the people were ready to attend services and to listen to the preaching, but when they found that the Gospel teaching involved a complete break with their old customs and habits they grew indifferent. Indifference later became hostility, and not once but many times the lives of the missionaries were in danger. Moreover, the Barotse etiquette forbade that anyone should take a new step before his superior in rank had set the precedent. Hence it was not until after Litia, the king's son, together with his friend, Mukamba, at a full service announced his conversion and his determination to break with heathenism and witchcraft, that converts began to come in, showing how many had been moved but had not dared to take the step of open profession.

Litia (afterwards known as Yeta III when he succeeded his father) and Mukamba (who became the first Christian prime minister) had been on their way to the training college of the French Protestant Missions in Basutoland, by the king's desire, but halting at Khama's town they had decided to go no further, and it was the influence of a young Bechuana convert and the example of the great Christian chief, Khama, that finally determined them to take this momentous step. *Then*, as M. Coillard wrote, " they could have gathered in hundreds ", but they wanted *real* not nominal Christians —men and women whose lives attested their faith, and these were few and far between.

The Sunday on which Litia and his friend, Mukamba, declared themselves Christians was the last of Mme. Coillard's life. This heroic woman died on 28th October, 1891. " When we were married ", wrote her broken-hearted husband, " she spoke these words to me, ' I have come to Africa to do the work of God with you, whatever it may be and wherever it may be, and remember this, wherever God may call you, you shall never find me crossing your path of duty '. It was more than a beautiful saying, it was the principle of her life." Hers is the earliest British woman's grave beyond the Zambezi.

A year after this, M. Coillard moved to Lealui, the capital, leaving the station of Sefula to M. and Mme. Adolphe Jalla. Lewanika granted a site for the Lealui station, a large ant-hill on the plain, the place where the sorcerers had always been burned, and covered with brushwood and human bones. It was not an easy post to occupy, just under the king's supervision, especially as for many months Lewanika was not in a good mood. During his exile he had heard of something called " British Protection " which his friend Khama had just obtained, and which he thought would be a good thing for himself. No sooner had the missionary arrived after Lewanika's restoration to power, than the chief desired him to write to the authorities to ask for this boon—of " British Protection ". M. Coillard declined both as a missionary and a Frenchman to mix himself up in so serious a matter of politics. Lewanika, not to be baffled, called a grand *pitso* at which he invited M. Coillard to be present and then to the astonishment of everyone, chiefs and guests alike, he delivered his ultimatum. " Chief Khama has teachers, but he also has *masole* (soldiers), so if you like (want) to have the missionaries ask *Satory* (Queen Victoria) to send us her soldiers." The chiefs, taken by surprise, violently objected, and after a two-day debate the *pitso* broke up in confusion and nothing more was heard of *Satory* or her *masole*. But Lewanika did not give up the idea. " Why not ask me what I want them for, myself ? " he inquired bitterly. He wanted protection against the Matabele in the south and against the slave raiding Mambari in the west, but also against the plotters in his own country. Moreover, but this he had hardly begun to realise, other webs were being woven around him. Concession hunters began to multiply at his court—harbingers of the great Chartered Company which was destined to take over the protectorate of this vast country.

This is not the place to enter upon an account of the important changes brought about by the political development except in so far as they affected the mission. The first representative of the Company, Mr. Lochner, arrived at Lealui in May, 1890. M. Coillard and his colleague, Adolphe Jalla, desired to avoid as far as possible any association with political matters. This was, however, very difficult as they were the only persons on the spot who knew the language and thus were forced to act as interpreters, and more or less as intermediaries in order to make sure that the king and his chiefs understood what they were offered, and what they were asked to do in making a treaty with the Company. Moreover, Mr. Lochner arrived very ill, and with most of his supplies lost on the journey up-river. In such circumstances it was a matter of sheer humanity for the only Europeans on the spot to offer him hospitality as well as to obtain supplies for himself and his followers. This inevitably identified M. Coillard and M. Jalla and their mission with Mr. Lochner in native eyes. Still the missionaries welcomed the treaty signed on 27th June, 1890, and M. Coillard wrote, " For my part I have no doubt that for the nation this will prove the one plank of safety. The Barotse are incapable of governing, and left to themselves, they would annihilate each other."

All would probably have been well had this treaty been put into force at once, but seven years were to pass before it was implemented. These were years of acute trial for the missionaries, though they were also years of patient, faithful toil to bear fruit later on. A continental traveller and explorer, Captain Alfred Bertrand, who visited Barotseland in 1895 recorded in his published account of his journey that " The results obtained by this handful of Europeans, animated by the spirit prevailing among them are astonishing ". And indeed a definite movement towards Christianity and away from the deadening cruelty and superstition of heathendom was perceptible. Perhaps this very fact stirred up a counter movement. Although M. Coillard had been at pains to try to make clear in public his own independence in the recent treaty negotiations, and although when Mr. Rhodes wrote to inquire whether he would accept the post of British Resident, his reply was " I cannot serve two masters ", no sooner had Mr. Lochner departed with the treaty than trouble began with a host of disappointed concession hunters and other persons who imagined that the Company's administration would interfere with their prospects, and who assured Lewanika that he had been betrayed into selling his country. The missionary was made the scapegoat, by natives and white men alike. One of the Europeans even contrived to install himself as Lewanika's " secretary ", and in that capacity to intercept all the up-river mail bags, incoming and outgoing, and to open all the letters and packets addressed to or by the Coillards. Lewanika, always prone to suspicion (for had he not been betrayed in the past by those who professed to be his friends ?) withdrew his help and countenance : the mission schools were deserted, the services neglected and even the lives of the missionaries definitely menaced. Fortunately the next year brought the ratification of the treaty. M. Coillard wrote :

> " Shortly after the death of Madame Coillard I received after nine or ten months passed without news, two voluminous mails bringing the news of the definite establishment of the British Protectorate over the Barotse country. This news reduced to nothing the calumnies representing the contract as simply delivering up the country to the exploitation of a commercial society. This was all that was needed to dissipate our political clouds. Lewanika says he rejoices in it."

Troubles however did not cease entirely. Owing to their hands being full with the settlement of Matabeleland, now Southern Rhodesia, it was still not for some years that the British South Africa Company was able to carry out its promise of sending a representative of the Queen, and until this was achieved, Lewanika's suspicions and caprices continued to harass the missionaries. Especially was this the case when the pioneers of the Primitive Methodist Mission arrived and asked permission to start work amongst the Mashukulumbwe (see page 25). Nevertheless, the people were gradually being persuaded to accept the benefits their missionaries believed themselves to be bringing with the Christian faith. These benefits were of a definite practical kind : educational, in the shape of schools and technical training, building, digging of canals, making of boats, growing of wheat, etc., and social, both in the shape of reforms and of medical help.

It was during the next few years (1891–1899) that these innovations began to spread. Lewanika had been very willing to accept the first two at once, and by degrees he sought to put in practice the most urgent of the social reforms also. But to the spiritual regeneration without which these matters could have little permanent value, he and his people long remained insensible.

Under the able direction of M. Adolphe Jalla and the Basuto catechists who were trained teachers, the school attendance increased. M. Jalla compiled school books, vocabularies, grammars, hymn-books, primers and a history of the nation. Later on Silozi, a modification of the original languge of the Barotse, displaced Sesuto, which was spoken in Livingstone's day and for some time after. The Reverend Adolphe Jalla also adapted the school material to this new language and later translated the Old and New Testaments and the *Pilgrim's Progress.*

Under Waddell's able tuition the Barotse had taken very kindly (often *too* kindly) to the use of tools, even though they sometimes applied them to strange purposes. They are by nature highly industrial, and now when the new station was opened on the plain near Lealui, major works began to be undertaken by the tribesmen in emulation of it. When the church was built, M. Coillard had a causeway thrown up from the plain part way from the mission station to the capital so that people could attend the services during flood-time. Lewanika at once set his workmen to raise another to meet it from his end : and when he saw the first canal being dug with the battered spades that had survived the wagon journeys, he said : " We can do better than that ", and before long several canals had been completed, one of them of twelve and a half miles in length.

With regard to social reforms, Lewanika was evidently moving towards a higher standard. Besides abolishing the trial by ordeal (poison or boiling water) at the capital in 1893 and the burning alive of people supposed to be convicted thereby, he announced that three villages should be built far away, to which accused persons should be banished, one for thieves, one for recognised " sorcerers ", and one for seducers of other men's wives. To supersede the system of " smelling out " he set up a service of police, who were also to put a stop to licentious dances and nocturnal disturbances. Persons who accused others of "sorcery" were themselves to be punished. He also endeavoured to suppress infanticide which was practised for many causes, sometimes in the case of twins, sometimes if a child cut its upper teeth before the lower ones and sometimes merely to get rid of an unwanted child. Also when his old prime minister died, he refused to allow the customary sacrifices of innocent persons to accompany the corpse, notwithstanding the plea of an old chief, overheard by M. Jalla. " Must he really go down alone to the Land of the Dead ? " But the reform he had most at heart and insisted upon with greatest severity, was the prohibition of strong beer-making and drinking—a fruitful cause of strife and bloodshed. So sternly was this enforced that when some of his chiefs, ministers of state, were found transgressing it, he had them brought to the open *khothla* and made to empty their pots of beer upon the sand, besides depriving them of all their appointments and honours because he said they had disgraced their office. These reforms were his own idea, and when carried through it was usually in the teeth of opposition from his chiefs, but it became easier to win support for them after the appointment of his Christian prime minister, Mukamba.

In 1895, M. Coillard was forced to return to Europe, owing to serious illness, and the responsibility for the mission fell on the Jalla brothers and their younger colleagues. A critical time ensued. The Chartered Company had still not begun to carry out the terms of the treaty, having its hands full with subduing the Matabele, and the Matabele in their turn, fleeing before the British advance, threatened to invade Barotseland from the south. Added to this a terrible epidemic of rinderpest swept the neighbouring countries, and all transport was held up for two years. This meant no European supplies and no barter goods to exchange for the necessaries of life. The natives not unnaturally seized the opportunity to force up prices unreasonably and on occasion to refuse to sell food at all and the missionaries suffered accordingly. Slaves—and this included all classes except the Barotse tribe itself—were not allowed to eat millet or sorghum. They were forbidden to build good huts or to wear good clothes, or even to possess things of any value that they had made themselves, and their lives were forfeited for the most trivial transgressions. To give an instance, a royal child was drinking milk ; his little slave and playfellow, no doubt hungry, asked for some, and for taking this liberty he was whisked away and killed. Almost imperceptibly these harsh restrictions had fallen out of use but the attitude of the chiefs towards subordinate tribes had not changed. These were the hunting ground for cattle and slaves, and when early in 1897 the council became aware that the British representative would soon be arriving and that such depredations would then be stopped, they determined to have one last fling, and proclaimed war against the Mashukulumbwe. This was all the more reprehensible since for some time Lewanika had been pursuing a policy of conciliation towards this tribe, so that they would be totally unprepared for a sudden attack.

The expedition was already mobilised in spite of M. Jalla's earnest remonstrances and was to start the next day. " We laid our troubles before God ", he wrote, " and a few days later I learned that the chiefs had petitioned the king overnight to give up this war." " The *Moruti* is right ", they said. Soon after this victory of peace the first British Administrator arrived (20th October, 1897) and the days of slave trading were ended.

Even this, however, did not solve all difficulties. Lewanika and his councillors, who had expected to see a band of soldiers, would not at first believe that Major Coryndon with his secretary, Mr. F. Worthington, and his small unarmed escort was really " the Queen's man ", and again the missionary was called in to mediate. The record in M. Jalla's journal of the three days' struggle with obstinate and sceptical chiefs is brief and to the point. " I succeeded in reconciling them."

The Resident announced that he was indeed the envoy of the Queen and his mission was to assist the king by his counsels, and to watch that his Concession should be observed . . . " The country of Lewanika is definitely declared a British Protectorate ; however, the country still belongs to the king and has not been bought by anybody."

Once accepted by the council of chiefs the appointment of the Resident in many ways strengthened Lewanika's hand in continuing to curb abuses, and the police force organised by Colonel Colin Harding eventually put a stop to the slave trading on the Portuguese border. Thus the year 1897 proved a turning point in the history of the country and consequently in the mission itself.

M. Coillard returned in 1898 with a band of young missionaries recruited from Europe, and the following year was signalised by two events which marked the effect that years of missionary work had brought about. Litia, now installed at Kazungula as Prefect of the Southern Province, was baptised with his wife and son, with his royal father's consent, thus making a public break from the national system of heathenism. Then also his friend, Mukamba (now his brother-in-law) as already recorded, became prime minister in the place of the old *Ngambela*, a determined die-hard. The king gave as his reason for choosing such a young man, " Mukamba is a Christian whose mind will be open to every kind of progress ".

It is a Barotse custom, when a minister of state is publicly inducted, for the other chiefs to address him on the duties of his office. Perhaps nothing could afford a more welcome proof of a changing outlook in the council of chiefs than the brief counsels directed to Mukamba on this occasion by some thirty or forty speakers. Here are a few samples recorded at the time :

> " You are the steer that leads the herd across the river to the opposite bank. Go forward always. If you turn back you will drown us all."

> " You have two ears, let one be for your king, and one for the nation."

> " It is a heavy task that is confided to you. You carry the country on your head, and the nation on your shoulders."

> " You are a Christian. Never forget it. Speak the truth always, even to your master."

Photograph by permission of Miss W. D. Arnot
F.S. Arnot.

Madame Coillard.

Rhodes-Livingstone Museum Collection

Rhodes-Livingstone Museum Collection
The Rev. Francois Coillard.

The arrival of the Coillard Expedition at the Zambezi, 1884.

Photograph by Rev. F. Coillard

Photograph by Rev. F. Coillard

Lewanika before setting out on his last raid against the Ba Ila.

Rhodes-Livingstone Museum Collection

Photograph by Rev. F. Coillard

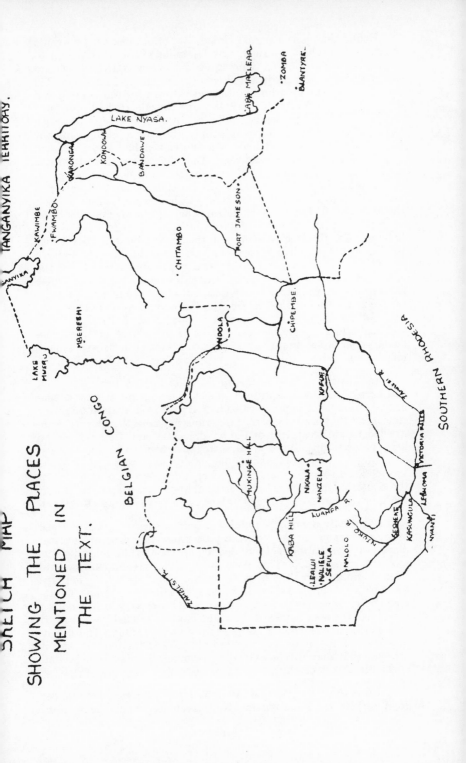

SKETCH MAP

SHOWING THE PLACES
MENTIONED IN
THE TEXT.

Before the pioneer period closed, two other noteworthy events occurred. The first, in 1902, was Lewanika's visit to England to attend the coronation of King Edward the Seventh. The second was the advent of a medical missionary, Dr. Georges Reutter. Till then the only doctor who had offered to work for the Mission had died a few months after his arrival ; and the climate had continued to take heavy toll of health and life. Almost a crisis had arisen when out of twenty-four young people who had recently come out to join the mission, eight had died, and eleven had had to return to Europe, invalided or widowed. Only five were left to reinforce the few surviving veterans, and disabling illness constantly hampered their work. It was in these circumstances that Dr. G. Reutter, a man of independent means, came out at his own expense and took the situation in hand. Just at this time the connection between malaria fever and the bite of the *anopheles* mosquito had become known. Dr. Reutter brought out the first mosquito-proof house (prefabricated) and had it set up in Nalolo near Lealui, raised above ground upon iron piles, and the missionaries readily submitted to the regime of a daily dose of quinine. All this is now a matter of course for the white man in tropical regions, but at that time it was a great innovation. In response to Dr. Reutter's appeal—a simple statement of the facts—friends started a movement to supply *all* the stations with hygienic houses, and, once these were installed, the change-over from chronic invalidism to normal health was almost miraculous.

As regards medical and surgical relief for the Barotse, which had been Dr. Reutter's primary object, this was not at first so successful. Simple dispensary cases had always been treated on every station as they still are, but for serious matters the natives were wedded to the treatment of the witchdoctors, and they refused to bring patients until they had exhausted their own resources, and then the white man was held responsible for any fatal issue. All sickness was ascribed to sorcery and, moreover, they were terribly afraid of the doctor's long knives ! In time, however, the happy results to those brave enough to submit to treatment gave courage to others.

Eventually a small hospital was built at Sesheke, and African assistants trained. A recent report from the present medical missionary, Dr. Ruth Picot, notified for *one* year 38,933 consultations and 164 in-patients. This good work still goes on, and several trained nurses carry on dispensaries on other stations. Perhaps the most valuable work has been for maternity cases, whose treatment by native custom was both cruel and useless, and if, as often happened, the results were fatal to the mother, the baby was buried with her, relatives having no means of infant-feeding. The happy results of skilled midwifery naturally impressed the natives, and it is hoped that they will be extended, for much remains to be accomplished in this department.

Before this time (1902) M. Adolphe Jalla had been able to render great service to Lewanika in giving evidence about the western boundary of Barotseland, which was the subject of the King of Italy's Arbitration Award and which, without his expert knowledge, might have deprived Lewanika of a large part of his kingdom. The award was finally published in 1905.

Lewanika's visit to Europe was a wonderful experience, both for himself and for the young men who formed his escort. It was also a great encouragement to those in Europe whose faith and sacrifices had contributed to bring about so great a transformation in the erstwhile ruler of barbarians. To the representatives of various good causes who had testified to their appreciation of his efforts to set his people on the right road, he addressed the following letter before leaving England, through his native interpreter and secretary.

" I am Lewanika.

I feel it is my duty to thank those of Great Britain for their kind reception—so friendly and honourable.

Secondly I must speak about the good work which has caused my country to progress, wrought by the hand of M. Coillard and M. Jalla and the other missionaries sent by the Paris Société des Missions.

The work of the missionaries and their cunsels have helped me to fight against many things, such as drunkenness, witchcraft, and many more things which I have tried to fight against, and they are coming to an end. Lastly I wish for many more missionaries to make my country go forward.

(*Signed*) LEWANIKA."

To Mr. Arnot, his earliest missionary, who spent the last evening with him, he said, "Yes, *Monere*, I am a black man, and with us the light dawns slowly, but I can say that I have learnt to pray to God, and I still hope I shall meet you in the Kingdom of God."

The Sunday after he returned to Lealui, he and nearly all the chiefs assembled at church and after the service of thanksgiving he spoke to the congregation. He said how astonished he had been to see in England what respect there was for God and His Law, and that even King Edward was crowned in a church. " I have seen", he said, "that the *thuto* (Christian teaching) is everything." "And ", he concluded, "it is in God you must rejoice and not in me, for it is God who has kept me from all evil everywhere and has brought me back to you safely."

The following year saw the first lines of the bridge laid over the Victoria Falls. On 27th May, 1904, the revered founder of the mission, the Reverend François Coillard, passed away in the midst of his work and was buried beside his wife at Sefula. A few days later, on 1st June, the railway reached Livingstone. The pioneer days were over, though others of the pioneer missionaries still lived on to continue the work begun under such difficulty, and when M. Adolphe Jalla died in 1946, he had completed fifty-six years of labour in the mission field.

THE THIRD PIONEER MISSION.

The Primitive Methodist Mission to the Baila.

While the French Protestant Mission was gradually establishing itself in the western part of King Lewanika's dominions, the eastern part was still wholly unevangelised and even to a great extent unexplored. The Reverend John Smith of Aliwal, in South Africa, consulted M. Coillard on behalf of the Primitive Methodist Missionary Society which was seeking a new field of labour, and on his advice they decided if possible to enter this region—the country of the Ila people (called by the Barotse, Mashukulumbwe) and of the Batoka. But for this it was necessary to obtain Lewanika's permission as these were nominally subject tribes. Accordingly the first party, consisting of the Reverend and Mrs. Buckingham and the Reverend A. Baldwin and an industrial missionary, trekked by ox wagon to the Zambezi, which they reached in August, 1890, having started from Kimberley in March. Their arrival took place at the most unpropitious moment, just after the treaty with the British South Africa Company had been concluded but not yet implemented (*see* page 18). The Barotse, and especially the chiefs of Sesheke, their minds inflamed by interested persons, at once identified the English missionaries with those " foreigners " whom they had determined to keep out of the country, and they treated them with the utmost indignity. The French missionaries at Sesheke and Kazungula, hoping to shield them, took their part, thereby incurring the same hostility.

This hostility culminated after they had been nearly a year at Sesheke awaiting the king's decisive reply to their request. At this time Lewanika's sister and co-ruler, the Mukwae, was governor of the Southern Province at Sesheke. During her absence one day, one of the newcomers had brought his colleague into the queen's court to show him how it was built, and traced a diagram in the sand with his foot. The native left in charge instantly accused them both of sorcery against the queen, who, on her return refused to see the missionaries herself, but summoned them to appear before the assembled chiefs. Mr. Baldwin was made to sit bareheaded in the sun, and scarcely had proceedings begun, when one of the chiefs flung himself upon Mr. Baldwin shouting " Seize him ! " and about five hundred men surrounded him. M. Goy threw his arms round him, but the mob, shrieking "Strangle him!", succeeded in tearing the two apart, and after they had tortured the " culprit ", as they considered him to be, he was again made to sit in the sun, covered with blood and dust, until the queen delivered her sentence, namely, that she consented to " pardon " them, but insisted on a heavy fine being paid there and then.

Lewanika, when he heard about it, was much displeased at the affair. He refunded the fine, but ordered the missionaries to quit the country at once. Eventually, however, he yielded so far as to say, "That they might stay to learn the language and customs of

[278]

his people ", but on no account might they go to the Mashukulumbwe nor yet to their neighbours the Batoka.

At his bidding the little party left Sesheke and came up-river to Lealui, leaving their wagons at Kazungula, where, on one pretext or another, they were detained for nearly two years longer. They could not easily get away as all the canoes belonged to the king, and he was not willing to lend them. He had, however, presented M. Coillard with a dug-out for his personal use, but when the latter lent it to Mr. Buckingham to go down to Kazungula and renew his stores, Lewanika could not contain himself for rage. " We had done him out of a good sum of money " (i.e. for the hire of his own canoes, which he had practically refused to lend). " What right had the *Moruti* to hire people (i.e. paddlers) out to this stranger ? " " Are they not the king's own slaves ? " And then he raised the great question : " What would their wages be ? " (These would, of course, pass to the king's pocket.)

Such was the contemporary record, and all the more extraordinary was Lewanika's complete *volte-face* soon afterwards. " The *Moruti* has conquered me ", and the ban was lifted. For several weeks before this the whole missionary body had been boycotted, and an order had even been sent secretly to strangle all the workmen who were engaged on M. Coillard's new mission station near Lealui. At last their perseverance, and M. Coillard's importunities on their behalf won the king's consent. But he insisted that they should bring their wagons up to the capital (three hundred miles through sand and rivers), and trek to their new destination from west to east. This made their route four times longer than if they had been permitted to enter the Mashukulumbwe country from the south.

The reason for this seemed to be that Lewanika had made up his mind to pursue a different policy towards the Mashukulumbwe— peaceful penetration instead of spoliation. M. Coillard wrote : " He is sending there himself to found a large village. He had, moreover, to repair the roads, he says : to make every inquiry on the route and even to send for some Mashukulumbwe who will themselves conduct the missionaries to their country. What good and great news this will be for all true friends of Africa ! "

Mr. Buckingham's party left Sefula on 6th July, 1893, and trekked eastwards through virgin forests, crossing seventeen unbridged rivers (at most of which each wagon had to be unloaded, dismembered and floated across) and on 6th December reached the Nkala river, a tributary of the Kafue. Here their first station was founded. Mr. Buckingham, however, did not long survive the hardships of those wandering years. He died in 1897, soon after the death of his champion, M. Goy. He unconsciously wrote his own epitaph in his message to the Primitive Methodist Missionary Committee, " My work has been that of a pioneer, and I have not shirked any difficulty, hard labour or privation in carrying out the purpose of the Connexion ".

Another party, with the Reverend F. Pickering and the Reverend W. Chapman, had founded a second station at Nanzela in 1895. Looking back on this, Mr. Chapman wrote, in his book, *A Pathfinder in South Central Africa* :

> " In considering some of the beneficial results achieved it must be borne in mind that only those who came in close contact with the people during our first years of work among them have any real conception of their spiritual and moral degradation."

In this they resembled their overlords, the Barotse, but in some other respects their conditions were different. There was no general submission to authority, no outstanding chief, except Lewanika, whom they grudgingly acknowledged, having no cause to love him, and he was a long way off. Moreover, he did not interfere with their internal affairs, contenting himself with levying tribute, and raiding for cattle and slaves now and again. Instead, there were many petty chiefs who had to be visited and won over singly, and who were constantly engaged in faction fighting. One result of this was that, until the British Administration arrived, the natives were apt to bring their disputes to the missionary as arbitrator which, no doubt, helped them to realise that there might be other and better ways of resolving difficulties.

During those early years dangers and privations were acute, and even later on, the second Matabele war, added to the rinderpest which swept away the cattle and much of the wild game, combined to cut off mission supplies from the south. Transport, food, health and housing all presented almost insuperable problems, and the attacks of wild beasts (lions and hyenas which even invaded the huts) seem to have been still more numerous and audacious than in the western country. The industrial missionary had resigned and at first the others had with their own hands to make bricks and put up buildings—dwellings, schools and churches. The natives were not very teachable ; it was extremely difficult to enlist their help for putting up the simplest shelter, and they were apt to strike on the slightest pretext or none at all. Their method of reasoning was baffling. " When the signal for rest was given, they all demanded pay for the half-day (strings of white beads) and because I refused, they shouldered their hoes and returned home. If I would not pay them for the half-day, was it likely I should pay them for a whole day ? " By degrees, however, they agreed to work and to wait even a week for their pay, secure in the certainty that the white man would not " eat " the first days and defraud them, and thus another useful lesson was learnt. But, even when their huts were built, the missionaries were constantly laid low with malaria, and between 1893 and 1905 the small staff lost five valued members by death, besides four children. Nor must the heroic endurance of the wives be forgotten. Upon them fell the training of native girls, the providing for their households, spending hours every day whilst the sellers of a stringy chicken or a few stalks of maize wrangled over the exchange of a string of beads or a strip of calico. They knew what it meant to have no other woman near them in the hour of sickness ; and to see their children fading before their eyes. All this called for great and unlimited patience. Yet the example of a Christian home was not the least of the forces making for righteousness in these primitive surroundings, and the presence of the children opened many doors and many hearts otherwise fast closed.

The language proved another obstacle. As in Barotseland the Sesuto tongue imposed by the Makololo was the *lingua franca* but the missionaries soon found that it was not understood so generally as they had been led to believe. It had been expected that the Baila would have learnt the language of their conquerors but, as time went on, it became evident that if the natives were to be successfully evangelised, they must eventually have books in their own tongue—the Ila language. The Lord's Prayer, and the Ten Commandments were the first passages to be translated, and it was a great day when the Ila people heard the first sermon preached and the first hymn sung in their own tongue. Sunday became known as " the singing day ".

The language study thus forecast was seriously undertaken by the Reverend E. W. Smith (the son of the Reverend J. Smith of Aliwal, *see* page 25), who joined the mission in 1902, and who has since become universally known for his distinguished linguistic and anthropological studies. Of his books, *The Golden Stool* is probably the best known. The Reverend W. Chapman wrote of him at this early date (1910) : " To know him and his work is to admire him. His handbook to the Ila language is second to none among books of that class, and will be found indispensable to Europeans entering the country who wish to learn the Ila language. He has also rendered great service in the preparation of school books and scripture translations."

Another member of the Primitive Methodist Mission should here be mentioned—Mr. J. R. Fell, whose experience has been of the utmost value to the Administration. He did not, it is true, join the mission until 1907, after the end of the real pioneer period, but still under very primitive conditions. He organised the Training Institute at Kafue, and later on became principal of the " Jeanes " School for supervisory teachers under Government service.

The Primitive Methodist missionaries, like nearly all others in Africa, keenly felt the importance of developing Christian education for the young, if the next generation was to be weaned from degrading superstitions. But, here, as elsewhere, it was extremely difficult to induce the parents to let their children attend regularly. " They at first decided that if we would take their children, feed them, clothe them and pay them for attending, they would allow them to come." By degrees matters improved in this respect, and by the end of the first five years a great and noticeable change had been effected in the social life of the people, and the Reverend

W. Chapman could write : " The country that was a closed book to us is now fairly open ; travelling which was once impossible is now rendered safe ; slave trading has been stopped in the neighbourhood of our mission ; no public trials for witchcraft (sorcery) now take place. The people are being taught to labour, and the respect and confidence of the natives has been gained, and the foundations of a great work are well and truly laid."

Shortly after this summary of results was written, the Chartered Company's first representatives arrived in the country (1897), and their Administration confirmed the peaceful settlement thus begun. The following year Lewanika came south to Kazungula to meet the Administrator of Southern Rhodesia, and Mr. Chapman and Mr. Pickering, who had long wished to meet Lewanika, decided to seek an interview with him there. He, too, was anxious to make their acquaintance and had repeatedly asked them to visit him. They found on arrival that he was already on his way north again, so after renewing their exhausted supplies, they returned to their own station at Nanzela and thence trekked on foot across the sandbelt to Lealui. The Reverend Adolphe Jalla introduced them to Lewanika, who talked with them freely, expressed his interest in their work amongst the Baila and promised he would do all he could to assist it. He also supplied them with canoes so that they could return by river instead of confronting the terrible sandbelt again.

Now that the missionaries had been received by their king as his friends the people paid them greater respect. The " boys " who had accompanied them loved to tell, and the people to hear, how the king had presented them with an ox, and lent them his canoes ; how the people at the king's town, and the king himself, attended church on Sundays, and how crowds of boys and girls attended school on weekdays. All this gave an impetus to the schools and even greater was the effect when, a few years later (1902) a King's Messenger arrived, who called the chiefs together and exhorted them strongly on the importance of education. Lewanika's message was imperative :

> " The opportunity offered by the missionary schools must not be neglected. The king commands you to listen to the teaching of your *Baruti* (missionaries)."

This emissary also brought a personal letter from Lewanika, who had just returned from his visit to England for the Coronation of King Edward VII :

" To the Reverend W. Chapman,

My friend,

Yours accepted with the greatest pleasure. We are still improving health yet. Trusting to hear the same from you. I enjoyed my visit to London and should like to see all the native chiefs to speak with them to tell them the news of England, to tell what I have seen with my eyes and what I have been told to do. Am really pleased for your kindness telling me about Mashukulumbwe as they do not care for educating their children. They shall send their children to get learned. The only thing for black man to do is to get learned. I have visited nearly all the churches while I was in England. I received a great reception from your church's people and they gave us some Bibles to cause us to tell others words of God. I will talk hard with the Mashukulumbwe chiefs about the schools as I did at Sesheke and Nalolo. Every chief who comes to see me I tell him to have a school opened in his district and children to be sent to school.

So my friend I will end with best wishes to you and Mrs. Chapman.

I remain,

Your friend,

KING LEWANIKA."

About this time the Northern Copper Company had begun to open up the mines in the rich mineral regions of the north-east. As there was no mission in the whole area, and finding that the Baila language was spoken there, Mr. Chapman deemed it advisable to survey the district and occupy the most suitable posts. After a long and extremely interesting exploration north of the Kafue River during 1904 the Nambala site was selected and opened by the Reverend W. Chapman.

Already in 1899 Messrs. Pickering and Baldwin had made an extended tour to the east and south-east of their two Baila stations (Nkala and Nanzela) and when they reached the Zambezi and noted the large population on its banks they reported that their Mission ought also to have stations amongst the Batonga living there. This project in later years was carried out, and in 1901 Mr. Hogg began work at Sijoba.* The large village of Kasenga was encountered at this time, but it was not till 1909 that the Reverend E. W. Smith was able to begin the work at this important station. Thus the Primitive Methodist Mission now possessed two spheres of labour, the Baila and the Batonga countries but both won at the cost of many sacrifices.

The Reverend W. Chapman wrote : " We crossed the Kafue River on a raft belonging to the Northern Copper Company [sic] and pressed forward to the new site, arriving there on 26th July, 1905. This event marks the beginning of a new chapter in the history of our Baila–Batonga Mission. We were to share in the general progress, for Africa is surely turning its face to the light. This is but the seed-time—who can tell how amazingly fruitful the harvest will be ? "

---

* In 1880 three Roman Catholic (Jesuit) Fathers had trekked from Wankie to Chief Mwemba's village, some thirty-five miles downstream from Sijoba's with the idea of founding a mission there. One of the Fathers had to leave almost immediately and after the death of one of the remaining two, by suspected poisoning, the Mission was abandoned. J.D.C.

With this new departure, the pioneer period may be said to have closed. Since then the mission has gone on from strength to strength and now occupies six stations and fifty outstations. Its headquarters are at 25 Marylebone Road, London, N.W.1.

NORTH-EASTERN RHODESIA.

The missions now working in North-eastern Rhodesia had in many respects similar experiences to those in the western region. Like them, they owed their inspiration to David Livingstone and to the enthusiasm generated by his appeals, and his example. Their history, however, was somewhat different, as in almost every case their present sphere of labour is an extension under more favourable circumstances of work begun in the severest pioneer conditions outside the Rhodesian borders, and before European nations had marked out their respective spheres of influence in this part of Africa. The vast country known earlier as the Marotse–Mambunda Empire, and to us as North-western Rhodesia, lay within clearly defined geographical boundaries, viz., the watershed of the Congo and Zambezi basins, and the great curve of the Zambezi itself. North-eastern Rhodesia comprises the country as far as Lake Tanganyika, a region rich in missionary associations, including as it does the site of Livingstone's death at Chitambo, but its actual occupation by various societies took place later than the pioneer period, and not till after civilised administration had reached it.

THE UNIVERSITIES' MISSION TO CENTRAL AFRICA.

In point of date, the first of these societies to be founded was the *Universities' Mission to Central Africa* which directly owed its origin to Livingstone's appeal in the Senate House at Cambridge on 4th December, 1857.

The following year the " Oxford and Cambridge Mission to Central Africa " was formed. The Universities of Durham and Dublin joined in, and by July, 1861, the first party, led by Bishop Mackenzie and starting from Kongoni at the mouth of the Zambezi on the east coast, had already reached the first objective namely " the tribes dwelling in the neighbourhood of Lake Nyasa " between Zomba and Blantyre. They had met Dr. Livingstone and conferred with him as to future plans ; and the original idea had been to follow in his footsteps and settle in the Zambezi Valley. But, as with other pioneer expeditions, sickness and misfortune attacked them from the first. They suffered also from the Arab slave traders, from raiding, and from the marauding of the Ngoni, a tribe of Zulu origin which spread terror and devastation all around Lake Nyasa. On 31st January, 1862, the Bishop himself died. This was a terrible blow but the mission heroically struggled on, encouraged by his successor, Bishop Tozer, until two years later it became evident, surrounded as they were by the slave trade, and by war, famine and pestilence, unable to obtain supplies, and their ranks incessantly thinned by sickness and death, that entrance into Central

Africa was closed for the time being. In 1864, therefore, the headquarters were removed to Zanzibar. This, however, was in no sense a retreat but a strategical withdrawal to a more promising base of operations, Zanzibar being the operative centre of the Arab slave trade.

Dr. Livingstone died on 1st May, 1873, and during the same year three notable events took place. The first anti-slavery edict was published in Zanzibar and the slave market closed, part of the slave market was purchased by the Universities' Mission; and on Christmas Day, upon that same site, was laid the foundation of what is now the Cathedral (consecrated on 29th June, 1903).

The Universities' Mission, however, never had lost sight of its primary purpose to evangelise the natives around Lake Nyasa, and this purpose had been steadily pursued during those intervening thirty years, concurrently with the work of the two Scottish Missions which had entered Nyasaland in the meantime. It is pleasant to read of the frequent friendly intercourse between the leaders of these missions and the mutual help afforded as need arose whether in matters of transport or in times of sickness.

In 1897, the British South Africa Company extended its rule over North-eastern Rhodesia, its officials entered upon "effectual occupation", and in 1907 British Central Africa became the Nyasaland Protectorate. The partition of " spheres of influence " amongst European nations in 1890 had created some difficulties for the Universities' Mission, part of its work now lying within the territory of Portuguese East Africa (Mozambique) and part within that of Tanganyika, assigned to Germany. The official history of the Universities' Mission to Central Africa says that the Chief Commissioner at Blantyre " was driven to proclaim a British Protectorate ", and Sir Harry Johnston was sent out to arrange the boundaries with the Portuguese. The highlands were to remain British and all the west side of the Lake. The east side was to be divided into five sections, of which the most southerly was to be British, the next two, Portuguese and the two most northerly, German. The island of Likoma, however, was to remain British because occupied by the Mission. The Lake itself was declared to be international water.

It was a great trial to the missionaries that so many of the villages where their work lay thus passed under the Portuguese regime but they went on perseveringly. The work of lay members should not be forgotten, especially Mr. A. C. Madan, a Senior Fellow of Christ Church, Oxford, who joined the Universities' Mission in 1880 and whose linguistic work, first on Swahili and later upon north Rhodesian dialects, has been of first importance. In 1899, Dr. Howard joined the staff, bringing with him the new discoveries about the mosquito as the origin of malaria fever, and determined to apply this knowledge to bettering conditions on the stations. Prophylactic measures were put into force ; better housing, mosquito proof buildings, clearance of bush around the stations, regular quinine dosage—and immediate improvements in health resulted. Later on medical work was organised amongst the natives and a hospital built.

On 4th December, 1907, the Universities' Mission celebrated its Jubilee at Cambridge, fifty years after Dr. Livingstone's memorable appeal in the Senate House ; and the formation of a Bishopric of Northern Rhodesia was proposed as a memorial and thank-offering. Three years later Bishop Hine entered his diocese as its first Bishop and spent the next four years prospecting for a suitable mission centre, covering 5,000 miles on foot ! The first synod of the diocese was held in 1927, and in 1935 the Church of the Holy Nativity at Ndola, in the midst of the Copperbelt, was constituted its Cathedral. " The Committee of the European Church agreed that the Church should be for all, irrespective of race or colour."

The Universities' Mission has always endeavoured to minister to the spiritual needs of the Europeans around them as well as to the natives, as do several other leading societies. In July, 1922, the Bishop presided over the Third General Missionary Conference in Northern Rhodesia which was attended by representatives of nearly all the missions in the Territory.

From the foregoing dates it will be noted that strictly speaking the pioneer days were over when the Universities' Mission extended itself into Northern Rhodesia. Earlier, its members had had to face the same experiences and to overcome the same obstacles as all other pioneer missions in Central Africa : privations, transport difficulties, opposition of chiefs and of the sorcerers' fraternity, sickness and death and, not least, the Arab slave trade and the constant raiding of the more peaceable tribes by the more warlike, such as the Ngoni. But, nothing daunted, they persevered, and the recompense has been seen in the converts whom they have felt justified in ordaining to responsible positions, not only as lay preachers but even as deacons and clergy and who for the most part have " by their diligence made their calling and election sure ".

THE LIVINGSTONIA MISSION.

The next to enter Nyasaland was the Livingstonia Mission (United Free Church of Scotland) in 1875. This mission gradually spread southwards, largely through the influence and often the actual agency of African converts themselves, European missionaries following them at their own request. The mission was initiated by Dr. James Stewart of Lovedale, and the first settlement was made at Cape Maclear on the southern end of Lake Nyasa, by the pioneers, Dr. Laws and his colleagues. Cape Maclear proved an unhealthy site, and the station was later removed further north to Bandawe. Dr. Elmslie and two others joined them and the work gradually extended into what is now North-eastern Rhodesia, including

Chitambo, the place where Dr. Livingstone died and where in his memory a station was planted in 1906 by his nephew and his grandson, Mr. Malcolm Moffat and Dr. Hubert Wilson.

The Livingstonia Mission is now so well known and has been so successful in winning Africans to the Christian faith and influencing the whole region for good that its terrible early struggles against the Ngoni can hardly be realised. What the Zulus were in South Africa and what the Matabele were in Bechuanaland and Barotseland, so were the Ngoni in this area. The Ngoni are a branch of the same aggressive, warlike stock whose ancestral ruler was the bloodthirsty Chief Chaka. They incessantly raided their weaker and more peaceable neighbours. It was said that these weaker peoples were almost driven into the Lake (Nyasa) by this relentless foe. "They had to rear their families, cradling them in the cracks of the rocks or crannies between the boulders to prevent their rolling off into the water."

Dr. Laws and his colleagues early recognised that the terror inspired by the Ngoni would prove an insuperable obstacle to mission work amongst their victims. The essential thing, therefore, was for the Gospel first to exercise its power among the Ngoni themselves. Long and difficult was the task, described as it is in Dr. Elmslie's book *Amongst the Wild Ngoni*, and even when a certain footing had been obtained and influence won, this gave rise to a new hindrance. The Ngoni had begun to realise that there might be certain advantages from having white men amongst them, especially in regard to medical help and technical training, and wished to keep these advantages for themselves and they resented the missionaries having any intercourse with the Tonga and others whom they regarded as inferiors, only fit to be plundered and enslaved. "Why do you not come up and live with us ? Can you milk the fish that you remain at the lake ? Come up and live with us and we will give you cattle. We are the rulers."

By 1882, an African evangelist. William Koyi, had the courage and faith to go and live among the Ngoni, and after long and patient efforts (including the learning of their language so as to converse freely with them) won their confidence and disarmed their suspicions. It became possible at last to establish schools and win converts, the first of whom were baptised in 1890. But, as in other parts of Africa, the influence of the Gospel manifested itself not so much in the numbers added to the Church as in the social uplift of the whole people. This was shown in a letter addressed to the mission leaders by Sir Harry Johnston, the Commissioner for British Central Africa, in April, 1896 :

"You will observe that in the new regulations extending the hut tax to all parts of the Protectorate I have exempted one district only, viz., that portion of the West Nyasa District which is occupied by the Northern Ngoni. My reasons for doing so are these : hitherto the Ngoni chiefs have shown themselves capable of managing the affairs of their own country without compelling the interference of the Administration of the Protectorate. They have maintained a friendly attitude towards the English and have allowed us to travel and settle unhindered in and through their country. As long, therefore, as the Northern Ngoni give us no cause for interference in their internal affairs, so long I trust they may remain exempt from taxation."

A young convert from the Tonga tribe, describing to a friend some special services held in 1897, wrote : " As I saw men with scars of spears and clubs and bullets on them, I said in my heart ' Can these be the Ngoni, submitting to God—the Ngoni who killed the Henga and the Bisa and other tribes ? ' " Another witness, the Reverend J. Henderson, wrote : " It was then that I realised the nature of the work that was being done among the tribe. It was the fighting men, the men in the prime of their strength, that the Gospel had laid hold of ".

The United Free Church was later granted a plot of ground around the spot where Livingstone's heart was buried, and within a few years a church was established there (in 1906), but apart from the work at Chitambo, the main extension of the Livingstonia Mission into North-eastern Rhodesia began in 1913.

Every society develops some special characteristic as time goes on, and the Livingstonia Mission has been distinguished for its medical work. In 1928 it could be said that it had a doctor on every station. But perhaps its leading feature has been the Overton Training Institution founded by Dr. Laws at Kondowi above Florence Bay on Lake Nyasa, which already in 1901 counted 500 students in training to be craftsmen, teachers or evangelists. Although the mission had not yet extended itself into North-eastern Rhodesia, a good many of the students were already drawn from various Rhodesian tribes who returned when their training was accomplished to turn it to good account in white employ.

The same may be said of the pupils trained in the Blantyre Mission of the Established Church of Scotland, occupying the region south of Lake Nyasa, numbers of whom have emigrated to Livingstone and other Rhodesian centres, where they are known as " Blantyres " and where their skill and intelligence command high wages. They have their own churches and pastors and form a valuable element in the native population.

The pioneer, Dr. Laws, of Livingstonia, was frequently referred to as the greatest living missionary—" A super missionary ". He was unique in variety of attainment, in capacity for all forms of work, in indomitable faith and patience and in magnificent achievement. (Yet) " No, no, no ", he exclaimed when reference was made to the transformation he had effected in Central Africa. " You must not put me in the foreground. God has used me for the purpose . . . but I want no credit." *

---

* From *Preachers I Have Heard.*

No sketch of the Livingstonia Pioneer Mission would be complete if it left out of account the work of Christian laymen, first in starting and financing it, and later on in relieving the missionaries of the secular work which had at first been unavoidable, thus setting them free for their evangelistic labours.

This ancillary help falls under three main heads : transport, commerce and exploration and the history of this mission, as recorded in the publication *Daybreak in Livingstonia* and other books, brings out in a most interesting manner the work of the pioneers in each of these three departments, and the way in which these burdens were gradually lifted from the shoulders of the missionaries and laid on those of equally earnest and devoted laymen.

The first expedition, in 1875, included besides the two ordained missionaries (Reverend R. Laws and Reverend J. Henderson), a carpenter, a blacksmith, an engineer, an agriculturist and a seaman : and the whole party accepted the leadership of Lieutenant Young of the Royal Navy who was granted two years' leave of absence for this enterprise—he having already ascended the Zambezi and Shire rivers in 1867 in search of Dr. Livingstone, falsely reported to be dead. For the expedition of 1875, Young brought a steel boat, built in sections to his own design, so that it could be carried past the Murchison Cataracts on the Shire, and put together again on Lake Nyasa. This was the *Ilala*, so named from the place where Livingstone died. It was the first of a succession of boats placed on the chain of African lakes, in the first instance for direct missionary service, and later on for the work of the African Lakes' Company, founded by a group of Glasgow businessmen of whom Mr. James Stevenson was the leading spirit. Mr. Stevenson had early perceived the importance of linking up the two great lakes, Nyasa and Tanganyika, by a practicable road, and had taken steps to have the 210 miles of route surveyed in 1879 by a lay member of the mission, Mr. James Stewart, c.e. The work was actually begun in March, 1881, Mr. Stevenson providing £4,000 towards the cost, of which £3,000 was a free gift. His desire was to open up Nyasaland to legitimate commerce. Livingstone had perceived and proclaimed that this was one of the best means of destroying the Arab slave-trade and the nefarious traffic in war material and European spirits, then beginning to spread into East Africa.

The African Lakes Company was first formed in 1878 under the title of the Livingstone Central Africa Company Limited, later changed to the African Lakes Company, and in 1893 it was reconstituted as the African Lakes Corporation Limited. From its inception the African Lakes Company refused to sell guns or ammunition, opposed the drink traffic, and endeavoured to send out as its agents men who could be relied upon to carry out these conditions. Mr. Stevenson would have associated the Livingstonia Mission with the enterprise, but the mission leaders felt they could not embark on commercial undertakings, however laudable. The African Lakes Company was therefore formed on an independent basis, but not with a view to immediate profit. For many years indeed it paid no dividend, but it proved a great benefit not only to the Livingstonia Mission but to the natives themselves by showing the latter how to obtain the calico and other goods which they really needed, by exchanging their own labour or their own produce. Moreover, as will be seen, it helped materially to break the power of the Arab slave traders.

Two young brothers, John and Fred Moir, were appointed managers of the African Lakes Company and they proved admirably fitted for their task both in character and capacity—fearless hunters, undaunted explorers and as the event proved, capable of organising prolonged and successful resistance to Arab aggression. It has been said with much truth that if the mission leaders in England and Scotland were morally the founders of Nyasaland, the Moir brothers upheld by Mr. Stevenson and his friends were its founders on the secular side. Both took an active share in the construction of the Stevenson Road, thanks to which they were able later on to extend the work of the African Lakes Company from its headquarters at Mandala near Blantyre in the Shire Hills to the north and west and even beyond Lake Tanganyika into what is now North-eastern Rhodesia. The construction of the Stevenson Road had cost the lives both of Mr. J. Stewart, c.e., and of his successor, Mr. McEwen, as well as those of many native helpers. Their work had not been in vain, since by 1885 there was now a clear route of 1,400 miles from the Zambezi mouth to South Tanganyika with only about 260 miles of land carriage throughout the whole of it. Not content with refraining from the sale of spirits themselves, the managers strove ardently to have the traffic in drink and fire-arms stopped altogether. At the Berlin Conference of 1884, attended by delegates from all the European states, Mr. F. Moir, Dr. Laws and others were successful in getting this prohibited throughout all the Central African regions, and when the British Government took over the administration in 1890, this prohibition was forcibly maintained. Amongst the Company's many activities, a vast nursery was laid out, and many kinds of fruit and vegetable seeds imported.

The lives of the scattered Europeans in the area had previously been constantly made precarious by the tribal warfare intermittently waged around them. Now the natives around Lake Nyasa were just beginning to have confidence in the white man when a new danger arose. Arab hostility suddenly seemed to flare up in a new form, quite different from the sporadic attacks to capture slaves from helpless villages which had always prevailed. This was a highly organised slave-raiding invasion force which seemed to centre in Zanzibar, and which in 1887 hurled itself against the Kaonde country northwest of Lake Nyasa, a region through which ran the Stevenson Road. After wreaking their usual brutality upon the wretched inhabitants they attacked the European outposts and first the African Lakes Company depot at Karonga, which had become a centre for hundreds of native refugees. " The Livingstonia missionaries and the Lakes Company had resolved never to fight except in case of utter necessity when by doing so they could save their own lives and those of the natives." But the Arabs refused to parley, demanding women, cows and goats, and hostilities became inevitable. The two white men at Karonga held out till they were joined by the British Consul and a few others, and eventually they were able to evacuate Karonga, and to maintain a sort of siege warfare against the Arabs in their stockades which from time to time they attempted to rush, but without success. The war once begun lasted nearly two years, and both the Moir brothers were severely wounded. It soon became clear that the conflict was really between the African Lakes Company and the Arab slave traders who were determined that European commerce should not oust their own traffic. The Sultan of Zanzibar adjured their leaders to desist. They kissed his letter and salaamed to his messenger but declined to obey. It was not until the spring of 1889 that Sir H. H. Johnston was sent by the British Foreign Office with renewed letters from the Sultan of Zanzibar to try and negotiate peace. In this he was successful. The Arabs were thoroughly tired out by the strenuous resistance of Mr. Fotheringham at Karonga and his few comrades (including Captain Lugard, famous in later years) and they seemed glad to surrender. A treaty was signed on 22nd October, and the British flag hoisted with all honours. The following year Nyasaland became a British Protectorate, and by an arrangement with the British South Africa Company, just incorporated, the western region was severed from British Central Africa and became part of North-eastern Rhodesia.

The London Missionary Society.

The London Missionary Society's work in East Africa was begun in 1877. " Your Society is the executor of Livingstone and we rejoice to know that your directors have accepted the trust ", said one speaker at their annual meeting ; and another, " There is no more important mission that you have undertaken than this to Central Africa ; important to commerce, to science, to Christianity, to the cause of truth and freedom '.

The first London Missionary Society party, consisting of six missionaries, led by the Reverend Roger Price, the survivor of the Helmore expedition of 1860, started for the interior from Zanzibar, their destination being Ujiji on the shore of Lake Tanganyika, the site of Livingstone's and Stanley's historic meeting in October, 1871. But after thirteen months' travelling under terrible conditions and subject to hindrances from the Arab slave trade, only three out of the six lived to reach their goal. Even after the first stations had been founded, misfortunes continued to pursue the missions, many members dying and others having to be invalided home. Nevertheless the gaps were filled as they arose and valuable explorations were made, especially by Captain Hore who eventually in 1883 brought out a steel life-boat in sections, *The Morning Star*, This was brought from the east coast on specially constructed light steel carts to Ujiji near the north end of Lake Tanganyika and there put together on the beach, to the astonishment of the natives, one of whom declared, " They had been promised to go to sea (i.e. on the lake) in a saucepan ! " This was almost the first of the boats which have played such a large part in the history of the missions around the African Lakes. Both this mission and that of the Free Church of Scotland will be remembered for their skill and perseverance in placing steamers on the African lakes ; steamers brought up in sections from the east coast, and put together on the shores of Lake Nyasa by the Livingstonia Mission, and of Lake Tanganyika by the London Missionary Society. The much larger vessel the *Good News* was brought out in sections along the Quilimane–Nyasa route to the southern end of Lake Tanganyika in 1883–4. The construction of this steamboat had been much delayed by the death of the engineer, Mr. Roxburgh, who had come out specially for this undertaking, and also by the loss in transit of certain fittings without which the boilers could not be set going. These were only some of the hindrances to pioneer transport.

The constant illness and frequent deaths among the missionaries, and the difficulties created by the Arab slave trade and tribal warfare, seemed insuperable obstacles to progress, and after ten years of struggle and disappointment the leaders decided to break fresh ground in less adverse surroundings. One of the chief troubles was that the African chiefs raided each other, often without the slightest pretext, in order to collect slaves and sell them to the Arab dealers. (The Livingstonia Mission had to cope with the same iniquity.) Accordingly in 1887 a new station, Fwambo, was opened, thirty miles south of Lake Tanganyika and well within the borders of what is now North-eastern Rhodesia, and in 1890 the station of Kawimbe was founded. During the intervening three years, the Europeans (traders, travellers and missionaries) had been beleaguered by an Arab advance on Lake Nyasa, and for over a year they had been entirely cut off, no mails arriving and scarcely any supplies. At the same time, the earlier route from the coast (Zanzibar to Ujiji) was closed owing to disturbances arising from the German occupation of Tanganyika, assigned to it by the European Conference of 1890. As a result, in 1898 the London Missionary Society handed over to the Moravian Missions its earliest stations, and all further advances were into North-eastern Rhodesia.

From the first, Swahili, the *lingua franca* of the coast, had been the medium of intercourse with the tribes the mission was seeking to evangelise, namely, the Amambwe and the Alungu. But Mr. Picton Jones and Dr. Mather had devoted themselves so successfully to the study of these tribes' own language that by 1891 it was possible to conduct at least one native service in it, and before long simple school books and Bible portions had been provided in the speech of the people of the southern end of the Lake and of the plateau, which had now been adopted as the working language of the mission.

The mission was now beginning to bear fruit in many ways— a fact attested by European travellers such as Lionel Decle and Miss

Mary Hall (1903) who in their published accounts recorded the great difference discernible between the untouched tribes and those which had come under Christian influence. It was long, however, before the days of danger ended. As late as 1895, the Awemba (or Bemba) tribe made a fierce attack upon the Alungu, carrying off booty and captives, mainly women, upon whom shocking barbarities were inflicted. Already in 1893, members of the London Missionary Society had visited Lake Mweru with a view to working amongst these Awemba but without success, their chief being opposed to having even a school started. However, in 1901, the society had definitely occupied Mbereshi near Lake Mweru, and this station has now become famous for its admirable girls' school, organised by Miss Mabel Shaw, as well as for the institution giving industrial training.

A new era had begun in 1891 when the British South Africa Company's Administration started, and by 1904, conditions had completely changed. Tribal warfare and Arab slave raiding had been arrested, and good roads made transport much easier. In consequence, the missionaries who had borne the burden and heat of the day found their work much less laborious, whilst on the other hand the altered spirit of the natives had greatly facilitated the establishment of law and order, a fact which was frankly admitted by the administration. Moreover, during these first ten years (1891–1901) of setting up civilised government, a great many Europeans passed backwards and forwards through the country bounded by the " African Lakes " (Tanganyika, Mweru, Nyasa and Bangweulu). These were officials, travellers, traders and contractors (such as those employed in putting up the African Transcontinental Telegraph) and many of them enjoyed the simple hospitality of the mission houses and their care in times of sickness. Already changes were observable in many directions, though these were, of course, not by any means universal.

The worst cruelties and more barbaric of the ancient rites were disappearing, for instance the poison ordeal for witch-finding was forbidden. Cleanliness both of the person and in the village was improving, and Sunday observance and attendance at church were spreading. New crafts too were being learnt, among them the building of square brick houses, of boats, wagons and furniture. Hospitals and local dispensaries were set up and welfare work and domestic training begun among the women. Mission schools were also set up and work done on the language and the translation of books. By 1928, 11,000 children were being educated in 288 schools, according to the Educational Code of Nyasaland. " The industrial work done at Mbereshi is of the very highest quality and shows what great effects on character such training may produce. While always keeping before it the aim of winning Africans to Christ, the London Missionary Society interprets its mission in the broadest sense, and looks to converting the whole man."* Naturally, however, the

---

* *The Way of the White Fields in Rhodesia.* Reverend E. W. Smith, D.D.

most important of all the missionary activities and the one on which they all depended was the work of evangelisation.

In addition to the Universities' Mission to Central Africa, the Livingstonia Mission and the London Missionary Society, which were the real pioneer missions in North-eastern Rhodesia, some other missions, which began elsewhere in primitive conditions and were later extended to this part of the Territory, should receive a brief mention.

THE DUTCH REFORMED CHURCH MISSION.

The well-known and distinguished missionary, the Reverend Andrew Charles Murray, was chosen to represent the Dutch Reformed Church of South Africa in the Nyasaland region in 1888. His work extended widely from the Chewa country in the south and west ; and when the Dutch Reformed Church of the Orange Free State joined the work in 1898, it was carried forward into the East Luangwa district of Northern Rhodesia and is now one of the largest missions in the country around Fort Jameson and westwards from that centre.

THE SOUTH AFRICAN GENERAL MISSION.

This mission is working amongst the Mankoya round Kaba Hill and Luampa, and amongst the Bakaonde at Mukinge Hill. Their work in these regions was initiated by Dr. Martyn Watney in 1923. Native dialects have been written down and translations of the scriptures made.

THE WESLEYAN METHODIST MISSION AND OTHERS.

The Wesleyan Methodist Mission began at Chipembi in 1912 and has been extended in the north to Broken Hill and in the south-west to the Zambezi, thus linking up with the Primitive Methodist Mission on the west. This mission was extended into Northern Rhodesia by the Reverend John White in response to the plea of a chieftain's son converted in the mines of Southern Rhodesia.

Important work in local languages has been accomplished by the Reverend C. M. Doke of the *South African Baptist Missionary Society* in the Luangwa district, its work dating from 1905, and now extending to Ndola and other stations on the railway.

The *Seventh Day Adventists* entered Batokaland in the same year and the *Brethren in Christ* (an American society) in 1906. This last was an extension from Southern Rhodesia by two courageous ladies, and is distinguished by its work amongst native girls.

The *Roman Catholic Mission* of the *White Fathers* (1891) and of the *Jesuits* (first attempted in 1878 and 1888) deserve a more detailed description than can be given here. The schools of the White Fathers have been cordially praised by education officers. Their work has proceeded mainly round Fort Jameson but also eastwards into Nyasaland and westwards to the shores of Lake Bangweulu.

It would be impossible in the space at our disposal to deal at equal length with all the missions that have entered Northern Rhodesia since the beginning of this century. There are said to be seventeen of them—possibly more : and there is room for them all. Most are working in harmony with each other and respecting each others' field of work, and the General Missionary Conference inaugurated at Livingstone in 1914 under the presidency of the Reverend E. W. Smith, D.D., seeks to promote co-operation and brotherly feelings amongst all Christian workers in the Territory.

Enough has been said to show how great has been the missionary contribution to the opening up of the Dark Continent—in the departments of language, education, medicine, anthropology and social reform. But perhaps the greatest accomplishment has been to develop the capacities and possibilities of the African himself, transforming many of the most primitive peoples into peaceable, intelligent and self-respecting members of the community and of the Church.

Truly it may be said : " The people that walked in darkness have seen a great light : they that dwell in the land of the shadow of death, upon them hath the light shined ".

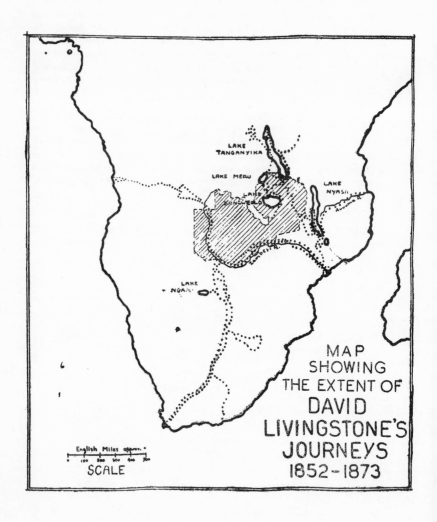

LAKE
TANGANYIKA

LAKE MERU

LAKE
BANGWEOLA

LAKE
NYASA

LAKE
NGAMI

English Miles approx.

SCALE

MAP
SHOWING
THE EXTENT OF
DAVID
LIVINGSTONE'S
JOURNEYS
1852–1873

9

DAVID LIVINGSTONE

A SHORT PORTRAIT
OF THE GREAT MISSIONARY—EXPLORER
BASED ON AN ACCOUNT BY

I. M. FLETCHER

OF THE LONDON MISSIONARY SOCIETY

1950

Based on an account by I. M. Fletcher of the London Missionary Society, and illustrated by passages from original letters and other documents in the collection of the Rhodes-Livingstone Museum and elsewhere.

" I had not the smallest idea of being honoured as I now am in my own country. I was engaged in simply trying to do my duty, without any expectation of fame ; and when I hear the kind expressions of approbation which have been made use of in reference to my past labours, I feel encouraged and my heart looks forward to what is to come."

How often are such expressions used as a matter of form on receiving an honour which has been coveted, hoped for, or even expected ! Spoken by David Livingstone, in his reply to Sir John Key during the session of the Court of Common Council of 21st May, 1857, when he was admitted to the Freedom of the City of London, these were words sincerely spoken. In his campaign to make known to the English public the horrors of the slave trade in Africa, Livingstone had done all he could in the writing of letters and articles to make himself and his travels known, yet the lionising he received in England during that year was beyond his expectations and not much to his inclination, so that it never turned his head. He did not covet fame for himself but as a means to rouse public opinion to the aid of his cherished cause—the abolition of slavery and the slave trade. His plea rang through the country—get rid of the slave trade, the " open sore of the world "—make it unprofitable by lawful, healthy commerce, and so force the Arab out of the business.

" I go back to Africa to try to make an open path for commerce and Christianity," were the closing words of his lecture given to the members of Cambridge University on 4th December, 1857.

Livingstone believed that by the opening up of Africa to legitimate trade and commerce the Arabs and other slave-traders would be forced to abandon this inhuman method of gain. To this end he had given his life not only to the evangelisation but to the exploration of Africa. In those days a map of Africa showed the interior as a blank, thought to be desert, and here was a man who had been all the way across it with a handful of native followers, travel-ling partly by ox and canoe, but mostly just walking. The story is amazing, firing the imagination in 1950 as it did in 1857. Here is thrilling adventure, the fascination of triumph over danger from man and beast and nature, glimpses into the great unknown ; and what possibilities for commerce, for civilisation and for humanity ! This man of middle height, worn and rugged of feature, slow of speech in the English tongue which he had used so seldom

[298]

for years past, gripped the select members of the Royal Geographical Society and their friends. He entranced the public in great gatherings in London and the provinces, he had audience of the Queen, he addressed undergraduates at Cambridge ; and he left them all with the sure and certain knowledge that his care, his thought, his whole life, was service to Africa.

David Livingstone was born on the 19th March, 1813, in one of the single-room flats belonging to the Blantyre Cotton Mills and now the Scottish National Memorial. His grandfather had been a Highlander from the Island of Ulva, and his father and mother brought him up to know many of the traditions of his Highland ancestry as well as to be pious and God-fearing. He grew up one of a family of five in a happy and industrious home. Later in life when the highest in the land were showering compliments on him he was writing of " my own order, the honest poor ". In fact, his parents were so poor that at the age of ten he was put to work in the cotton mills, first as a piecer and then as a spinner. In spite of fourteen working hours a day he found time to study, notably Latin, at an evening class from 8 to 10 p.m.

" The dictionary part of my labours was followed up till twelve o'clock or later, if my mother did not interfere by jumping up and snatching the books out of my hands. I had to be back in the factory by six in the morning, and continue my work with intervals for breakfast and dinner till eight o'clock at night. I read in this way many of the classical authors and knew Virgil and Horace better at sixteen than I do now," although he once confessed, late in his life, to be " as unfit for study in the evenings as ever I had been when a cotton spinner." !

In addition to a wide interest in reading he would as a boy scour the country with his brothers in search of botanical, geological or zoological specimens. Indeed, his interest was not always confined to fossil specimens as such and a neatly poached trout or salmon not infrequently graced the Livingstones' table as a result of David's rambles.

Brought up as he was in a God-fearing home, David Livingstone's thoughts turned early to religion.

" It was my privilege to enjoy the instruction, example, and prayers of pious parents."

It was, however, not until about his twentieth year that he began seriously to consider becoming a missionary. An appeal to the churches by a certain Gutzlaff on behalf of China fired his imagination and determined him to aspire to becoming a missionary, moved by " the claims of so many millions of his fellow-creatures and the complaints of the scarcity, of the want of qualified missionaries ". From this time his " efforts were constantly directed towards that object without any fluctuation ".

Livingstone's reasons for becoming a medical man lay within his resolve to become a missionary. Considering that the healing of the body would be the best way to reach the souls of the Chinese, he started straight away with such equipment as he had to study medicine. He found time for long country excursions with his two brothers " collecting simples ", identifying them from a book, and trying to learn their uses. The habit of noticing and noting was probably far more useful than the immediate knowledge gained ; in fact, without this power—already well-developed—Livingstone could never have given that close attention to accurate detail that later made the world wonder, and the Cape astronomer write, " he has fixed his geographical points with very great accuracy and yet he is only a poor missionary ".

During the years 1836–1838 he was able to spend time studying medicine and theology at Glasgow University and in 1838 he made application to the London Missionary Society to become a missionary to China. His application was provisionally accepted and he was called to London to meet the directors. China, however, as a result of the opium war, was a forbidden country for Europeans, so that Livingstone's hopes of going there faded rapidly. At this point he met Dr. Robert Moffat, who was in England creating interest in his South African Mission at Kuruman. He spoke of the smoke of a thousand villages to be seen to the north, and of the need of a man of pioneering interests who would not be content to settle down in an old station. So was Livingstone's course set for the fulfilment of his resolve—he decided to go to Africa. First he returned to Scotland to take his medical diploma and was then ordained on the 20th November, 1840. On the 8th of December he embarked on the ship *George* and set sail for Africa.

Livingstone described his voyage in several letters to his friends telling them how glad he was when a split foremast and lack of fresh water necessitated a month's stay at Rio de Janeiro, where kind-hearted peasants offered every hospitality ; and how he had enjoyed a showerbath under a waterfall, running the risk of having his clothes stolen and being made to look foolish.

He took a scientific interest in seasickness, too, and writes while still at sea :

" I should have been delighted to have assisted you when passing through that grievous ordeal, seasickness. It is indeed a dolorous predicament to be in, a man and his wife and the stomachs of both making efforts to quit their bodies every time the head is elevated, is really a melancholy spectacle. I pitied but could not cure. The only cruelty I was guilty of and I am not quite sure but I should have done the same to you if you like my friend here had rashly quoted the text to me before the sickness began ' Two are better than one '. I was quoting the same text to him when both he and his spouse were turning their stomachs inside out into one basin—I think this will give you some idea of what you may expect. It is as bad as you can picture it in your imagination. I did not feel it."

At last he arrived in South Africa, with orders to stay at Kuruman until Robert Moffat returned from leave in England and to await definite instructions.

As it was nearly two years before Moffat came back to his station Livingstone had time to look around. He reached the mission station of Kuruman in Bechuanaland on 31st July, 1841, and describes his arrival to his friend Prentice :

" Through the gracious care of our heavenly father I have at last reached this which is to be my resting, or rather halting place for a little. We left Algoa Bay on the 20th May and reached this on the 31st July, a pretty long period you think but through the whole it has been so pleasant I never got tired of it. The wagons are very comfortable affairs indeed, little houses in fact, so you may expect to set up housekeeping long before you are surrounded by mud walls. I could tell you a great deal about the country but any book of travels will supply a better account of it than I can. . . . I find this a pretty spot but as it is winter it wants most of its charms. The church is the largest I have seen on any mission station. The walls are built of stone and so strong they resemble those of a battery. The gardens are excellent but the number of the people is much smaller than I expected to find."

He was twenty-eight years old, unknown and unnoticed by the public ; just a young Scottish doctor, " determined to devote my life to the cause of missions, thereby endeavouring to evince my love and gratitude to Him ' who though rich, yet for our sakes became poor '." So he had expressed himself five years previously in his offer of service to the London Missionary Society, dated Blantyre, 5th September, 1837.

His colleague at Kuruman was a man eighteen years his senior, Roger Edwards, and barely two months after Livingstone's arrival the two set off northwards to explore with a view to founding further mission stations. He writes again to Prentice :

" You have heard of the great success said to have attended missionary efforts in this locality. It is great but coming from England it is invisible, or nearly so. Those who had to deal with Bechuanas 20 years ago and those who have seen them far in the interior alone can appreciate the change. Don't expect to find such amiable christians as you read of in the South Seas, etc. It is quite different round here. Don't expect to find chiefs friendly to receiving missionaries. In general they are hostile and when friendly it is generally for the purpose of ' milking ' them. . . . Within 100 miles of this to the north and north East the chiefs are all hostile. They indeed receive us with a show of apparent friendship but they likewise tell us they do not want our Gospel for it teaches men to put away their wives and this they are determined not to do, and most of their people taking courage from the countenance of their chiefs are bitter scorners and opponents. Several of these chiefs have removed further away for the express purpose of being beyond the reach of the Gospel."

Almost immediately on arrival Livingstone had formed the opinion that the London Missionary Society should expand its activities preferably to the more thickly populated north.

" I mentioned that the tribes near us to the North and N.E. are all hostile to Christianity. The different villages in the other directions are not so but these are all taken possession of by Griqua town missionaries. In fact they have nearly encompassed us. Don't imagine I am sorry at it. I love to see their arms encircling and ready to grasp us for it will force us towards the dark interior, if no other motive compels us this will. We shall have no one to itinerate to but people of the north. There are very few people on this station and very few in the surrounding localities, unless you consider 700 as a large population for K. and within 14 miles of this 1,300 or 1,400. The people are far off. There are many 80 or 100 miles to the North East, but all or nearly all are bitter opponents to the gospel."

Accordingly he and Edwards undertook a journey of 700 miles and selected a spot 250 miles north of Kuruman, Lelepole in Bakwain territory, as a suitable place for a mission station. As neither Moffat nor any definite instructions from him had reached Kuruman before their return, Livingstone went off again, this time by himself, living amongst the natives so that he might learn their language and their ways of thinking. These solitary expeditions gave Livingstone much valuable experience in the treatment of the native peoples, and before he had been a year in the country he was already showing that ability to control Africans and to inspire their loyalty that later became such a marked characteristic. During these journeys also he passed within ten days' march of Lake Ngami of which he had heard already at the Cape and which he was to discover in 1849.

Six months before the return of the Moffat family on 13th December, 1843, he received the long-awaited letter from the mission directors authorising the formation of the new station in the interior. " The dark interior " was already beginning to grip him ! In his reply to the directors of the London Missionary Society he says, " May the Lord enable me to consecrate my whole being to the glorious work " ; while the thrill and pride of the pioneer are in the words he wrote to his friend, Prentice, on 9th October, 1843, " I have been further into the interior than any other European " (that being between two and three hundred miles north of Kuruman).

As the Bakwain people had been driven from Lelepole in the meantime, the new outpost was started at Mabotsa in the land of the Bakhatla where Livingstone could work among both them and the Bakwain. He describes it in glowing terms to his friend :

" I returned a few days ago from the erection of a hut at the Bakhatla, a tribe situated a little more than 200 miles north of this. It is the nearest point in the interior where an elligible spot can be found, and we have by this step taken possession of it for a station. A lovelier spot you never saw, a hill in the rear is called *Mabotsa* (a marriage feast) may the Lord be with the missionaries who labour there so that many may thence be admitted to the marriage supper of the Lamb."

Here, with his newly married bride, Moffat's eldest daughter, Mary, and Roger Edwards, he settled down to missionary routine, attending to planting and building, to teaching and healing, to talking and to preaching. It was soon after settling at Mabotsa, when the people were having trouble with sheep-stealing lions, that Livingstone led the hunt against them in which his arm was badly mauled, leaving the marks by which his body was later identified. Here, too, Livingstone's dominant personality showed itself in his inability to live peaceably with Edwards who, in his turn, resented a younger man taking the lead and, probably unwittingly, ordering him about. Edwards exaggerated his grievances, Livingstone could not see that he had any, and the position became so strained that, in 1846, the Livingstones moved forty miles further on to Chonuane in Sechele's country.

Here Livingstone built himself a house and again began all the activities of a mission station. From the first, Sechele himself showed great interest and after three years was baptised a Christian, but conversions among his followers were few though, as Livingstone said, " real progress has been made ". His work he described as :

" Building, gardening, cobbling, doctoring, tinkering, carpentering, gun-mending, farriering, wagon-mending, preaching, lecturing on physics according to my means beside a chair in divinity to a class of three."

The Livingstones were unable to stay long at Chonuane. The want of rain was fatal to agriculture and about equally fatal to the mission. Many of the surrounding Dutch farmers were unfriendly and hostile to Livingstone's cherished scheme of planting native evangelists among the tribes. The necessity to move was apparent, and in February, 1847, the Livingstones, followed by the chief and all his tribe, moved to the banks of the Kolobeng River where a mission station was again set up. A typical day's work at Kolobeng he describes in a letter to the Reverend D. G. Watt :

" We get up as soon as we can—generally with the sun in summer, then have family worship, breakfast and school, and as soon as these are over we begin the manual operations needed —sowing, ploughing, smithy work and every other sort of work by turns as required. My better half is employed all morning in culinary or other work and feeling pretty well tired by dinner time we take about an hour's rest then, but more frequently without the respite I try to secure for myself she goes off to her infant school and this I am happy to say is very popular with the youngsters. She sometimes has 80 but the average may be 60. My manual labours are continued till about 5 o'clock. I then go into the town to give lessons and talk to anyone who may be disposed for it. As soon as the cows are milked we have a meeting in Sechele's house which brings me home about half past 8, and generally tired enough—too fatigued to think of any mental exertion. I do not enumerate these duties by way of telling how much we do but to let you know a cause of sorrow I have that so little of my time is devoted to real missionary work."

The hostility of the Boers continued, however, and lack of rain again made a move imperative. Livingstone had already made several short journeys around Kolobeng and now determined to explore the possibilities of founding a mission station to the north of the Kalahari Desert in the country of Sebituane, Chief of the Makololo. Just before he started, messengers came from Lechulatebe, chief of the lake people, asking him to visit that country and giving such an account of the quantity of ivory that the cupidity of his Bakwain guides was aroused and they became quite eager to be there.

On 1st June, 1849, in company with two English hunting friends, Oswell and Murray, Livingstone set out to find the reported lake (Ngami), hoping that on its further shores would be a suitable settling place, or if not there, in Sebituane's sphere of influence, further on in his actual domains. The journey took two months, and Lake Ngami and the river Zouga were discovered in August, 1849 ; but the party could not go across the lake because of the opposition of Lechulatebe who did not want them to meet Sebituane. Livingstone sent his report of the expedition to the London Missionary Society, and also to Captain Steele, a friend made on one of his 1841 to 1843 journeys. The latter showed his work to the Royal Geographical Society. In 1849 the Society voted him a sum of twenty-five guineas " for his successful journey in company with Messrs. Oswell and Murray across the South African desert, for the discovery of an interesting country, a fine river and an extensive inland lake ". The president of the society frankly ascribed Livingstone's success as an explorer to the influence he had acquired as a missionary among the natives and Livingstone thoroughly believed this to be so. Thereafter he kept the Royal Geographical Society in touch with all his explorations. Detailed observations of all kinds reached London as to the kind of country he had passed through, and its inhabitants both human and otherwise, with deductions as to future possibilities. In addition, the Astronomer Royal at the Cape, Sir Thomas Maclear, received sheet after sheet of astronomical observations carefully taken and recorded day by day.

Defeated in his endeavour to reach Sebituane in 1849, he set out again from Kolobeng in 1850, while Oswell went back to the Cape to bring up a boat to attempt a crossing of Lake Ngami. Livingstone took with him his young wife and children and Chief Sechele and again the party got as far as Lechulatebe's, and again failed to reach Sebituane and the Makololo, as fever and tsetse drove them hurriedly back. On their return they met Oswell who escorted them all to Kolobeng and later they went on to Kuruman to recuperate. Livingstone wrote to the Rev. W. Fairbrother :

" My Dear Friend,

" I had almost concluded that your bowels of compassion for us poor Hottentots had got into a state of hopeless constipation when I was cheered by some small symptoms of amendment in the shape of a note, you dared not call it a letter and I am glad of it for if you had I should have set you down among the great potbellies who modestly say ' I shall give my mite ' and the mite means the same thing as it did in the case of the old man you and I saw at the missionary meeting at Brentwood (or ford) so carefully fishing out five shillings from among the sovereigns—But you promise amendment, very well, better late than never. I write you now as a matter of conscience for I think I answered your note after receiving it about two months ago. I am not quite certain but I wish to make sure and I have very little to write about. We came out here on account of my wife's health, she was troubled with an affection of the nerve of motion of the right side of the face. It became quite paralysed but am thankful to say it has regained its power. We were proceeding to the Cape for the sake of surgical assistance. I require my uvula excised, but we were prevented from proceeding and now we hear our station is again menaced by the Boers and I feel anxious to be back again. They are great plagues to the progress of missions these same boers. Each has his big bible which he never reads. Each has his horse and gun with which he can kill the blacks. They look upon themselves as the peculiar favourites of Heaven. That they resemble the children of Israel when led by Moses. And the blacks are the descendents of Cain and may be shot as so many baboons. Sechele once warned one of them to depart out of his country—this as the French say created a great sensation among them. It was worse than Balaam's ass palaver with her mad jockey, but the worst feature in their case is they all believe themselves to be Christians and the miserable delusion is kept up by their ministers who I am not proud to say are generally Scotchmen. I saw two of them called Faure and Robertson baptizing their children by hundreds. They did not like to see me and when they returned to the colony propagated some slanders which they had collected among the boers against myself. We hear that the natives and boers have got to fighting—two have been killed on each side.

I fear the natives will ultimately go to the wall. They cannot stand against the European—they must ultimately go to the Kalahari desert and the regions where fever prevails so much that Europeans can't live."

It was at this time that Livingstone conceived the idea that was to dominate his later journeying—the desire and determination to find a passage to the sea :

" We must have a passage to the sea either on the eastern or western coast. I have hitherto been afraid to broach the subject on which my perhaps dreamy imagination dwells."

His first attempt to further this new resolve was another effort, and this time successful, to reach Sebituane. He set out again with his family and Oswell, in 1851, enduring incredible hardship from wild beasts, insects, and this time from lack of water.

" The supply of water in the wagons had been wasted by one of our servants, and by the afternoon only a small portion remained for the children. This was a bitterly anxious night ; and next morning, the less there was of water, the more thirsty the little rogues became. The idea of their perishing before our eyes was terrible ; it would almost have been a relief to me to have been reproached with being the entire cause of the catastrophe, but not one syllable of upbraiding was uttered by their mother, though the tearful eye told the agony within. In the afternoon of the fifth day, to our inexpressible relief, some of the men returned with a supply of that fluid of which we had never before felt the true value.

" No one knows the value of water till he is deprived of it. We never need any spirits to qualify it, or prevent an immense draught of it from doing us harm. I have drunk water swarming with insects, thick with mud, putrid from other mixtures, and no stinted draughts of it either, yet never felt any inconvenience from it.

" My opinion is, that the most severe labours and privations may be undergone without alcoholic stimulus, because those who have endured the most had nothing else but water, and not always enough of that."

Livingstone found Sebituane " unquestionably the greatest man in all that country ". Sebituane received Livingstone with great kindness, but unfortunately he died of pneumonia within a few days of the meeting so that the high hopes of friendship never grew. Livingstone had received permission to travel in Sebituane's wide dominions and in August, 1851, he and Oswell arrived at the Zambezi at Sesheke. This was thus the first time the explorer set foot in Northern Rhodesia. The discovery that the Zambezi flowed in this area was also a great geographical feat. The immediate object of the journey—the discovery of a suitable place for a new mission station was, however, not fulfilled and the party returned to Kolobeng. At this time, in spite of financial difficulties, Livingstone had reluctantly to decide to send Mrs. Livingstone and the children to England to recover their health and escorted them to the Cape for that purpose. This step caused him great sadness. He wrote to the directors of his society :

" Missionaries expose their children to a contamination which they have had no hand in producing. We expose them and ourselves for a time in order to elevate those sad captives of sin and Satan, who are the victims of the degradation of ages. None of those who complain about missionaries sending their children home ever descend to this. And again, as Mr. James in his ' *Young Man from Home* ' forcibly shows, a greater misfortune cannot befall a youth than to be cast into the world without a home. In regard to even the vestige of a home, my children are absolutely vagabonds. When shall we return to Kolobeng ? When to Kuruman ? *Never*. The mark of Cain is on your foreheads, your father is a missionary. Our children ought to have both the sympathies and prayers of those at whose bidding we become strangers for life."

While at the Cape, Livingstone put himself under the instruction of the Astronomer Royal, Mr. (afterwards Sir) Thomas Maclear, who became one of his best and most esteemed friends. His object was to qualify himself more thoroughly for taking observations that would give perfect accuracy to his geographical explorations. Maps drawn by him and also by Arrowsmith from his observations may be seen in the Rhodes-Livingstone Museum and Royal Geographical Society's collections. At this time Livingstone became even stronger in his determination to carry the gospel to an ever wider field and by paving the way for legitimate commerce to make it possible to stamp out the slave trade.

He left the Cape on 8th June, 1852, and reached Kolobeng to find his personal possessions looted and his home gutted. The station had been destroyed by a Boer commando under Pretorius, who had long been a declared enemy of Livingstone.

After some difficulty Livingstone got guides to take him to Sebituane's country, now ruled over by his son Sekeletu, and in 1853 he arrived at Linyanti, the capital of the Makololo. The country was flooded and malaria rife—only too obviously not a healthy place for European settlement.

" I would like ", he says in his *Journal*, " to devote a portion of my life to the discovery of a remedy for that terrible disease, the African fever. I would go into the parts where it prevails most, and try to discover if the natives have a remedy for it. I must make many inquiries of the river people in this quarter."

In his journal he asked himself, " Am I on my way to die in Sebituane's country ? Have I seen the end of my wife and children ? "

The chief, Sekeletu, decided to accompany Livingstone into Barotseland where they proceeded for a considerable distance up

[307]

the Zambezi River. Livingstone went to the limit of the Barotse country but found no healthy locality for settlement so he decided to try to find a way to the coast on the west via St. Paul de Loanda.

On his journey Livingstone, who had already met with slavery on the Boer pattern, now met it for the first time as practised by the Portuguese, where tribe raided tribe and sold their captives for European goods. He never grew accustomed to the sight of slave gangs on the march, not even in later years when he was obliged to accept the hospitality of slave dealers. The journey to Loanda took six and a half months, the final departure from Linyanti being 11th November, 1853, and arrival at the west coast 31st May, 1854. Livingstone had none of the equipment considered essential on an exploring expedition ; just twenty-seven natives and a few necessaries, including his instruments, his journal, beads for barter, some tusks to sell on Sekeletu's behalf, and ammunition for the larder's sake. His followers needed a great deal of managing, though they were devoted to him and, once beyond Sekeletu's jurisdiction, the journey northwards to Katima and then more or less due west was far from easy going. Rains rotted his tent and softened the natives' feet. Livingstone was often ill with fever, and with the old affection of his throat, for which he had had his uvula excised at the Cape. Some of the chiefs through whose territory he passed refused food and behaved in a threatening manner. When about 300 miles from Loanda he came to the farthest inland settlement of the Portuguese in Angola, Cassange, where he sold Sekeletu's tusks for a favourable price. He rested at Loanda for nearly four months, living with and being cared for by the one and only English inhabitant, Mr. Edmund Gabriel, the British Commissioner for the Suppression of the Slave Trade.

While at Loanda two navy captains then in port pressed Livingstone to return to England ; but in consideration of his followers, far from home and with hostile tribes between, he resisted the temptation and set off on the return journey to Linyanti on 20th September, 1854. All were loaded with good things which did not see the journey's end owing to the rapacity of those whose countries they traversed.

All this time Dr. Livingstone was making very careful astronomical observations, in order to determine his exact positions and sending elaborate letters to the Geographical Society. His astronomical observations were regularly forwarded to his friend the Astronomer Royal at the Cape for verification and correction. The long journey to Loanda had proved that this would never become the wagon route for trade about which he dreamed, and so once again at Linyanti Livingstone prepared to try the eastward trek, hoping that this way might prove a possible trade route.

He left St. Paul de Loanda on 24th September, 1854, and arrived at Linyanti on the 11th September, 1855. From there he set out eastwards along the Zambezi, hoping it would prove to be his commercial highway to the coast. It was on this journey that he discovered the famous " Musi watunya ", the great falls he named after Queen Victoria. He sailed down the river from one of the islands with Sekeletu in his canoe, and on 21st November, 1855, he first saw the Falls. In his sketch-book he made a water-colour drawing of them and in his journal he describes his discovery thus :

" 21st November, 1855. Having left Sesheke on Monday the 13th currt. we sailed down to the confluence of the Chobe, to the town and island of the Makololo called of Mparia from which Lecuane was expelled. It is on a low hill composed of igneous rock having chrystals of serpentine (?) diffused through it each coated with a pellicle of green copper ore. Proceeding down the river next day we were detained some hours by a strong East wind raising waves which threatened to swamp the canoes. In the evening we reached the village of Molele at Nampene island at the beginning of the rapids and there were obliged to leave the canoes and proceed along the bank on foot. The rapids extend all the way down to Mosioatunya a distance of at least 30 miles. In the evening we remained at the village of Nambowe opposite an island called Chondo. Next day we reached the village of Maroamosia at the island of Sekote which is called Kalai and on the day following we went down to the falls of Mosioatunya or as it was called antiently Shungue. After 20 minutes sail we viewed for the first time the vapour, or as it is appropriately called ' smoke ' arising exactly as when large tracts of grass are burned off. Five columns rose and bended in the direction of the wind against a low ridge covered with trees and seemed at this distance (about 6 miles) to mingle with the clouds. They were coloured white below and higher up became dark probably as the vapour condensed and returned in showers. Having got small and very light canoes farther down we went in the care of persons very well acquainted with the rapids and sailed swiftly down to an island situated at the middle and on the Northern verge of the precipice over which the water roars [Livingstone Island]. At one time we seemed to be going right to the gulph but though I felt a little tremous I said nothing believing I could face a difficulty as well as my guides. The falls are singularly formed. They are simply the whole mass of the Zambesi waters rushing into a fissure or rent made right across the bed of the river. In other falls we have usually a great change of level both in the bed of the river and adjacent country and after the leap the river is not much different from what it was above the falls. But here the river flowing rapidly among numerous islands and from 800 to 1,000 yards wide meets a rent in its bed at least 100 feet deep and at right angles with its course or nearly due East and West, leaps into it and becomes a boiling white mass at the bottom ten or twelve yards broad. Its course is changed also. It runs or rather rolls and wriggles from East to West until it reaches what above

was its left bank then turns a corner and follows or rather is
guided by the fissure away in its usual route of S.E. and by E.
The lips of the rent are in some parts not more than fifty or
sixty feet apart. The southern lip is straight and except at the
West corner which seems inclined from a split in it to fall into
the gulph is straight and level with the general bed of the river
above. Its wall is quite perpendicular. The northern lip is
jagged, several pieces having fallen off and five or six parts
have the edge worn down a foot or two. In these when the
water is low as it now is the falls divide themselves and from
each ascends a column of vapour which rises from 200 to 250
ft. three of these falls throw more water each now at low water
than the Falls of Stonebyres do when the Clyde is flooded.
At the parts where portions have fallen in the fissure it seemed
150 feet wide. The entire length is certainly not less than 600
yards and there are at present at least 400 yards of water which
looks about 2 feet thick. The measurements are given as
approximations only. My companions amused themselves by
throwing stones into the gulph marvelling that a stone an inch
or two in diameter should disappear before reaching the foaming
waters. The depth below which receives the whole body of the
water must be very deep. The Eastern half of the rent which
receives most water never exposes its bottom. In peering
down over the edge we could see only a dense white cloud with
two rainbows on it. A smart shower from the ascending columns
falls when the wind shifted Eastwards and soon drenched us
to the skin. This falls almost constantly on the Southern lip
and a thick bank of evergreen trees enjoy perpetual showers.
Several little streams are formed and run down that side but
never reach more than half way, the ascending vapour swills
them up into the air with it. When the river is full the noise
is said to be terrific and the vapour seen ten miles off. The
water is said to well up in surges to the opposite lip.

" Returning with Sekeletu on the following day I planted
a lot of peach and apricot stones and coffee seeds on the island
which being already covered with trees seemed well adapted to
be a nursery. The spot selected for experiment was one which
is visited with a fine sprinkling of the condensed vapour many
times daily. The parts nearer the gulph are adapted for water
plants only and a curious sort of polypus flourishes. We gave
directions for the construction of a fence to prevent the hippo-
potomi from treading down our seedlings and as this climate
requires tender plants to be frequently moistened I have no
doubt but Mosioatunya will prove a more careful nurseryman
than any of the Makololo would be.

" The Chiefs Sekote, Mokuime and Licuane appropriated
the three larger falls as places at which they prayed to the gods
or departed spirits—the roar of the waters were well fitted to
inspire feelings of awe. Sekote was a Batonga chief and he and

Licuane enjoyed despotic sway over the fords of the river. On Kalai, as Sekoti's island was called, we saw the grave of his father surrounded by 70 large elephants' tusks stuck in the ground the points turned inwards. About 30 others were placed as sort of gravestones over the members of his family. They think in cases of sickness that the departed are angry with them for not offering food, etc., etc. There were fifteen skulls placed on poles of persons who had been executed and a pot which when opened they believed would inflict death on those they hated. As the island is surrounded by a strong current these Batonga felt themselves quite secure and excelled in pride and cruelty. A party of Bamangwato were, on pretence of ferrying over the river, ferried onto an island and cruelly left to perish. They took possession of their wives and children. Sebituane arranged better having induced the chief to sit by him until all were over on the other side, Sekote having ferried the Matabele over to attack Sebituane the latter expelled him from his island and he now lives with Mosilikatse."

So "through more narrow escapes than any man living" he came to Tete where he left his sixty or seventy followers, and finally, on 26th May, 1856, nearly four years after leaving the Cape, saw the sea at Quilimane. With a promise to come back and take his men home to their tribe Livingstone returned to England via Mauritius, landing at Dover in December, 1856.

He returned to England as a missionary in the service of the London Missionary Society. During his stay, while writing his *Travels* and being made much of as an explorer, the question of his future had to be decided. There never came to his mind any doubt as to his missionary calling, that was sure and unchanging. Some supporters of the London Missionary Society, however, did not feel that the funds should be used for his, to their idea, very indirect means of evangelisation. He himself, having tasted the freedom of authority and found it congenial, with all goodwill towards the society to which he owed his opportunity, felt that to be receiving a missionary's salary and so to be under orders would be limiting and irksome to his independent spirit.

During his stay in England he was received by the Royal Geographical Society, who pronounced his feats of exploration to be the greatest of their age. His scientific accuracy made all his observations of supreme value both in cartography, zoology, palæontology and many other fields which his varied curiosity led him to investigate. Traveller, geographer, zoologist, astronomer, missionary, physician, and mercantile director, did ever man perform the duties of each with such painstaking accuracy and so great success ? Much of his time at home was spent in writing, and his *Missionary Travels* was published in 1857 and had a huge success, more as a record of travel perhaps than of missionary activity. He himself wrote of his life and of his decision to leave the London Missionary Society :

" Nowhere have I ever appeared as anything else but a servant of God, who has simply followed the leadings of His hand. My views of what is *missionary* duty are not so contracted as those whose ideal is a dumpy sort of man with a Bible under his arm. I have laboured in bricks and mortar, at the forge and carpenter's bench, as well as in preaching and medical practice. I feel that I am ' not my own ', I am serving Christ when shooting a buffalo for my men, or taking an astronomic observation, or writing to one of His children who forget, during the little moment of penning a note, that charity which is eulogised as ' thinking no evil ' ; and after having by His help got information, which I hope will lead to more abundant blessing being bestowed on Africa than heretofore, am I to hide the light under a bushel, merely because some will consider it not sufficiently, or even at all *missionary* ? Knowing that some persons do believe that opening up a new country to the sympathies of Christendom was not a proper work for an agent of a Missionary Society to engage in, I now refrain from taking any salary from the Society with which I was connected ; so no pecuniary loss is sustained by any one."

He left for Africa again on 10th March, 1858, as leader of a Government expedition to explore the Zambezi, holding the Government appointment of British Consul, " for the promotion of commerce and civilisation with a view to the extinction of the slave trade ". He described his expedition to Professor Sedgewick of Cambridge :

" That you may have a clear idea of my objects I may state that they have something more in them than meets the eye. They are not merely exploratory, for I go with the intention of benefiting both the African and my own countrymen. I take a practical mining geologist from the school of mines to tell us of the mineral resources of the country. Then an economic botanist to give a full report of the vegetable productions— the fibrous, gummy and medicinal substances together with the dyestuffs—everything which may be useful in commerce. An artist to give the scenery. A naval officer to tell of the capacity of the river communications and a moral agent to lay a christian foundation for anything that may follow. All this machinery has for its ostensible object the development of African trade and the promotion of civilisation but what I tell to none but such as you in whom I have confidence is this, I hope it may result in an English Colony in the healthy high lands of Central Africa—(I have told it only to the Duke of Argyll). I believe the highlands are healthy—the wild vine flourishes there. Europeans with a speedy transit to the coast would collect and transmit the produce to the sea and in the course of time, say when my head is low, free labour on the African soil might render slave labour which is notoriously dear labour quite unprofitable. I take my wife with me and one child. We erect

[312]

an iron house near the Kafue to serve as a depot that we may not appear as vagabonds in the country and may God prosper our attempts to promote the welfare of our fellow men.

" With this short statement you may perceive our ulterior objects. I want you to have an idea of them."

Financed mainly by Government, he set out fairly well equipped, with a European staff of six. This included Dr. (later Sir) John Kirk, Thomas Baines, known for his own later explorations in Matabeleland, and Richard Thornton, a mining geologist who was dismissed by Livingstone in 1859 for alleged inefficiency, went exploring with Baron von der Decker in the regions of Kilimanjaro, rejoined the Zambezi expedition two and a half years later, and died on 21st April, 1863, after performing a difficult journey while still weak from fever, in order to get food for his companions. When engaging Thornton, Livingstone explained the purpose and plan of the expedition :

" The main objects of the expedition to which you are appointed Mining geologist are, to extend the knowledge already attained of the geography and mineral and agricultural resources of Eastern and Central Africa, to improve our acquaintance with the inhabitants, and to engage them to apply themselves to industrial pursuits and to the cultivation of their lands with a view to the production of raw material to be exported to England in return for British manufactures. And it may be hoped that by encouraging the natives to occupy themselves in the development of the resources of their country a considerable advance may be made towards the extinction of the slave trade, as the natives will not be long in discovering that the former will eventually become a more certain source of profit than the latter.

" 2. As mining geologist you are specially charged with the duty of collecting accurate information respecting the mineral resources of the country through which we are to travel, and you are required to furnish me with reports thereon, and on the geology generally of the parts visited for the information of Her Majesty's Government. Taking for your guidance the hints furnished by Sir Roderick Murchison, you will carefully examine those parts of the country which may be pointed out to you as capable of being visited without risk to your person or health, specimens of the fossils that may be found must always be brought away as evidence of the conclusions to which you have arrived respecting the age and relations of the different deposits, and drawings will be made by Mr. Baines for the general collection of the Expedition.

" 3. The Expedition will proceed as quickly as possible through the lower portion of the Zambezi and the efforts of every 'member will probably be required to facilitate the

[313]

DAVID LIVINGSTONE
[*Rhodes-Livingstone Museum Collection*]

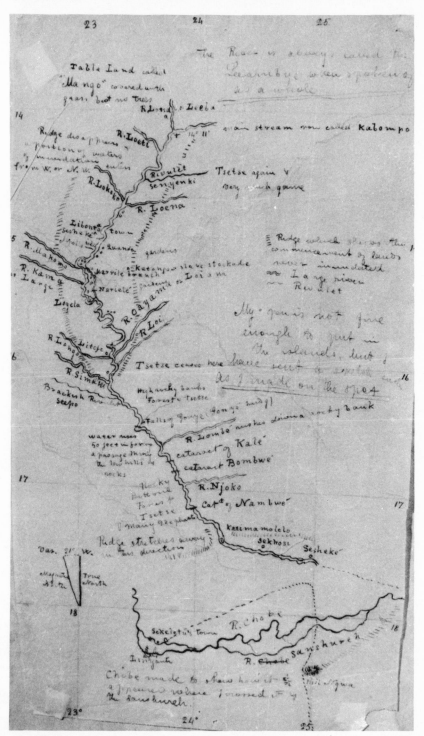

HOLOGRAPH MAP OF PART OF THE UPPER ZAMBEZI VALLEY, BY DAVID LIVINGSTONE, 1853
[*Rhodes-Livingstone Museum Collection*]

DAVID LIVINGSTONE'S COLOUR SKETCH OF THE VICTORIA FALLS, 1860
[*Rhodes-Livingstone Museum Collection—on loan from Dr. Hubert Wilson*]

" THE HORRORS OF THE SLAVE TRADE "

[Reprinted from " Livingstone's Last Journals "]

Steamer Pearl, at Sea,
16 April 1858

Richard Thornton Esq.

Sir

The main object
of the expedition to which
you are appointed Mining
geologist are, to extend the
knowledge already attained
of the geography, and
mineral and agricultural
resources of Eastern and
Central Africa, to improve
our acquaintance with the
inhabitants, and to engage
them to apply themselves
to industrial pursuits and
to the cultivation of their land.

transit of the luggage to Tete. While there you will have an opportunity of examining the seams of coal which crop out in the rivulets Moatize, etc. etc. a few miles to the North Eastward of Tete, and you will spare no pains in reaching a sufficient depth from the surface to enable you to form an opinion as to the quality of the mineral where it has not been subjected to the influences of atmospheric agencies, as should serviceable coal be found at this spot (which may be considered the limit of the comparatively deep water navigation of the river) it would be far more valuable than elsewhere and its discovery will well repay the time devoted to a careful search for it.

" 4. Having ascended to some eligible spot beyond the confluence of the Kafue and Zambezi the iron house will be erected and experiments in agriculture will be set on foot partly with a view to promoting the health and comfort of the Expedition, and still more in order to ascertain the agricultural capabilities of the country. Whatever knowledge of soils you may possess will now prove of great value and you are expected to communicate it freely for our guidance.

" 5. The iron house being established as a central depot explorations will be made in various directions in company with the Makololo, and botanical and mineral and zoological collections will be deposited at the central station, but though these explorations and collections are very desirable you will understand that Her Majesty's Government attach more importance to the moral influence which may be exerted on the minds of the natives by a regulated and orderly household of Europeans setting an example of consistent moral conduct to all who may congregate around the settlement, treating the people with kindness and relieving their wants, leading them to make experiments in agriculture, explaining to them the more simple arts, imparting to them the religious instruction as far as they are capable of receiving it, and inculcating peace and goodwill to all.

" 6. It is hoped that no occasion will ever arise in which it will be necessary to use our fire arms for protection against the natives but the best security from attack consists in so acting as not to deserve it and letting the natives see that you are well prepared to meet it. You are strictly enjoined to exercise the greatest forbearance towards the people, and while retaining proper firmness in the event of any misunderstanding to endeavour to conciliate as far as possibly can be admitted with safety to our party.

" 7. Your own principles will lead you in all your dealings with the people to follow the strictest justice but it is necessary to remind you that even the *appearance* of over-reaching or insulting must be carefully avoided. No native must be employed unless a distinct understanding has been come to in the presence of witnesses as to the amount of remuneration to be given. It will greatly facilitate your intercourse with the people in the middle of the country if you acquire the Sichuana language.

" 8. You are distinctly to understand that your services are engaged for two years unless any unforeseen accident should happen to the Expedition, when you will be set free as soon as an opportunity is afforded for returning to England.

" 9. I hand you the appendices No. 1 and 2 for your information in order that should any useful plant or new animal come under your observation while engaged in your other duties you may communicate with the head of the Expedition. While it will be necessary to employ our firearms to procure supplies of food and in order to secure specimens of animals and birds for the purposes of natural history the wanton waste of animal life must be carefully avoided, and in no case must a beast be put to death unless some good end is to be answered thereby.

" 10. Finally you are strictly enjoined to take the greatest care of your health. Avoid all exposure to night exhalations and should you be troubled with drowsiness, constipation or shivering apply promptly to Dr. Kirk for medical advice. Trusting that our Heavenly Father will watch over you and that you will return to your friends after having performed your duty with honour, I heartily commit you to the care of over-ruling providence."

Later Livingstone sent Thornton's papers and journals with a covering letter to his brother, George Thornton, and the journals themselves show the true worth of Richard Thornton.

" It is with sorrow that I have to convey the sad intelligence that your brother Richard Thornton died yesterday morning about ten o'clock. He became ill on the 11th currt. of dysentery and fever, and no remedy seemed to have much effect. On the 20th he was seriously ill but took soup several times, and drank claret and water with relish. We then hoped that his youth and unimpaired constitution would carry him through—the diarrhoea had nearly ceased, but about six o'clock in the evening his mind began to wander and continued so. His bodily powers continued gradually to sink till the period mentioned when he quietly expired.

" He was attended to most assiduously by Dr. Meller during the whole course of his illness and as he was aided by the advice of Dr. Kirk you may rest assured that everything was done for his recovery that could be suggested.

" Owing to the insidious way in which the delirium crept on him, I regret that he never had an opportunity of expressing any wish respecting his affairs—Dr. Meller was by him the whole night. Dr. Kirk and I were at hand and sleepless but nothing fell from his lips as last words to survivors.

" We buried him to-day by a large baobab tree about 500 yards from the first cataract and 300 from the right bank of the Shire—and there he rests in sure and certain hope of a glorious Resurrection.

" I enclose a lock of his hair : I had his papers sealed up soon after his decease and will endeavour to transmit them all to you exactly as he left them. The chief part of his property is at the Mission station below this, but it will be preserved with care, mere trade goods sold, and everything likely to be valued by his relatives sent home.

" He had two men from Zanzibar, Ali and Mabruck whose wages and expenses home must be paid. I fear the saleable effects will not cover these. He has left some debts at Quillimane. Those to Manoel at Tette incurred in behalf of the Mission and Expedition and amounting to Sixty Pounds will be paid. It is understood that he ordered goods for that amount to Manoel. This may arrive in time to countermand that order.

" I would have taken the papers, journals, etc. with me at once to Quillimane, but feared that they might get damaged in an open boat. I close this sad letter with a heavy heart, and with the prayer that the Almighty Disposer of all events may comfort those to whom its contents will bring much sorrow."

By the time the expedition reached the mouth of the Zambezi Livingstone was already suffering from diarrhoea, but in order to get as soon as possible out of the fever-ridden mangrove swamps he had the three sections of the specially built launch the *Ma-Robert* (Mrs. Livingstone's African name) put together at once. Livingstone also felt in a difficult position at the head of this enterprise. He realised that a civil enterprise had not the habits of discipline and obedience of a military expedition and also he knew himself to be unaccustomed to command such men as were now under him.

The first notable achievement of the expedition was the discovery of the advantages of the Kongone entrance of the Zambezi. He knew the Kebrabasa rapids and gorge existed some thirty miles beyond Tete, but he thought the difficulties were exaggerated by the Portuguese desire to keep others out, and that it was only a matter of blasting to make the great river navigable through to the interior.

The launch proved more trouble than it was worth, with engine trouble, terrific fuel consumption, and too great a draught.

" We have found the Pinnace too heavy for the engine in low water where we are obliged to go slowly and cautiously and I leave it at Pita."

Four expeditions to the Kebrabasa at last shattered Livingstone's most cherished and much-talked-of scheme, to his bitter disappointment.

" The vessel we have—the *Ma-Robert*—is such an awful botch of a job. I have been obliged to take up our baggage in driblets having passed over 1,700 miles at least and we have to cut a ton of wood for 7 or 8 hours steam—a current of 3¼ knots holds her back so that she cannot gain an inch and so does a stiff breeze. I have applied to government again for the *Bann* [the vessel originally offered to the expedition but considered unsuitable by the attached naval officer] and if she is not granted then I have ordered £2,000 to be expended on a vessel of my own. We could have passed up the rapid of Kebrabasa in February last had the vessel possessed any power."

He sent home for a new boat to be built, and meantime set about exploring further north, up the River Shire. On the first trip the party went as far as the great cataract which he named Murchison, after his friend Sir Roderick of the Royal Geographical Society. A good deal of time was spent up and down the Shire River and back to the store dump at Kongone. The party disembarked on one occasion at Chibisa, and, walking on, looked one day for the first time on Lake Nyasa. This was on 16th September, 1859, whereupon Livingstone wrote home for a boat to be constructed at his own expense to sail on the waters of the lake that lawful commerce might oust the slave trade he found being carried on extensively in those regions.

" We have traced this river [the Shire] up to its origin in Lake Nyassa, in South Latitude 14°25'. . . . Well, we found that there is only a small partition between Nyassa and Tamandua (Shirwa), but we could not examine it as we were on foot, and had been longer away than we promised. Along this partition all the slave trade and other trade must pass in order to get away to Moscambique and other ports on the East Coast. We met a large party with an immense number of slaves and elephants' tusks, coming from Cazembe's country and bought some fine specimens of malachite from them— they were not Arabs but looked somewhat like them—an awfully blackguard looking lot. When they knew we were English and saw our Revolvers they slipped off by night probably thinking the same of us as we did of them. An English establishment up here—missionary and mercantile, would eat out the slave trade, for the Babisa and other native traders, would not go a month farther (to E. Coast) for the same prices we could give here."

Here tribe fought tribe and sold their prisoners for cloth, and here, later, the trails he blazed for freedom were used by the Portuguese for the slave traffic. Here Livingstone's resolve was strengthened to put first the liberation of the African people. His rediscovery of Lake Nyasa meant that nearly 250 years had gone by since the first European, a Portuguese by the name of Gaspar Bocarro had set eyes on the lake. During that time, so far as we are aware, no other European had made the journey to the lake. Of equal importance with his rediscovery of the lake was Livingstone's discovery of a high, healthy region for settlement that became known as the Shire Highlands.

" As we are below the rapid and our establishment is at Tette we are examining the country adjacent. The Shire promised best so we went up a hundred miles of Latitude from its source and found it a fine river for a steamer. It really does come out of the Lake Nyanja (Nyasa) but a little above this its navigation is obstructed by Cataracts of the same rock and nearly in the same Latitude as Kebrabasa. . . .

" There is a high mountain near its entrance called Marambala—it is 4,000 ft. high and a fine point for a health station. It is well cultivated on the top, having hills and dales and flowing fountains there. Lemon and orange trees grow well so do pineapples."

By the end of 1859 the need for the new boat was so imperative that Livingstone decided to fill in time until its arrival by taking home the Makololo who still wished to go. The journey, not being part of his commission, was not prolonged, though he spent time making closer, more adequate examination of the Victoria Falls, and visited both Sesheke and Linyanti, where were the graves of the mission party (the Helmore-Price expedition) he had intended to meet and settle with Sekeletu but had arrived too late—unfriendliness had been the party's portion and fever had killed most of them. These regions also now bore the usual traces of the results of African tribal warfare.

Back at the coast where the *Ma-Robert* had sunk, came the arrival of the new boat *Pioneer* on 31st January, 1861. The Portuguese being unwilling to open their hinterland to free trade, Livingstone's instructions were now to explore the Rovuma River about 600 miles further north in the hope that this river might prove another way to Lake Nyasa. As a band of missionaries under Bishop Mackenzie had arrived at the same time as the *Pioneer*, Livingstone was obliged to take them under his care and guide them in their settlement. As it was not possible to go far up the Rovuma on this first trip he turned his attention once again to the Shire with the missionaries, whom he left to settle at Magomero.

Because of lack of medical aid and supplies, and the difficulties of work in a land where there was tribal warfare and slave raiding in continual operation, the mission's immediate life was short. Some members of the mission party, including the leader, died en route, and the new bishop—Tozer—insisted on retiring to Zanzibar.

On this journey Livingstone's expedition met with many evidences of the slave trade, and was instrumental in setting free a gang of eighty-four men and women.

" On 15th July last we went up to the Manganja highlands East of this in order to shew the bishop an eligible country for his mission and no sooner did we cross the brow of the plateau than we discovered that the Portuguese had set up an extensive system of slave hunting in the very country to which the mission had come. The first party headed by a well known slave of one of our friends had eighty four captives. While enquiring who gave the adventurers leave to make war and of the captives how they came to be bound, the Tette men escaped into the bush so I handed these and the captives of three other Portuguese parties over to the mission as a beginning of the school. A detached portion of a tribe called Ajawa had been incited by Portuguese who followed the path taken by Dr. Kirk from this to Tette to attack village after village of Manganja kill the men and sell the women and children to them for calico worth here from 1/– to 2/6 each. . . .

" There is an active export of slaves from some one of the ports of the Zambezi probably from one near the Lindi or Massangano. We never knew slaving carried on at such a rate before in the Zambezi. Senhor Cruz the great slave trader has married the Governor's eldest daughter and St. Filipino the the younger, so with the French flag to cover it all is comfortable. I feel a depression from seeing Portuguese following in my footsteps which neither sun, long marches, Hunger, Thirst nor even fever ever produced."

This was the one and only occasion when Livingstone used fire-arms against the Africans, as it was also the first occasion that he came directly in conflict with Portuguese authority. He had to make up his mind as to the proper course of action with regard to the slave gangs being driven to the coast. Day after day he saw their dead bodies on land and in the water, estimating that only one in ten of those captured ever reached the market. He could do no other than liberate where possible. The leader of the first party caught was a half-caste Portuguese slave personally known to him, and from whom he was able to prove that the Portuguese Government was actively concerned. Livingstone came later to realise that the Government deliberately encouraged the slave trade as part of its policy.

Mrs. Livingstone, who had come out with her husband in 1858, but had been obliged to stay in Kuruman for her health, now rejoined her husband in January of 1862 when the party was at the coast once more. Mrs. Livingstone had come on board the H.M.S. *Gorgon* which also brought the *Lady Nyassa*, the steamboat for the new lake which had been awaited for so long. Unfortunately the *Pioneer* in which Livingstone and his wife and their party were to proceed up river was delayed rather long in the fever-haunted area of Shupanga, and Mrs. Livingstone succumbed and died on 27th April, 1862, four months after their reunion. This was the bitterest blow of Livingstone's life. "It is the first heavy stroke I have suffered and quite takes away my strength. For the first time in my life I feel willing to die", he wrote in his journal.

Even in his sorrow Livingstone could not be idle. The *Lady Nyassa* was put together, but as the season was too far advanced she could not be got to the lake. To fill in the time, therefore, the party again explored up the Rovuma.

"We went up the Rovuma 156 miles or 114 as the crow flies and touched twice on the slave route from Nyassa to Keelwa [Quiloa]. The *Gorgon* [the new naval boat] will do a good deal I believe to stop the stream of 20,000 slaves annually which comes along that road for the Red Sea and Persian Gulph and I am anxious to get up to the source of that trade to do what we can there."

In 1863 they were ready to carry the *Lady Nyassa*, again dismantled, over the road they had been constructing past the Murchison Cataracts. Above the cataracts it was intended she should be launched and taken to the lake whose name she bore, to trade and keep that area free from slave raiding. Nothing actually happened, the road was not finished, the boat never saw the lake, for at this point Livingstone was recalled for political interference with Portugal, his actions in freeing slaves and writing to Portuguese officials on this subject having been misinterpreted.

"Get possession of the ivory trade as I proposed to do on the lake and you render the trade in slaves unprofitable. I tried it though unintentionally in the Makololo country. Slave merchants came from Benguella to the subject tribes East of that people and annually carried off large quantities of ivory and slaves. The ivory was purchased for hoes and Sekeletu—having many smiths under him who yield an annual tribute in hoes—I suggested that he should purchase the ivory of the Eastern tribes with them. He did so for the sake of the profit on the ivory and the Benguella traders ceased to go to that district. One of them told me that it was better to get slaves nearer the coast if no ivory was to be obtained for them to carry. The fact of the matter is slaves cost so much for sustenance when a long way from the coast that without ivory they are a losing speculation. It was a knowledge of the plan I had for stopping the slave trade of Iboe and Mosambique as well as that to Quilloa that made our Portuguese friends frantic. Now slaving goes on faster than ever."

[325]

The highway Livingstone had opened was being used by Portugal for the extension of the very curse which he was spending his whole life to eradicate.

He sailed the little *Lady Nyassa* across the Indian Ocean, docked her in Bombay, and, taking the first boat from there, was back in England on 23rd July, 1864. Looking back on the work of the last six years, while deeply grieved that the great object of the expedition had not been achieved, Dr. Livingstone was able to point to some important results—notably the discovery of the Kongone mouth of the Zambezi and the navigability of the river and the ascertaining of the capacity of the soil, and, most important, of the exposing of the fountain-head of the slave trade.

The year 1864–1865 Livingstone spent in England, lecturing, speaking, visiting his family and friends, and staying with the Webbs at Newstead Abbey, where he rested somewhat to recover his health. He looked, he said,

". . . very old and grey and face wrinkled like a gridiron. A barber offered to dye my hair for 10/6. I must be very good tempered for I did not fight him."

While at Newstead Abbey he wrote his book *The Zambesi and its Tributaries*.

". . . all my time is absorbed in writing another book. I am literally over head and ears with copy, proof, revise, and copy, proof, revise again, till my eyes are sore. . . . I would have gone off . . . but for the belief that in this work I am affording information which may lead to the Governments of the world putting a stop to the farce played so long by that of Portugal on the East Coast and of pretending to dominion while doing nothing but shutting it up from the rest of the world as a gigantic slave reserve."

He had intended it to be merely a short book, a panegyric against the monstrous slave trade of the Portuguese, by whom he was, rather naturally, misunderstood.

" It is manifest ", wrote Dr. Lacerda, the great Portuguese traveller, " without the least reason to doubt, that Dr. Livingstone, under the pretext of propagating the Word of God (this being the least in which he employed himself) and the advancement of geographical and natural science, made all his steps and exertions subservient to the idea of . . . eventually causing the loss to Portugal of the advantages of the rich commerce of the interior, and in the end, when a favourable occasion arose, that of the very territory itself."

During his year's stay in England the Royal Geographical Society proposed to him a third journey into Africa, the objects of which he set out in the preface to *The Zambesi and its Tributaries*.

"Our Government have supported the proposal of the Royal Geographical Society made by my friend Sir Roderick Murchison, and have united with that body to aid me in another attempt to open Africa to civilising influences, and a valued private friend has given a thousand pounds for the same object. I propose to go inland, north of the territory which the Portuguese in Europe claim, and endeavour to commence that system on the east which has been so eminently successful on the west coast : a system combining the repressive efforts of Her Majesty's cruisers with lawful trade and Christian missions—the moral and material results of which have been so gratifying. I hope to ascend the Rovuma, or some other river north of Cape Delgado, and, in addition to my other work, shall strive, by passing along the northern end of Lake Tanganyika, to ascertain the watershed of that part of Africa."

The first part of the scheme was his own and the second proposed by the Royal Geographical Society, but only £1,000 was put up by Government and Geographical Society combined. This to anyone less single-minded than Livingstone would at once have appeared inadequate. However, he set out for his third and last period in Africa on the 19th August, 1865. As he wrote to Professor Sedgewick in March :

"It would take a long time to tell you all I feel. I am living with a friend whom I made in Africa, Mr. Webb of Newstead Abbey and cannot move till the book is done. I am pretty well through with it and then after a short visit to my mother in Scotland am off again to try and get a way into the Interior North of the Portuguese. My appointment gives me wide enough scope and if I saw a beginning made with lawful commerce and christian missions I think I could lie down in my grave and rest in peace."

All the way through his journal and letters at this time runs a thread of excitement to make new discoveries, yet there is still the underlying purpose of the " good of Africa ". " The Nile sources are valuable to me only as a means of opening my mouth with power among men ", he wrote to his brother John near the end of his life in December, 1872. It was Livingstone's friend, James Young, who made this going back to Africa possible by giving £1,000 for the expedition that was expected to take not more than two years, but actually culminated in Livingstone's death eight years later.

He went straight to Bombay, sold the *Lady Nyassa* ; then, with a set of men, partly Sepoys and emancipated Africans from the Nassick training school, sailed across to Zanzibar on a boat he was to present to the Sultan from the British Government in the person of Sir Bartle Frere, Governor of Bombay—a gesture which pleased the Sultan mightily. From Zanzibar he wrote to Sir Bartle Frere :

"In the slave market here I saw at different times from 70 to 300 slaves exposed at once for sale. Northern Arabs and Persians are the chief purchasers. They have their dhows in the bay or southwards picking up what they can in slaves from Portuguese and Malagasse. They cannot go North till April or May partly because the exportation coastwise is prohibited, but chiefly because the wind wont let either Northern or Zanzibar dhows go north. The prohibition, you see, is exactly in accordance with the laws of nature. We must never go contrary to the laws of nature. This is modern philosophy. As soon as the monsoon changes all the dhows will crowd North. Then we have no prohibition. This is true philosophy but not slave trade suppression policy.

"The slaves swarm here, and the majority are Manganja. Their prices when I was in the market were from 7 to 20 dollars. I see little chance of their lot ever becoming better ; so long as they are about on a level with their Arab masters it will do very well. Master and man partake of the general indolence and barbarism but with the advance of civilisation or trade and luxury their lot becomes harder. The lust of gain in the master must always increase the hardships of the slave—so if we wish well to the slave we must wish the Arabs to remain in a state of barbarism. We must not interfere with the status of slavery however, if I might venture to say it we perpetrate a monstrous mistake in allowing slaves to be carried coastwise or anywise in order not to injure the status of slavery here—we virtually uphold it."

With a queer collection of animals including camels, mules, water buffalo and donkeys, the expedition disappeared into the hinterland and, with the exception of H. M. Stanley, Livingstone was seen no more by white men. The animals, intended as an experiment in resistance to the tsetse fly, all died through the rough treatment of their keepers. All these men were either dismissed or deserted except for five faithfuls including Susi and Chuma who were with him to the end. Trouble with carriers was one of the trials that continually beset Livingstone during this exploration. In addition the expedition proved far longer and far more expensive than had been anticipated.

The journey started up the Rovuma River and on to Lake Nyasa, proving conclusively that this was no waterway to the lake, then round the south end and on north-west towards the south of Lake Tanganyika. From Lake Nyasa Livingstone wrote to Professor Sedgewick :

"I have taken a sore longing to write to you though I have not the faintest prospect of being able to send a letter to the sea coast. The Arab slave traders on their way thither avoid me as if I had the plague. In six or seven cases they set off across country as soon as they heard that the English were coming and dashing through bush and brake here is a more serious affair than with you for the grass is generally over one's head in the hollows—as thick as a quill in the stalk and often intertwined with creepers. I would fain have spared the slaves who were thus dragged, but the masters took care not to look me in the face. One sagacious old leader who had about 800 slaves in his party, hearing that, after a march of eight days through a fine country completely depopulated by the slave trade, we were nearly famished, and that we were just at hand, came forward and presented a bag of flour and an ox. I daresay he had some genuine goodness in him though it looked like taking the ' bull by the horns '.

" To give you an idea of the country it is a gradual slope from the coast up to within forty or fifty miles of this Lake. The first 80 miles or so are covered with dense forest, the only bare spaces being the clearings of the inhabitants. The rock where it can be seen is coarse grey sandstone with blocks of silicified wood lying on it. This overlies coal. Beyond the sandstone we come on gneiss and sometimes granite, there the forest is scraggy but it is still so thickly planted that one can rarely see the horizon. About 200 miles inland the country becomes undulating and on the crests of the waves one sees mountains all round—great rounded granite masses—igneous rocks appear among these masses and large patches of ferrugious conglomerate are met with. The country is still rich in soil but the trees are small as we attain greater altitude—and the number of running rills in the mountainous district is quite astonishing. I counted in one day's march no fewer than fifteen flowing burns. These are the sources of the Rovuma."

The highlight from a geographical point of view was the discovery of Lakes Mweru and Bangweulu. Livingstone never knew that the search for the Nile sources so far south was a wild goose chase (" I hope I am not premature in saying that the sources of the Nile arise in from 10°–12° south—in fact where Ptolemy placed them ") though, still making careful observations, he settled the source of the Congo and gave the world much useful information.

The story of this long, last journey in Livingstone's life reads like the tale of a weary wanderer through whose wanderings there is ever the fixed determination, carried out often through sheer will-power, to go on until the task is finished. His health was broken and his constitution undermined by the travels and hardships of earlier years ; he seemed, though only in his fifties, to be an old man, with less ability to control and inspire, but with a greater gentleness and more consideration than before. His journeyings took him north, into the land of the Manyema, west of Tanganyika, to Bambarre and Nyangwe, into Cazembe's country, where he tells of the mining of copper, and right round both Lakes Mweru and Bangweulu.

[329]

One day a carrier deserted with his medicine chest, and all search for him proved fruitless. Livingstone depended so much on drugs to keep him alive that this was a hard loss to bear, sickness through damp and fever and indigestible food being ever with him. He was only enabled to carry on so long, though so painfully, because of the care of the few faithful Africans who were as sons to their father, watching over him and carrying him in a litter when he could not even sit on the one donkey that had withstood both the tsetse and the " care " of its keepers. He was now often obliged to travel in company with Arab slave raiders, who were mostly considerate and helpful to him personally even while they continually intercepted his mail for fear of his exposure of their nefarious trade, and allowed their slaves to steal the stores he ordered from the coast and which he needed so badly. Amongst the letters that did get through were several to Oswell telling of his hopes and fears and adventures.

He was continually at the mercy of those around him ; Arab caravans moved so slowly and stayed so long in one place that, as he travelled with them, he was bound to become associated with their activities in the African mind. Chiefs refused him canoes or prohibited his entry into their territory or, once in, would not let him go. On one such occasion a show of force bluffed the chief of an island in the middle of Lake Bangweulu into speeding his departure with all the canoes he needed. Often it was wars that caused delay, or the rains making country impassable. At such times Livingstone side-tracked to make sure of some geographical detail, or just sat, sick in body and mind, and waited.

So the years passed with very little news reaching the outside world. England resounded with lamentations at his loss but his friends would not believe him dead. Sir Roderick Murchison and his friends of the Royal Geographical Society organised a search-party under Mr. E. D. Young, who cast anchor at the mouth of the Zambezi on the 25th July, 1867. The steel boat, *The Search*, was successfully carried past the Murchison Cataracts, reassembled and sailed to Lake Nyasa, where Young found definite news of Living-stone's passage. The object of his journey was thus accomplished and he returned to England at the end of the year.

Livingstone's headquarters were at Ujiji and stores were sent to his depot at Unyanyembe, but Livingstone did not reach there himself again until 1871—robbed of all his goods, his medicine chest lost, racked by fever and even starvation, he was a living skeleton.

" A hungry time we had in passing through the dripping forests of the Babisa country—no animals to be shot and the people had no grain to sell. Mushrooms in plenty though but woe's me good only for exciting dreams of the roast beef of byegone days—no salt either. This causes the gnawing sensation to be ceaseless but we got through by God's great mercy. Sugar we have forgotten all about and roast a little grain to make believe it is coffee but we have got to a land of plenty and are going to have our christmas feast tomorrow. We had nothing to celebrate it when the day passed but won't be balked of it for all that. I am excessively lean but take on fat kindly as do some races of pigs."

There at Ujiji he was found a few weeks later by H. M. Stanley of the *New York Herald*, who had been sent out to Africa to find the great explorer—rather as a newspaper sensation. Stanley's party left Zanzibar in September and reached Ujiji in October shortly after Livingstone himself had arrived there tired, hungry and ill. An excited cry from Susi, " An Englishman, I have seen him ! " brought Livingstone to his feet, and the bewildered old man, stooping, " pale and wearied, with a grey beard, wearing a bluish cap with a faded gold band round it, a red-sleeved waistcoat, and a pair of grey tweed trousers," faced the smart, fit American. The meeting at that moment in that place, though not unexpected by Stanley, produced a feeling of embarrassment which has given their greeting as almost a catch-phrase to posterity, though at the time the formal expression covered deep emotion. " Dr. Livingstone, I presume ? " " Yes ", and a handshake was all the watching Arabs and Africans heard or saw.

Refreshed with clothes, food, letters and companionship, Livingstone refused to go back with Stanley : there were points still unsettled that he must see about. After a long wait at Unya-nyembe on the Zanzibar route, where the two had parted, for the stores and carriers Stanley promised, Livingstone again disappeared in his search for the Nile sources and the world saw him no more.

Livingstone was growing gradually weaker, slowly killed by malaria and dysentery. On the 21st April he wrote in a shaky hand in his journal, " Tried to ride, but was forced to lie down, and they carried me back to vil. exhausted." His pains were excruciating and his weakness excessive. Carried in a litter he arrived at Chitambo's village in Ilala and his faithful attendants built a hut to accommodate him. There he died—on his knees beside his rude bed, at the last in an attitude of prayer.

Susi and Chuma, Livingstone's old attendants, now became the leaders of the party. It is they who tell of his lonely death at Chitambo's village, south of Lake Bangweulu, of the burial of his heart under a tree, of the reading of the funeral service and the carving of the inscription by Jacob Wainwright, a Christian Nassick boy, who came with the stores sent by Stanley ; and of the long journey with their " father's " body and possessions. On the way to the coast the party met, in October, an expedition which had come out to relieve Livingstone under the leadership of Dillon, Cameron and Murphy. Chuma told them of the death of Livingstone and they wished to bury him there in Africa. Chuma, however, was adamant, and the explorer's body was sent to England ; Susi and Chuma were brought to England also to tell their story. It was Jacob Wainwright, short and squat and black, who guarded the coffin all the way home, and was among the bearers at the funeral in Westminster Abbey of the man, known and still honoured all over the world, but loved particularly by the Africans whose descendants still speak of him with awe and reverence.

In appearance Livingstone had been a short man with a bushy moustache, and a keen, piercing eye. His words were always gentle, and his manners were always kind ; as a leader it was a privilege to follow him, and he knew the way to the hearts of men. This picture was given by an African in 1880, describing the donor of a coat a missionary found him carrying and which is now in the Scottish National Memorial at Blantyre. Another African, who as a small boy saw Livingstone, said, in 1928 :

" He made a path through our land, and you his followers have come, God's Light-bringers, and more come to-day."

He opened the eyes of the British people to the horrors of the slave trade so effectually, creating such pressure of public opinion, that even before his death a mission was sent to Zanzibar to treat with the Sultan. Sir Bartle Frere, the leader, was unable to persuade Barghash to sign the treaty, and hoped that a more efficient naval patrol would be enough. Public opinion was not satisfied, however, and Dr. Kirk, with the might of the British navy behind him, presented an ultimatum which caused the Sultan to sign without further delay. On 5th June, 1873, while Livingstone's body was still a long way from the coast, the slave market at Zanzibar was closed for ever, and the sea route banned, though the slave traders still used land ways to the north until these too were forbidden. The " open sore of the world " was fast being healed.

Travellers, inspired by Livingstone, explored and charted more and more of the country. Traders and merchants made their plans to build roads and railways, to encourage settlement and the export of raw materials. Missionary societies gave lives lavishly that the highway into Africa might become a Christian way. Sir Bartle Frere, the president of the Royal Geographical Society, said of Livingstone's work and ideals :

" The object of Dr. Livingstone's geographical and scientific explorations was to lead his countrymen to the great work of christianising and civilising the millions of Central Africa. You will recollect how when first he came back from his wonderful journey, though we were all greatly startled by his achievements and by what he told us, people really did not lay what he said much to heart. They were stimulated to take up the cause of African discovery again, and other travellers went out and did excellent service ; but the great fact which was from the very first upon Livingstone's mind, and which he used to impress upon you, did not make the impression he wished, and although a good many people took more and more interest in the civilisation of Africa and in the abolition of the slave trade, which he pointed out was the great obstacle to all progress, still it did not come home to the people generally. It was not until his third and last journey, when he was no more to return among us, that the descriptions which he gave of the horrors of the slave-trade in the interior really took hold upon the mind of the people of this country, and made them determine that what used to be considered the crotchet of a few religious minds and humanitarian sort of persons, should be a phase of the great work which this country had undertaken, to free the African races, and to abolish, in the first place, the slave-trade by sea, and then as we hope, the slaving by land."

Livingstone's spirit lives on in all, and their number is great, who can say with him, " May God grant me life to do good to this poor Africa ". For, to quote from the speech of Sir John Key (to which the opening paragraph of this paper was the reply), after eulogising scientific discovery and commercial possibility :

" Yes, Sir," he said, " what we are now doing for the evangelisation of this distant continent is but the commencement of the liquidation of that righteous debt with which all Christendom is chargeable for Africa's protracted wrongs."

And the greatest pioneer of this liquidation was David Livingstone.

10

LUNDA RITES AND CEREMONIES

V. W. TURNER

1953

INTRODUCTION

In many parts of Northern Rhodesia the ancient religious ideas and practices of the Africans are dying out, through contact with the white man and his ways. Employment in the copper mines, on the railway, as domestic servants and shop assistants; the meeting and mingling of tribes in a non-tribal environment; the long absence of men from their homes—all these factors are contributing to the breakdown of religions which stress the values of kinship ties, respect for the elders and tribal unity. But in the far north-west of the Territory, this process of religious disintegration is less rapid and complete; if one is patient, sympathetic and lucky one may still observe there the dances and rituals of an older day. In Mwinilunga, for instance, where I did a year's field-work as a research officer of the Rhodes-Livingstone Institute, I was able to attend many rituals of the Lunda people and obtain material on others from informants. I gradually became aware of a vast and complicated system of ceremonial practices going on around me rather as one picks out the skyline of a distant city in the growing dawn. It was an astonishing and enriching experience to note the contrast between the relatively simple and monotonous economic and domestic life of these hunters and hoe-cultivators and the ordered arrangement and colourful symbolism of their religious life. Limitations of space unfortunately prevent me from doing full justice in this paper to the subject of Lunda ritual; what I hope to do is to convey some impression of how even illiterate and ill-equipped human beings in the backwoods of history have been able to create a consistent and harmonious religious structure.

To underline the contrast mentioned let us take a brief look at the Lunda in their daily, secular existence. There are about thirty thousand of them in Mwinilunga District, dispersed in scattered villages, each of about a dozen huts, over seven thousand square miles or so of deciduous woodland, cut up by hundreds of streams and young rivers flowing down towards the Zambezi. To the west of the Lunga River, that roughly divides the district from north to south, live the Ndembu, to the east of it the Kosa, both groups calling themselves Lunda and claiming to have come from the land of the great Congo chief, Mwantiyanvwa. In the two centuries following this migration, both Kosa and Ndembu Lunda seem to have lost what central authority and military organisation they may have possessed at first, and have broken up into small, virtually independent chiefdoms. In the late nineteenth century Kanongesha the Ndembu, and Musokantanda the Kosa, senior chiefs, whose ancestors had led the respective war-parties from Mwantiyanvwa, were still respected by their junior chiefs, but had little direct control over them. Much intermarriage took place with the simply organised Mbwela peoples the first Lunda had conquered. Later, Ovimbundu slave-traders and Lwena and Tchokwe slave-raiders from Angola, encouraged by the Portuguese, completed the disintegration of these virtually isolated outposts of Mwantiyanvwa's empire, now grown weak in the homeland itself. But the Lunda, like emigré aristocrats at Cannes or Biarritz, in their talk by the village fires still live in the strenuous and heroic past. Whatever time and raids have done to them, ' We are the people of Mwanti-yanvwa ', they say, and that is that!

Following the conquest, in the absence of cattle, hunting rather than war became the chief masculine occupation, associated with slash-and-burn cassava and millet cultivation by the women, the cassava being grown for food and the millet mainly for beer. Although succession to headmanship and inheritance of what small property they had passed on the mother's side from brother to brother and mother's brother to sister's son, women did not remain in their matrilineal villages as adults, but went to those of their husbands. In this custom of ' virilocal marriage ' the Lunda differ markedly from such matrilineal peoples as the Bemba and Lamba of Northern Rhodesia, among whom men go to their wives' villages on marriage. The core of a Lunda village, therefore, was and still is a small group of male matrilineal kin, whose mothers, sisters and sisters' daughters may be scattered over a wide area in the villages of their husbands. I mention this peculiar feature of their village organisation as it will help us to understand certain aspects of their ritual. The divorce-rate is and always appears to have been high, one reason, I think, being the pull exerted on women living at their husbands' villages by their male kinsfolk, brothers and sons, who reside continuously together. Another consequence of the residential arrangement is competition between a young man's father and mother's brother for his allegiance, resulting in frequent transfers from one village to another of the junior menfolk.

The picture we get, therefore, of the social organisation is of a highly mobile and fluctuating population tied together by small knots of male matrilineal kin in common village residence. But there is a widely spun network of kinship ties uniting all these dispersed groups. By marrying out its womenfolk in all directions, so to speak, each village entrusts other villages with the upbringing of its own junior matrilineal members and receives theirs in return. In this way every man who joins his mother's brother as a young adult has been brought up on the closest terms with his father's kinsmen as a boy. Thus, if the core of a village consists of ten male relatives it is possible that the village is collectively related through their fathers with ten other villages near and far, a bond of warm affection which is free from the poison of mutual sorcery accusations. The advantages of such a wide range of friendly kinship to a society of wandering hunters are obvious.

[337]

Broadly speaking, Lunda rituals fall into two main types: (1) Life-crisis rituals; and (2) Rituals of affliction. Now both these terms require some explanation. What, for instance, is a ' Life-crisis '? Briefly, it is an important point in the physical or social development of an individual, such as birth, puberty or death. In most of the world's simpler societies and in many ' civilised ' societies, too, there are a number of ceremonies or rituals designed to mark the transition from one phase of life or social status to another. We have christening and graduation ceremonies for example, the first to indicate the arrival of a new social personality on the human scene, the second to celebrate the successful outcome of a long and often painful learning process and the launching of a new breadwinner. But these ' crisis ' ceremonies do not only concern the individuals round whom they are centred, they also mark changes in the relationships of all the people connected with them by ties of blood, marriage, cash, political control and in many other ways. When a Lunda woman bears her first child, a boy let us say, she may be presenting her brother, a village headman, with an heir, while her husband becomes a father and her mother a grand-mother, with all the changes in behaviour and status involved in these new relationships. And so her society itself undergoes changes along with her own important passage from young wife to mother. Whatever society we live in we are all members of one another; our own ' big moments ' are ' big moments ' for others as well.

Space only permits me to deal with a few Lunda life-crisis rituals—boys' circumcision ceremonies, girls' puberty ceremonies and funeral rituals. I have selected these three for the Curator has asked me particularly to describe the role of masked dancers, and traditionally masked dancers (*makishi*) only appeared at boys' circumcision ceremonies and important funerals. Moreover, these three rituals are the occasions of big public gatherings, whereas other ' crises ' such as a woman's first pregnancy, child-birth and divination for a child's name are associated only with small intimate groups.

RITUALS OF AFFLICTION

Now what is meant by ' Rituals of Affliction ' ? The answer to this question pinpoints the major theme of Lunda religious life. For some reason or other Lunda have come to associate misfortune in hunting, women's reproductive disorders and various forms of illness with the action of the spirits of the dead. Furthermore, whenever an individual has been divined to have been ' caught ' by such a spirit, he or she becomes the subject of an elaborate ritual, at which many people from far and near attend, devised at once to propitiate and to get rid of the spirit that is thought to be causing the trouble. These statements give rise to a further chain of questions. What sort of ' spirits ' are said to afflict the living those of relatives, of strangers, ' nature spirits ' or ' demons '?

The answer is simple and unambiguous. They are the spirits of deceased relatives. The Lunda term for such a spirit is *mukishi*, plural *akishi*. I would like to make it clear from the outset that *akishi*, 'spirits', must not be confused with *makishi* (singular *ikishi*, Lwena *likishi*), which means 'masked dancers at initiation or funeral ceremonies' or the costumes in which they appear. For the sake of convenience I would like to use Professor Wilson's term 'shade' rather than 'spirit' or 'ancestor spirit' for *mukishi*. Rightly or wrongly 'ancestor spirit' suggests 'remote or distant ancestor' to most people, and these uneasy inhabitants of the 'unquiet grave' are always the spirits of those who played a prominent part in the lifetime of the persons they are troubling.

Why do the shades 'come out of their graves', as the Lunda put it, to plague their kinsfolk? Various reasons are alleged, the most important being that the latter have 'forgotten' them or that they have acted in a way that the shades have disapproved of. 'Forgetting' implies neglect to make an offering of beer or food at the *muyombu* trees planted as living shrines in the centre of villages or omitting to mention their names while praying there. It may also mean neglecting to pour blood from one's latest kill down an opening made in a hunter's grave, 'for the shade to eat'. It may simply consist in forgetting the dead 'in one's heart'. 'Disapproved conduct' may mean causing a quarrel in the kin-group, going away from the dead person's village to live elsewhere or disobeying a wish expressed in his or her lifetime. But whatever the reason there is usually thought to be something rather distinctive and important in being 'caught by a *mukishi*'. To begin with, one becomes the central figure of a great ritual gathering, all of who earnestly desire that one should get better or have better luck. Then, if one has undergone successful treatment, one is entitled to become a minor 'doctor' (*chimbuki*), when the same ritual is performed for other people, perhaps progressing in time to the role of principal doctor. Thus, the way to religious fame is through 'affliction'. I have often heard doctors or diviners reply to the question 'how did you learn your job?' by the words, 'I started by being sick myself', meaning that the shade of one of their relatives afflicted them with illness. So that there is a double meaning in being caught by a shade. One is punished for neglect of their memory, but at the same time one is chosen or 'elected' to be a go-between in future rituals that put the living into communication with the dead. If the ritual fails in its purpose and one's sickness or bad luck continues, it may be a sign that one has not properly atoned for one's offence. It may mean, on the other hand, that one is being attacked by the witchcraft of the living, but witchcraft falls outside the scope of this paper.

What are the ways in which a shade comes to afflict one? They fall roughly into three main types: (1) the shade of a hunter may cause his kinsman to miss his aim, fail to find animals to shoot or drive animals out of range; (2) the shade of a woman may cause her kinswoman to have various reproductive troubles ranging from sterility to suffering a series of miscarriages; (3) shades of both sexes may cause their living kin of both sexes to become ill in various ways, such as ' wasting away ', ' sweating and shivering ' or ' pains all over the body ', to use Lunda descriptions of symptoms.   To these three modes of affliction correspond three principal kinds of ritual to remove them, which may be described as: (1) Hunting Cults, (2) Fertility Cults, and (3) Curative Cults; the first being performed for men, the second for women and the third for both sexes. The mode of affliction and the rite to dispel it are both known by the same name.   For instance, if a woman suffers from prolonged and painful menstruation she is said to have been ' caught by a shade which has come out in *Nkula* ' and the rite to rid her of the shade is also called *Nkula*.   Within each ' Cult ' are a number of separate rituals, those of the Hunting Cult being arranged in a graded order while those of the other Cults have no fixed order of performance. The afflicting shade in a given ritual is said to have been itself afflicted in the same way while it was alive.   Thus patient, leading ' doctor ' and lesser ' doctors ' and the shade itself belong to a single, sacred community consisting of the elect and the candidate for election.

PART I

LIFE-CRISIS RITUALS

INITIATION CEREMONIES

Although both boys and girls undergo initiation ceremonies the form and purpose of the ceremonies differ widely in either case. Boys, for instance, are circumcised, but there is no cliterodectomy of girls. Boys are initiated collectively, girls individually. Boys are initiated before, girls at the onset of puberty. The main purpose of boys' initiation is to inculcate tribal values, hunting skill and sexual instruction; that of girls' initiation to prepare them for marriage, which follows immediately in the great majority of cases. Boys are secluded and taught in the bush; a grass hut is built in the village itself for girls. Other striking differences exist which will be brought out in the descriptions below. The main points to notice, however, are the contrast between the *group* nature of the boys' ceremony and the *individual* nature of the girls'; the emphasis on obedience to the discipline of the elders and endurance of hardship in the boys' as contrasted with the emphasis on sex and reproduction and the freedom from manual work associated with the girls' ceremony, and the *bush* setting of the former as compared with the *domestic and village* setting of the latter.

Mukanda, the Boys' Initiation Ceremony

To all Lunda men of about middle age or over *Mukanda*, the boys' circumcision ceremony, is the most wonderful of all rituals. True it is beset with real and imaginary dangers, but its whole atmosphere is pervaded on the one hand with reverential awe and on the other by a strong sense of masculine comradeship. It used to be the very basis of tribal solidarity—one was neither a man nor a Kalunda if one had not passed through *Mukanda*. Today the Missions offer an alternative and far more hygienic circumcision operation at Kalene Hospital, but the traditional ceremony is still held in outlying areas. It is a mystical drama of manhood in the course of which the fundamental values of tribal life are expressed and driven home in the most vivid form. In the eyes of older Lunda a mere physical operation is no substitute for the grand and ancient mystery. But younger parents are tending to send their sons to the ' Mission Mukanda ' because it is less costly in cash, time and trouble.

Phase 1.—*Preparation*

The initiative to hold *Mukanda* lies with any headman who thinks that he can afford to feed and house large numbers of parents who will come from distant regions of Lunda country to be near their children at the bush school. Great is his honour and fame who successfully sponsors one. His first act is to send the most spirited lad in his village to a powerful ' doctor ', called *Mbimbi*, who possesses the apparatus and medicines required to perform the circumcision. When he reaches the latter's village the lad says, ' Old man *Mbimbi*, you are lazy and your knife is blunt. You are now no good at circumcising boys. In fact, it's no use calling you to my uncle headman So-and-so's village '. *Mbimbi* is not angry at this reviling but takes some special medicine called *isaku* and puts it on the boy's brow, telling him to return to the village and ask the people to brew much beer. This boy is known from now on as *Kambanji*, or ' war-leader ', the most important of the novices. He returns, tells the headman that *Mbimbi* is favourable to the performance and is then sent to notify the local chief and the headmen of adjoining villages that *Mukanda* will be held from his uncle's village. The news spreads like wildfire across Lunda country and messengers soon arrive from quite remote areas, even from other senior chiefdoms, asking if boys can be sent from them to this headman's *Mukanda*. If the answer is in the affirmative the parents of these boys brew beer and assemble foodstuffs and accompany their children to the village of *Mukanda*. During the ceremony the women will have to provide a constant shuttle service of supplies between the *Mukanda* area and the home villages. *Mukanda* always begins when the rains have ended and continues until the end of the dry season, when agricultural activities recommence.

When about fifty or sixty boys have been assembled, *Mbimbi* is told to bring his outfit of knives and medicines to the village. The ensemble is known as *mfunda*, which also means ' foreskin ' and refers to his primary medicine which consists of the cindered foreskins of previously initiated boys mixed with herbal medicines. *Mfunda* comprises a receptacle made from a bush-baby's skin, carried by two arrows bound together near the barbs and fixed to the skin at the feathered ends. One of the arrows is the type used with arrow-poison, the other an ordinary arrow. In the receptacle are kept a short, sharp circumcising knife (*ntewulu*), medicines appropriate to different phases and circumstances of the ceremony and a small phallus-shaped calabash, called *kadiwu*, into which the foreskins of the boys are placed after removal to form the basis of future *mfunda* medicine. Normally, *Mbimbi* keeps his apparatus hung up in the bush on a forked post not far from his hut. On no account may it touch the ground or it will lose its efficacy. If a woman or an uncircumcised boy happen to touch it they will catch leprosy. When he reaches the village of *Mukanda*, *Mbimbi* hangs it up on a special pronged stick in the centre of the village.

[342]

Other officiants are now chosen. One is called *Chijiku wa-Mukanda*, ' the keeper of the fire of *Mukanda* ', who lights and tends a fire about a hundred yards from the village, the nearest women may approach to the circumcision lodge, during the whole period of the school. Another is known as *mfumu watubwiku* or *mfumu wanyadyi*, literally ' husband of the novices ', whose duty is to teach the novices (*anyadyi*, singular *mwadyi*) the sacred songs and dances of *Mukanda*, bush-lore and sexual matters, during their seclusion. Each boy is given a *chilombolo*, a ' guardian ' or ' nurse ', usually a senior relative, who will also instruct him and look after him. The senior *chilombolo* is called *Chilomboji* and he supervises the carrying of food from the sacred fire (*ijiku daMukanda*), to which the women bring it from the village, to the novices in the bush. The boys are frequently beaten by these officiants during *Mukanda* if they make mistakes, and if they act in a stupid or disrespectful way afterwards their parents will rebuke the guardians for not chastising them sufficiently. Some of the boys, too, are given titles. Next in importance to *Kambanji* is *Kaselantanda*, who may be the headman's son. After him is *Mwanta waMukanda*, ' chief of *Mukanda* ', who is the son of the keeper of the sacred fire. The last boy to be circumcised is called *Kajika*, ' he who closes ', a humorously disgraceful title. Each novice's mother is called *Nyamwadyi*. During the period of *Mukanda*, only titles and not personal names are employed, and special sacred terms are given to common utensils and other objects used in it.

The evening before *Mukanda* proper begins, the sponsoring headman, *Mbimbi*, and the keeper of the sacred fire assemble before the *nyiyombu* trees which are planted as shrines to the village shades. In the order mentioned each man takes his own ball of white clay (*mpemba*), applies it to the tree, draws three lines from the tree to himself and finally anoints himself beside the eyes and draws a line upwards from his navel. White clay is a symbol of purity, good will, good health and communion and is always applied as a prelude to prayer to the shades. The headman mentions each of the village shades by name, refers to his or her status and past deeds and prays that no mischance should befall the novices from sorcery, witchcraft or the breaking of taboos while in seclusion. *Mbimbi* calls on the spirits to witness that he has never yet allowed a novice to die as the result of circumcision. The keeper of the fire promises them that he will observe the correct customs and not allow ritually dangerous persons, such as those who have broken the prohibition on sexual intercourse, to pass beyond the fire.

Now the sacred fire is lit by steel and flint and a big dance follows lasting all night, in which women for the last time play a prominent part. From now on the parents of the novices must abstain from intercourse until the circumcision scars are completely healed, otherwise they will not heal quickly, and indeed the boys' lives may be in danger.

Phase 2.—Separation

Mbimbi and a number of assistant circumcisers spend the night together in the bush. Next morning, all the boys are made to sit on a single long mat near the sacred fire. The women are near them. The circumcisers arrive and the women weep and lament for their sons. The circumcisers now set up a three-posted frame rather like a goal made of *mukula* (*Pterocarpus Angolensis*), a wood which secretes a red gum and often symbolises blood. A functionary called *Chimbu* or ' Hyaena ' calls to the boys to pass under the ' goal ' or *mukuleku*. When the boys and *Mukanda* officials have done so, *Chimbu* prevents the distraught women from following them.

The boys are now taken to a place in the bush about a mile from the village where they spend the rest of the day erecting the circumcision lodge, called *ng'ula*, a long hut thatched with leaves instead of grass. It has only one doorway, facing east towards the sunrise. Behind it is a cleared space called *kwifwilu danyadyi*, ' the death-place of the novices ', where circumcision takes place.

Phase 3.—Circumcision

This event occurs next morning. Another *mukuleku* is erected in the *kwifwilu danyadyi*; from it long poles of *mukula* wood are placed end to end in a line along the ground; at intervals small termite mounds (*mafwamfwa*) are placed upright, each with a sort of shallow basin scooped out of the top; a long string of bark peeled from the *musamba* tree is carried over the tops of the ant-hills. Each boy is made to stand by an ant-hill, several large and small drums are brought up and the fathers and male relatives begin to drum and chant the *Mukanda* refrain, ' The child is feeling the pain of circumcision, you see it with your own eyes '. Each guardian stands behind his charge. The circumcisers who again spent the night in the bush are suddenly brought in on the backs of male relatives each with his knife and medicines. The drumming grows louder and louder. The guardians throw the novices on their backs and kneel behind them clasping them firmly. Now *Kambanji*, *Kaselantanda* and *Mwanta waMukanda* are circumcised in that order by the great *Mwimbi*, one cut being made above and one beneath the penis before a circular cut is made removing the foreskin. The other doctors now begin to circumcise, each dealing with approximately seven boys. Lunda boys unlike novices in many other tribes are expected to yell and struggle; the powerful singing and drumming is to hide the noise from the women waiting by the sacred fire. The bark-string is set alight and as soon as each boy has been circumcised he stands over the termite mound holding his penis in the smoke. This is supposed to communicate the ' binding up ' qualities of the bark-string to the wound and make it heal quickly. Another smaller piece of *musamba* bark is inserted in the end of the penis to prevent urination through fright. While circumcision is going on pots and calabashes containing medicines have been placed near the sacred fire. Some are to prevent the familiar spirits of sorcerers and witches from attacking the novices. Others are to defend the fire and the novices from the inimical influences of persons who have recently had sexual intercourse and whose close approach would cause sacred things and persons to lose their efficacy.

Mbimbi places a magic clay pot (*izawu*) containing medicines in a hole in the ground at the circumcision site, and inserts a sprig of *muyombu* to invoke the shades to witness the circumcision and protect the novices. Directly after each boy is circumcised he is passed over this *muyombu* in the pot before standing over the termite-mound.

Mbimbi collects the foreskins and puts them in his *kadiwu* calabash. The boys are now taken to their lodge (*ng'ula*) and are forbidden to enter or even look at the circumcision site again. If they do, they will contract leprosy, the general sanction against breaking a *Mukanda* taboo. Women, however, were summarily put to death if they were found near the lodge.

After two days the novices are taken to a stream, where they wash off the stains of blood. *Mbimbi* applies medicine, composed of *musenji* and *musafwa* bark pounded in cold water, to the circumcision scars. Then they are given *kasanji* leaves to chew which they apply round the glans as a bandage. After a week the same medicines are applied warm.

If a boy should die during *Mukanda* he is not buried, but simply thrown on a cinder-pile near the lodge and covered gradually with the ashes of successive fires. His mother must not be informed until the initiation school is over when she is silently handed the plate she has sent his food on—broken.

After circumcision *Mbimbi* is not allowed to enter the lodge, but comes from time to time into the adjacent bush and sings to the novices who may revile him violently without their abuse being returned.

Phase 4.—The Dance of the Makishi

When about three weeks have passed after circumcision, the novices are instructed by *mfumu watubwiku* to go into the bush to procure large quantities of bark string from the *katochi* and *muzawu* trees. They come back peeling the string off as they walk. This string is taken by the guardians and other officiants to the sacred circumcision place. *Mfumu watubwiku*, the instructor in the mysteries of *Mukanda*, now sends a message to the keeper of the sacred fire to tell the women to brew about a dozen calabashes of beer. He explains that if the beer is poured out on an ant-hill the *makishi* ' will come out of the ground '. The women take the beer from the village to the sacred fire and the guardians remove it to the circumcision site where the officiants and other elders are by this time rapidly weaving the *makishi* costumes from the bark strings. The *makishi* dancers themselves have not been seen at this *Mukanda* before, may have come from a considerable distance, and remain anonymous after the dance. Costume-makers and dancers get very drunk and when they have finished the costumes begin to clap their hands and sing songs appropriate to each *ikishi*, while the boys in the lodge tremble with fear for, like the women, they believe that the *makishi* are indeed supernatural beings. The masks are not made at the ceremony, but have been taken from large calabashes buried in former circumcision sites where the blood had fallen and looked after by *Mbimbi*. After a while the *makishi*, one by one, enter the lodge and completely terrify the boys who huddle together away from them as they approach. Traditionally, I am told, the Lunda, unlike the Lwena who have many, possessed only two *makishi*, whose names were *Mvweng'i* and *Katotoji* (corresponding to the Lwena *Katotola*). *Mvweng'i* appeared first and was ' a very big *ikishi* ' who had a laterally extended mask and wore animal skins. He stood in one place making a gentle but sinister undulating movement (*ku-punjila*) and beating two sticks together, known as *ayingongu* (singular, *chingongu*); for this reason *Mvweng'i* is sometimes known as *Sachingongu*. *Mvweng'i* is particularly terrifying to women for a reason which will be explained later. *Katotoji* (see *Katotola* in the Museum) carries a stick and is said to wear a grass kilt and collar at *Mukanda*. When they have had their fill of scaring the boys the *makishi* proceed to the village and scare the women there. *Katotoji* climbs trees and hangs upside down from them or rushes up the roof of a house and straddles it. When they advance on women, the latter must pay them beads or cash to avert misfortune. Finally they disappear into the bush again, to be seen no more until the next *Mukanda*.

Recently the Lunda have borrowed a number of *makishi* from Lwena and Luchazi sources, such as *Chizeluki* (' the madman '), *Chileya chawambanda* (' the fool of women '),[1] *Ndondo* (' the one with the disease-swollen stomach '), *Kalelwa* and *Chikumbukumbu* (meanings uncertain), and many others. In considering the meaning of these strange visitations, however, it is best to stick to the authentically Lunda *makishi*, for what has a distinct meaning in one society and culture loses its original significance when borrowed by another.

Opinions differ among the authorities as to the meaning of these masked dancers. Professor Baumann thinks that they are ' demons of the bush ', but this does not get us much further. Professor Gluckman regards them as ' ancestor spirits ', but this identification is emphatically denied by Lunda themselves, who say ' *akishi* (" shades " or " ancestor spirits ") are dead people whom we knew alive; but *makishi* were never men like us, they stay in *Mukanda*.' Everybody thirsts for explanations of enigmas; that is why detective fiction sells so well. With some trepidation, there-

---

[1] Corresponding to the Lwena *Mwana pwevo* and Tchokwe *Mwana pwo*.

fore, I will hazard my own guess as to the significance of the two Lunda *makishi*. *Mvweng'i* symbolises male authority over women; *Katotoji* stands for the authority of seniors over juniors. *Mvweng'i* appears in a cult of affliction, affecting female fertility, called *Isoma*, where it is supposed that a shade, offended by the neglect of a living pregnant woman relative, ' says to *Mvweng'i*, " come let us go and catch this woman " ' (informant's statement). The woman then dreams both of the shade and *Mvweng'i* who is doing his swaying dance and eventually has an abortion or miscarriage. The swaying is associated with the premature ' sliding-out ' of the child. The *Isoma* ritual is performed to rid her of the shade and important features of the performance are the swaying dance (*ku-punjila*), and the singing of *Mukanda* songs by those taking part. Thus *Mvweng'i*, distinct from the afflicting shade, is seen as the means by which the latter ' blasts ' the woman's reproductive powers. *Mvweng'i* is regarded as a male *ikishi*, unlike ' female ' *makishi* (personated, however, by men, since women must not approach the lodge) such as *Chileya*. *Katotoji* appears again in sorcery beliefs as an animated wooden figurine (*nkishi*) which can be sent, stick in hand, by its owner to attack invisibly the latter's junior kin. It is animated in the first place by inserting a blue duiker's horn in its forehead, containing medicine, among the ingredients of which are pieces of bark string from the costume of a *Katotoji* used at *Mukanda*, blood from a junior kinsman killed by the sorcery of the witch-doctor who is ' giving his client *Katotoji* ' and certain herbal preparations to render it invisible. All chiefs are supposed to own a *Katotoji* which is said to wander round the villages after dark, beating belated children to death with its stick and striking with impotence men who come out of their huts to urinate.[1] There is a purpose behind this apparently wanton malice for Lunda believe that a sorcerer increases his own virility and vigour with every victim he kills. From the anti-social uses of *Katotoji* a clue may be found to his social function. The stick he carries at *Mukanda* summarises in one dreaded object all the sticks employed by the elders to beat the novices at *Mukanda*. The *Katotoji* of sorcery strikes down only the juniors or inferiors of its owner. The *Katotoji* of *Mukanda* keeps the young in lively awe of their elders. If we consider that the power of the shades is a kind of extension of the authority of the elders, as Professor Wilson does for the Nyakyusa people, we might go some of the way with Professor Gluckman and concede that the *Makishi* stands for ' ancestral authority ' in general rather than particular manifestations of the dead.

I cannot explain the other ' borrowed ' *makishi*, except to suggest that as some of them seem to represent diseases or madness they may be regarded as having a ' prophylactic ' (to use Professor Wilson's term) function against such disorders. The belief that by depicting or enacting what one wishes to avoid one will be immune from it in future is fairly widespread in ' primitive society '.

[1] C. M. N. White, 1948. " Witchcraft, Divination and Magic among the Balovale Tribes ". *Africa*. Vol. XVIII No. 2. April. cf. p.100.

Before leaving the fascinating and speculative topic of the *makishi* it is worth pointing out that they are collectively associated with the bush, the domain of the Lunda male, especially of the hunter, with ant-hills, which symbolise in hunting cults both masculine sexual power and huntsmanship in general, and that they are feigned to rise up from the blood-saturated site of circumcision, a circumstance that seems further to connect *Mukanda* with the hunting cults in which the symbolism of 'shed blood' is a regular theme.

Phase 5.—*The Novices in Seclusion*

How do the novices spend their time in seclusion? Their activities are many and varied, consisting on the one hand of instruction in sacred matters and mystical lore and on the other of instruction in practical and useful arts such as hunting and fishing lore and techniques, the manufacture of bird snares and traps and basic knowledge of the uses of herbal medicines.

Their only clothing is a girdle of woven string called *fwefweta*. They eat together from a long table of woven branches (*kaweji*) outside the initiation lodge. The mother of each boy makes a separate fire while *Mukanda* lasts, devoted exclusively to the cooking of cassava mush for her son. The boys must provide their meat and fish relish by their own efforts. Each novice carries with him wherever he goes a small wand of *kabalabala* wood which he must put beneath him if he wishes to sit down or go to sleep. Shrines to the shades of hunters, consisting of peeled sticks, forked near the top, are often made of this wood, a typical hunter's 'medicine'.

A fence of brushwood, called *mukoliki*, extends in a circle from the lodge enclosing an open space, also known as *ng'ula*, in which the boys sleep, *kambanji* only using the lodge. They sleep two and three together on a single mat for warmth, for it is very cold in May and June and they are not allowed blankets. The guardians sleep nearby and if a boy wishes to urinate he must call his guardian and hop with him on one leg to the ash-pile, afterwards slapping his open hand on his clenched fist, 'to make him strong'. The boys must rise at dawn and go to bed at sunset, singing a song to the sun as they do so. Meanwhile their relatives of both sexes—other than *Mukanda* officiants—sleep near the sacred fire and sing 'My child is crying, mercy on my child, mother is far from *Mukanda*' at dawn and sunset.

Among other sacred matters boys are taught ancient Lunda traditions about their Congo homeland and myths about the first man and woman. They receive instruction on sexual matters, and sing songs enjoining on them certain food taboos which do not hold good during *Mukanda*, but afterwards must be maintained until late middle age. Among these forbidden foods are a large number of striped and spotted animals and birds the eating of which will cause leprosy with its streaks and blotches on the skin. They include zebra, bushbuck, blue duiker, serval and genet cats, certain species of mongoose, striped mice, guinea fowl, a type of small striped kingfisher and a songbird with a spotted head called *mulundu*. Other birds and fishes with red markings will, if eaten, cause one to bleed to death from cuts; these include the red-legged, bare-throated francolin, the red-loury and a red-breasted bream. If one eats the elephant-shrew its elongated snout will make the foreskin grow long again and impede sexual intercourse. These taboos are rigorously observed after *Mukanda* and I know a man who was circumcised in 1919 who only started to eat the red loury in 1946 and has not yet dared to eat zebra flesh.

This brief account by no means exhausts the list of the novices' activities. The even tenor of their lives is interrupted about four months after circumcision, when the scars are considered fully healed, by a ceremony known as " the cleansing of maturity ".

Phase 6.—' The Cleansing of Maturity '

This implies a further washing in the river for the boys and a big beer-brew and dance for the parents at the sacred fire. The initiative to hold the dance comes from the boys and their parents may now resume their normal activities such as sexual intercourse, visiting relatives and friends in other villages, and may even return to their own villages for a while. But the boys must remain in seclusion for another two months and the officiants continue to perform their duties.

Phase 7.—The End of Seclusion

Shortly before the boys return to their mothers, they are given *mfunda* medicine to eat by *Mbimbi*, made from their own burnt foreskins and herbal medicines including *kapwipu* and *mubang'a* bark. Then they are given tortoise meat. These foods will give them ' a strong penis '. After this an elder covers himself completely with a cloth and makes a hole in it, through which he inserts his male member. This character is known as *Nyakayowa*. Each of the novices goes through the motions of copulation with *Nyakayowa*, who says, ' Tomorrow you will return to mother. Each guardian will carry back another guardian's novice. Ohé, how the mothers will cry when they see the wrong children on the backs of the guardians.'

Phase 8.—The Coming-out Ceremony

The parents all forgather at the sacred fire the day before the coming-out ceremony and dancing and drumming go on all night. Just before dawn the novices are led to a cleared site in the bush called *kafotu*. Meanwhile *mfumu watubwiku* and the guardians take burning brands from the initiation fire and burn down the

[349]

lodge, covering the circumcision site with the ashes. The boys must not look at the blaze, lest the stripings of flame should stripe them with leprosy.

Now each novice is striped ' like a zebra ' by his guardian with spaced rings of white clay, thick bands round his face rendering him unrecognisable. In each hand he carries a stick of *kapepi* wood covered with alternate rings of black and white. Black for Lunda symbolises death, uncleanness or misfortune according to the context; white, as we have seen, stands for purity, good health, reconciliation and atonement with the ancestors and good luck. Thus, the intermediate condition of the novices between ' death ' of their old childhood selves and the birth of a new relationship with their group,[1] a new ' life ', between ritual impurity and ritual cleansing, is well expressed. Each boy wears a collar of stiff grass round his neck and a kilt of stiff grass round his waist (both called *nkambi*). He is lifted onto the back of another boy's guardian and keeps his head bowed, beating the sticks above his neck as the guardians in procession carry their charges to the sacred fire where the parents are assembled. When the latter see them coming they are seized with uncontrollable excitement. The drums beat, all sing ' *Twamuswekele, twamusoleli* ', ' We have uncovered him, we see him in public ', and the women surge forward, desperately anxious to find out whether their sons are safe. Each runs to her child's guardian and after close scrutiny discovers that he is carrying another boy. Bitter wailing breaks out as at a funeral, as the women, fearing that their children have died, rush frantically from guardian to guardian, seeking out their sons. When they find them at last, they seize their hands, try to blow in their ears (the Lunda kiss) and cry out their gratitude to their proper guardians. Finally the procession makes off into the bush again (a process known as *kufumpa niswewa*), followed for a time by the jubilant mothers who sing the praises of their sons.

The mothers return to prepare a feast, including great quantities of meat, for the boys. These have gone to a stream to wash off the white clay, shave their heads neatly along the hairline and cast their grass kilts and collars into the water. Each mother has given the *Chilomboji*, the chief guardian, a fine new cloth for her son. The latter is no longer in an ' intermediate ' state, he has definitively entered his new status of full Lunda-hood (to use a term of Mr. Cunnison's) and can now marry when he is old enough. Meanwhile, the food cooked by the mothers is set out in a long line at a special clearing called *Katewu*, a little distance from the sacred fire. Only men can carry it there, for *Mukanda* has not yet quite finished, and the novices sit down together with the guardians and officiants for a communion meal, eating in small groups of friends.

After they have eaten they are carried by their guardians to the sacred fire where the local chief, his headmen and councillors and a

---

1 White beads are wound round a new baby's wrist.

great throng of Lunda from all over the country are waiting. A big wooden slit-drum (*chikuvu*) has been brought from the capital village and it begins to rumble as it is beaten by the rubber-headed drum-sticks. The boys, assembled in line, dance each in turn, *Kambanji* first, the impressive solo war-dance of the Lunda, the *ku-tomboka*. Anointed down the brow and beside the eyes with red clay, symbolising the spilling of blood, with a red loury feather in his hair, the dancer, breathing heavily like an angry bull, gesturing fiercely with a battle-axe in his hand, prowls round the ring of on-lookers breaking into a convulsive dance with laterally jutting hips and flying legs. Traditionally *ku-tomboka* was danced by the war-leader (*kambanji*) of a chief after the Lunda had defeated their foes and brought the severed heads of the latter before the chief. In this case a keyhole-shaped hole would be scooped in the ground and in it placed a cup containing beer mixed with the blood of their enemies. The hole imitates and symbolises a Lunda grave, and the last act of *ku-tomboka* was the drinking of the beer and blood by the war-leader *kambanji*, who flung down the cup and its dregs into the hole.

After *Kambanji*, *Kaselantanda*, then *Mwanta waMukanda*, ' *tomboka* ' before the chief, then the others, last of whom is *Kajika* who smites the drum with his open hand to mark the end of the coming-out proper.

The boys now retire to one large mat and *Kambanji* addresses the chief, ' I am now a big man, even I myself. You are a fool and a rogue, a useless person. I warn you, from now on don't eat your food alone, but share some of it with us your children.' This licensed disrespect which *Kambanji* enjoys towards chief and circumciser is a form of compensation for the pain and humiliation the boys have had to endure from older men. Now the keeper of the sacred fire steps forward and says to the chief, ' O chief, we came to ask you for fire (refers to the chief's giving permission to hold *Mukanda*, not to an actual torch). We have looked after these children well. Now count them; not one is missing.' *Mbimbi*, the circumciser, *Chilomboji*, the leader of the guardians, and *Mfumu waTubwiku*, the instructor in sacred matters, now ask the parents for payment in cash or kind. The boys themselves had received small gifts from the onlookers while they danced, known as *nshing'a*. The lesser guardians are paid privately later.

Next day, each boy's set of relatives gives him a sheep or a goat and they eat, again in groups of particular friends, for the first time in the village, in secular society. Two days afterwards they wash in the river, using *Mukanda* medicines (including portions of the litter of *Kambanji's* bed and ashes from the lodge fire) and castor oil used to anoint them in the lodge. This is to prevent them giving leprosy to girls with whom they may have sexual intercourse in the next few weeks, for even young boys of about seven to eleven, as most novices are, take part in games of a sexual nature with girls

[351]

in the bush. After this last precautionary cleansing the guardians marshal their charges by chiefdoms and villages and lead them home. *Mukanda* is over.

Nkang'a, the Girls' Initiation Ceremony

The following account is mainly based on the observations of my wife, as there are certain aspects of the ceremony from which men are excluded. However, as in *Mukanda*, big public dances mark the opening and closing phases of *Nkang'a*.

Lunda women maintain that *Nkang'a* surpasses *Mukanda* in beauty and impressiveness. It is not, however, so elaborately organised and usually concerns only a single girl. There are three phases, ' going-in ' (*kw'ing'isha*), seclusion (*kunkunka*) and ' coming-out ' (*kw'idyisha*).

Phase 1.—' *Going-in* '

The marriage of a young girl frequently takes place before puberty, although the girl will often remain with her parents until the end of *Nkang'a*. When a girl begins to show obvious signs of sexual development (growth of the breasts rather than first menstruation is the principal criterion of development), her parents and matrilineal relatives decide that *Nkang'a* should be performed for her. At this age the girl is expected to become shy in the presence of her husband or betrothed, a modesty which must continue until the end of the ceremony. There is a strong taboo on the husband coming to see her during seclusion. As with the Bemba, described by Dr. Audrey Richards, Lunda hold that there is danger inherent in full adult sexual intercourse as distinct from the sexual play of children. Only a protracted and exacting ritual can remove this danger and adequately prepare a woman for the role of wife and mother.

The evening before *Nkang'a* begins, at sunset, the girl's mother and the woman selected to be her guardian (*Nkong'u*, literally ' midwife ') go to the *nyiyombu* tree-shrines of the village (either her mother's or father's village, although the former is preferred as the site of *Nkang'a*), and pray with white clay (as in *Mukanda*) to the shades that the girl, henceforward known as *Kankang'a*, should be preserved from bad luck or bad health, be immune from sorcery or witchcraft (the sorcery figurine *Nyalumayi*, for instance, can only be animated by a *Kankang'a's* blood—possibly menstrual blood, but we have no explicit information on this point)—and that she should ' ripen ' quickly. The girl must first that night or eat only a small amount of cassava mush without relish. But no taboos of food-avoidance or sexual continence are placed on her parents. *Nkong'u* (the ' guardian ') may or may not be a relative of the girl, although she is often her older married sister, full or classificatory. She it is who selects the site of the ' going-in ' ceremony, centred around a *mudyi* (*Diplorrhyncus*) tree just outside the village ring of huts. Now *mudyi* medicine is generally associated with nurture, probably from the fact that the tree secretes milky fluid when the stem is cut. *Mudyi* sticks are used to cover the afterbirth which is buried in a shallow hole behind the mother's hut. Chewed *mudyi* leaves are applied to the breasts of a foster-mother to stimulate a flow of milk. Midwives use them as an ingredient in medicine to produce an easy delivery. Generally, in fact, they symbolise birth and nurture.

Next morning, just before dawn, the *Kankang'a* girl novice is taken from her hut by women of the village where the ceremony is being held, naked save for a blanket, and carried to the *mudyi* tree (always a sapling, signifying youth), where she is laid on a duiker skin. An arrow draped with white beads around the feathered end is inserted in the *mudyi* sapling. This represents her husband (the term for marriage-payment, *nsewu*, also means ' arrow '), the *mudyi* stands for the girl and the white beads symbolise good will and union. She will wear these beads at her ' coming-out ' dance. Meanwhile, the village women begin to dance, in a close ring singing and clapping, round the girl who is entirely covered by her blanket. The songs are of a teasing and highly sexual nature, belittling the mother of ' only one child ' or of ' bald children ', extolling female desire, warning against quarrelling in the hut or bickering with co-wives. The novice has to lie perfectly still on one side until midday when she is lifted on to her other side, although her guardian comes and massages her periodically. Gradually, women drift in from other villages, men appear with drums, the large *kayanda* drum together with two small *mong'fuza* (' scolds ') drums forming a popular combination, and two circles of dancers take shape, one composed mainly of women, although men sometimes jocularly join it, circling the novice, and the other of men and women, a flirtatious and cheerful group who sing the ' latest hit tunes ' of the district, while the other group tends to adhere to the traditional *Nkang'a* songs. Strong rivalry between the sexes is a marked feature of *Nkang'a* and I have seen the women in a body bear down on a circle of male dancers and spiritedly tell them off for making too much noise. Since *Nkang'a* is a sort of festival celebrating womanhood, the men had to defer, however reluctantly, and ' break it up ', like a crowd of soldiers ' ticked off ' by a sergeant!

In the early afternoon, the novice's father enters the women's circle points to the girl and chants ' Are the *twins* well? ' The women reply, ' Yes, well ', emphatically. Twins represent an almost embarrassing excess of fertility. We shall meet with a ritual devoted to the theme of twins under Fertility Cults in a later section. Then the women pluck *mudyi* leaves and pass them round over each other's heads.

About four o'clock a simple grass hut (*nkunka*) is built in a space in the village circle of huts by the novice's bridegroom and his brothers. When it is made, one of his brothers straddles the

[353]

hut with his legs. The bridegroom may not do this himself on account of the taboos of *Nkang'a* for it represents his sexual rights over his bride.

Shortly afterwards, the women gather leaves from the *mudyi* tree, run to the hut where the bridegroom lodged the previous night and hide them under the thatch of the roof. Later these leaves will be taken by the novice's mother to the bridegroom's village.

At six o'clock the girl is lifted up and carried on her guardian's back, still wrapped in her blanket, to where the men are dancing and they run three times round the dancers. She is then taken to her grass seclusion hut and her groom is called in to kindle a fire inside it by means of flint and steel. If he cannot do it quickly he is taken to be impotent and in former times another husband would have been found for the girl. Nowadays, however, he may use store matches, which guarantee early success! Then all except the guardian, the novice and a young female relative of the latter, who has not yet attained puberty, called *Kansonsera* (' she who kindles the fire '), withdraw, and the guardian puts the novice to bed. *Kansonsera* must perform most of the domestic chores for the novice, who is under taboo not to do the traditional women's work, such as making a fire, cultivating, drawing water, preparing and cooking food, during the whole period of seclusion. *Kansonsera* is often the novice's younger sister, but, like *Nkong'u*, may not necessarily be closely related. I have, indeed, seen a young uncircumcised boy in this role, able to enter the seclusion hut because he had not yet undergone *Mukanda*.

At sundown people from surrounding villages far and near gather for a dance that continues until sunrise. Food and beer are provided by the parents of bride and groom. A lot of stealthy cuckolding goes on, stimulated by the dancing and drinking and fights break out sporadically between husbands and lovers. It is essentially a dance for the younger people and much of the sexual jealousy is caused by the fact that men marry about eight years later than women so that their contemporaries of the opposite sex are already long-established wives.

Phase 2.—Seclusion

The seclusion of the girl novice is not nearly so complete as that of the boys at *Mukanda*. Any day she can be seen in a small compound enclosed by a fence of reeds or grass practising the innumerable traditional dances in which she will be obliged to show her skill when she ' comes-out ', supported by clapping and singing female relatives. She may even leave this compound to relieve herself in the bush. Should she go out, however, she must cover herself with her blanket, held well forward over her eyes, and walk in a crouching posture, ' like a sheep ' as Lunda say, accompanied by her faithful little attendant *Kansonsera*. If she sees public rituals and dances, the ceremony must be abandoned and indeed her relatives may die. Men are not normally allowed into the enclosure, but an exception is made in the case of the *ikishi* dancer, *Chileya chawambanda*, a character who in recent years has become a sort of secular mountebank or clown, giving public performances as far from Mwinilunga as the Copperbelt from a wide repertoire of dances. I have seen *Chileya* dancers on two separate occasions giving girl novices dancing lessons in the sacred enclosure, clad in their masks and costumes which confer a sort of honorary female-ness on them.

The *Nkong'u* guardian or instructress does not do a full-time job but comes to instruct the novice after she has done her own work for the day. The basic instruction given is in sexual matters, childbirth and child-rearing. One reason given us for the seclusion period was that during this time the novice's sexual organs were widened by various techniques such as the daily use of an artificial phallus made of the root of the *kambanjibanji* tree, a tall tree that grows in the evergreen forest beside streams. The sooty outer coat of *mudyi* bark is collected to blacken her labia, thereby en-hancing her sexual attractiveness. For the same purpose cicatrices are made on the lower part of her abdomen and on the small of her back as a species of erotic ' braille '. As regards actual instruction in sexual matters, emphasis is placed on pleasing the husband sexually rather than on being faithful to him. ' Never tell your husband the name of your lover ', warns the wordly-wise instruc-tress, ' for your first lover is always your friend; do not make him an enemy '. There is in this a basic recognition of the fact that ultimately the children belong to the mother and her matrilineal relatives, that although a father has ties of strong affection with his children they are not his in the sense that they will succeed or inherit from him. Thus, what he seeks in a wife is first and foremost a pleasing sex-partner. Not that correct marital behaviour goes unmentioned. On the contrary, politeness and hospitality to a husband's relatives and guests, hard work for him in his gardens and a civil demeanour towards him at all times are enjoined as correct, but they are not so much presented as virtues as good common sense.

Certain *Nkang'a* medicines are to make a woman fruitful; this is expressed in a dance for women in which they hold up empty baskets to the men and challenge, ' We have done our work (of making the novice fruitful). Now it is up to you. Here are the baskets, fill them with children.' Other dances, to be described later, at the coming-out ceremony, have the same object. Much of a novice's time in seclusion is taken up with the rehearsal of dances dramatising female fertility. Other dances, such as the close circling *danse du ventre*, represent the Lunda method of sexual intercourse, and are taught in the privacy of the seclusion hut itself.

During the whole seclusion period the novice may only speak in a low voice and must adopt a modest mien to her elders. She is

[355]

permitted to amuse herself by playing an instrument sacred to girl's seclusion, known as *nkunkandimba*, which is a simple bundle of three bows held pressed against a calabash resonator. The plucking of the strings often serves to summon relatives from the village to wait on her.

Certain food taboos are enjoined; she must not eat fish or the leaves of cassava, sweet potatoes or spinach, lest the ' slippery ' nature of these should cause her baby to ' slip out '.

Phase 3.—' Coming-out '

The length of the seclusion period is highly variable being dependent on such factors as the amount of food and beer that can be mobilised for the coming-out dance, the bridegroom's plans and the degree of sexual maturity reached by the girl in seclusion. If her first menstruation occurs during seclusion she must be taken to a river and washed in it with water and medicines. But the size of the breasts is the principal sign that a girl is ready to be ' taken out '.

A big all-night dance is the prelude to her emergence the next day. One feature of the dance is a sort of ' push-of-war ' between the bridegroom's party and that of the bride while the drums beat loudly. The bride's mother then calls out ' How much beer have you brought? I have ten calabashes.' The bridegroom tries to exceed this number and finally the calabashes are exchanged.

In the morning the women, somewhat hoarse and weary, take the girl out of the seclusion hut and sit her down in a small enclosure screened off by mats called *hakatewu*, similar to that used by the boys when they are coming out of *Mukanda*. It is slightly to one side of the village and in it the novice and her little ' fire-maker ' are given ritual toilets. The women scrupulously comb their hair and braid it, singing popular love songs, songs from the boys' initiation ceremony and songs of extreme sexual frankness. The girls are shaved round the hair-line, washed, decorated with beads, the white beads from the going-in ceremony being placed on the novice's hair, and finally rubbed all over with a mixture of red clay and castor oil. They are dressed in skirts only, leaving the breasts bare, rattles are attached to their calves (see photograph II) filled with medicine to make them strong and strips of cloth to make them dance well may be fastened to the wrists of the novices. A ' mud-pack ' of red-clay and oil is plastered over their coiffures. The women waiting on the novice have a communion beer-drink together. After she is properly arrayed a ritual meal of chicken and cassava mush is brought in which all the little girls present share (see photograph I). The head of the fowl is offered to the novice as part of the teasing she must endure with modest humility from her elders. She is fed by others for she is not allowed to touch food with her hands, which she must hold clenched by her temples, while her gaze is cast down. This is because she has not yet been ' opened ' by her bridegroom

I.—Communion Meal before ' Coming-out ' Dance at Girls' Initiation Ceremony.

The *Kankanga* is seen at the left, anointed with castor oil and with a coiffure o red clay mixed with castor oil. Her left hand is clenched and may not be opened until she has slept with her husband. *Kansonsera* (see text), similarly anointed, is on her left.

During her toilet she has been admonished to behave as a good wife should by her instructress.

When all is ready, the girl is led out, screened by a mat. She approaches the village by a roundabout route, then down the main path where a crowd is waiting for her behind the drums, which are played by her male relatives. She seems shy of entering the circle which forms before her and when she does so goes bent double with humility and shame. Then she straightens out and with her *Kansonsera* does the stamping dance, characterised by restricted leg-movements and thrust-forward breasts that is appropriate to *Nkang'a*. Now she has to show how well she has mastered Lunda traditional dances, essential knowledge among a people so steeped in

[357]

ritual. One dance imitates the movements of fishing, perhaps
indicating, as Dr. Richards' Bemba material suggests, that the great
fertility of fishes is hoped for. She also wears a cluster of medicated
rattles on the small of her back, where her husband will hold her in
bed at night, and these she must shake rhythmically. In the course
of another dance she passes a cloth bundle or carving representing a
child to the men in the circle, asking them ' to give her a baby '.
In another she dances with an eland-tail switch, traditionally carried
by headmen and important elders, symbolising her new mature
status. Another expressive dance dramatises the conflict of co-
wives; novice and assistant in turn snatch an axe, representing the
husband, from one another, and are finally reconciled. Older
women join in the dance in the ring and a cup is passed round for
small gifts (*nshing'a*). I have seen beads, soap, store fountain pens
and bottles of scent thrown in beside money. The ' tariff ' for

II —' COMING-OUT ' DANCE AT GIRLS' INITIATION CEREMONY.

Male matrilineal relatives of the *Kankang'a* play the drums. She holds
an eland-tail switch in her left hand and a cloth in her right hand. Note the
numerous strings of beads round her neck and breasts.

relatives, expressed in terms of cash, is 3*d*. for a matrilineal and ½*d*. for a patrilineal relation.

After this dance the ceremony normally blends with the full marriage ritual, which I am describing in a separate paper. After the coming-out dance the girl is considered to be sexually prepared for marriage, instructed in correct behaviour towards her husband and her in-laws, and potentially fertile. If, as sometimes happens, marriage does not follow *Nkang'a*, the novice's genitals are said to become narrow again and her sexual temperament to become more frigid (*wafwa mw'itala*, literally, ' dead in the house ').

Some Comments on Initiation Ceremonies

Some of the main differences between the boys' and girls' rituals have already been pointed out. With regard to the difference between the collective nature of the boys' and the individual nature of the girls' ceremonies, the comment of a Lunda woman is perhaps illuminating, ' If many girls and their instructresses were away at once for a long time, who would work in the gardens, fetch water and cook for the men? ' Since the agricultural work of men was in the past confined to clearing and burning the bush and some preliminary hoeing in the early rains and since they did no preparation or cooking of food, but spent most of their time in irregular hunting and shooting, their withdrawal in large numbers from economic activities would not produce such a marked effect.

In a sense, *Mukanda* qualifies a man for entrance into the hunting cults and *Nkang'a* prepares a woman to take part in the fertility cults. However, the life-crisis rituals are common to all Lunda and automatic, while hunting and fertility cults depend upon the affliction of individuals by individual shades and are not automatic.

It is interesting that the main theme of *Mukanda* should be productive activity (i.e. hunting), while that of *Nkang'a* should be reproductive activity. Women's economic activity, which is, when all is said and done, essential to the existence of the community, is hardly ritualised at all, while that of men is saturated with ritual. Hunting and sex for men, sex and motherhood for women seem to be the values underlined most strongly in life-crisis rituals, with respect for elders and superiors, dramatically and awesomely embodied in the boys' *makishi*, a constant element in both.

FUNERAL CEREMONY

As in most societies the amount of ' pomp and circumstance ' at a funeral depends on the wealth and importance of the dead person. Professor Radcliffe-Brown has said that funerals are concerned more with the living than the dead. It has been mentioned previously that in all life-crisis rituals changes take place in the relationships of all those people closely connected with the subject of the ritual. When a person dies, all these ties are snapped, as it were, and the more important the person the greater the number and range of ties there are to be broken. Now a new pattern of social relationships must be established: if the dead person was, for instance, a headman, a successor has to be found for him; his heirs must divide his inheritance among them; someone must be responsible for his debts; the fate of his widow must be decided, and everyone who stood in a particular relationship with him must know where they stand with regard to his heirs and successor. But before all these things can be done a period of adjustment must take place, an interval during which society passes gradually from the old to the new order. Among the Lunda this period coincides with the time that a mourning camp, *Chipenji* or *Chimbimbi*, lasts.

It is during this period that the shade of the dead is thought to be most restless, forever trying to revisit the scenes and communicate with the people it knew best alive. Lunda believe that without the ritual of mourning the shade would never lie quietly in the grave, but would be constantly interfering in the affairs of the living, jealous of every new adjustment, such as the remarriage of its widow, or the appointment of a successor of whom it would have disapproved, and indeed might afflict with illness all those people who should have honoured its memory by holding a funeral gathering, but omitted to do so.

There are many kinds of funeral ceremony among the Lunda, ranging from the private burial of a baby by its father under a *mudyi* tree near the village to the long public mourning attended by elaborate ritual of an important chief. In this paper I will describe only one kind, which I witnessed personally—the funeral of a village headman.

The Funeral of a Headman

Phase 1.—Until Burial

In the past a headman was buried in his own hut which was pulled down after the funeral ceremony, the village moving to a new site. But today, when capital may have been invested in huts made of sun-dried brick and cash-crops, such as rice and groundnuts grown near the village, a compromise solution is sometimes made by burying the headman in the bush between the village and the village graveyard where commoners are interred. The interment usually takes place the morning after the day of death. Immediately a death occurs messengers are sent out from the dead man's village to all parts of Lunda country where close matrilineal relatives of the dead are living to summon them to the funeral camp. Other messengers go to the chief of the area and others to the kin on the father's side. But, perhaps most important of all, a report is made to the head of the *Mung'ong'i* Society, a group of ritual officiants whose task is to prevent the shade of the dead man coming back to trouble his relatives and neighbours and to discipline and

instruct young boys, both circumcised and uncircumcised, in the
' Mystery of *Mung'ong'i* ' (*mpang'u yaMung'ong'i*, literally, ' enclosure of *Mung'ong'i*). This high officiant—one might almost
call him ' priest '—is none other than our old friend *Mbimbi*, the
Chief Circumciser at *Mukanda*, and the medicines he uses are the
medicines of *Mukanda*, carried in his *mfunda* (see page 342). In
Mung'ong'i, however, he is known as *Samazembi*, from *izembi*, the
name for a dead person's hut.   This identification of the high
officials of boys' tribal initiation and of the funeral ceremony of
men important in tribal life is most interesting.   As we shall see
presently, *Mung'ong'i*, like *Mukanda*, has the function of instilling
respect for the elders into the young.

When news of the death is received at the village of one of the
relatives, immediately the women begin to weep in a demented
high-pitched voice, praising the qualities of the dead man and
lamenting their own grievous loss, while the men sit in little silent
groups by the verandahs of their huts; afterwards they prepare to
set out for the funeral camp.

At the village of the dead wailing and lamenting goes on continuously, augmented by condoling cries of new arrivals.   The
body of the dead man is laid extended on the bed in his own hut,
while his widow or widows sit at his feet and bewail.   The corpse
is anointed after death with castor oil, which is pressed in under
each joint, and the mouth is washed with water.   Then a line of
white clay is drawn from the navel downwards and the shade is
enjoined to return and kill the sorcerer who had been the cause of
death, for nearly every death is thought to be the work of sorcery
or witchcraft.   Some men during their lifetime drink a special
medicine, called *mwiyanawu*, which is said after their death to kill
the sorcerer and all his matrilineal kin.   If the dead man was sterile
a line of charcoal is drawn from his navel, between his legs and up
to the small of his back, ' to make him die for ever ', i.e. to prevent
him ' returning ' in dreams or to influence divination to give a newly
born child his name, which involves the inheritance of certain of his
characteristics.   An arrow is inserted into the bed near his head.
After the funeral this arrow will be taken to a diviner in a sheaf of
similar arrows and the diviner will be asked to select the correct one
which is said to contain the name of the dead.   If the diviner is
successful he will be engaged by the relatives of the dead to divine
the name of the sorcerer who killed him.

Meanwhile, *Samazembi* proceeds to the village of the dead and
takes up residence in the dead man's hut, where he remains throughout the period of mourning, only emerging to take part in the
Mung'ong'i ritual.   He summons together a group of officiants,
known as *Tudang'u* (singular, *Kadang'u*), who consist of persons
who have undergone the *Mung'ong'i* ritual.   He then instructs
them in their duties, the most important of which are dancing and
singing through the villages of the neighbourhood, shaking two

[361]

small hand-rattles, in order to keep the restless shade out of them. For this office *Tudang'u* receive small sums of money or gifts in kind, which they place in a long basket kept in the hut of the dead, to be distributed among them by *Samazembi* at the end of mourning. At least one *Kadang'u* must dance throughout the entire mourning period. They take it in turns to sleep in the *izembi*, but I have seen *Tudang'u* taking surreptitious naps in the villages! If *Samazembi* gets to hear of such a breach of correct ritual behaviour he is entitled to punish the refractory *Kadang'u* by fixing him by the neck in the fork of a tree, a punishment formerly meted out to slaves. He will not be released until he pays a large fine.

During the night before burial the widows must keep wake at the corpse's head, and other close relatives must come and sit in his hut. The other members of the *Chipenji*, funeral camp, must sleep outside the *izembi*, while the *Tudang'u* chant the poignant and plangent lamentation songs, shaking their *nzenzi*, hand-rattles. If the dead man had drunk *mwiyanawu* medicine the gathering must sleep on the bare ground, otherwise they may use mats.

Phase 2.—The Day of Burial

Now let us go in thought to an actual burial; a general account cannot possibly convey the strong feeling-tone of the ceremony. When we arrive at the village at about 8 a.m., the body is still in the hut; with it are the dead man's brother and sister and some close female relatives who moan and bewail most heart-rendingly. This expression of grief is conventional; it must not, however, be immoderate, otherwise the mourner may fall under suspicion as a witch who is trying to put others off the scent—' The lady doth protest too much, methinks '. The remains of a fire can be seen in the hut and a bottle of oil and calabash of water for washing and anointing the corpse. A sprig of *muneku* leaves, the typical funeral medicine, is placed in the doorway, and a calabash has been hung upside down on a nearby tree. Just outside the hut, to the left of the doorway, stands a group of women who had lost husbands through death. In front of the hut female relatives from the dead man's own village are assembled. A short distance away from these, a large group of men, including several neighbouring headmen, sits round a fire. Still further away is a group of women from other villages. To the right of the doorway two *Tudang'u* are putting the finishing touches to a rough pole stretcher which will serve as a bier.

The sister of the dead breaks into a long grieving monologue about how good he was, how kind to his relatives, which sharpens in sorrow as the ' sextons ' enter the hut. The widows meanwhile stand silently the other previously widowed women and widowers. The corpse is securely lashed on with bark-string to the bier, which is then lifted a few paces beyond the doorway. Now two former widows lead the new widows between them in file, hand in hand, in a circle round the corpse, the woman in front carrying a faggot of firewood and a bunch of leaf-medicine. Then they lead them away to the village ash-pile where at first they squat in silence.

A party of male grave-diggers or sextons (*tumfundi*) gathers behind the carriers of the bier and they proceed to the site of interment. The closest living male relative of the deceased, called *Nyamufu* ('mother of the dead') presides over the burial. The other sextons may be relatives, neighbours or *Tudang'u*. There does not appear to be a taboo on close relatives of the deceased taking part in the digging of the actual grave, a taboo that is found in many parts of Africa.

The grave itself is of a keyhole shape. The first-clods taken out are placed to one side of the hole. When the hole is about six feet deep, the body is placed on its side in the slightly flexed position of sleep with its head to the west. It is covered once more with the blanket and a few personal possessions of the dead, such as cloths, blankets and plates, may be put in before the grave is filled in, the first-clods removed being the last to be replaced. During the burial relatives roll on the earth, beat themselves with sticks and make as if to kill themselves. Shreds of the dead man's clothing are fastened on the right arms of the sextons, who now go to a stream to cleanse themselves and their hoes from the impurity of death. Meanwhile at the village the widows have been bewailing in the ash-pile and scattering ashes over themselves. Cassava roots have been taken from the dead man's garden and everyone eats a portion raw. Three roots are thrown on the threshold of the *izembi* hut. When the sextons return they halt at a cross-roads near the village and ask for grass from the thatch of *izembi*, castor oil to anoint themselves with and a cassava root from the three on the doorway. When these are given them *Nyamufu* lights the grass and each man holds his feet over the flames. Then each eats a piece of the root. All sit down and *Nyamufu's* wife cooks food and sends it to them. After this all forgather in the village and discuss the dead man and his qualities.

Phase 3.—The Seclusion of the Widows

At dawn on the following day *Nyamufu* takes the widows to the cross-roads. They carry water and firewood; with the latter a fire is made, with the water they are washed. They have already exchanged clothes with female relatives. Now *Nyamufu* shaves their heads completely. Since the death of their husband they have not slept, nor will they sleep for another day. When the hair of the senior wife has grown so that it completely covers her scalp again, it is a sign that the mourning period is over, usually about a month after shaving. On the day of the funeral the widows fasted; this fast will be broken the evening after washing and shaving.

The next thing *Nyamufu* does is to build a grass hut (*nkunka*), identical to that used by girls at puberty, for each widow, near his own, where she must remain in seclusion until the end of the mourning. It is doctored with herbal medicines, including the ashes of *musosu* leaves.

The morning after the building of *nkunka* the widows are taken to the bush and a tree is found that has been completely uprooted by wind and rain. A broken tree with its stump still rooted must not be chosen otherwise the shade of the husband will visit them every night in dreams. *Nyamufu* digs a small hole, places in it, broken, the calabash hung up at the time of burial near the dead man's hut, containing medicines and water, and washes the widows with them. Then he puts a lid on the medicine and earth on top of that, saying, ' Husband do not come and make your wives dream '.

Many medicines are kept in the *nkunka* with which each widow is washed at night, to prevent dreams and free her from the shade that wants to stay near her. She is not allowed to leave the door open in the daytime for fear that the shade may enter. She must go into the hut at sundown, keeping the door shut until dawn, when she may come out, shutting the door behind her again. She must not sleep on her back. The medicine is heated in a clay pot every evening. She washes her own hands and body with it, but another woman must wash her head and legs. She must not eat at night and must cook only enough for her own needs; if any food is left on her dish, the husband will come back and eat with her. She must not eat from the same dish as, nor at the same time with, a woman whose spouse has not died, lest the occasion bring back too strongly the memory, and with it the presence of the shade, of her own husband. She must not speak in a loud voice, but only in a whisper, or else the shade will hear and return. She exchanges household articles such as cups and plates with her neighbours so that the shade will be misled. She may even temporarily exchange her garden, ' Otherwise the husband might come and say, " Here you are using the things I used myself. Why? I will return and sleep here." ' She must wear her cloth girded up between her legs, in case the shade tries to resume sexual relations. She may not work in her gardens during seclusion. I do not know whether young widows continue to cook for their children during seclusion, for I have only seen older women in this condition.

Phase 4.—The Mung'ong'i Ritual

The funeral gathering is fed largely from the cassava gardens and livestock of the dead man. But his other relatives, and especially his widows, are expected to help out from their own resources. The female kin of the deceased must cook for the mourners. Until the camp breaks up its most important function is the nightly performance of *Mung'ong'i*. The *Tudang'u* have a separate fire from the rest. Only one of them is masked, *Kadang'u kamashika* (the ' *Kadang'u* of fever or malaria '), and is called an *ikishi*. Two others are named: *Kadang'u kakusomeka* (' the

[364]

Kadang'u of escaping from traps '), who wears an inverted bird's feather stuck upright in the hair above the brow, and *Kadang'u kansala* (meaning unknown to me), who wears a high crown of hornbill feathers, but they are not thought of as *makishi*, for they are not *masked* dancers.

On the night following burial *Samazembi*, the *Tudang'u* and others already initiated in *Mung'ong'i* withdraw to the nearest point where two paths cross, clear all the grass away around it, cut two lengths of *mukula* and setting them at an angle to one another bind them at the tops with bark string. A strong fence is made round this ' shrine ' at the junction of the paths and a big fire is lit in the enclosure. Then all the small boys at the mourning camp are rounded up and taken into the enclosure. *Samazembi* daubs himself with white and red clay and cuts a pair of stilts. Drums are brought in and beaten. Each father present tucks his son between his legs. Suddenly all the *Tudang'u*, *Kadang'u kamashika* last, rush in and begin to pinch and beat the boys unmercifully while their fathers put up a half-hearted resistance to them. The whole time *Samazembi* walks about on high stilts, a strange and awful figure in the firelight, gleaming white in the air. At daybreak the boys are taken to a river to wash, then taken to the cross-roads and instructed by *Samazembi* in the *Mung'ong'i* mysteries. *Mung'ong'i* is performed almost every night of the *Chipenji* until the *Mudyileji* mourning dance ends the task of the *Tudang'u* and the camp disperses.

Phase 5.—Mudyileji, The Mourning Dance

Towards the end of *Chipenji* much beer is brewed for the final dance of mourning. Before sunset on the night of *Mudyileji*, *Nyamufu*, the dead man's nearest relative, other near relations and the *Tudang'u* go to the cross-roads where so much ritual has taken place, carrying a small calabash (*kaswaha makombelelu*, ' the little calabash of prayers ') and a stick. The stick they plant in the ground. Then *Nyamufu* addresses the shade of the dead man by his inherited name, asking it to leave them in peace because they have done everything possible to give it a notable funeral. After praying in the manner described above with white clay (*ku-kombela*), he breaks the calabash and impales it on the stick.

As they return to the village cries of grief break out afresh. When they enter it the drums begin to thud and the *Tudang'u* start to dance. Dancing and the singing of mourning songs continue all night. The dance of *Kadang'u kamashika* is the most impressive performance imaginable. In some ways this *Kadang'u* seems to represent the shade itself, thus differing from the *makishi* at *Mukanda*. A screen of mats is put up against the hut of the dead and from it the lesser *Tudang'u* one by one emerge. A thin treble squeaking like that of a bat comes from behind the screen. Suddenly the screen is removed. One expects to see something un-

III.—*Kadang'u Kamashika* THE *Ikishi* WHICH DANCES AT FUNERAL CERE-
MONIES OF IMPORTANT MEN.

Note the 'tears' under the 'eyes'. See description in text.

canny, but there is nothing there! Suddenly one sees a strange figure leaping and cavorting convulsively, behind a lane of women stretching from the hut of the dead to the drums about thirty yards away. This abrupt and unexpected appearance has a terrifying effect on the children who scream and shrink back. *Kadang'u kamashika* (see sketch III) with its huge, round, top-heavy mask radiating feathers and with a beard of flat grasses, its skirt of bushy grass, and its contrastingly slim limbs circled with alternating rings of white and red, looks almost as though it will fly apart, arms and legs jerking away from the body. It runs round the outside of the village first like a huge and stealthy crab and returns to the threshold of the hut of the dead. Then it slowly advances on the drums, squeaking plaintively. Every now and then it halts, puts its left hand, which clasps a bunch of medicine leaves, on its heart and sags forward on the staff in its other hand. Sometimes it performs a *pas de deux* with one of the lesser *Tudang'u*, sometimes half a dozen *Tudang'u*, some with knives in their hands and all shaking rattles (there is a rattle at the end of the masked *Kadang'u's* staff), interweave and intone together. Men drum while women chant and clap. The masked *Kadang'u* has a disconcerting habit of taking itself off into the crowd and thrusting its squeaking round face into that of a baby who fairly yells its head off with fright. At other times it leaps off into the bush and comes back from unexpected directions. No wonder that the women give it money when it bears down on them!

Phase 6.—The Cleansing of the Widows

Early next morning the matrilineal relatives of the dead lead the widows to the ash-pile once more and there wash them and anoint them with castor oil. Then *Nyamufu* shaves their hair-line at the front and gives them a brand-new white cloth. After they have been shaved, *Samazembi* and the *Tudang'u* disappear from the scene, their work ended. Close relatives of the dead, who have also shaved their hair off after the burial, wash and shave off their hair-lines also. The widows and the mother or sister of the dead are then given white beads.

Two days afterwards, the brothers of the widows come for them. Cloths of a colour other than white are given them by the relatives of their husband, and the latter go with their own relatives to the villages of the widows. At each of the widows' villages, a payment called *mpepi* is made to the husband's kin for secluding her and giving her medicines to rid her of the jealous shade. As a final act of purification the widow is told to cover herself with a blanket in the nearby bush and perform ritual intercourse with a relative (a classificatory grandson is preferred) of her husband. The latter is expected merely to insert the tip of his member into the widow, ' to receive the shade ' (*ku-tambula mukishi*) back into its own family. If complete coitus took place the *mukishi* would not be released from her body.

The widow can now marry again if she wishes. If she has not observed the correct funeral customs, however, the unexorcised shade of her husband will make things extremely unpleasant for her next spouse, lying between the pair at night and beating the new husband until he pines to death. Widows, unless they are of slave origin, are never inherited by the dead man's heir. The gardens made by a widow at her husband's village belong to her and she can sell them when she returns to her own village.

Comments on the Funeral Ceremony

The funeral ceremony displays many features typical of Lunda ritual in general. The open nature of the gathering not restricted to a narrow kin group, the existence of a society of ritual specialists to exorcise and repel the restless and dangerous shade, the division of labour between ritual officiants, all bear an unmistakable stamp. The role of the *Tudang'u* in asserting male authority over women has not yet been stressed, but they have power to fine a woman who laughs in their presence or whom they see carrying a basket or calabash on her head. In this the *Tudang'u* resemble the *Makishi* at *Mukanda*. Again, the idea that one progresses in a cult from initiation to high ritual office, entering it first by being afflicted by a spirit, is present in *Mung'ong'i*, where the little boys are terrorised by the *Tudang'u*, one of whom, *Kadang'u kamashika*, is thought to portray the shade of the dead man, and are henceforth entitled to become *Tudang'u* themselves, advancing gradually to the status of *Kadang'u kamashika*, perhaps in old age even to that of *Samazembi* himself.

The month following death is considered to be the period when the shade is most to be feared. True, the shade is always ready to come out of its grave afterwards to 'catch' a neglectful relative with sickness, sterility or bad luck, but for this one apprehensive month it may even kill, or strike a whole village with an epidemic. Even people who were reckoned benevolent in their lifetime display a ghostly ferocity. The shade 'runs round the village' like *Kadang'u kamashika* and 'runs through the bush from village to village'—wherever the dead man was well known, in fact. We may regard the funeral ritual as a sort of spiritual barricade against the cunning and unremitting attempts of the dead to regain its lost honours. It refuses to accept a new dispensation, a society that goes on without it. Thus it must be both cajoled and coerced into remaining quiet.

At any rate that is how the Lunda look at the matter. The sociologist would say that the behaviour of the shade and the ritual to control it are reflections both of the anxiety and fear of persons whose regular social existence has been violently disrupted by the death of a prominent member, and of their earnest desire to create a stable new pattern of living, a task which can only be carried out successfully if old habits are completely replaced and do not clash with new ones.

PART II

RITUALS OF AFFLICTION

Among Lunda the term *wukolu* has various meanings. It can denote ' good health ', ' good luck ' or ' strength '. But to understand what it means to Lunda we must not look at it through European spectacles and regard it as referring merely to a state of physical well-being. For behind it is the idea that one is ' well ' because one is on good terms with the shades, that one is doing one's duty by them through making offerings of beer or food to their shrines and by behaving piously in accordance with their wishes. But ' good health ' is felt to be a negative condition, associated with the absence of interference rather than with the actual assistance of the shades. It implies placid mediocrity, colourless virtue. The way to positive success in life, to eminence and celebrity, lies through a breach of *wukolu*, a stroke of bad luck or sudden sickness. Such interruptions in the peaceful flow of life are thought to be caused by offended shades, as we have seen above (pages 5–7). ' Things must get worse before they get better ' is the dominant theme of Lunda ritual life, recalling the Book of Job. The state of mind and body that follows the placation of a shade one has offended is considered more desirable than that which existed before affliction. When one becomes the subject of a ritual, one becomes ' sacred ' (*kumbadyi*, ' to the side '), one is ' set apart ' from the profane run of humanity, and some of this sacredness persists after one has been cured, or made atonement to the shade which is the same thing. Through contact with the shade one attains ghostly power, and can become a doctor in future rituals.

HUNTING CULTS

The high value set on hunting as a male occupation has already been pointed out in connection with boys' initiation where the basic values of the Lunda people are taught and expressed.

To us, hunting is merely an economic or sporting activity, in which, granted a natural talent in the beginning, skill is increased with practice. The Lunda do not look on it in this way. A young man receives a ' call ' to be a great hunter, much as a person has a call to become a missionary in our own society, i.e. he receives a message from a supernatural source telling him that he has a vocation. In the case of the Lunda youth, the message comes in the form of dreams about the shade of a famous hunter relative, accompanied by bad luck at hunting. On consulting a diviner he learns that the shade wishes him to become a famous hunter and that he must enter the hunters' cult by having the first of its rituals performed for him. From that time forward the same sequence continues—bad luck and dreams followed by ritual to win the favour of the shade, followed in turn by greater success at hunting —until the hunter is acknowledged to be a master of his profession. Huntsmanship may thus be seen as acquirement of increasing

[369]

supernatural power through successive degrees of initiation into a cult of the hunter shades. This power enables him ' to see animals quickly ', ' to draw them to where he is ' and ' to become invisible to them '.

Formerly there were two distinct hunters' cults, but one of them has almost died out. This was *Wubinda*, ' hunting with bows, spears and traps'. The second cult, *Wuyang'a*, ' hunting with firearms ', developed with the introduction of the muzzle-loading gun into Mwinilunga by Ovimbundu slave traders from Angola in the nineteenth century, and after existing side by side with *Wubinda* for many years has now almost entirely replaced it. Nevertheless, *Wuyang'a* has adopted many of the medicines and ritual practices of *Wubinda* and even two of the actual rituals of that ancient cult.

For the purposes of the present paper it will be sufficient to state that *Wubinda* consisted of five separate rituals in a graded series, most of them concerned with different forms of bad luck in hunting brought on by hunter shades and one, *Ntambu*, the aim of which was to secure that the afflicted hunter would be reincarnated as a lion or leopard after his death and thus go on hunting in spite of it.

The two rituals borrowed from *Wubinda* by *Wuyang'a*, called *Mukála* and *Chitampakasa*, are both designed to remove particular modes of affliction with bad luck. In the former, the invisible shade is thought to stand on an ant-hill and whistle the game away from the approaching hunter. In the latter, the hunter just does not get even a glimpse of game, but wanders vainly through the bush. The interesting point here is that the four rituals that comprise *Wuyang'a* proper are arranged in an orderly series and celebrate increasing proficiency in hunting. But this steady advance goes against the grain of Lunda belief; *therefore*, two rituals concerned with *affliction* are retained from the older cult. The theme that one must suffer to succeed still continues. *Mukála* or *Chitampakasa* are inserted between each step in *Wuyang'a*, providing a sort of legal fiction that the success celebrated is the consequence of placating an offended shade.

The four rituals of *Wuyang'a* are:
(1) *Kuwela*, ' to wash oneself ', performed for a novice, who has been given the loan of a gun by an established hunter and shot several animals with it. During the ritual he washes himself with special *Wuyang'a* medicine.
(2) *Ku-sukula*, ' initiation in huntsmanship ', when the budding hunter comes under the tutelage of an established hunter who teaches him bush-lore and hunting medicine. This hunter is known as *Mama daWuyang'a*, ' mother of huntsmanship ', while the novice is known as *Mwana daWuyang'a*, ' child of huntsmanship '.

(3) *Ku-telekesha*, 'causing to cook', in which the hunter, who has by this time killed many animals, provides a communion meal for an assembled company of hunters, consisting of special portions of meat reserved for hunters, such as ears, lower jaw, heart, lungs and small intestine, and cassava mush, cooked by the hunter's senior wife. The ritual is ended by the hunter taking a special hunter-name, from a set of names reserved for hunters.

(4) *Mwima*, only performed by great hunters who have killed by the hundred. It is an elaborate glorification of the hunter at which many attend. Only a handful of such hunters exist.

A detailed account of Lunda hunting ritual will be published in the *Rhodes-Livingstone Journal*. It might, however, be of

IV.—SHRINE TO THE HUNTER SHADES ERECTED IN FRONT OF THE HUT OF A GREAT HUNTER.

The main shrine is the small thatched hut (*Katunda KaWuyang'a*). Antelope skulls and horns are placed on poles. *Ayishing'a* forked sticks may be seen to the right with *mukata* satchels containing *mahamba* teeth slung over them. Guns are resting on the thatch of the shrine. In the front centre may be seen *ndamba* strigillators and hand-rattles. The trees to the left of the photograph are *nyiyombu* shrines planted to the village shades (see text). Hunters' belts and pouches lie beside the strigillators in the right foreground.

interest to mention some of the material objects used in these ceremonies. These fall into four main groups: (1), Cult objects; (2), Hunters' equipment; (3), Musical instruments; (4), Medicines.

(1) *Cult Objects*

These may be further subdivided into two categories: (*a*) those that are considered to be intrinsically sacred, and (*b*) those that are consecrated for the purposes of the particular ritual.

Among the former may be mentioned the permanent hunters' shrines that are a conspicuous feature of most Mwinilunga villages. These vary considerably in shape and size, from a single peeled stick forked near the top to a miniature hut, as shown in photograph IV. These sticks, called *ayishing'a* (singular *chishing'a*), are cut from five species of trees which have in common the property that string cannot be made from their bark; if they were ' string-trees ' their use as medicine would have the effect of ' tying-up ' the hunter's ability to see the game and shoot straight. They are also resistant to termites. Duiker and other woodland buck are said to relish the young shoots of these trees and the *ayishing'a* are sharpened to a point to resemble the horns of an antelope. A dead hunter is buried in a sitting position with a *chishing'a* between his clasped hands, touching his lips and brow and emerging from the surface of the grave. When a hunter relative makes a kill he must pour some blood down this *chishing'a* ' to feed the shade '. Whenever a hunters' ritual is performed a new *chishing'a* is cut for the occasion and inserted in the village next to the older ones, ' to join the new ritual to *Wuyang'a* '. The small hut called *katunda* is regarded as the occasional home of a particular hunter shade related to the maker of the hut.

Hung on the fork of a *chishing'a* or contained in a *katunda* is a curious satchel of white canvas called *mukata*. One finds that women and uncircumcised boys are not allowed to approach it. If a woman goes near it, one is told, she will suffer prolonged and painful menstrual bleeding and will perhaps die. If a boy goes near it, he may bleed to death when he is circumcised. The satchel has long strips of rolled cloth as carrying straps wound round fragments of the dead hunter's clothing. If one pays *nshing'a* of 6*d.* to its owner he will lift up the flap of the container and expose a curious spectacle. Two cowrie shells embedded in a paste of dried blood surmount a human front upper incisor tooth. The shells are known as ' the eyes ', the whole composition is known as ' the face ', and the tooth itself is called ' the *ihamba* '. The *ihamba* is the tooth of a dead hunter with a hunter-name and it is inherited by one of his relatives, usually a matrilineal relative, of a similar rating in *Wuyang'a*. In some respects it may be likened to a charm, containing a part of the power and luck of the dead man, and it is carried by its inheritor in its *mukata* satchel (worn over the right shoulder) when he goes hunting. At other times it seems to be regarded as a special manifestation of the hunter's shade, as it is thought to be able to fly about invisibly and fix itself in the body of a person of either sex who has offended it. A ritual is performed to remove it, also called *Ihamba*, in which the doctor, who is usually a *Mwima* (see page 371) hunter, 'sucks out' the tooth from the patient's body (a deft conjuring trick) through a goat's or sheep's horn. The tip of the horn has been cut off and the hole is plugged with beeswax, which is then pierced with a reed and sucked on over a slit in the patient's flesh made by a razor. Such ' extracted ' *mahamba* are sealed up in small calabashes with beeswax and placed in a bundle of grass (also called *katunda*) which is then inserted in the fork of the *chishing'a*. These *mahamba* are not carried in *mukata* satchels. At an *Wuyang'a* ritual, a company of hunters assembles, each with his inherited *ihamba* in its satchel. All are hung up on the freshly cut *chishing'a* and at one stage of the ceremony are taken down to be ' fed ' with scraps of meat and cassava-mush provided by the hunter who is holding it. Now we see why women and uncircumcised boys must avoid an *ihamba*—because it gives power to shed blood.

Among those objects consecrated in and through the ritual are: a flat round winnowing basket (*luwalu*) into which herbal medicines are placed after they have been collected in the bush by the hunterdoctor before the shrine is set up; a small clay pot (*kanung'u*), in which the communion meal of meat is cooked, and a larger pot in which the sacred cassava-mush is stirred by the hunters' gunmuzzles; a calabash containing honey-beer (*kasolu*) used for a communion drink, and various other tools and utensils brought in contact with the shrine and ' magnetised ' by it, so to speak, with sacredness and ritual power.

(2) *Hunters' Equipment*

First and foremost item of hunters' equipment is the muzzleloading gun, usually an ancient flintlock or Tower musket. I have seen one fearsome-looking object, about five feet long, with a brass plate on the butt indicating that it had been made in America in 1861. They are often resplendently decorated with coils of copper wire or glinting with polished iron or brass studs. Often eland or duiker tails hang down from the trigger guards and animals' teeth and the horns of small buck may be tied to the stock as charms. Originally they were exchanged for a slave apiece and the history of their former owners can be recounted for some time back. Bitter quarrels take place over their inheritance, often between a dead hunter's son and his sister's son, the ' legal ' heir.

Another important item is a rawhide belt and pouch made from a single piece of leather, called *ngonga*. The pouch is square, rather like the case of an old-fashioned Brownie camera. It contains cartridges, powder, home-made bullets, a metal striker, a small flint and some tinder of dried moss. It may also contain small blue duiker horns used to mimic the call of the female duiker and

[373]

attract the males. Barkcloth wadding for the gun may be placed in it. In addition, there are many medicines and other magical substances to be described below.

Hunters also carry light, sharp, well-balanced bush-axes in their belts and small skinning knives, similar to circumcision knives.

(3) *Musical Instruments*

In addition to the large drums (*kayanda*, related to *iyanda*, a meal mortar) carved from a single piece of wood and covered with antelope hide, pegged into the rim, and small *mung'fuza* drums (from *ku-fuza*, ' to scold '), there are other instruments peculiar to hunters' rituals. Most prominent of these is a hollow indented bar of wood, called *ndamba*, which is stroked rapidly with a stick, producing a rhythmic strigillating sound. Iron axe-blades are clinked together to make a sound known as *ku-konkomwena* (literally, ' to address '), which is supposed to ' make the shades come quickly '. At hunters' funerals xylophones (*ndimba*) are played.

(4) *Medicines*

In a hunter's pouch are a number of medicines, the most important of which, called *mpelu* medicine, is contained in small packages. Among its ingredients are hair from albinos and Europeans, which, coming from ' white ' persons, is considered lucky (see pages 343 and 350 for white symbolism); splinters of wood from a chief's or a European's house, ' to give power '; bits of roots which cross the motor road, to make the hunter swift ' like a motor-car '; nail-parings of Europeans or chiefs and earth from their footprints, ' to make one liked ' by these important beings; rootlets taken from the earth where a girl lay during the *Nkang'a* ceremony (see page 352 *et seq.*) 'to give power', and various other unidentified objects. Other medicines in the pouch are portions of the wing-case of a Goliath beetle, ' for strength ' again and the purple wings of a hornet to give ' stinging ' power and accuracy to the hunter's bullets. In a galago's skin he wraps powdered red clay with which to anoint himself and others at hunting rituals; the red symbolism of ' blood that is shed ' is a dominant motif in both *Wubinda* and *Wuyang'a*.

Medicines collected in the bush before an *Wuyang'a* ritual is performed include a creeper called *mukondakanyi*, ' which creeps cautiously towards other trees in order to catch them ' (just so does a hunter creep up on animals and catch them); *kaswamang'wadyi* grass, which is braided and tied round the *chishing'a* (*ku-swama* means ' to hide ' and *ng'wadyi* is the ' bare-throated francolin '). When this grass grows tall in the late rains it provides cover for francolins and guinea-fowl; it is hoped that its use in ritual will make the hunter ' invisible ' to his prey. Leaves from three kinds of tree are bound together to make a medicine-broom for splashing liquid medicine of pounded leaves on the bodies and equipment of hunters—these are, *mukombukombu* (from *ku-komba*, ' to sweep '), *mututukambululu*, which has nectar-filled flowers and will draw many people to the ritual as bees are attracted to the flowers, and in the same way will draw many animals within range of the hunter's gun, and *muhotuhotu* (from *ku-hotumona*, ' to attract '). Lunda say that sweeping with medicine makes a man ' white ', meaning both ' pure ' and ' invisible '. When he is ' pure ' he is also attractive and ' beautiful '; he draws people towards him; even animals will be fascinated by him. There is an overtone of ' sexual attraction ' in this strange concept.

Firewood is cut from a white wood called *mweya*, with the usual ' white ' symbolism of ' good-luck ' and ' well-being '. This firewood will cook the sacred communion meal.

As for the human performers in *Wuyang'a*, the hunters take the leading role in the public rituals, the importance of each hunter's contribution being in accordance with his status in the cult. Hunters' wives, mothers and sisters have a distinct, if limited, role, but non-hunters, male and female, even close kin of the subject of the ritual, have little to do except to admire the Nimrods of the bush.

V.—The Principal Officiant at the *Ku-telekesha* hunters' ritual (see text) dances the *Wuyang'a* Dance, axe in hand and scowling.

[375]

When I was in Mwinilunga I attended many rituals concerned with women's reproductive disorders and heard of many more. In a sample of nineteen women whose ritual histories I recorded not one had failed to have such a ritual performed for her and one old woman had been the subject of four separate rituals. Now, is there any medical basis for these widespread cults connected with reproductive troubles? My evidence is slight but suggestive. Figures supplied to me by the lady doctor at Kalene Mission Hospital in August, 1951, revealed that out of ninety women accepted as normal pregnancy cases sixteen or nearly 18 per cent. underwent abnormal deliveries. My wife was asked to assist at about half a dozen cases of prolonged childbirth or miscarriages in the villages adjoining our camp in about three months. Many women showed clear signs of anaemia and some revealed that they had frequent periodic troubles. It may well be that the modern prevalence of these disorders is associated on the one hand with the shortage of meat and fish in many areas, such as the north-west corner of the district where game has almost disappeared, and the low protein value of the staple crop, cassava, on the other, which has only one eighth the protein value of millet. Lunda do not keep cattle and their small stock is not adequate for their meat requirements.

However, although these ' fertility ' (or rather ' infertility ') rituals are on the increase nowadays, most of them seem to have existed in the far past, coming, as Lunda say, ' from Mwantiyanvwa '. The theme of ' affliction ' we have already met with in *Wuyang'a* crops up again. The woman who has miscarriages, abortions or an excessive menstrual discharge, or who is sterile, is thought to have offended a shade who ' comes out ' of the grave and ' sits ' in her body until propitiated by one or other of the women's rituals prescribed by a diviner. I found that a woman's mother's mother was by a long way the most frequently offended shade, afflicting women in twelve out of twenty-five cases where I could trace the relationship. After her came a woman's own mother, in five instances, and next her older sister, in two. This seemed significant in view of the fact that women, through whom succession and inheritance are reckoned, go to their husbands' villages on marriage, often far away from their own villages, and may in the course of time cease to remember their older kin on the mother's side who have died. Moreover, when they were young girls they would have spent most of their time in their father's villages where they would have been living with their mothers. But, in spite of spending so much of their lives away from their ' own ' villages, they are still expected to send their sons back to them when the latter reach puberty, and if they themselves are divorced or widowed their matrilineal villages are regarded as their sanctuaries until remarriage. It would seem therefore that being ' caught ' by a matrilineal shade serves as a sharp reminder that their own first loyalty is to their matrilineal villages and that they bear children not for their husbands, but for their mother's brothers and brothers ' back home '. And we find that ' forgetting ' the shade is the usual cause of affliction (see page 339).

Four rituals are performed for women with reproductive troubles: (1), *Nkula*, when a woman has an excessive flow of blood at menstruation; (2), *Wubwang'u*, when a woman has had or expects to have twins, or when she seems to be sterile; (3), *Isoma*, when a woman has had a number of stillbirths or abortions; and (4), *Chihamba*, which can be performed for sickness as well as for reproductive disorders and for men as well as women. *Nkula*, *Wubwang'u* and *Chihamba* can also be performed for ailing children, in which case mother and child are treated together. Often the husband is treated with the wife, ' to make him sacred and taboo (*kumbadyi nakwajila*) ', for he must eat with her and sleep with her, and intimate contact between sacred and profane persons or things is thought to be dangerous, or at the least to nullify the effects of the treatment. Each of these rituals has three well-marked phases: (1), *Ilembi* or *Ku-lembeka*, consisting of a treatment and dance to make the subjects ' sacred '; (2), a period of seclusion, during which they are partially or entirely separated from everyday existence and have to observe certain food taboos; and (3), *Ku-tumbuka*, a further treatment and dance which celebrates the end of seclusion and prepares the ' patients ' to enter ordinary life again.

Since each of these rituals is at least as elaborate as the girls' initiation ceremony, I can do no more, in the limited space of this paper, than pick out a few features they possess in common and give a brief outline of the salient characteristics of each.

The principal doctor at each ritual is a man, although they are women's rituals. But he must have been made ' sacred ', either as child or husband of a woman undergoing a particular ritual, before he could have been taught the medicines and procedure appropriate to it. Each doctor (*chimbuki* or *chimbanda*) tends to specialise in one or other ritual, although some doctors know the techniques of many. Usually he has a leading woman doctor as assistant and a throng of minor doctors who are women supposed to have been cured by previous rituals of the same type. An initial payment— nowadays from 2*s.* 6*d.* to 4*s.*—is made to the male doctor to secure his services; food and beer are given to the women doctors. If a cure is effected and the woman successfully bears children, the doctor is paid 10*s.* or £1, which he may divide among his assistants as he thinks fit. The patient herself and her husband usually provide the money. Holding a ritual is an expensive business in terms of Lunda wealth. It costs 3*s.* 6*d.* in diviner's fees, over a pound for the doctor, and a great expenditure of cash, time and labour to provide food and beer for the assistants and the general gathering. In addition, the rules of seclusion often forbid a woman to draw water, work in her cassava gardens and carry the roots to her kitchen, thus depriving her family of her economic services for several months.

Each separate performance of *Ku-lembuka* and *Ku-tumbuka* has three main stages: (1), the collection of medicines; (2), the construction of a shrine; and (3), a long period of drumming, singing and dancing, interspersed with treatment of the patient by the doctors, who wash her with medicine, address the afflicting shade at the shrine and perform various ritualistic actions. The patient usually sits passively before the shrine, but may on occasion join the circle of women dancing round her or even dance by herself.

Each type of ritual has its own special drum rhythm, its own 'theme song', its own combination of medicines, and its own stylised behaviour, expressed in dancing and gestures, and its own type of shrine and ritual apparatus.

Three main categories of people usually take part in these rituals: (1), men and women who have been patients themselves for the particular ritual and hence can act as major or minor doctors (*ayimbuki*); (2), matrilineal and patrilineal kin of the wife and husband patients (the term for 'patient' is *muyeji* and is also used for an unlucky hunter who is being treated in an *Wuyang'a* ritual; it really means 'a person afflicted by the shade of one of his or her relatives'); and (3), other Lunda, who may or may not be related to the patients, but come to take part in the dancing and drinking, for each ritual, especially the final phase, is the occasion for a public festivity, a general tribal gathering recruited, it may be, from several distinct chiefdoms. If the headman of the village where the ritual is being performed knows its techniques and medicines he will act as principal doctor, but the doctor need not necessarily be related to the patients. As a general rule membership of the cult gives one a more important role in the ritual than kinship with the patient.

Some comments on the individual rituals:

(1) *Nkula*

Much of the symbolism of this ritual is connected with blood. For instance, doctors and patients are anointed with red clay, a red cock is sacrificed and bark and roots from the *mukula* tree (*Pterocarpus angolensis*), which exudes a red gum when cut, are the principal medicines for washing the patient and giving her to drink. Since the purpose of the ritual is to cure the patient from prolonged menstrual bleeding, other medicines are used to prevent bleeding. Such are *museng'u* and *musoli* roots and leaves taken from trees from which hunter's forked pole shrines are made. It will be remembered that these poles are placed in the graves of dead hunters and that blood of animals is poured down them for the hunter's shade to drink. In the same way it is hoped that the patient's bleeding will be 'drunk up' by the medicine.

The doctor makes a tiny grass hut (*katala kankula*) behind the patient's hut, a big fire is made in front of her own hut and at one stage in the proceedings the doctor places his flat *luwalu* medicine-basket firmly on her head and makes her roll her head while he presses it down. She must then work her way backwards, still rolling her head under the *luwalu*, to the small hut, repeating this process, from fire to *katala*, four times.

All the medicines of *Nkula* are heated and mixed with red clay. During seclusion they are kept in a small calabash called *ilembu* (from which the *ku-lembuka* phase gets its name and which figured prominently during it) and she must wash herself with them, sitting on a small stone, at dawn every morning, splashing them, mixed with castor oil, over herself and her husband.

After a big final ceremony at night, during which she and her husband march round a huge fire, carrying a bow between them on their shoulders and followed by a procession of women doctors chanting the theme song of *Nkula*, ' one child, only one child, a single bangle round the leg ' (referring to the thin copper bangle worn by an only child), the doctor gives her a carved wooden effigy (*nkishi*) of a baby, made of *mukula* wood, which she must sleep with or carry on her back and hip, until she has borne a live child. Other songs describe the shade, which has come ' in *Nkula* ', as dancing the *ku-tomboka* dance of war-triumph (see page 351) on the woman's verandah, again with reference to the theme of ' spilt blood '.

(2) *Wubwang'u*

This ritual, based on the affliction of a woman with twins by a shade, has been made the expression of ' the joyous struggle ' between men and women. The theme of the ritual is conflict, contradiction, paradox, with the battle of the sexes strongly underlined. Psychologically a conflict has been set up between jubilation at the excessive, almost embarrassing, fertility represented by giving birth to twins and the acute economic anxiety involved in rearing them. This paradoxical emotion finds expression in lascivious banter between the sexes who revile and abuse each other in the most uninhibited way. Lunda are normally rather prudish in mixed company; at *Wubwang'u* complete freedom of expression in sexual matters is almost rigorously observed!

All the symbols in *Wubwang'u* are arranged in pairs. Some of the medicines are collected from the dry bush, others from the streamside; there are *two* principal medicines, one, a tree called *Katawubwang'u* is taken from the bush, the other, a creeper called *moluwawubwang'u*, from the streamside evergreen forest. Back at the village fronded branches of the bush medicine trees are used in the construction of a shrine a few yards in front of the patient's hut as uprights for a diminutive semi-circular ' fence ' (*chipang'u*), while the *molu* creeper is threaded laterally across them. A partition of branches is made across the centre dividing it into *two* compartments. The male doctor, who carries a *double* hunting-bell, is assisted by a principal woman doctor. At the river he anoints

the patient with powdered white clay from a phallus-shaped calabash (*muswayi*), while the woman doctor anoints her with red
powder from the large shell of a freshwater mollusc (*nkalakala*),
symbolising the female sexual organ. The bush itself generally
symbolises masculinity, as it is the domain of the hunter; the
streamside symbolises womanhood as it is from streams that
women draw water and beside which they make their maize and
pumpkin gardens.

Twins and the mothers of twins are entitled to put a ring of
white clay round their right eye and of red clay round the left eye.
Children, who are allowed to go with the doctors to collect medicine,
are also decorated with white clay. If at birth the navel cord was
wrapped around the left shoulder a ring of white clay is put round
the left eye; if round the right shoulder the right eye is ringed; if
around both, both are circled with white. Women whose children
were born without any trouble have a spot of white clay on each
cheek and another on the brow.

When the procession of doctors, twins and children returns from
the woods, each person bears a leafy branch in his hand. The
principal doctor carries his *luwalu* basket which contains, in addition
to bark chips from all the medicine trees, domestic plants such as
cassava (one root from the bush gardens and one from the river
gardens), maize-grains, beans, ground-nuts, sweet potatoes and
millet seeds.

After the *chipang'u* has been made (see photograph VI) a small
calabash of honey beer is placed in one compartment, while a chunk
of black mud from the river-bed is put in the other, on which a clay
pot called *izawu* (used in many rituals) dotted with red and white
clay is then placed. Some of the bark chips and domestic plants
are put in the pot which is filled with water. Some beer is poured
into it from the calabash, more beer is poured along the sides of the
chipang'u and the *luwalu* is placed over the pot as a lid. An arrow
is inserted behind the pot, point downwards, and a leaf of the castor
oil plant is draped over the arrow. The beer in the calabash is
called *nkaka wamumbanda*, ' mother's mother ', and is said to *be*
the shade. It is drunk by the women doctors in a sort of communion ceremony.

Periodically the patient is sprinkled with medicine by the male
doctor, who uses a leaf-broom. She sits facing the shrine in a
modest attitude rather like a girl at initiation. But there is nothing
modest about the songs of the dancers, mainly women, who swirl
and laugh in a stamping ring round the shrine. Amorous pleasure
is likened to ' tickling grass ', to ' sweet honey ' and a man declares
himself to be ' a veritable witchdoctor of fornication '. The drums
change to a furious, heady, unsteady, jovial rhythm; the leading
woman doctor blows white powder from her mouth over everyone.
Men in numbers join the circle of dancers. All leap in the air,

raising and lowering both arms repeatedly; the men revile the women's genitalia and the women deride the small size of the men's. Everyone roars with laughter while the more bashful admirers of

VI.—Shrine for the *Wubwang'u* Ritual (see text).

In the flat *luwalu* basket in the foreground may be seen bark-chip medicine, a cassava root, beans, peas, millet grains and ground-nuts and the shell of a freshwater mollusc containing powdered red clay. The calabash in the right compartment of the *chipang'u* (see text) contains honey beer for a communion drink. The clay pot in the left compartment contains medicines and rests on a slab of black river mud.

the heroes in the circle hold their sides at their sallies. Everyone speaks at once. The women break into the *Mukanda* song supposed to be sacred to boys' initiation. The male doctor bashes his basket down hard on the arrow (a symbol of the male sex) while another man dives through his extended legs. The effect of this battle of the sexes is said ' to give strength ' to the patient; the provocative language is said, if she is pregnant, ' to help the baby to grow '.[1] Analogously, it is thought that intercourse, after pregnancy has been established, strengthens the unborn child.

The climax comes at sundown when the male doctor collects up his ritual equipment, puts the arrow between his big toe and second toe, and, holding the *luwalu* basket aloft and with the patient

[1] If the patient is a twin she is expected to have twins herself.

clasping him round the waist, both hop on their right legs into the patient's hut. Later that night she is washed with the remaining medicine in the pot.

When a woman has successfully borne twins she dances round all the neighbouring villages, wearing only a peraminal band with a flap over the pudenda. This flap she causes to fly up and down as she dances, and she is followed by a crowd of women and children.

After *Wubwang'u* women are secluded for about a month during which they must refrain from eating fish, which being slippery will cause the child to ' slide out ' prematurely. Nor must they take cassava from the soaking pools or draw water from the rivers or wells. After *Ku-tumbuka* (see page 377) the doctor gives his patient a wooden carving of a baby, as in *Nkula*, but made of *katawubwang'u* wood.

(3) *Isoma* (from *Ku-somoka*, ' to slip out ')

This ritual is designed to get rid of a shade which is causing a woman to have a series of abortions or miscarriages. On page 347 we noted that the shade ' coming in *Isoma* ' is supposed to be assisted by the *ikishi Mvweng'i*, which sways about like a woman giving premature birth. There are no drums at the *ku-lembuka* ceremony and *Mukanda* songs are sung throughout. Most of the medicines are taken from fruit-trees, to make the woman fruitful. Bark-scrapings are taken for splashing on the patient and her husband with a leaf-broom. *As in all fertility rituals* no tree from the bark of which string may be obtained is used for medicine, as this would ' tie up the baby in the mother's womb '. No young children, except those of the doctor himself, are allowed to be present at *Isoma* or they will become very ill.

The ceremony takes place in the bush at the source of a stream. Two holes (*makela*) are dug about four feet deep, connected by a short tunnel (*mwina* or *ikela dakuhanuka*). At the head of the farther hole a fire is kindled and a container of thick bark filled with water and medicine is put on it to heat; at the foot of the nearer hole a broken calabash containing cold water and the same kind of medicine is placed (see photograph VII). To the left of the nearer hole a fire is kindled at which the men sit; to the right a fire for women is made. A red cock with tied legs is laid to the left of the upper hole. The patient enters the nearer hole and stands on the right side; her husband also enters and stands on the left. Both are stripped to the waist. The patient is given a small white pullet to hold. The doctor standing on the left of the nearer hole splashes cold medicine, first on the patient then on her husband with a leaf-broom. Then the patient crawls through the tunnel, followed by her husband, and the doctor dances to the farther hole and splashes hot medicine on them in the same order as before.

[382]

This 'splashing on' is really a ritual within a ritual. It is called *Ku-chilika* or *Ku-kupula* and means 'to drive away familiars sent by witches and sorcerers'. Since children have died before this ritual is held there is a chance that *wuloji*, 'witchcraft or sorcery', is afoot, and that the diviner's attribution of the trouble to a shade is incorrect. This is strikingly brought out in the text I

VII.—THE SPLASHING-ON OF MEDICINE AT THE *Isoma* RITUAL TO DRIVE FAMILIARS AWAY FROM THE PATIENT AND HER HUSBAND.

The doctor holds a leaf-broom in his hand and dips it alternately in the hot medicine in the bark container behind the patients and in the cold medicine in the broken calabash in front of them. A tunnel connects the two holes Part of the white chicken held by the woman patient can be seen.

recorded of a doctor's words as he splashed on medicine. 'What about this husband? Some of his wife's children have died. Strange, strange! Perhaps his mother-in-law has *Tuyebela* (women's familiars of variable shape; they may appear as jackals, cats, owls or rats or as diminutive humans with inverted feet; they capture a living relative of a witch as food for witches' necrophagous feasts, substituting in his village a false semblance which sickens and dies; they are matrilineally inherited by women from female relatives, not made by medicine as men's familiars are). Perhaps his wife's mother's brother has an *ilomba* (a male sorcerer's familiar with the body of a snake and the face of its owner; it is 'grown' in an antelope horn at the source of a river and kept in a hole under its owner's hut or in a nearby pool; when it is shot by a witchdoctor, its owner dies too; it normally devours the "shadow" (*mwevulu*) of its victims who are usually matrilineal kin of the sorcerer). If this is so, let them go back to their huts and not trouble these people. Why did her second child die? Perhaps because of *andumba* (another word for women's familiars) or *ilomba*. Let them go back to her relatives so that her children may be born alive. Perhaps there is a woman in this village who steals human meat, special meat, perhaps the meat of one dead. If she has eaten these children, let her familiars go back to where they came from!'

While this incantation goes on the men on the left of the holes and the women on the right start to sway their hips in rhythm (*ku-punjila*) and chant the song 'My child is swaying about'. Now one doctor stands by each hole and the two splash on hot and cold medicine alternately, slapping the brooms on their hands to scatter the drops and shouting ' *Yepoo!* ' as they do so.

This continues from about ten a.m. to three p.m. and many *Mukanda* and *Mung'ong'i* (see page 343 *et seq.* and page 380 *et seq.*) songs are sung. Near the end two doctors take the red cock and hold it over the hot medicine while all sing the circumcision song of *Mukanda*. Feathers are plucked from the living bird and strewn in the hole by the hot medicine, some over the couple in it. Now the principal doctor cuts the cock's head off and pours the hot blood in the hot medicine. Then the other doctor sprinkles blood in both holes and in the cold medicine. Finally both doctors sprinkle hot and cold medicine on both patients. The assistant pours cold water on the couple, then takes the cock into the bush and plucks it, collecting the feathers and putting them in the nearer hole.

The couple go off carrying the white pullet. The patient is given a white cloth to wear by the doctor. The doctor puts beans, cassava and sweet potatoes in the farther hole, as food for the shade. His assistant throws the broken calabash and cold medicine into the nearer hole and the doctor himself throws the ashes of the fire and remaining faggots into the other hole, but upturns the bark container over the medicine. The holes are not filled in but abandoned.

The husband has previously built his wife a grass seclusion hut (*nkunka*), set back a little from the village and will build a fence round it in which the white pullet will live. If she bears and rears a child to the toddling stage the chicken will be given to the doctor. The red cock will be eaten by the doctors that night.

The doctor now gives her the horn of a bushbuck stuffed tightly with a special medicine and put unsealed in a small basket on her head, which she must carry wherever she goes while living in seclusion. She may not go near water or soak cassava or eat fish during this period. If she does she will become sick and the baby she is carrying will be at the mercy of the offended shade. She is also given a phallus-shaped *muswayi* calabash filled with a root-medicine pounded with a white juice. Whenever she wishes to go outside she must smear it on her temples.

She and her husband must have a separate fire and cook only from that. She may not enter the centre of the village, but only creep round outside. She is forbidden to eat flesh of the bushbuck, giant rat, wild pig, hippopotamus, eland, situtunga, blue duiker, yellow-backed duiker, elephant and the male roan antelope. She must not wash or shave her hair until her child can take its first steps.

When she ' comes out ' her head is shaved and she eats from the same pot as all the other women. As many of the tabooed foods as are available are cooked in it. Then follows a dance of rejoicing, held at night.

Since *Chihamba* is really a curative ritual although it is also performed to remove female reproductive troubles I will deal with it below.

CURATIVE CULTS

Chihamba and *Kalemba* seem to be the only truly indigenous Lunda cults to cure sickness or disease, unless we include the anti-witchcraft ritual of *Kaneng'a*. Other cults I have seen or heard of, such as *Kayong'u*, *Tukuka* and *Masandu*, are of Lwena (Lovale), Luchazi or Tchokwe origin and are characterised by hysterical tremblings, ' speaking with tongues ' in foreign languages, and other symptoms of dissociation. In these introduced cults also the doctor gives medicine to himself as well as to the patient and both give way to paroxisms of quivering, very unpleasant to behold. In *Tukuka* and *Masandu* women play a far more prominent role than in the traditional Lunda rituals. These two rituals are becoming very popular in north-west Mwinilunga and are often performed for persons suffering from T.B. The shades who cause the disease are said to be those of Europeans or of members of other tribes like the Lwena and part of the treatment consists of giving the patient European foods, served by a ' houseboy ', miming

European dancing in couples, wearing European dress, and singing up-to-date songs such as ' We are going in an aeroplane to Lum-wana '.

Kayong'u is often performed for patients with breathing difficulties and part of the treatment consists in placing the patient under a blanket with a steaming pot of leaf medicines and making him inhale the steam. It is also performed for a person who has dreamed that a shade wishes him to become a diviner.

Kalemba is not often seen nowadays and I have no reliable information about it, except that it was a women's ritual and a woman dancer-doctor with her face covered in white clay and carrying a *luwalu* containing specimens of all the Lunda food crops performed a solo dance.

Ihamba has been mentioned above (pages 372–3). Although it appears to be of Lwena-Tchokwe origin it has been incorporated into the *Wuyang'a* hunters' cult. It, too, has become popular in the north-west where there are many villages and little game. It gives non-hunters a kind of vicarious participation in the hunters' cult and illustrates the tenacity with which a people will hold on to their cherished values even when their material basis has gone.

Chihamba

The typical symptoms of a patient who has been caught by a shade ' in *Chihamba* ' are ' pains in the whole body ' and ' shivering and fever '. *Chihamba* is said to be ' a very big drum (i.e. " ritual ") like *Mukanda* ', with very many people coming to perform in it. The first, *Ku-lembeka*, phase takes place between sunset and about ten p.m. and is an intimate affair at most involving the people of a few neighbouring villages. Then follows a period of partial seclusion, during which the patient must avoid such foods as the doctor prescribes and refrain from intercourse with his or her spouse at night and lover (*ndowa*) by day. But the *Ku-tumbuka*, going-out ceremony, is long and complicated, lasting two nights and days. At about seven p.m. on the night it begins, a huge fire is made in the patient's village, many drums are beaten and the patient is doctored on the doorway of his hut, medicines used being *musoli*, *mukula* (see pages 344 and 378), *mutututambululu* and *mukombu-kombu* (see page 375). A white cock is sacrificed and hung on a stick head downward. The doctors eat a ritual meal of beans, peas, maize and cassava in the patient's hut, which is partitioned by a mat. The principal doctor, called *Kavula*, goes to the other side of the mat and speaks in a throaty guttural voice a special ritual dialect also called *kavula*, in which indecencies prevail. This phase is called *Kantong'a*.

At sunrise, after an all-night dance, *Kavula* catches the patient by the neck and handles him roughly. This is the signal for everyone to indulge in horseplay and ribaldry with one another.

[386]

VIII —*Tukuka* RITUAL.

The doctor is washing the patient (in an advanced stage of T.B.) with medicine from a meal mortar, just after dawn. The women doctors holding rattles have frequently gone into convulsive trembling fits during the singing and drumming, which has continued throughout the previous night. These women claim that they have themselves been cured by the *Tukuka* ritual and this gives them the right to act as minor officiants in subsequent performances of *Tukuka*.

Everyone rushes into the bush, men chasing women, and much sexual intercourse, leading in some cases to illegitimate births, takes place. This is a sort of Bacchanalia.

Towards the end of the afternoon, the doctors prepare a sacred site in the bush. The inner sanctum, called *isoli*, is composed of a semi-circular enclosure covered with leaves partitioned down the middle, with a stick placed transversely across the opening to serve as a door. At some distance a much larger semi-circular fence, called *mukoliki* (as at *Mukanda*) is made, also with a stick for door. A sacred path is cleared in the bush from the village of the patient, through the door of *mukoliki*, to the door of *isoli*. Outside *isoli* to the left of the door stands a meal-mortar, striped with red and white clay, full of medicine. Inside, to the right of the door, stands *Kavula* himself. On the other side of the partition is his chief assistant. Behind the *isoli* or *chisolu* sits another doctor making a costume of bark-string for *Kavula*, interwoven with *nzenzi* ankle dancing-rattles (again recalling *Mukanda*, when the *makishi* are made). Meanwhile, the patient and other people who have already passed through *Chihamba* as patients wait outside the *mukoliki* fence. Uninitiated persons have already been driven back to the village with bows and arrows by the initiated. Initiates all have special names by which alone they are known in the cult. About an hour before sundown, the patient is called in to visit *Kavula*. Beans and new maize are cooked within *isoli* by the chief assistant. The patient eats these after drinking medicine from the mortar, first with the cupped left hand then with the right. *Kavula* speaks to him throatily asking him his business. ' I am very sick ', ' Good ! *Nzambi* (the High God) helped you to me. Now go away. You are better. Don't forget to wash in the medicines I gave you every day '.

After the patient the initiates come, one by one, each bearing a string of beads, to greet *Kavula*. The beads are payment for the privilege of seeing him. After drinking from the mortar, they enter and see *Kavula* dressed from head to foot in rattles. ' He *is* the shade (*mukishi*) ', Lunda say. They say further most emphatically that *Kavula* is *not* an *ikishi* or masked dancer, like *Katotoji* (pages 346–7) or *Kadang'u Kamashika* (pages 366–7). The initiates take two rattles and beat *Kavula* with them, first on the knees, next on the neck and finally on the top of the head. Then *Kavula* dances himself with a rattle in each hand while other doctors beat drums. He sings guttural songs in his own weird and indecent dialect. At sunset the visits cease and drumming, dancing and revelling continue at the village.

At six a.m. the following morning beans are cooked, *Kavula* teaches the patient the medicines of *Chihamba* and they eat the beans together. *Kavula* then concludes the ritual by planting a cutting of cassava near the patient's doorway.

II

SOME
AFRICAN POISON PLANTS
AND
MEDICINES OF NORTHERN RHODESIA

W. GILGES

1955

FROM THE PREFACE TO THE
SECOND IMPRESSION, 1964

Owing to the considerable popularity which this paper has enjoyed it has proved necessary for a reprint to be published. The opportunity has been taken of correcting certain minor errors which were present in the edition published in 1955 and of bringing the botanical names up to date. In this we were greatly assisted by Mr. D. B. Fanshawe, Principal Scientific Officer, Division of Forest Research, to whom we are deeply grateful. There are no other major alterations to the text though a brief list of suggestions for further reading has been included at the end of the paper.

The Central African bush offers to the amateur botanist a rich field for collecting, and the satisfaction of frequent discoveries. While the more stately timber trees have been fully described, the humbler denizens of the bush, shrubs and herbs, are still an almost untouched field where happy hours can be spent in collecting, observing and discussing with the local population the names and merits of the individual plants. Away from the line of rail, where the paraffin tin culture has not taken complete hold of the people, much of the human life is centred round the trees and shrubs, which for large areas represent the only available raw material.

A little iron smelting is done here and there, a few craftsmen survive, fashioning knives, hoes, adzes, spear blades and arrowheads and repairing muzzle-loaders (often illegally) but wood and the produce of the soil constitute the material on which village life is built. It is, therefore, not surprising that folklore and superstition are intimately connected with the bush and that the knowledge of its trees and shrubs is great and extensive. The African, like the Spaniard, hates trees and would like nothing better than to clear large tracts of land of them. He may, to show his higher state of knowledge and experience, plant some imported gum trees round his village, he may when transferred from Nyasaland to the North-Western Province carry with him the seeds of a pink jacaranda, and plant them near the school where he teaches, but for the indigenous trees he has little love. He knows them well and uses them extensively with no thought for conservation and replanting and when one travels through the almost limitless " green desert " one can understand that to him the riches available at his doorstep seem limitless.

It is great fun after a day's collecting to discuss with the local worthies the names and uses of the various specimens gathered. It is usually the older people who possess the greater knowledge, while the younger, often with some school education, have lost much of this lore

[391]

and consider one's interest in a mere plant as amusing, if not somewhat crazy. In typical African fashion, heated arguments often ensue until a local expert clearly crystallizes out and from then on holds the floor. Women very rarely contribute to the discussion, as they are taught to keep quiet in the common assembly. Once only did I get some Luchazi girls to volunteer information and, with much giggling, their own version of a story was given.

I have found here and there educated Africans who retained pride in their tribe and had become experts on its history and folklore. They, although somewhat grudgingly admitting that a few of the white men's thoughts were not bad, some of his material goods even better, considered that their own way of living was well worth preserving and they had collected almost with scientific interest all items of tribal tradition and knowledge. These people were a gold mine of information. They also appreciated one's interest in their tribes, thoughts and way of life.

My collecting was either done in the immediate neighbourhood of the station or on medical tours. Specimens were pressed as soon as camp was reached and they were shown to the local villagers either in a fresh, partly dried or completely dried condition. It never seemed to make any difference whether the " experts " were dealing with the fresh or herbarium specimen, they recognised either equally well. Their information was frequently checked. I felt satisfied that if the same name had been given to a plant by three different groups of people as widely separated as Balovale, Kabompo Boma and the Kabompo mouth for instance, there could be no doubt it was the accepted tribal name. Standards on medical use were sometimes more difficult to obtain and such details are included in the following account only if at least two sources gave the same information, or if the statements made by one member were enthusiastically supported by the whole group to which he belonged.

Three specimens were collected of every species—whenever possible—one retained for my own collection, the other two were sent to the Herbarium of the Royal Botanic Garden at Kew, and to the National Herbarium, Pretoria, for identification. While most of my specimens could be identified as to genus, the species identification was often impossible as neither Kew nor Pretoria had any comparable material— a pointer to the dearth of botanical specimens from this part of the world. Now and then the identifications given by the two Herbaria were different. The taxonomy of the Central African Flora is still in a state of flux, and names will probably be changed frequently for a long time to come until these plants have been collected and studied more

[392]

thoroughly. Often different names are really synonyms for the same thing and are kept on more through local tradition than for rational motives.

" Medicine " in Africa is not only the drug taken to cure disease, it is the poison to kill the enemy, and it is also the charm worn round the neck to prevent conception, it is the witchcraft with its evil influence as well as the cylinder oil the " Bwana " puts in his motor car to improve its performance.

The sanitary inspector with his DDT spray, the political speaker who can attack the Government with impunity, the surgeon who is lucky in the results of his operations all possess " strong medicine ". Medicine is therefore not only the powdered bark or the infusion, the quinine tablet or the scabies ointment, it is also the personal power, for good or evil, inherent in some people and reaches into the world of the mind and the soul.

The African seems unable to weigh up risks and his fears are usually of a vague, undefined nature and cannot easily be overcome. When discussing an operation with a European, the questions raised usually are: how much will it hurt, how long will it take, what is the risk to life, what will it cost ? He does not require concrete answers to definite questions—he is just afraid and whether the operation advised is a slight or major one, no arguments will move his fears. This fear of the unknown surrounds him always, the evil spirit of sorcerers, the avenging ghost of his dead ancestors, the strange manners of alien masters, the wild animals of the bush, the long dark nights when hyenas prowl and the witches' brew is concocted. There is also the fear of starvation in a population living normally at subsistence level, the fear of losing their land or fishing rights to newcomers, the fear of disease and death. It is against this background that African folklore must be studied.

The old Continental proverb that for every ill a herb is growing, for every disease a medicine can be found, is also firmly believed in central Africa. Pathological concepts like cancer and pneumonia which are in common usage in even the most primitive communities in Europe are completely foreign to the African, and his herbalist treats patients by the symptoms they produce. A rational therapy can, therefore, very rarely evolve, although it is quite possible that through centuries of trial and error certain potent drugs have been detected and are being used quite effectively in the same way as the

[393]

" galenical's " in European pharmacy were prescribed long before experimental pharmacology either confirmed or disproved their usefulness. As in ancient Greece or medieval Europe, African medicine disdains experiment and relies on authority for its teachings.

When there is a host of remedies for one disease or syndrome, one can draw with certainty the conclusion that none are really effective and the multitude of concoctions, infusions, enemas, etc., that are prescribed for such ills as venereal disease illuminate the fact that the African pharmacopoeia contains no single effective remedy against these and many other common diseases. The Bantu herbalist has no scales and no clear idea of dosage. He may be very heavy-handed with dangerous drugs and incur fatalities, which would probably number many more if the African were not very resistant to overdosage even of European-dispensed remedies. He has a much tougher constitution and shows less side effects with many of the potent drugs like sulphones, sulphanilamides or salvarsan.

The following is an account of my enquiries into the medicinal and other uses to which trees and shrubs are put. The local name added is in Lovale—all other vernacular names are given in the Appendix. If no locality is mentioned, the account applies to the Balovale and Kabompo districts of the North-Western Province, bordering on Angola, from where most of the tribes concerned emigrated.

I found it easier to reproduce the statements given to me in the form they were made by my informants. A sentence such as : " the infusion enters her vagina and cures her " should therefore be read as coming from the African herbalist who is praising his wares and does not imply my belief in the efficacy of the medicine.

There are some vegetable poisons which even to a tough African constitution can prove lethal, and deliberate or accidental poisonings are fairly frequent. A widely distributed creeper *Abrus precatorius—Mukenyenge*—produces small red seeds—" lucky beans "—which are known to be poisonous and children are warned against them. A tough coat makes them usually indestructible and they pass through the digestive tract unchanged. If, however, these beans are taken crushed the toxic principle, Abrin, can produce death rapidly. A Livingstone man was found dead on a bush path. In his basket several of these beans were detected and although no direct trace of the poison in the man's organs could be demonstrated, an extract of the *Abrus* seeds injected into white mice produced petechial haemorrhages in many organs and severe enteritis as was found in the body of the deceased.

[394]

Witchdoctors who want to kill somebody make an effigy of that person and put *Abrus* seeds in place of ears. A decoction of the roots is taken for chest trouble. Crushed leaves are mixed with boiling water and the steam is used to soothe inflamed eyes.

Another very potent poison is contained in the roots of *Erythrophleum africanum—Mukoso*—the toxic principle being a digitalis like glycoside. When taken in small doses it acts as a remedy for chest trouble but a rather liberal portion of the sun-dried root scrapings poured into some enemy's beer eliminates him with certainty and for ever. The wood of this stately tree is hard and is used for pounding-sticks, furniture and buildings. It makes good wedges for hoe handles and the bark is useful for burning clay pots.

Species of *Indigofera*—mainly small shrubs—are very common but not many are as yet identifiable. Poisonous properties of some *Indigoferas* have been previously described. One case observed by me concerned a young African wife who consulted an old herbalist woman on account of her sterility. Root scrapings of "*Kajiha Misongo*" were introduced into her vagina. She died after twelve hours. The dissection again revealed multiple pin-point haemorrhages in many organs. A decoction of the roots is used against gonorrhoea and head lice while a decoction of the whole plant is given as an enema in bilharzia. Hot fomentations prepared with it are useful in cases of snake bites and burns.

An infusion of the roots of *Markhamia sp.—Kapasa kalyongoho* —a large tree—mixed with beer, kills your enemy or rival in two to three hours. Root scrapings introduced into the vagina are equally efficacious.

Physostigma mesoponticum—a leguminous herb—produces seeds of doubtful potency. A young Chewa girl had attempted suicide with about six of these after a violent quarrel with her mother but recovered from the resulting gastric upset within two days.

The most famous of the intra-vaginal poisons is *Securidaca longipedunculata—Muyise* or *Mutata*—the " Violet Tree ". This poison represents the accepted means of suicide for Lovale women: two such cases are described in detail below:

On April 9th, 1952, a Lovale woman was brought to hospital by her relatives because " she had poisoned herself by inserting roots of the *Mutata* tree into her vagina ". Although badly shocked she was able to tell her story, which was as follows: A man offered her three

[395]

shillings to live with him. This she had done for some time but now felt that he might as well marry her. When she asked him, he became very annoyed, told her that he would leave and demanded his three shillings back. She felt so depressed that she wanted to die and inserted some powdered roots of *Mutata* into her vagina. The relatives, on hearing this, cleared out her vagina and rushed her to hospital.

On admission the patient was found to be an elderly African woman in a severely shocked condition. Her body felt cold and clammy and the pulse was rapid (over 130) and hardly perceptible. Her temperature was normal. She vomited repeatedly and complained of palpitations but no pain. Her condition deteriorated steadily and she died about twelve hours after admission. A post-mortem examination was carried out with the following findings: multiple sub-mucous haemorrhages in the following organs—larynx, trachea, bronchi, stomach, intestines, bladder and uterus. Large haemorrhagic area in left lung. Complete necrosis of vaginal mucosa.

A second case occurred on June 6th, 1952. The dead body of a Lovale woman was delivered to the mortuary with the following history: After a quarrel with her husband involving the sum of twopence, this woman had threatened to kill herself. She repeated her threat next morning, but was not taken seriously. In the afternoon the husband, however, found her lying in her hut, very ill and weak. To help her, he called another woman who discovered parts of a root in the vagina, took her to a stream and washed her out. The death occurred during the following night. The symptoms as described by the villagers were: persistent vomiting, restlessness and severe abdominal pain, haemorrhages from vagina and extreme weakness. This all happened while I was on tour, a post-mortem examination, therefore, could not be carried out.

Medical officers stationed at Balovale have, in their annual reports, repeatedly mentioned this form of suicide, e.g. in 1943 Dr. J. W. O. Will reported eight deaths from this cause in the Balovale District. Amongst them were two young girls who had the root introduced into the vagina by an African doctor in an effort to procure abortion.

From local information available it appears that the *Mutata* tree is very common in the Balovale and Mwinilunga districts and that its poisonous properties are well known to the populace. Suicide per *Mutata* seems, however, to be confined to the Balovale people; even in Barotseland where cases also occur it is restricted to tribes of Balovale origin. Informants are emphatic that the root scrapings are only poisonous when introduced into vagina or rectum or worn in the armpit for a long time.

A number of other cases have been seen and dissected. The picture was the same in every instance. One concerned an old woman who had been accused of witchcraft and rather than face ostracism by the village had killed herself. The root scrapings contain much methyl salicylate and possess therefore the characteristic odour of oil of winter-green. The smell is supposed to drive snakes away. The roots are also soaked in water until a thick paste is obtained. This is applied to cuts made into the legs for all sorts of inflammatory conditions. The Luchazi use an infusion of the roots as mouth washes in toothache.

As a contraceptive measure the scrapings of inner skin of roots are added to gunpowder and mixed with cold water. This brew is drunk through an old used axe or hoe handle that has been thrown away for a long time. When drinking the woman must stand at the crossroads and face west. Leaves pounded with water with salt added are taken for coughs. The oil gained from the winged seeds stains furniture and is also applied in the form of a salve.

The genus *Strophanthus* is well known in European medicine and a highly diluted extract of a West African species is used extensively on the Continent for the treatment of cardiac failure. Not much is known of the local *Strophanthus welwitschii—Mimbapanda*—a common creeper with violet flowers and a large spindle-shaped seed pot—but it is not surprising that it also contains an active toxic principle. An infusion of the roots is used against gonorrhoea. Given in an overdose this might easily prove fatal. Two such cases occurred in Balovale in 1951. The roots are also mixed with oil and then employed against scabies. It acts as a charm against snake-bite. Cobras are supposed to peel the bark of the plant and eat it.

Tephrosia vogelii—Wusungu—is well known all over southern Africa as a fish poison and is cultivated in many villages for that purpose. When the leaves are thrown into a pool, the fish are temporarily paralysed and can be picked up from the surface of the water. Powdered leaves are rubbed into the skin in cases of measles and will also rid a dog of fleas.

Many plants are used as " charms ". Here are some examples:

Acacia polyacantha ssp. campylacantha—Muzeze. The roots of this common tree have a smell that is intensely disliked by snakes. They will leave a house when these roots are kept among the rafters. At crossing points in the rivers, they will keep crocodiles at bay. In the Eastern Province a child sleeping restlessly is washed with an infusion of the roots. The bark can be used for ropes, the pods contain edible seeds and the wood is good for hoe handles. In Nyasaland this tree is considered an indicator of fertile soils.

Afrormosia angolensis—Muvambo—produces very strong, heavy timber—one of the hardest woods in the country. Among the Luchazi a man who wants to improve his sexual potency cuts off the penis of a live goat, ties it sandwich-fashion between two slabs of this wood, and boils it in water. The broth is then taken. A cold infusion of the roots is used as an ordinary tonic and also for chest troubles. In Fort Jameson the steam inhaled from boiling water with the leaves of this tree is considered a good cure for headaches. There is an African saying that without this wood many a man's children would go hungry, as it is used for much spare-time carving.

Cassipourea ? sp. If the villagers want to find out whether a person is a witch, they give him an infusion of bark and roots. If he vomits it up his guilt is established beyond doubt.

Eugenia angolensis—a small shrub with edible fruit. It must however not be eaten at the beginning of the rainy season, otherwise heavy rains may flood the district.

Maytenus senegalensis—a riverside shrub—provides a remedy aginst snakebite. " Cut off the snake's head, burn it together with the roots, mix the ashes with oil and put it on the victim's tongue and at the site of the bite. If the snake has not been killed, drink an infusion of the leaves. "

Lonchocarpus capassa—Mutomatoma—This is a lucky medicine ! Anyone with pieces of this tree on him will generally be liked by people and be agreeable to his employer. No information was available whether the wearer's own behaviour and anxiety to please contributes to the success. Among the Tonga a decoction of the leaves and roots is given to disputants who appear before a witchdoctor for the settlement of an argument. The wood makes good axe handles.

Psorospermum febrifugum—Muhota. In the Eastern Province this is believed to act as a charm against being seen by wild animals. For this purpose it should be worn in one's hair. To entice somebody's husband away, put it on the wife's fireplace.

Strychnos innocua—Mukolo—A piece of bark together with bark from other trees is used by mourners to dab the head and upper part of their bodies after a funeral. Produces the " Kaffir Orange ", an edible fruit of pleasant taste.

[398]

Syzygium cordatum—Musombo. A beautiful evergreen tree growing in moist localities, mainly along river banks. Pounded leaves, bark and roots are soaked in water and applied to the breasts of mothers to produce more milk. Amongst the Chewa it is worn by pregnant women, when they learn that their husbands have committed adultery, to prevent their babies being deformed. Birth defects to the children often happen as a punishment for husbands' infidelity.

This tree belongs to the same family as the guava and also produces an edible fruit.

*Trichilia emetica—*Cape or Natal Mahogany. Roots and bark are used in the Eastern Province to tame doves, pieces being tied to the cages. Before building a dovecot, women place part of the root in the hole made for the first pole. Roots are also placed near water where doves come to drink. The oil from the beans is used as an ointment.

Wingandia urens—" Elephant's Ear " or " Chimbuzi Plant "—*Mupapati—*of rapid growth and with very large leaves. Used in Lusaka to hide the " piccanin kaya " and amongst the Ngoni as a love charm.

Certain trees have acquired almost a sanctity with the tribes, others have been preserved for the use of chiefs or are planted at the graves of their leaders. One of the very few trees that the woodman's axe will spare is *Musuhwa*, a species of wild fig. What a difference one or two of these majestic trees with their evergreen foliage will make to a village ! Wonderfully cool shade they provide, instead of the parching heat that seems to penetrate into every corner of a village devoid of trees.

The *Muyombo* is a sacred tree and is used for spirit worship. Its botanical name is *Lannea stuhlmannii.* When a new village is started a cutting of *Muyombo* is always planted on the site by the headman. When a close relative visits the village the following ceremony takes place. The host and guest go and kneel at the village *Muyombo,* they place a small coin at the base of the trunk and sprinkle it with dry *mpemba* (white clay). They then make a mark with the *mpemba* on the trunk of the tree, on the host's forehead, and on the guest's forehead, and they ask that the guest shall stay well in the village during his visit.

Also the same ceremony is performed two or three days after the birth of a baby in the village. *Mpemba* is put on the tree and on the umbilicus of the baby and it is named. When a person is sick and goes to visit an African doctor, he is often told by the doctor that he can be cured by planting a *muyombo* outside his house. This invokes his ancestral spirits and he then lives well. This can only be done once in a lifetime, for once the ancestral spirits have been called, they stay with the person indefinitely.

When two enemies wish to end their quarrel they meet at the *Muyombo*. A white chicken or a perfect goat or sheep (no sores on them) is killed and the blood is sprinkled at the base of the *Muyombo*, the meat is divided between the two. *Mpemba* is also sprinkled at the base of the tree and rubbed on the abdomens of the two people.

*Vangueriopsis lanciflora—Musole—*is also a " *lihamba* " in the same way as *Muyombo*.

When a person is suffering from nightmares and headaches an African doctor will probably tell him to plant a *musole* cutting. Chalk or meal is scattered round the cutting.

A decoction of the roots is given to pregnant mothers to make their babies strong and to barren women to cure their sterility. It produces an edible fruit and hard wood for porridge spoons and drinking cups for infants.

*Albizia versicolor—Mulungwe—*was a tree which under tribal rule was strictly reserved for chiefs. Only for them was the wood used and Chief Ndungu's beautifully carved drum is an example of Mulungwe's contribution to a chief's regalia. The roots of this tree are soaked in water and the liquid is used as a substitute for soap. In the Eastern Province an infusion made from the bark is applied to sore eyes and to skin rashes and also taken for puberty troubles.

*Ricinodendron rautanenii—Mungongo—*is also looked upon as a sacred tree. Its wood is very soft and used for carving sun helmets. The nuts are edible and are tied round the ankles to cure pain in the legs.

Much of the tree lore is of course pure superstition, and I have collected a few examples of uses tree parts are put to, which by no stretch of the imagination could be called rational.

Acacia: ? *seyal* or *pilispina—*" fever tree "*—Mungonga—*A woman with abdominal pain will sit in a cold infusion of the roots. The infusion then enters her vagina and cures her.

[400]

Afrormum ?sp.—" Wild Ginger "—*Muntundu*. Tubers are used to cure a condition called *Manyanga* or *Visongo* which makes the limbs jerk and shake. The roots are cut into strips and these are tied to the affected parts. The sick person sits on the ground and drums are beaten. If during the drumming the limb jerks it is certain that the person suffers from *Manyanga* and the treatment begins. *Mutundu* roots are pounded with leaves from other trees, mixed with water and the mixture is massaged into the limbs. Roots are used in a sitz-bath for women with retained placenta or abdominal pain.

The tubers are sweet and edible. So is the fruit. Both can be used to make a refreshing cold drink.

Combretum psidioides—*Mulamata*—To increase the milk supply of a lactating mother her breasts are washed with an infusion from its roots.

Combretum microphyllum—a climber very common in the low-lying parts of the Eastern Province especially the Luangwa Valley, covers in September and October the highest trees with a mass of scarlet flowers. The valley people crush the roots and mix them with scrapings from the stem and dog's faeces and burn the mixture. The ashes are given in relish or food as a remedy against lunacy.

Combretum ghasalense—*Mombomba*—Among the Chewa and Ngoni, children suffering from convulsions are washed with an infusion from the roots. The Lovale use the same infusion as a cough remedy.

Cassia ? singueana—An infusion is made of the roots and used to wash children who suffer from general anaemia or from a disease called *Ndulo* or *Tsempho* which they have contracted because their father sleeps with a woman other than his wife (Eastern Province).

Kigelia pinnata—Sausage Tree—*Muvunguvungu*. A thin baby is rubbed with pieces of the fruit, but only the body. If through ignorance the head is also rubbed it will develop a hydrocephalus. If the breasts of mothers are rubbed with pieces of the fruit the milk supply will increase.

Ochna ? pulchra—*Muhongo*. Roots if boiled with water then mixed with flour and taken as a porridge by a youngster of twelve or thirteen will make him a proper man when meeting a girl. (Eastern Province). In Balovale oil is extracted from the fruit and used as a salve.

Schrebera trichoclada—*Muhaswa*—a tree easily recognisable by its pear-shaped, hard fruit. Weak babies are bathed in the decoction of the bark to make them strong. The wood is used to carve spoons,

Vitex mombassae—Mumbomba—Mumbomba wacilunga—" for the men " refers to the practice of young boys of putting the sap on the scrotum to make the penis grow bigger. As the sap has caustic action it occasionally causes severe swelling and pain.

The largest group comprises those trees and shrubs which supply some of the straight medicines without magical frills. Although it cannot be assumed without proper investigation that many of them are really effective, it would be rash to label them all as useless. Active principles in plants are newly discovered every day; the recent finding of a substance in a species of *Rauwolfia* which is capable of lowering a high blood pressure, and the discovery of antibiotic factors in garden cress are cases in point. It may well be that to an enterprising pharmacologist some hidden values in our native flora might one day be revealed.

Anthocleista liebrechtsiana—Mupapala. A riverside tree with large evergreen leaves—a typical representative of the " *Mushitu* " tropical fringing forest. Fresh leaves are placed on wounds.

Asparagus racemosus—Kafuhwakashi. " Fishbones " on account of its thorns. A decoction of the roots is given against gonorrhoea.

Pachycarpus lineolatus—Likuvi. A piece of wood from this tree is put into the fire. When the hot sap emerges this should be collected and rubbed onto an itching skin (Eastern Province). In Balovale the people use the roots to catch birds. They are sprinkled amongst grain, when the birds eat them they become unconscious. The birds are then caught and eaten.

Baissiaea wulfhorstii—Mukangula. A very common creeper with small white flowers, abundant at Balovale aerodrome. The leaves are boiled and used as a fomentation.

Baphia obovata—Kachiva. A small tree, flowering profusely for several months, has masses of sweet-pea-like blooms of white or delicate pink shades. Invades soils eroded and spoilt by cassava cultivation.

The leaves are crushed, mixed with water and salt and used to cure sores. An infusion of the leaves as a face wash overcomes giddiness. As a remedy for measles, they are pounded and soaked, the cold infusion is mixed with ash and smeared over the body. The wood is hard and used for gun stocks. The roots pounded in a mortar give a substitute for soap.

[402]

Bauhinia variegata—is used by the Chewa in the treatment of syphilis and diarrhoea. The fruit is edible when green.

Bauhinia macrantha—*Muhwichichi*. Leaves are pounded, mixed with salt and cooked in water. While still warm the liquid is squeezed over wounds. A diarrhoea medicine is made from the roots. For this purpose they are mixed with *Mukenge* (?) roots. Half of the mixture is boiled with water, from the rest a cold infusion is made. The cold draught is drunk first, followed by the warm one. In the olden days *Makishi* suits were made from the bark. Now people use *Mufufu* (?).

Brachystegia longifolia—*Musamba*. A cold infusion of the bark soaked for about half an hour makes a good medicine for stomach troubles or worms. For an enema the bark is soaked overnight. This tree produces much honey when flowering in December, and a good cloth is made from its bark. The wood is hard but easily attacked by borers. The roots produce string for fishing nets and baskets, but are not as strong as *Mukenge*.

Cathium anomocarpum—*Mukonowakasenda* or *Kasembelela*. Powdered leaves mixed with white clay and water, and made into a paste are applied to small-pox spots. The wood is very strong and is used to build granaries which last as long as ten years.

Cathium venosum—*Mukonowakasenda*—" Legs of the Blue Duiker" or *kasembelela wacipwevo*—" Of the Women ". A cold infusion of the roots makes a man strong and is also a good dog medicine. Small boys use branches as spears.

Landolphia camptoloba—*Mumbungo*. The Luchazi use an infusion of the fruit as eyedrops in conjunctivitis. Produces an edible fruit. " Best bush rubber ".

Cassia obtusifolia—*Kajiha Musongo*. A decoction of the roots is a remedy for gonorrhoea.

Cissus buchananii—*Kukulumbe*. In Fort Jameson a remedy against sneezing.

Combretum apiculatum and *laxiflorum*—*Muhuhu*. Dry stems are burnt and the ash mixed with white clay and water. A person suffering from conjunctivitis must put his face into the mixture several times.

Combretum gossweileri—*Mufufwa*. A decoction of the roots is given for heart trouble.

[403]

Combretum molle—Mulamata. The leaves are used in the same way as those of Muhwichichi. A decoction of the inner bark, either orally or as an enema, is taken against stomach troubles. The leaves pounded and soaked in water will make a red dye.

Combretum zeyheri—Muhuhu. The powered bark is introduced into the vagina during menstruation to stop the flow of blood. The ash of the bark makes an eye lotion. Branches are used for making baskets and chairs. In the Eastern Province the leaves are crushed, mixed with oils and used as embrocation. An infusion produces a good remedy against diarrhoea.

The Combretums are a large family, with some magnificent trees, others are climbers and a few are small shrubs. They are easily recognisable by their four-angled seeds.

Copaifera baumiana—Mupa. The roots are used by pregnant women when suffering from abdominal pain. The Luchazi boil the roots in water, skim off the fat and employ this as a remedy against scabies. Branches crackle when thrown into a fire and are used to frighten toddlers. When they crawl too near, a branch is thrown into the fire, the noise of the explosion gives the infant a fright and it will not go near a fire again.

Croton megalobotrys—Mupupu. An infusion of the roots makes thin babies fat.

Cryptosepalum maraviense—Mukuve wacana. A decoction of the roots is given against hookworm and the pounded leaves against scabies. It has honey-producing flowers and is a food plant for the edible caterpillar. A small shrublet *wacana*, eight to ten inches high, growing on the plains.

Dalbergia ?sp.—Mujimbejimbe. An infusion of the roots for stomach-aches. Used as a gargle for toothaches and by women for abdominal pain.

Dalbergiella nyasae. Roots and leaves are given in diarrhoea and syphilis and threads from the bark are worn round the neck to cure conjunctivitis (Eastern Province).

Dialium engleranum. Syn. simii—Musala. Infusion of bark for eye lotion. The following prescription produces a medicine for dysentery. " Cut the roots into small pieces, mix with a little meal, boil till cooked. Take one spoon at a time for three days only. " Very bitter and poisonous in overdose. The fruit is edible, often eaten boiled with meal. The wood is hard and the flowers honey-producing.

STROPHANTHUS WELWITSCHII

TEMNOCALYX OBOVATUS

MEMECYLON SAPINI

CHRYSOPHYLLUM MAGALISMONTANUM

Dichrostachys cinerea ssp. nyassana—Kaweyi. Leaves and roots are smoked against tuberculosis in the Eastern Province. A very thorny, twisted small tree, often a shrub, with characteristic seed pods—also called lantern tree. Bright pink flowers appear in October-November and are much visited by bees.

*Diospyros batocana—*Ebony*—Munjongolo.* Root scrapings mixed with fat are applied to cuts made into leprous spots. Also used as a remedy against scabies. The leaves are pounded and soaked in cold water for about half an hour, then used as an enema. The bark is poisonous. After millet has been soaked in the river for beer-making and is put on a mat to dry, it is covered by the leaves to improve the flavour. The fruit is edible but only as a starvation diet. A very dark tree with dark green leaves and a hard wood from which spoons, combs and other small articles are carved.

Diplorhynchus condylocarpon—Muli. Fruits and roots are used, boiled and the steam inhaled in the treatment of chronic cough and pulmonary tuberculosis. Women use milky latex to remove pubic hairs. The latex also provides the glue to stick feathers onto arrows. The roots, in the same way as those of *Mulamaka*, are given for stomach troubles, mixed with maize or millet flour. Porridge spoons and gun stocks are made of the wood. The edible caterpillar *Makilakila* feeds on the leaves. One of the commonest trees.

Dioscorea ? buchananii. Inhalation of steam from boiling leaves is prescribed in cases of general anaemia and oedema (Eastern Province). Grows as a creeper near streams.

Eriosema psoraleoides. Used in the treatment of syphilis. A flowering shrub of the Eastern Province.

Faurea speciosa—Muzwezwe. Crushed and soaked roots are helpful in ear infections. An infusion of the leaves can also be used as eardrops.

Colophospermum mopane—Mopane—Mushivi. A warm infusion of the leaves is drunk early in the morning against stomach troubles, and the bark produces an infusion employed in the form of an enema. The small red fruits are edible and rich in oil which is a good stain for furniture. This species produces some magnificent evergreen trees with the typical butterfly leaf.

Maytenus cymosus. Inhalation of boiling leaves is employed against tuberculosis (Eastern Province).

[409]

Holarrhena febrifuga. Roots are boiled with milk. Young boys who are passing through puberty are washed with the milk. It also acts as a snakebite antidote and is used in treatment of venereal diseases. A most beautiful tree when covered with white blossoms (Eastern Province).

Holostyon baumii—Tambakondo. For killing lice, roots are powdered, mixed with water and put on the hair with a stick.

Hymenocardia acida—Mupepe. The burnt and powdered roots are used in cases of mouth infections. Leaves are soaked in water, then boiled and the steam inhaled against headaches. Leaves are placed on the roof of a house to protect it from lightning (Eastern Province).

Isoberlinia angolensis—Mutovo. Roots are taken for stomach troubles. The wood is rather soft, used for roofing and furniture.

Julbernardia paniculata—Munyumbe. The bark is soaked and the juice poured onto the anus of a person suffering from a kind of dysentery causing sores round the anus. The bark of young trees makes good string. The wood is hard but quickly attacked by borers.

Maprounea africana—Kavulamume. A decoction of roots as face-wash in eye troubles. The sap is used to dress the penis after circumcision.

Mimosa pigra—Chikwata. Ashes from burnt roots are sprinkled over leprous patches. A typical mimosa which folds its leaves together when touched, with very wicked thorns. It grows along rivers and dambos, and is completely submerged in the flood waters for three to four months every year.

Lannea discolor. The inside of the bark, ground fine, is a good medicine for diarrhoea. Leaves are a remedy against fits and also helpful in the treatment of boils and abscesses. Edible fruit—known in South Africa as " Boom Druif " or " Tree Grape ".

Ochthocosmus lemaireanus—Chikuku. Steam from boiling leaves for cold and inflamed eyes. Swollen testicles are treated by applying the burnt roots to skin incisions.

Paropsia brazzeana—Muvangwa. Infusion of roots in cases of gonorrhoea or as a gargle in toothache. The Luchazi use the fruit for headaches and nasal troubles. Seeds are readily taken by birds and therefore used as bait. One of the commonest under-shrubs of the *Brachystegia-Isoberlinia* woodlands.

Phyllanthus ? *reticulatus.* The Chewa and Ngoni give parts of the plant in cases of anaemia and intestinal haemorrhages.

Pseudolachnostylis maprouneifolia—Musalya. The bark is employed to make enemas and a decoction of the roots for stomach troubles. Hard wood, the fruit is eaten by buck.

Psorospermum baumii—Katunya. The boiled root makes a good remedy for scabies and lice and also a good mucilage.

Pterocarpus angolensis—Kiaat—Mukula. Ash obtained from burnt seeds is applied to inflamed skin, also to bleeding gums. The reddish sap under the bark heals sores quickly and in the form of an enema gets rid of intestinal parasites and is also used against ringworm infection of the scalp. A decoction of the roots acts against gonorrhoea and worms. Leaves are used to lure fish into traps. In one case seen the leaves had been pounded and packed into the rectum to cure backache, resulting in purging and passing blood for forty-eight hours. Another case concerned a young woman who packed *Kiaat* sawdust into her vagina to " make the husband hot ".

Rhus kirkii. Low riverside shrub, parts of it are given in menstrual disorders.

Salix subserrata. A " willow tree " fringing the Kabompo River for many miles. The leaves are used as laxatives for humans and domestic animals.

Sapium ellipticum. The roots are boiled and applied as fomentations to babies with large spleens.

Sesamum angolense. An infusion of the leaves as eyedrops in measles. Eaten as vegetables (Eastern Province).

Strobilanthopsis linifolia—Munguwamasa. Decoction of roots used against gonorrhoea. Honey-producing flowers.

Swartzia madagascariensis—Mutete. Leaves mixed with salt are a cough medicine. An infusion of the seedpods is given in stomach troubles. Roots taken raw or as a hot infusion act as a sexual stimulant. Powdered seedpods are a fish poison; though only mildly toxic to human beings they can be used to procure abortion. The wood is very hard and dark. Trees are of small size only and the wood available is mainly used to carve walking sticks, handles for fly switches and similar small objects. The seedpods which look like brown, thin " frankfurters " are eaten by eland and cattle.

[411]

Temnocalyx obovatus—Kamashito. Smoking the leaves will cure a cough.

Terminalia brachystemma—Mwuea. Decoction of roots is given in diarrhoea, also produces a black dye.

Vitex doniana—Chikamba. In the Eastern Province it is prescribed in one form or another against anaemia and in Balovale against gonorrhoea. The fruits are edible. Those of *Vitex pooara*, which may be synonymous, are eaten in the Transvaal.

Ziziphus abyssinica—Mupundukaina. Ash from burnt leaves mixed with salt is used as a throat paint in cases of tonsillitis, hot leaves for fomentation in pneumonia (Eastern Province).

Xylopia tomentosa—Mujimbijimbi. Decoction of roots used against stomach troubles. Pieces of roots are put into the nostrils to cure headaches.

Tribes to whom starvation is frequently a real threat can be expected to make a use of anything edible within reach. A great number of wild-growing plants and their fruits have in the course of time been found to be palatable. At times of scarcity the children are sent into the bush and told to collect their own food. At boarding schools only the cassava meal is supplied, all other " relish " the pupils are expected to find themselves. A few examples are mentioned below.

Alvesia rosmarinifolia—Mufunyafunya. Used for salting food.

Annona senegalensis—" Custard Apple "*—Mulolo.* Produces an edible fruit, the size of a plum, orange-coloured when ripe and smelling like a pineapple. Ripens very slowly—that is why the fox lost the hairs on his tail while waiting for *Mulolo* to ripen.

Coleus esculentus—Ntambaya Mulima. Roots eaten as potatoes.

Dioscorea ? abyssinica. Roots are edible.

Dissotis princeps. Roots are eaten and taste like cassava or sweet potatoes and have aphrodisiac properties. They are also used as soap. Riverside shrub of the Eastern Province.

Erythrococca menyharthii—Lindumbwa. The leaves are eaten as a vegetable.

Flacourtia indica—Mufupu. Edible fruit—also used in the treatment of syphilis (Eastern Province), a related species is known as the " Batoka Plum " in South Africa.

Hibiscus sabdariffa—" Rosella "*—Dikelenge.* Edible fruit, leaves are also soothing for a cough.

Memecylon—Muzele. Blue-black fruit with pleasant taste. Stains like a mulberry. Pounded roots are used as eye-lotion and the leaves as a dressing for festering skin.

Parinari curatellifolia—Mucha. Edible fruit, produces sweet beer which becomes very strong when left for three days. The kernels are also edible nuts, they are mixed with spinach-like vegetables as relish and are very useful when starting a fire. An infusion of the bark is used as an enema. The *Mucha (Mpundu* in Nyanja) is a very stately evergreen tree and produces masses of fruit.

Bauhinia petersiana. The pods are edible when boiled (Eastern Province).

Centemopsis gracilenta. Used as a vegetable (Eastern Province).

*Ochna pulchra—Kafuko—*and probably other *Ochnas* as well, and there are a number of species—are a valuable source of oil. The fruit is boiled in water and the fat skimmed off the surface.

Phyllanthus muelleranus, Syzygium guineense. Both have edible fruit.

Other trees and shrubs producing some edible parts have been mentioned before where their magical or medicinal properties seemed to be considered more important than their value as food. These were: *Acacia polyacantha ssp. campylacantha; Eugenia angolensis; Strychnos innocua; Syzygium cordatum; Ricinodendron rautanenii; Aframomum biauriculatum; Bauhinia variegata; Vangueriopsis lanciflora; Dialium engleranum; Diospyros batocana; Colophospermum mopane; Lannea discolor* and *Vitex doneana.*

On other plants with edible parts information only was collected, specimens were not always available and botanical identification often impossible.

Uapaca species: *Mundengondengo; Mabula; Tuminamawone; Mupopolo.*

*Mupopolo—*probably *Uapaca kirkiana—*produces a very palatable somewhat floury fruit.

[413]

*Pistia stratiotes—Lungwe—*a floating water-plant. Used as salt; after drying and burning the ash is leaked out in a calabash.

?*Landolphia* ?*Carpodinus: Mbungombungo,* also the bigger relative: *Mbungokashinakayi.*

Syzygium, several species—*Musombosombo,* also probably *Mundurunduru.*

Mufungofungo—Anisophyllea quangensis, a violet fruit when ripe, the size of a plum, eaten raw. A small tree and a shrub in the plains.

Mufumbelele—Diospyros undabunda. A tomato-like fruit, slightly tart, with large seeds.

Musakala " Stemvrugte ". *Chrysophyllum magalismontanum— Musongosongo:* ? *Ximenia caffra.*

Muchacha—Parinari capensis—similar to *Mucha* but a small shrub in the plains.

Mutengulu—Oldfieldia dactylophylla: Kazongwe.

Other edible plants or fruits belong to *Mungangamena* (leaves are eaten raw). *Kasaimakalum* (edible fruit). *Misonyesonye* (orange-coloured fruit). *Nyamalomo Mungondo, Shamba, Mungindo, Mwiyi, Kakoha* (children eat the roots of this small plant). *Yikahu* (grass with fleshy roots, eaten raw, sometimes used to make cake). *Mukulikuli, Mususu, Mpawa.*

It has always been a surprise to me to find with what eagerness the people in and around Balovale were ready and willing to talk about their medicines. Was it that they found my interest in their methods pleasing ? Was it an exchange of information amongst colleagues ? Or was it to show off their knowledge ? Whatever the reason, information was readily forthcoming. I remember a wicked old Luchazi who brought bundles of dried leaves, roots and stems and told me about their uses. How far he was a herbalist and how far a witch-doctor I could never fathom, but I regret that I shall never possess his knowledge of African psychology and his art in the treatment of his fellow men, that, coupled with my scientific medical knowledge, might have made a most useful combination.

Some of his plants were unfortunately sterile, possessing no flowers or seeds and could not, therefore, be botanically identified. Below is given some of the information he imparted to me. The names are those used by the Luchazi tribe.

Musase and *Musondosondo.* An infusion of the roots left for three days in a gourd, is given as an enema in a case of prolonged labour. An overdose might be fatal.

Mumbambakhunga. The steam bath of the leaves heals sore eyes.

Munieni. A decoction of the pounded seedpods is given against gonorrhoea. The inner part of the roots is put into the nostrils for severe headache and cough. The bark is used in the same way as the seedpods. The infusion should stand for three days.

Mutukumishi. The leaves are dried, put into a hole near a man's hut, then the leaves together with others are burnt. He sits over the hole so that the smoke reaches him. This will develop his penis. The roots are chewed and then rubbed onto the penis to enlarge it.

Mpawa is used as a dressing for wounds and ulcers.

Muchingini. The roots act against gonorrhoea, given either orally or as an enema. They are also a sexual stimulant.

Kakumbi. A woman who has been sterile for a long time finally becomes pregnant after consulting African doctors. She will clothe her baby in the bark of this tree and the baby will live to become an adult. The child is called Bihemba—" a gift of medicine ". The roots are taken to make seine nets.

Muvumba Noka. A shrub with strongly scented leaves. The steam from the boiling leaves is inhaled.

Muneko. The leaves are used as hot compresses and applied to the neck of a sick child.

Mulolo. A decoction to be given to premature babies.

Tsingoyahanda and *Muhasu.* A cold infusion of pounded leaves is employed as eye-lotion.

Ntandakembe. The roots are very poisonous orally as well as per vagina.

Mukenge. The powdered bark is introduced into the vagina during menstruation to stop the flow of blood. The root bark makes strong baskets. Mukenge roots also play a role in some rather gruesome proceedings which came to the light of day through the boasting of an old woman—a self-confessed witch. A young female child or grandchild of the witch had to be strangled and its heart cut out. A piece of the child's heart mixed with Mukenge roots was then introduced into the brain case of a mole and from then on the mole became the witch's familiar to do her bidding and carry out her orders.

Chivumbanoka. Crushed leaves are introduced into the vagina to ease the after-birth pains.

Hanyani. A sweet-scented grass introduced from Angola. It smells like lemon, makes a good tea and is also drunk as cough mixture.

Mononyanemba. The sap of the roots is given against gonorrhoea. Boiled roots as an enema: if it is left in too long it may poison the patient. The seeds produce an oil.

Kashimakaluku. The leaves are used for steam baths or hot fomentations. The scrapings of the roots in the form of a decoction are a medicine for general sickness.

Munganamena. The leaves are a cough medicine.

Muzele Kavangu is poisonous. So is *Muhonga Ndumba* which given as an infusion in water or beer kills a person in five minutes.

Mukivi. Root scrapings are a fish poison—also used as an enema. Small branches make good toothbrushes. The wood is hard.

As a contraceptive measure the following prescription was given:

Cassava leaves are pounded, mixed with water, the fluid is strained and left in the bottle for two days. *Kachinga* roots are dug up, boiled and the infusion is put into another bottle for two days. Then the contents of both bottles are poured into a third bottle which must be hidden, the husband must under no circumstances discover its whereabouts. When the woman is menstruating she drinks some of this concoction for two days, keeps the rest for another month, takes more of it during her next monthly period again for two days and repeats the performance a third time. After this she breaks the bottle between her legs standing in the doorway. She will then be sterile until her death.

As a last group there are those trees and shrubs which provide timber or sharp thorns. One of the latter is *Acanthus montanus*, a thistle-like shrub of the *Mushitu*. It is called *Mutuvapoko* ("stick him

knife ") or *Mutuvatumbi wacikulo* ("stick the rat of the riverbank").
To prevent rats from climbing poles, a few leaves with spikes downwards are tied round the poles.

Afzelia quanzensis—Pod Mahogany—*Muvulatowo*. The very
large seedpod—bigger than a man's hand—containing ornamental
black and red seeds. The wood is used for planks and dug-out canoes,
also for drums, bowls and furniture. The bark is applied to an aching
tooth.

Blepharis buchneri—*Mutuvapoko*. Used as an instrument of
torture, especially for witches on the way to the place of execution.
Other thorny branches (*Acacias*, etc.) and leaves are also employed for
this unpleasant procedure.

Brachystegia spiciformis—*Mupuchi*. Soft wood, makes poor canoes
which last only about two years. Bark cloth and sacks from this tree
are of poor quality. Roots provide strings for seine nets. Flowers in
July and is then much visited by bees.

Burkea africana—*Msese*. Soft wood, but poles are durable. Wood
splinters as wedges for hoes and for handles. Bark makes a good fire for
burning clay pots. Flowers in October and produces much honey.

Cryptosepalum pseudotaxus—*Mukuve*. *Pseudotaxus* refers to the
similarity with the European yew (*Taxus*). It not only resembles the
yew, but just like the European tree produces wood ideal for bows. The
bark is used to make bee-hives, mats and ropes. An infusion of the
bark is good as a cough mixture. A most beautiful evergreen tree, much
liked by bees in search of honey, it indicates to the Luchazi land on
which they like to settle. Unfortunately it is not very flame resistant
and the annual bushfires take a heavy toll of this species. It is the
Balovale substitute for a Christmas tree and when hung with decorations
and full of burning candles looks surprisingly like the real thing.

The *Mukuwe*, like many other trees, has a poor relation on the
sandy plains *Mukuwe Wamcana*—the previously mentioned *Cryptosepalum maraviense*. It is interesting to speculate how these dwarf forms
have been evolved. On the one side in the bush there are stately trees,
a few yards away in the plains the same plant occurs, much reduced in
size but otherwise hardly different in leaves or flowers. The beautiful
Ochnas have their small cousins which hide their flowers amongst the
grass stems. The *Syzygium* (*Musombo*) is represented in the plain by
Musombosomo; the *Parinari curatellifolia* (*Mucha*) by the dwarfish
Parinari capensis (*Muchacha*). The *Combretum microphyllum*, with its

[417]

bright scarlet flowers, climbs the highest tree-tops in the Luangwa Valley; its nearest relative, *Combretum platypetalum*, hardly lifts its equally beautiful red flowers above the sand in the North-Western Province. Like all other *Combretums* this lovely plant possesses four-angled seeds but these are coloured in the most delightful cyclamen hues. In August and September they provide the one spot of colour on those long, weary, sandy paths, yet the local population has never shown any interest in the plant. Its beauty makes no appeal to them and according to the old rule, no use—no name, it has no name.

The process of detribalisation is going ahead fast in almost every corner of Africa. The bus and the lorry—and the saucepan radio—have broken through the isolation which surrounded many districts till a few years ago and are bringing to the deepest bush some of the advantages of urban life. Many old customs disappear—the filing of teeth is one of them—others are adapted to more modern conditions. The folklore surrounding " medicine " is perhaps the last to go. This is not surprising, as even in the most progressive western communities the " Quack " and vendor of miracle drugs still flourishes, in spite of all the advances modern medicine has made. While the sophisticated African town-dweller may ridicule his primitive brethren in many ways, he is just as much subject as they are to the beliefs and fears surrounding *Muti*. A big trade in potent herbs is conducted between Balovale and the Copperbelt, of which aphrodisiacs and contraceptives provide a large proportion. Even in Johannesburg the native herbalist sells his wares at the foot of multi-storey buildings, as if the twentieth century had never happened. The study of African medicines is a fascinating one and it has occasionally practical importance in puzzling medical and criminal cases. If these notes stimulate interest in the pharmacology of the African bush they will have served their purpose.

I am grateful to the Director of Medical Services, Northern Rhodesia, for permission to publish this paper.

[418]

For Further Reading

FANSHAWE, D. B. ... *Fifty Common Trees of Northern Rhodesia.* Published by the Natural Resources Board in co-operation with the Forest Department, Lusaka, 1962.

FANSHAWE, D. B. AND HOUGH, C. D. ... *Poisonous Plants of Northern Rhodesia.* Forest Research Bulletin No. 1, Lusaka, 1960.

GITHENS, THOMAS S. *Drug Plants of Africa.* African Handbooks No. 8, University of Pennsylvania Press, 1948.

REYNOLDS, BARRIE ... *Magic, Divination and Witchcraft among the Barotse of Northern Rhodesia.* London, 1963.

SYMON, S. A. ... *African Medicine in the Mankoya District, Northern Rhodesia.* In Rhodes-Livingstone Communication No. 15, Lusaka, 1959.

TURNER, V. W. ... *Lunda Medicine and the Treatment of Disease.* Rhodes-Livingstone Occasional Paper No. 15, 1964.

SELECT CHECK LIST OF SOME NORTHERN RHODESIAN TREES AND PLANTS WITH THEIR USES WHERE KNOWN

BOTANICAL NAME	PAGE	COLLECTED AT	LOVALE NAME	LUNDA NAME	LUCHAZI NAME	EASTERN PROVINCE NAME	USES
Abrus precatorius	6	B	Mukenyenge	—	Mukube	—	Black magic. Hoehandles.
Acacia macrothyrsa	—	FJ	—	—	—	Chitongololo	Medicine.
Acacia polyacantha ssp. campylacantha	9	FJ	Muzeze	Musese	—	Chitongololo	Charm. Medicine.
Acacia seyal or A. pilispina	11	B	Mungonga	Muzeze	—	—	Medicine.
Acalypha chirindica	—	B	Mutuvapoko or Mutuvatuumbi wa Cikulo.	—	—	—	Unknown.
Acanthus montanus	22	B	—	—	—	—	Thorns.
Adenia gummifera	—	B	—	—	—	—	Unknown.
Adenodolichos ?bequaerti	—	B	—	—	—	—	Unknown.
Aframomum biauriculatum	11	—	Mutundu	Mutungunu Mushindwa.	—	—	Charm. Food (tubers, fruit).
Afrormosia angolensis	9	FJ	Muvambo	Muwan'a...	—	—	Charm. Carvings.
Afzelia quanzensis	22	B	Muvulatowo	Mwala	—	Mupapa	Woodworking. Medicine.
Albizia anthelmintica	—	FJ	Musakayaze	—	—	Masango Kawereka.	Charm.
Albizia antunesiana	11	FJ	Mulungwe	—	—	Mtanga	General Woodwork.
Albizia versicolor	18	FJ	Mufunyafunya	—	—	Mtanga	Wood for Drums. Medicine.
Alvesia rosmarinifolia	—	B	—	—	—	—	Salt.
Ancylanthus fulgidus, bainesii	19	B	Mufungofungo wa cana.	—	—	—	Food (fruit).
Anisophyllea quangensis	—	B	Mulolo	—	—	—	Food (fruit).
Annona senegalensis	18	B	Mupapala	—	—	—	Food (fruit). Medicine.
Anthocleista liebrechtsiana	12	B	—	—	—	—	Salt. Medicine.
Antidesma venosum	—	B	—	—	—	—	Unknown.
Asparagus racemosus	13	B	Kafukwakashi	Kafwankaji	Winkalawewa	—	Medicine.
Azanza garckeana	—	B	Mukushi	Mukushi	—	—	Unknown.
Baikiaea plurijuga	—	—	—	—	—	—	General woodworking (Rhodesian teak).
Baissiaea wulfhorstii	13	B	Mukangula	Mukangula	—	—	Medicine.
Baphia ?massaiensis	—	B	—	—	Mwama	—	Unknown.
Baphia obovata	13	B	Kachiva	Mwinji or Munze	—	—	Medicine.
Barleria sp.	—	B	—	—	—	—	Unknown.

Species	Code	No.	Vern. 1	Vern. 2	Vern. 3	Vern. 4	Uses
Barleria ?ventriculosa	FJ	—	—	—	—	—	Unknown
Bauhinia sp.	FJ	—	—	—	—	—	Unknown.
Bauhinia fassoglensis	B	—	—	—	—	—	Unknown.
Bauhinia macrantha	B	13	—	—	—	—	Medicine.
Bauhinia mendoncae	B	19	—	—	—	—	General woodworking.
Bauhinia petersiana	FJ	—	Muhwichichi	Muhwititi	—	Mpondo	Food (fruit).
Bauhinia punctata	B	—	—	—	—	—	Ornamental tree.
Bauhinia urbaniana	FJ	13	Muhwichichi	Muhwititi	—	—	Bark for ropes.
Bauhinia variegata	B	—	—	—	—	—	Medicine. Food (fruit).
Becium sp.	B	—	—	Kapachi	—	—	Unknown.
Bersama abyssinica	B	22	Mutovapoko	—	—	Msekese	Medicine.
Blepharis ?grandis ?buchneri	B	—	Mumanga	—	—	—	Thorns.
Brachystegia bakerana	B	—	—	—	—	—	Bark for ropes.
Brachystegia ?bussei	B	13	Musamba	Musamba	—	—	Woodworking.
Brachystegia longifolia	B	—	—	—	Mukongolo	—	Woodwork. Bark for nets and medicine.
Brachystegia spiciformis	B	22	Mupuchi	Mupuchi	Mutundwa	—	Medicine. Woodwork. Bark for string and nets.
Brackenridgea arenaria	B	—	—	—	Muwuta Kafunkaji	—	Food (fruit).
Bridelia cathartica	B	—	Chilama	Chilama	—	—	Medicine.
Buchnera foliosa	B	—	—	—	—	—	Unknown.
Buchnera prorepens	B	—	—	—	—	—	Unknown.
Bulbine asphodeloides	B	—	—	—	—	—	Unknown.
Burkea africana	B	22	Msese	Wezenzeli	Msese	—	Woodwork.
Byrsocarpus orientalis	B	—	—	—	—	—	Unknown.
Canavalia ?rosea	B	—	—	—	—	—	Unknown.
Canavalia virosa	B	—	—	—	—	—	Unknown.
Canthium anomocarpum	B	13	Chikuvangu / Mukonowakasenda	Kasebeleli	—	—	Wood for poles. Medicine.
Canthium gueinzii	B	—	Pundukaina	—	—	—	Food (fruit). Medicine.
Cathium venosum	B	14	Mukonowakasenda	Kasebeleli	—	—	Medicine.
Cardiospermum halicacabum	B	—	—	—	—	—	Unknown.
Cassia mimosoides	FJ & B	—	—	—	—	—	Unknown.
Cassia obtusifolia	B	14	Kajihamusongo	—	Lueni	—	Medicine.
Cassia occidentalis	B	—	Cinyalala	—	—	—	Medicine.
Cassia sp.	FJ	12	—	Mwang'Izembi	—	Mtantha Nyerere	Charm.
Cassipourea sp.	FJ	9	—	—	—	Mavi	Charm.
Centemopsis gracilenta	FJ	19	—	—	—	Chiomba	Food (leaves).
Chrysophyllum magalismontanum	B	20	Musakala	Nkululumbi	Liboha	—	Food (fruit). Medicine.
Cissus buchananii	FJ	14	Kukulumbe	—	—	—	Medicine.
Cleome hirta	B	—	—	—	—	—	Unknown.
Coleus esculentus	B	•18	Ntamba ya Mulima	—	—	—	Food (roots).
Clerodendrum buchneri	B	—	Liambadyapata	—	—	—	Unknown.
Clerodendrum sp.	B	—	—	—	—	—	Unknown.
Colophospermum mopane	B	16	Mushivi	Mushiyi	—	—	Woodwork. Medicine.

BOTANICAL NAME	PAGE	COLLECTED AT	LUNDA NAME	LOVALE NAME	LUCHAZI NAME	EASTERN PROVINCE NAME	USES
Combretum apiculatum	14	FJ	Muhuhu	Kakunjika Muka-nda.	Muhuhu	—	Woodwork. Medicine.
Combretum ?collinum	—	FJ & B	Chilunguveva	Mweya	—	—	Medicine.
Combretum ghasalense	12	FJ	Mombomba	—	—	Kalama	Medicine.
Combretum gossweileri	14	B	Mufufwa	Mufumfwa	—	—	Medicine.
Combretum laxiflorum	14	FJ	Muhuhu	Muhuhu	—	Chitungulu	Medicine.
Combretum microphyllum	12	B	—	—	—	—	Medicine.
Combretum molle	14	B	Mulamata	Muhuma	—	—	Medicine.
Combretum platypetalum	23	B	Mulamata	Mavunguvungu	—	—	Unknown.
Combretum psidioides	11	B & FJ	Muhuhu	Muhuhu	Mutobowacikulo	—	Medicine.
Combretum zeyheri	14	FJ	—	—	—	Kalama-chimpa-nasa.	Medicine. Woodwork.
Combretum zuluense	—	FJ	Mundumbwa-ka-vaya.	Katombwangu	—	Kalama	Medicine.
Copaifera baumiana	14	B	Mupa	—	Mumpa	—	Medicine.
Crossopteryx febrifuga	—	B	—	—	—	—	Unknown.
Crotalaria sp.	—	B	—	—	—	—	Unknown.
Crotalaria amoena	—	B	—	—	—	—	Unknown.
Crotalaria aculeata	—	B	—	—	—	—	Unknown.
Crotalaria grandistipulata	14	B	—	—	—	—	Medicine.
Croton megalobotrys	—	B	Mupupu	Mumfumpu	Chilama	—	Unknown.
Cryptolepis brazzai	15	B	Mukuve wacana	Kakubi	—	—	Unknown.
Cryptosepalum maraviense	15	B	Mukuve	Mukungu	Mukube	—	Medicine.
Cryptosepalum pseudotaxus	22	B	—	—	—	—	Wood for bows. Bark for ropes and beehives.
Cyphostemma fugosioides	15	B	Mujimbejimbe	Mutatambululu	Mukungu Palanga	Nkula Singa	Unknown.
Dalbergia sp.	15	FJ	Mujimbejimbe	—	Musakayaze	—	Medicine.
Dalbergia ?nitidula	15	FJ	—	—	—	—	Medicine. Charm.
Dalbergiella nyasae	15	B	Musala	Musala	Musala	Kafunda	Food (fruit). Medicine.
Dialium englerianum	15	FJ	—	—	—	—	Medicine. Bark for ropes.
Dichrostachys cinerea ssp. nyasana	18	B	Kaweyi	Mubanga	—	Nyalumpangala	Food (roots).
Dioscorea ?abbyssinica	15	FJ	—	Ikon'i	—	—	Medicine.
Dioscorea ?buchananii	15	B	Munjongolo	—	Muzongolo	—	Food (fruit). Medicine.
Diospyros batocana	—	B	Chivala	Mwidima	Muhemuhe	—	Toothbrushes.
Diospyros lycioides	—	—	Mutowa	Chivala	—	—	Food (fruit).
Diospyros mespilliformis	—	B	Mufumbalele	—	—	Mchenja	Food (fruit).
Diospyros undabunda	20	—	Muli	—	—	—	Wood for small articles.
Diplorhynchus condylocarpon	15	B	—	Muli. Mwidi	—	Mtowa-Mtombozi	Medicine.

Species	Auth.	No.	Native name 1	Native name 2	Native name 3	Native name 4	Uses
Dissotis sp.	B	—	Kabitenya				Unknown.
Dissotis falcipila	B	—					Unknown.
Dissotis princeps	FJ	18					Food (roots). Medicine.
Dolichos sp.	B	—					Unknown.
Dombeya rotundifolia	FJ	—					Unknown.
Dombeya tanganyikensis	FJ	—					Unknown.
Ectadiopsis oblongifolia	FJ	15	Muzovu	Kajingalwidi		Chidyamkwere	Medicine.
Eriosema psoraleoides	FJ	—					Medicine.
Erythrina sp.	B	18					Unknown.
Erythrococca menyharthii	B	6	Lindumbwa				Unknown.
Erythrophleum africanum	B	—	Mukoso	Musesi Wehama	Mukoso	Kapiyopiyo	Food (leaves).
Eugenia sp.	B	—					Wood. Poison.
Eugenia angolensis	FJ	9					Unknown.
Fadogia sp.		—					Food.
Faurea speciosa		16	Muzwezwe	Mushokoto		Chiyere	Food.
Ficus sp.		—	Mulemba				Woodwork. Medicine.
Ficus dekdekena	FJ	—	Musulhwa	Ikanda			Unknown.
Ficus pygmaea	B	—	Muminamboma				Sacred tree.
Ficus sp.		—				Mkandambazo	Sacred tree. Bark for rope
Flacourtia indica	B	18	Mufupu	Mumfumpu			Food (fruit). Medicine.
Garcinia smeathmannii	FJ	—	Musolesole				Wood for poles. (?) Fruit.
Globimetula braumii	B	—	Chisuku				Birdlime.
Grewia bicolor	B	—					Unknown.
Grumilea sp.	FJ	—	Mutuhu			Nsazichulu	Medicine.
Hannoa chlorantha	B	19	Dikelenge	Ndambala			Unknown.
Hibiscus sabdariffa	FJ	—	Mungondo	Mungondu			Food (fruit).
Hirtella eglandulosa	FJ	16					Unknown.
Holarrhena febrifuga	B	16	Tambakondo			Ndombozichipeta	Charm.
Holostylon baumii	B	—					Unknown.
Homalium abdessammadii	B	16					Unknown.
Humularia megalophylla	FJ	6					Unknown.
Hymenocardia acida	B	—	Mupepe	Mupepi	Mutateya		Medicine.
Indigofera sp.	B	16	Kajiha misongo	Kajiha musong'u	Mubuta		Medicine.
Indigofera sp.	FJ	—					Medicine.
Indigofera emarginella	B	16					Unknown.
Ipomoea ?marmorata	B	16	Mutovo	Mutowa			Unknown.
Isoberlinia angolensis	B	12					Woodwork. Medicine.
Jatropha curcas		—	Munyumbe	Mwanda	Munyumbe		Unknown.
Julbernardia paniculata	B	—	Muvunguvungu	Muvunguvungu		Muvungula or Mvungutsi	Woodwork. Medicine.
Kigelia pinnata	B	—					Medicine.
Kotschya strobilantha	B	—					Unknown.
Laggera brevipes	B	14			Muheta		Unknown.
Landolphia camptoloba		—		Mumbwengeleli			Food (fruit). Medicine.
Lannea sp.	B	16	Mumbungo		Mumbungo		Food (fruit).
Lannea discolor	FJ	—	Sakawumbu			Kaumbu	Food. Medicine.

BOTANICAL NAME	PAGE	COLLECTED AT	LOVALE NAME	LUNDA NAME	LUCHAZI NAME	EASTERN PROVINCE NAME	USES
Lannea stuhlmannii	10	B	Muyombo ...	—	—	—	Sacred tree.
Lantana rugosa	—	B	—	—	—	—	Unknown.
Lepidagathis macrochila	—	B	—	—	—	—	Unknown.
Lepidagathis perismilis	—	B	—	—	—	—	Unknown.
Leptactinia benguelensis	—	B	—	—	—	—	Unknown.
Leptoderris harmsiana	—	FJ	—	—	—	—	Unknown.
Lonchocarpus capassa	9	B	Mutomatoma ...	Mulela ...	—	Chinpakasa ...	Wood for handles. Medicine.
Loranthus oleifoleus	—	B	Chisukulu	—	—	—	Birdlime.
Mallotus oppositifolius	—	B	—	—	—	—	Unknown.
Maprounea africana	16	B	Kavulamume ...	Kavulamumi	—	—	Medicine.
Markhamia sp.	7	B	Musase or Kapasa Kalyongono.	Kapase ...	—	—	Poison.
Markhamia obtusifolia	16	B	—	—	—	Mtungamphansi	Unknown.
Maytenus cymosus	9	FJ	—	—	—	—	Medicine.
Maytenus senegalensis	19	B	Muzele ...	Kaban'a Kachina	Muzelekavangu ...	—	Charm.
Memecylon sapini	16	B	Chikwata ...	Kayisa ...	Mungonga ...	—	Food (fruit). Medici
Mimosa pigra	—	B	—	—	—	—	Medicine.
Monotes dasyanthus	—	B	Munyanya ...	Chimpampa	—	—	Unknown.
Monotes elegans	—	B	Kanyungi ...	Kayuvasovu	—	—	Medicine.
Mucuna irritans	—	B	Kafuko Kafuko-wamcana.	Musang'u	—	—	Unknown.
Ochna pulchra	19	FJ	—	—	—	Kachale ...	Food (fruit).
Ochna pulchra ssp. offmannii-ottonis	—	B	—	—	—	—	Unknown.
Ochna richardsiae	—	B	Chikuku ...	—	Chikuku ...	—	Unknown.
Ochthocosmus lemaireanus	17	B	—	—	—	—	Medicine.
Olax dissitiflora	20	B	Mutengulu ...	Kazong'we	Makala ...	—	Unknown.
Oldfieldia dactylophylla	13	FJ	Likuvi ...	Kapofu ...	—	—	Charm. Medicine.
Pachycarpus lineolatus	—	B	Muhanyi	—	—	—	Unknown.
Parinari sp.	20	B	Muchacha ...	—	Munchauch	Mpundu	Food (fruit).
Parinari capensis	19	B	Mucha ...	Mwicha	Muvangu	—	Food (fruit). Medicine.
Parinari curatellifolia	17	B	Muvangwa ...	Mwangalala	—	—	Medicine.
Paropsia brazzeana	—	B	—	Chifui ...	—	—	Unknown.
Paullinia pinnata	—	B	—	—	—	—	Unknown.
Pavetta Onitidulu	—	B	—	—	—	—	Unknown.
Pavetta pygmaea	—	B	—	—	—	—	Unknown.
Peltophorum africanum	—	B	—	—	—	—	Unknown.
Phyllanthus mulleranus	19	B	Muliasefu ...	Muliasefu	—	Mpaca ...	Food (fruit).
Phyllanthus ?reticulatus	17	FJ	—	—	—	Kapiulambuzi ...	Food (fruit). Medicine.

Species		No.					Use
Phyllanthus welwitschianus	B	—	—	—	—	Kabobo	Unknown.
Physostigma mesoponticum	FJ	7	—	—	—	—	Poison.
Phytolacca dodecandra	B	19	—	—	—	—	Unknown.
Pistia stratiotes	B	—	Lungwe	—	—	—	Salt.
Pleiotaxis sp.	B	—	—	—	—	—	Unknown.
Pleurostylia africana	B	17	—	—	—	—	Medicine.
Protea sp.	B	—	—	—	—	—	Medicine.
Pseudolachnostylis maprouneifolia	B	—	Kaholawubisu / Musalya	Chelemu / Kabalabala musadya	Musa	—	Medicine.
Psorospermum baumii	B	17	Katunya / Muhota	Muhotahota	—	Kavundula	Medicine.
Psorospermum febrifugum	FJ	9	—	—	—	—	Charm. Medicine.
Psychotria sp.	B	—	Mufunyi / Mukula	—	—	—	Unknown.
Pteleopsis anisoptera	B	17	—	—	—	—	Laths for houses.
Pterocarpus angolensis	B	—	—	—	—	—	Woodwork. Medicine.
Pterocarpus chrysothrix	B	—	—	—	—	—	Unknown.
Pygmaeothamnus zeyheri	B	—	—	—	—	—	Unknown.
Raphionacme longifolia	B	—	—	—	—	—	Unknown.
Rauvolfia caffra	B	17	—	—	—	—	Unknown.
Rhynchosia sp.	B	11	—	—	—	—	Unknown.
Rhus quartiniana	B	—	—	Muhilu / Mulela	—	—	Unknown.
Rhus kirkii	B	17	Mungongo	—	—	—	Medicine.
Ricinodendron rautanenii	B	—	—	—	—	—	Food (fruit). Sacred.
Rothmannia englerana	B	17	—	Kambulafita / Mutundu	Mumwameme	—	Unknown.
Salacia ?bussei	B	17	—	—	—	—	Medicine.
Salix subserrata	B	12	—	—	—	—	Unknown.
Sapium ellipticum	B	7	—	—	—	—	Medicine.
Sapium oblongifolium	B	17	Muhaswa / Muyise Mutata	Kataubwangu / Mutata	Muhasu / Mutata	—	Unknown.
Schrebera trichoclada	B	—	—	—	—	—	Unknown.
Securidaca longipedunculata	FJ	—	Chiseke	Kun'nayi	—	Sope. Delele	Poison. Medicine.
Sesamum angolense	B	17	Kavuvu	Kavuvu	Kabuhu	—	Food (leaves). Medicine.
Sesbania sesban	B	8	—	—	—	—	Fishing rods.
Sida cordifolia	B	—	—	—	—	—	Bark for chairs.
Sphenostylis erecta	B	—	—	—	—	—	Unknown.
Stereospermum kunthianum	B	17	Mungu-wa-masa	Kalyamba / Mbwengeleli kashinakaji	Kombokombo	—	Ornamental tree.
Strobilanthopsis linifolia	B	8	Mimbapanda	—	wa Msiwakalulu	—	Medicine.
Strophanthus welwitschii	B	—	—	—	—	—	Medicine. Arrow poison.
Swartzia madagascariensis	B	17	Mutete / Mukolo	Kapwipu / Muhwila	—	Mzimbiri	Medicine. Food (fruit).
Strychnos innocua	B	9	Mutunga	Mutungi	Mwitwi	—	Food (fruit). Medicine.
Strychnos spinosa	B	—	Mujimbikolo	Munjumbe	—	—	Food (fruit).
Strychnos sp.	B	—	—	—	—	—	Unknown.
Syzygium congolense	FJ	10	Musombo or Mundukundu	Musombu	—	Chiyele	Woodwork. Charm. Medicine.
Syzygium cordatum	B	—	—	—	—	—	Food (fruit).
Syzygium guineense	FJ	19	Chimomomomo	Musombu wa pata	—	Mafuwu	Medicine.
Syzygium guineense ssp. huillense	B	—	—	—	—	—	

BOTANICAL NAME	PAGE	COLLECTED AT	LOVALE NAME	LUNDA NAME	LUCHAZI NAME	EASTERN PROVINCE NAME	USES
Tacazzea apiculata	—	B	Kajingaluli	—	—	—	Medicine.
Tamarindus indica	18	FJ	—	—	—	Bwembe	Food (fruit).
Temnocalyx obovatus	—	FJ	Kamashito	—	—	Maso-ang'ombe	Medicine.
Tecoma stans	8	B	Kapasa	Kapasi	—	—	Unknown.
Tecoma mollis	—	FJ	Kapapati	Kapapati	—	Ulembe	Arrow poison.
Tephrosia vogelii	18	FJ	Wusungu	Ululu	Wusungu	Wombo	Medicine. Fish poison.
Terminalia brachystemma	—	B	Mwuea	Mweya	—	—	Medicine.
Terminalia sericea	—	FJ	Mufunji	Nyakafunji	—	—	Woodwork. Bark for dye.
Terminalia silozensis	—	B	—	Muvewa	—	—	Unknown.
Thonningia sanguinea	—	B	—	—	—	—	Unknown.
Tinnea vestita	—	B	—	—	—	—	Unknown.
Trachyandra arvensis	—	B	—	—	—	—	Unknown.
Trachycalymma pulchellum	—	B	—	—	—	Msikisi	Medicine.
Trichilia emetica	10	FJ	Mugindu	—	—	—	Charm. Medicine.
Tricalysia cacondensis	00	B	Mukombakomba	—	—	—	Unknown.
Tricalysia angolensis	—	B	—	—	—	—	Unknown.
Trichilia quadrivalvis	—	B	—	—	—	—	Unknown.
Triumfetta dekindtiana	—	B	—	—	—	—	Unknown.
Turbina shirensis	—	B	—	—	—	—	Unknown.
Uapaca kirkiana	19	B	Mupopolo	—	—	Msuku	Food (fruit).
Vangueriopsis lanciflora	11	B	Musole	Musoli	Musole	—	Sacred tree. Charm. Wood for carvings.
Vernonia ampla	—	FJ	—	—	—	Masoya	Unknown.
Vernonia amygdalina	—	B	—	—	—	—	Unknown.
Vernonia colorata	—	FJ	—	—	—	Msoyo	Unknown.
Vernonia glaberrima	—	B	Musoli	Masola	—	—	Medicine.
Vigna ?esculenta	—	B	—	—	—	—	Unknown.
Vitex buchananii	18	B	Chikamba	Kazongu	—	Mfifya	Medicine.
Vitex doniana	—	FJ	—	—	—	—	Unknown.
Vitex madiensis	12	B	Mumbomba	Kashilumbulu	—	Mfutu	Medicine.
Vitex mombassae	—	FJ	—	—	—	—	Unknown.
Vitex payos	—	B	Kavulu	Funfunya	—	—	Unknown.
Waltheria indica	10	FJ	Mupapati	—	—	Kalamatila	Bark for ropes.
Wigandia urens	—	B	Musongosongo	Musombolombo	—	—	Charm.
Ximenia caffra	20	B	Mujimbijimbi	Mututambululu	Muzimbazimba	—	Food (fruit).
Xylopia tomentosa	18	B	—	—	—	—	Medicine.
Xysmalobium ?membraniferum	—	B	—	—	—	—	Unknown.
Ziziphus abyssinica	18	—	Mupundukaina	Mupundukaina	—	—	Medicine.

12

THE FISHING DEVICES
OF
CENTRAL AND SOUTHERN
AFRICA

P. I. R. MACLAREN

1958

PREFACE

PETER MACLAREN was Fisheries Officer for the Zambezi Basin region in Northern Rhodesia from 1952 until his tragic death last year. Prior to his coming to Northern Rhodesia he had served in Nigeria in a similar capacity. In the course of his work in Africa he had made a special study of the many different methods used by the African for catching fish and his knowledge and notes on these were extensive. Just before his death he had virtually completed an important monograph on the fishing devices of Southern and Central Africa for publication in the Occasional Papers series of this Museum.

We most gratefully acknowledge the generous permission given by Mrs. Maclaren that has now enabled us to publish this paper, which has been prepared for publication by Mr. B. G. R. Reynolds, the Keeper of Ethnography at the Rhodes-Livingstone Museum.

This paper is a memorial to the energy, interest and scholarly approach with which Peter Maclaren always tackled his subject. Those of us who were fortunate enough to be among his friends have not only suffered a personal loss but know that had he lived his contribution to African ethnography would have been considerable.

J. DESMOND CLARK.

LIVINGSTONE,
25th November, 1957.

EDITOR'S NOTE

When this paper was handed to me for editing the text was already complete and, except for the addition of the footnotes which are based on my own fieldwork, is exactly as the author intended it for publication.

The greater portion of the editing has been concerned with the gathering of references. In a few instances it has proved impossible to obtain full information; these references are listed separately.

The help of the Rhodes-Livingstone Institute, Lusaka, the Director, Department of Game and Tsetse Control, Chilanga, in obtaining references, and the kind permission of the Northern Rhodesia Government to reproduce the tribal map of Northern Rhodesia are gratefully acknowledged.

B. G. R. Reynolds,
Keeper of Ethnography.

SOUTHERN AFRICA

L. RUDOLPH

L. KYOGA

L. VICTORIA

L. GEORGE

AGARASI R.

L. ALBERT

L. EDWARD

L. KIVU

UELE R.

STANLEYVILLE

CONGO R.

COQUILHATVILLE

KASAI R.

OUBANGUI R.

CORISCO IS.

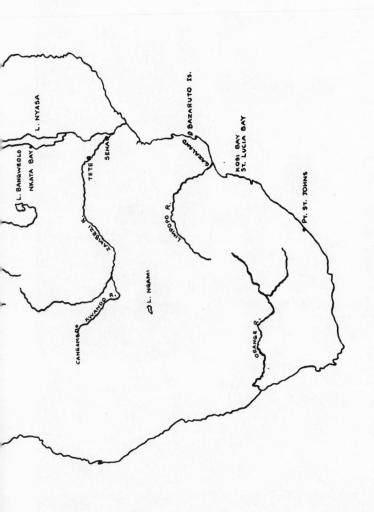

LUVALE WOMEN DRAG FISHING.

Introduction

The material culture of the fishermen of Central and Southern Africa is described, and as far as possible vernacular names for the various devices and methods are listed. The role of fishing in the social organisation of the people is not dealt with nor are the intricate subjects of magic and ritual.

Although the fisheries of Northern Rhodesia are dealt with in the greatest detail an attempt has been made to cover completely the whole of Africa south of latitude 7° S., while information from the remainder of the southern hemisphere has had perforce to be drawn upon less fully. As a matter of convenience the major Bantu subdivisions are followed—Western, Eastern and Southern*—in discussing similarities existing between the devices in this south-central area and adjoining regions. Attention is given to those devices which are absent, and to those which were previously undescribed, among which may particularly be mentioned the combined draw and lift net of Barotseland, and the " dark-hut " spearing technique of the Kafue Twa.

The evidence as to whether any similarities are due to a diffusion in culture or to adaptation in the face of similar needs and conditions is examined, but the drawing of conclusions from the findings in the former case is left to those better acquainted with the history of the complicated tribal movements that have taken place in East, Central and Southern Africa.

Errors and omissions will undoubtedly come to light, and the many unavoidable generalisations will need to be qualified in the light of further study. The justification of publishing these findings in their present state, however, lies in the undisputed need to focus attention on native culture before it ceases to exist in its aboriginal form.

Sources of Information

The accounts of travellers, ethnographers and fisheries investigators have been drawn upon, as well as the personal knowledge of administrators, missionaries and others. In addition, the writer has had five years' experience as Fisheries Officer in Northern Rhodesia, and five years in Nigeria. The full list of informants and literature cited is given in an appendix.

---

* WB, EB, SB.

It is difficult to single out those for special mention, but I am particularly grateful for information supplied by Mr. W. Lammond about the Luapula Valley, by Mr. J. B. Thompson about the Lundi-Sabi area of Southern Rhodesia, and by Dr. J. Desmond Clark about Southern Africa generally, to supplement the literature and material available in the Rhodes-Livingstone Museum. Library facilities freely afforded by this Museum and by the Rhodes-Livingstone Institute, Lusaka, must also be acknowledged.

Among the more comprehensive publications concerning Northern Rhodesia are W. V. Brelsford's study of the Unga on Lake Bangweulu, Max Gluckman's of the dwellers in the Central Barotse Plain, and C. M. N. White's of the role of hunting and fishing in Luvale society. These all treat in great detail with the social organisation of the tribes, which is of such importance in those peoples in which communal fishing activities play a large part. Authors dealing in detail with neighbouring parts of Africa are Baumann and Hambly (Angola), Ricardo (Rukwa), Ricardo-Bertram, Lowe and Hoole (Nyasa), Goffin, Johnston, Weeks and especially Sautter (Congo) and Poll (Tanganyika).

To avoid encumbering the text, page references have been deliberately omitted, except in the case of works in which the data quoted cannot readily be traced.

Vernacular Languages

J. Moffat Thompson's account (a) of the native tribes of Northern Rhodesia refers to seventy-three tribes and some thirty dialects, attributable by him to six main groups. His classification is given below,* although the grouping of the languages for the Northern Rhodesia Government's interpreters' tests is now slightly different. Those dialects in which names of devices have been recorded are italicised, and beneath are added the tribes from outside the Territory to the devices of which reference is made. The accepted modern practice is to use only the roots of tribal names, but in making quotations the form adopted by the author is followed.

The extent to which the names can be attributed to the particular dialects is most uncertain. Some words, such as *mono* (valved trap), are particularly widespread and can be accepted as belonging to each dialect. In other cases the names have been recently adopted along with the actual devices, and in yet other cases the informant has picked up the name of a strange device in some area where he has seen it used because there is no word for it in his tongue. On the whole, and as might be expected, the fishing tribes have accurately defined terms for their gear and practices, while those tribes with little or no fishing

* *Vide* Appendix.

[434]

tradition apply loose words such as correspond to " net " or " trap " to any article with which they are confronted. Only those names definitely identified by myself or by writers obviously familiar with the gear concerned have been italicised. Plurals are in some cases added.

The map in Thompson's paper delineating the tribal areas of Northern Rhodesia has been incorporated in a pair of military maps showing the tribal areas of Kenya, Uganda, Tanganyika, Nyasaland and Northern Rhodesia. Boone, in a recent paper, has dealt with the Belgian Congo tribes and Baumann and Hambly those of Angola. Southern Rhodesia and Mocambique are poorly documented, except in Seligman's general survey, but Schapera's two studies, of the Bantu and Khoisan peoples, cover South Africa.

Classification of Devices

Although a universal classification of fishing gear has been attempted [Burdon] it is cumbersome, and for the most part inapplicable to the material of this paper. The system followed below is entirely arbitrary, and chosen only for its simplicity and convenience; this accounts for the grouping together of a number of apparently dissimilar devices.

Care has been taken to reduce to a minimum the descriptions of the manufacture and operation of services which have already been dealt with fully in the literature.

A. FIXED INSTRUMENTS

I. Barriers

Barriers are fixed engines erected to impede or concentrate the movements of fish, and do not by themselves effect their capture. They are used in combination with valved and unvalved traps, sieves, or enclosures, and names are applied rather loosely to the whole or the parts. They vary from vast structures of sticks and stones such as span the entire Luapula River to small affairs of mud and grass. Medium-sized barriers are the most common, made of reed mats.

Except where they are used in conjunction with organised drives, barriers are essentially placed to intercept the natural movements of fish to and from breeding, feeding or nursery grounds, which movements are themselves largely linked with the seasonal rise and fall of the water level. It is probable that barriers in general are not as destructive as is widely believed, despite their heavy catches, because on most watercourses the major fish movements appear to take place at the peak of the floods, at which time the erection of barriers is as a rule impossible. However, the Unga of Bangweulu, where currents are not strong, block the interstices of their barriers with doors until the water level is low enough for the insertion of traps [Brelsford]. Incomplete barriers, or guiding fences placed in a V or a W formation with traps at the apices, have only been seen in Barotseland; Worthington (*b*) found them on Lake George, and Roscoe on Lake Victoria. They are more effective in tidal areas such as the Niger Delta.

The most primitive type of barrier, a rock wall, is not to be expected in inland waters, and in fact apart from a record from Likoma Island on Lake Nyasa, where gaps in such barriers are blocked with valved baskets (Mzumara), the Kalahari Bushmen weirs and the Hottentot *Vywers*, described below in the section on South Africa, are the only examples.

I	Lungu ...	...	? Wamba.
II	Senga ...	...	? Wamba.
	Chewa	...	Biyo.
	Nyasa-Tonga	...	Biyo.
III	Bemba ...	...	*Masanda*; *Bwamba* (*Mamba*); Icansa (Ifyansa).

Ushi ...	...	*Bwambi*; *Cansa* (Fyansa).
Kaonde...	...	Cipanda (Vipanda); ? Mivubu.
Unga ...	...	*Isando* (temporary door in gap).
Shila ...	...	*Bwamba* (earth and sticks); *Mabandu* (fence); *Mbelo* (gap).
Bwile ...	...	*Wamba* (*mamba*).
Lamba ...	...	Ifipanda; ukwalila (to use).
Tonga ...	...	*Isasa* (reed); *Masasa amabu.*
Ila ...	...	*Masasa* (reed); *Masasa amabu*; *Mielo*; Lutele Kushinkidzna (to dam). ˅
We ...	...	*Duando Lujalilo.*
V Lozi ...	...	*Bualelo* (*maalelo*) (embankment); *Siandi* (*liandi*) (reed fence).
VI Lunda ...	...	*Bwamba.*
Luvale ...	...	*Malilo* (*walilo*) (earth and sticks), Makalila (sod bunds); Lungando (Mangando) (reedmat fence).
WB Luimbi	...	*Walelo.*
Ovimbundu	...	*Olunja.*
SB Shona ...	...	Rusose.
Hlengwe	...	*Luanso.*

(a) Valved baskets

These are the normal retaining device used in barriers throughout the Bantu region, and in fact valved baskets have a wider world distribution than any other item of fishing gear. In size they vary from 12 inches long to 6 feet or more, and in cross-section they are circular or egg-shaped. They are made of grass, whole reed or split reed, and commonly fish are removed by untying the bunched longitudinal strips at the apex. In other more flattened types the edge further from the entrance is unlaced for the removal of the catch. Small lifting handles have been noted only in the Luapula Valley and Barotse-land,* while in the latter area a special prefabricated unit of a trap and its adjoining section of screen is found. Lifting handles running the length of the trap are noted only in Angola [Baumann]. Despite the widespread use of valved baskets in the Central African region, their construction has not reached that stage of perfection that Worthington (c) and others report on Lake Victoria.

---

* And in the Middle Zambezi Valley.—EDITOR.

The valves are made of the same material as the main trap. The component strips run inwards and upwards so that an unbound frieze of sharp ends of roughly the same cross-section as the average fish to be caught projects into the trap. As there is a certain amount of " give " in the ends of these strips extra large fish are able to force their way in. Two-chambered traps, with a pair of valves, that are such a feature of West Africa and the lower Congo (Southern) are not recorded in Central Africa except on Lake Victoria [Fosbrooke and Worthington (c)] and on Lake Nyasa, possibly because *cylindrical* valved traps in this area are rarely baited or set away from barriers. Spherical and subspherical valved traps are described below.

In the Luapula-Mweru region otters do so much damage to valved traps in dambo swamps that these have to be protected with a fence of strong stakes.

I Lungu ...	...	*Mono (myono)*.
II Nyasa-Tonga	...	*Mono (miyono)*; mkurura (small); *chana (viana)* (valve).
Nyanja ...	...	*Mono (myono)*; Mvuma (valve).
III Bemba ...	...	*Mono (myono)*; Bwamba (mamba) (in mud banks); Kupinde Isande (in reed screens); Banasabila munangi (extra large).
Ushi ...	...	*Mono (myono)*; Kang'anda (otter guard).
Tabwa ...	...	*Mono (myono)*.
Kaonde...	...	*Muvuwa (mivuwa)* (general); Musalala (small); Ciwinja or wa ngwashi (large).
Unga ...	...	*Mono (myono)*; *Fwambi* (valve).
Shila ...	...	*Mono (myono)*; Cimpangu (otter guard).
Bwile ...	...	*Mono (myono)*.
Lamba ...	...	*Mono (myono)*; *Mfwambi* (valve); Umunsala and Munanga (unspecified types).
IV Tonga ...	...	*Mono* (myono).
Ila ...	...	*Mono* (myono); *Buvhwazhi* (valve).
We ...	...	*Mono* (myono).
V Lozi ...	...	*Lukoko (makoko)* (small); *Ndjamba (lindjamba)* (large).
VI Lunda ...	...	*Mono (myono)*; fwambi (valve); ? Kabindi (small); ? Lupupo (large).
Luvale ...	...	*Ngombe namwala* (very large); *Muvuwa* (smaller); *Chilazo* (valve).

[438]

Mbunda	...	? Mizua; kulunga (to set); ku-kuata (to catch with).
WB Luba ...	...	*Muteko*.
Chokwe	...	*Mutso* (mitso).
Luimbi	...	Muziwa or Mawala (with handle along whole trap); Yilazo (valve).
EB Swahili	...	Dema or Lema.
SB Shona ...	...	Duwo (maduwo) (? general for all baskets).
Karanga	...	Duvu.
Shangana	...	Lisole.
Hlengwe	...	*Muvasa*; *Usonje* (mouthpiece).
Bavenda	...	Mhoma.

(b) Unvalved baskets

In small streams where there is a steady flow without too great a risk of spates long conical reed traps are inserted in the gaps of barriers. Small fish are retained in them by the force of the water. Similar but much stronger cones, up to 15 feet long, are lowered into rapids, particularly where the flow is concentrated between rocks, and in such cases the barrier is a natural one. This type of trap is most highly developed along the Congo near Stanleyville, where immense scaffoldings have to be erected in the torrents to secure the cones.

Unvalved constricting cones, possibly derived from the above, are dealt with below.

I Lungu ...	...	? Chono.
III Bemba ...	...	Musalala.
Ushi ...	...	Kampasa; Kambila.
Kaonde...	...	*Yamba*.
Unga ...	...	Mutubi.
Shila ...	...	Musasu.
IV Tonga ...	...	(Mono).
Ila ...	...	Tulengo.
VI Lunda ...	...	Musalala.
Luvale ...	...	*Likinda* (*makinda*) (occasionally, also applied to small valved traps).
WB Chokwe	...	*Tsongo*.
Lumbi ...	...	*Matsinda*.

[439]

(c) Sieves and jumping gaps

Water flowing through a barrier may be led over a reed box or platform or through a pocket-shaped basket, so that small fishes are left stranded. Such sieves are found in the Luvale and Barotse regions, and the latter are also a handy shape for emptying enclosures. Very much greater sieves (*ngola*) are placed at the apices of barriers across the Uele in the Congo [Depasse and Mathieu].

Brelsford records the Unga of Bangweulu catching fish in mats or nets after leaping the gaps in barriers around breeding grounds, and on Nyasa grass platforms serve the same purpose [Bertram]. The Hlengwe catch in conical baskets fish jumping over barriers up to which they are driven [J. B. Thompson].

III Unga ...   ...   Cimpampa (jumping rack).

IV Tonga ...   ...   Cisasa (sieve).

VI Luvale ...   ...   *Cikanga (Vikanga)* (pocket-shaped sieve-
baskets); cisunga mundoli (gap in
barrier jumped by fish).

(d) Enclosures with valves or doors

When barriers are made of reed mats, enclosures of the same material are often included, the valves being vertical and converging pieces of mat. The enclosures are placed between the barrier and the bank, or at the apex of converging fences. Double valves were noted in Barotse, where also in some cases sections of the barrier are removed at certain times of the day to allow fish to enter the enclosed water from the main Zambezi. Hughes refers to large enclosures round spawning areas on Lake Bangweulu with falling doors which are released by canoemen at night, and on the middle Congo watchers release the doors of enclosures when fish enter and strike pliant canes on which are strung rattles [Depasse]. Fish are normally extracted from the enclosures with spears, but occasionally small baskets or hand nets are used. The Luvale set their barriers and enclosures particularly for the spawning run of the barbel *Clarias* [White].

The enclosures, typical of the Zambezi and Kafue rivers, resemble closely the *osageru* of the Jaluo of Lake Victoria [Worthington (c)].

III Bemba ...   ...   ? Luando.

IV Tonga ...   ...   *Lusasa.*

Ila   ...   ...   *Lusasa*; Masasa amabu; manda; kukusola
cimpinda (to set).

V Lozi   ...   ...   *Siandi (liandi).*

VI Luvale ...   ...   *Lilela (Malela).*

[440]

II. Isolated Traps

(a) Valved baskets

As mentioned above, the *cylindrical* valved basket is not normally used on its own (as it is in West Africa), there being records only from Lake Nyasa and the Hlengwe [Thompson]. The itumba of the lower Luapula Valley is in the shape of a squashed sphere, with two opposing entrances. It is set unbaited among vegetation in shallow flooded areas, and also in barriers. Derived from this is the *litumba* of the Luvale and Barotse, found in great abundance along the Zambezi, although according to the Paramount Chief and others it was only introduced about 1943 by Luvale fishermen. It is made in shape and size like a petrol drum, again with two opposing entrances. It is interesting to note that the Baganda on Lake Victoria set a large basket trap called *ntumba* among reeds where fish breed [Roscoe]. Spherical traps similar to those of the Lunda are widely used on the Stanley Pool [Sautter]. In the Rhodes-Livingstone Museum is a large pear-shaped trap with a single valve at the flattened base, from the Lukanga Swamp, where it was said to be used by the Lenje and most probably also by the Kaonde and Twa. I have met with nothing of this nature in the field in Northern Rhodesia, but Graham depicts exactly similar traps on Lake Victoria.

In the south-west arm of Lake Tanganyika are vast three-chambered traps suspended in deep water and baited with grass to catch silurids and other fish, attracted probably by the animal life sheltering in the grass. The mouths of the three chambers face inwards and the fish are reported to enter the space so formed from below, though according to Poll (*b*), who also found four-chambered traps, they enter from above. The *saika* trap of Lake Nyasa appears to attract fish with the same kind of bait. It is a lump of floating sudd bordered with reeds and backed with a hanging trap into which *Clarias*, searching for worms in the sudd, are said to slide [Lowe]. A similar device, a ring of floating weed around a valved trap set mouth upwards, is also recorded on Lake Nyasa [Bertram]. A large baited cone-shaped basket with a funnel in the neck leading to a spherical bowl was used on Lake Victoria in 1911 [Roscoe], and a baited openwork cage with two entrances on Lake Tanganyika in 1860 [Burton], but I have been unable to find any mention of other three-chambered pots in Africa.

I	Lungu ...	...	*Cisowi* (*Visowi*) (three-chambered).
III	Tabwa ...	...	*Fisowi* (three-chambered).
V	Lozi ...	...	*Litumba* (*Matumba*) (barrel-shaped).
VI	Lunda ...	...	*Itumba* (sub-spherical).

Luvale ...   ... *Lizakasa* or *Litumba* (*Matumba*) (barrel-shaped).

EB Baganda   ... *Ntumba.*

WB W. Tanganyika   *Kisoke* (three-chambered).

(b) Baited enclosures

These only differ from those used alongside barriers by standing on their own and being baited. The same names are often applied to both. They are simply made by placing a mat or screen vertically in the shallows with a heart-shaped cross-section, so that the two ends form the valve. In the case of the Barotse *Katamba* the trap has a built-in base, enabling it to be moved as required. A similar screen is set spirally by the Hlengwe [J. B. Thompson]. Cassava or mealie meal is the usual bait.

There are no records of baited traps or enclosures with trigger-released doors, such as are found in parts of the Congo [Goffin, Sautter], nor is there any artificial feeding of enclosed fish such as the Bangala of the upper Congo River carry out, in the form of cassava peelings and cut-up snails [Weeks].

III	Bemba ...	...	? Lusando.
IV	Tonga ...	...	? Lusasa.
	Ila ...	...	? Lusasa.
V	Lozi ...	...	*Katamba* (*tutamba*).
VI	Luvale ...	...	*Lilela* (*Malela*).
SB	Hlengwe	...	Cizungalaka.

(c) Constricting traps

The Lozi and Luvale set a trumpet-shaped cone, spirally woven and pliant, among grass; it is about 3 feet wide and 4 feet long, and bears a close resemblance to the rodent traps of Central Africa, in which the victim is constricted when it tries to retreat from the tube. The fish, pushing its way through the swamp, enters the trap and is prevented from withdrawing by the erection of its fins as is well shown in Goffin's illustration of a Congo silurid held by its spines. Sautter, too, mentions constriction traps on the Stanley Pool. The Kimwani of Lake Victoria use a similar trap in specially cleared swamp channels for *Protopterus* [Fosbrooke]. Identical traps are found in India [Hornell, p. 145].

Both the Lozi and the Luvale make similar constricting cones out of fibre netting held open by stick rings 18 inches across; the latter place them in barriers up to which fish are driven or lured with bait [Baumann and White].

The Vachokwe, Luchazi and Babunda fish the Kwando River of East Angola in small bark canoes, and set small conical string nets, attached to stakes, with their openings upstream [Hambly]. It is possible that Johnston's record from the Basoko of round nets to gill fish, baited and kept open by creepers, and Hewitt-Ivy's from the Bavenda of gill nets on triangular frames apply to nets of this nature.

V Lozi ... ... Kafula (tufula) (small); Lufula (mafula) (large) (spiral cone).

VI Luvale ... ... *Lunguwa* (*Tunguwa*) (net cone); *Likasa* (spiral cone).

Luchaze ... Likanza.

WB Chokwe ... Lunguwa (net cone).

Luimbi ... Kanguwa (net cone).

III. SHELTER ISLANDS

The practice of erecting shelters to which fish are attracted is not as prevalent in the Rhodesias as in neighbouring areas. On Lake Albert [Worthington (*a*)], in Nigeria [Maclaren] and in Mocambique [Costa] clumps of grass are surrounded with nets or screens some time after having been placed in position and the fish removed, while naturally existing shelters are also so fished. On the lower Congo large areas of vegetation are surrounded [Sautter], and on the Shire River in Nyasaland patches of papyrus [Borley]. On the upper Congo light branches and leaves are thrown on the surface of an area of water enclosed by nets on all but the upstream side [Weeks].

At Sitoti near Senanga on the upper Zambezi piles of stones are said to be erected in which small mormyrids called *lininga* take cover. The piles are later surrounded by unvalved baskets and the stones removed to another site, thus exposing the fish. A similar use of fishes' instinct to take shelter has been noted near Mongu, where hollow balls of clay are placed in pits on the flood plains and later lifted out [Mitchell-Heggs]. In Nigeria hollow sections of bamboo [Maclaren], in the Gabon hollow logs [Kingsley] and on the Zambezi at Mambova bottles and drums are put to the same purpose, although in the last case a bait of mealie meal is added.

Lozi" ... ... Liungwe (Maungwe) (piles of stones).

? Manganja ... Nsilo (surrounding papyrus clumps).

B. NETS

Net twine is prepared from a variety of fibres, among which cotton has not been noted. As a rule the fibre is rolled on the thigh, to produce a yarn of only moderately uniform thickness; very fine yarns are particularly subject to variation. The yarns are normally twisted into a two-ply yarn. Breaking tests on Lake Nyasa net fibres are recorded by Bertram.

Nowadays, however, most gill nets (except in Barotseland) are made with nylon or, in the case of small nets for subsistence fishing, with sewing cotton, while draw nets are made with the nylon fibres laboriously stripped out of vehicle tyres. Rayon fibres are not popular for the same purpose because of their excessive springiness.

The head and foot ropes of gill and draw nets are made of coarse two-ply fibre twine, and still coarser fibre is twisted up into the two- or three-ply pulling ropes of draw nets. Tests on these fibre ropes were also conducted by Bertram.*

There is little doubt that the netting shuttle is a very recent introduction to the area. Apart from Nyasaland fishermen and a few Mweru dwellers who have been in contact with Greek fishermen there, the makers of nets throughout Central Africa do not use a shuttle, merely pulling the twine through, the mesh being taken up with the fingers. Nor is there any evidence of any mesh gauge or mesh stick other than the fingers of the left hand. A recent survey of netting knots and needles [Maclaren] has shown that the only areas of the world without the simple open-ended shuttle are Central and South Africa and the Americas, while only aboriginal Central and South Africa lack the mesh gauge.

All game nets I have examined in the region have been made with a vertical reef knot or its loose form, the cow hitch. In finer nets, such as are adapted to fishing, the prevalent knot in Northern Rhodesia is the mesh knot from over, which has a wide distribution in Asia and the Pacific, but which is less common in neighbouring parts of Africa than the reef. Alongside this mesh knot from over is a minor variation which produces a reef knot with a twist. I have on several occasions seen these two knots made by the same man at the same time, pointing to a lack of definite knotting pattern. The whole subject is treated in greater detail in the paper referred to.

It is reasonable, therefore, to associate with these deficiencies (of the shuttle and the mesh gauge) a relative paucity of nets, and the historical evidence is that in most areas nets other than game nets and small hand nets have been introduced since the advent of settled conditions.

In the upper Zambezi Valley and on Lake Ngami, however, nets (of unspecified type) were known in the middle of the last century [Livingstone (a)], and on Lake Nyasa there appears to be a more widespread tradition of " netmanship " than anywhere else in the area, as evidenced by the presence of the open-ended netting shuttle and the use of net preservatives [Bertram]. Bark and root extracts are still used on the west side of Lake Nyasa to tan small nets.

* Floats and weights are discussed below.

I Lungu ...	...	Mututu (float).
II Nyanja ...	...	Ukonde; Kafumba, akalanji (float).
Nyasa-Tonga ...		*Mkwau* (*Mikwau*); sila (masila) (float); Kalanje (large central float).
III Bemba ...	...	*Isumbu* (masumbu); Mpepa (float).
Kaonde...	...	Bukonde.
Shila ...	...	Ubukonde; Utumbushye, ichiloli, mpepa (floats).
Bwile ...	...	Utumbushye, ichiloli, mpepa.
Lala ...	...	Kombe.
Lamba ...	...	Ukwikashya (to fish with a net).
IV Ila ...	...	Kanyandi.
VI Lunda ...	...	Bukonde (makonde); Cibulo (fibulo) (floats).
Luvale ...	...	Lioji (Lioshi) (Myoji).
Mbunda	...	Ku-tamba mu-nanda (to use nets).
WB Mbundu	...	Mawanda.
Chokwe	...	*Wanda*; Liozi.
Luimbi	...	*Wanda*.
Yombe ...	...	Nkonde.
SB Shona ...	...	Ushashi.

I. GILL AND TANGLE NETS

As there are no shoals of standard-sized fish in any of the waters under consideration gill nets in the strict sense are not employed, for the nets entangle their catches as much as they gill them. The same net may be employed in a variety of ways, so that the classification below is loose.

The most widespread method is to set the net overnight, as a vertical wall of netting, with floats along the head line and, generally, with weights along the foot line. The ends of the net are secured to grass or trees, and if the water is deeper than the net a float is attached to a stone tied to each end. On the big lakes the nets are bottom-set—that is, they float from the bottom upwards and not as usual from the surface downwards. On Lake Bangweulu and Lake Mweru floats of light wood often made from the *cipolo* nodules from the bark of a tree are threaded onto the head ropes, but elsewhere grass, reeds and papyrus form the floats. On the upper Zambezi, particularly, grass is used. Three-foot lengths are doubled and bent onto regularly spaced top meshes; there is no head rope and the hanging of the net is maintained by the foot rope, which is generally unweighted. Alternatively, there may be a head rope but no foot rope. The grass floats are said to last less than a week, but are easily replaced. They do not catch in the net and make its handling an easy matter. Weights, if used, are of baked clay or of stones clumsily tied to the foot line. Lead has not yet been adopted.

In shallow waters, particularly where there are no canoes, tangle nets are held erect by stakes a few feet apart, and the fish are driven into the nets by fishermen splashing the water. On the Kalungwishi River the *Alestes* jump so energetically that the nets have to be held above the water. Such driving is also used with floating nets, particularly in Barotseland and the Luapula area, where a special plunger on the end of a stick is employed to make deep reverberations in the water.

The same nets, with light floats and no weights, are drifted down the Luapula by the current, and on the Zambezi the Lozi and Luvale use them either as encircling nets or set them in the form of a spiral which later is closed up; they cunningly manipulate their small canoes by gripping the long paddle between neck and shoulder. Goffin records drift nets used as above on the Congo at Stanley Falls, Sautter on Stanley Pool and Poll (*a*) refers to the Kiluba drifting such nets or setting them in a circle.

On the western shore of Lake Nyasa and on Likoma Island small nets, with floats and weights, are staked among rocks by a pole at either end and fish are driven in by swimmers, sometimes in water several fathoms deep. The smaller-meshed nets catch rock-haunting *mbuna*, and the larger ones *Bagrus* guarding their nests. These nets can also be dragged by two men in the shallows.

In the same area the Tonga set a small floating net from canoes and attract fish to it with a light in a third canoe.

Little gill nets of a unique type have been photographed by Poll (*b*) on the west side of Lake Tanganyika. One kind (luku) is in the form of a flag the side of which measures one metre. Several such flags are attached to cables running vertically from floats to the lake bottom; the other is triangular floating vertically in a bamboo frame. Both have shining white fibres at the intersections of the meshes which apparently appear to large fish to resemble the gleam of fodder fish. A third net also depicted by Poll is elliptical. It is placed between stones and fish are chased into it by children; in appearance the net resembles a dip net.

NOTE.—The Valley Tonga, or BaWe, of Gwembe, use a gill net mounted on an elliptical stick frame which is in turn lashed to the end of a long pole. The net is set overnight in the Zambezi, the butt of the pole being driven into the bank and a forked stick being used to support the shaft. The dimensions of a typical specimen collected in 1956 are: Frame, length 7 feet 6 inches by 2 feet breadth (maximum); pole, length 12 feet; stretched mesh, 4 inches. Smaller specimens are used as dip nets.—EDITOR.

I Lungu ...	...	Isumbu (Masumbu); Buloshi; ? Sumbwa (staked net).
II Nyanja ...	...	*Ndangala*; *Ukonde*; ntambula.
Nyasa-Tonga	...	*Ndangala* (gill net); *Chilepa* (underwater stake net); *Ngongongo* and *Mudundo* (floating net to which fish are attracted by light—Mwenji).
III Bemba ...	...	*Isumbu* (*Masumbu*); *Lioshi* (drift nets); Ndala; Kabelekete; Ukuteya (to set); ukusoa (driving).
Ushi ...	...	Bukonde (Makonde); Chaoshi.
Tabwa ...	...	Buloshi.
Kaonde...	...	Ukonde.
Unga ...	...	*Isumbu* (Masumbu); Kusakila (driving).
Shila ...	...	Ubukonde; Ka Belibeti; *Seuseuta*; Kusowelesha and *Ukutumpula* (driving) with *Akaoma* (*utuoma*) (plungers); Kamukuta (staked net).
Bwile ...	...	Ubukonde; *Kabeliketi*; *Amaseuseuta*.
IV Tonga ...	...	? Ntangala.
We ...	...	*Lusabwe* (*Masabwe*) (stake nets).
Ila ...	...	Kanyandi.
V Lozi ...	...	*Kanyandi* (*Tunvandi*).
VI Lunda ...	...	*Seuseuta*; Ukutumpula (driving) with Kaoma (plunger).
Luvale ...	...	*Kalenge* (small, generally weighted); Lioshi (mioshi); *Kulalika* (to set overnight); *Kukuvulwila* (to drive into nets).
WB Luba ...	...	Mukonde; Maliba; Kitumpa (plunger).
W. Tanganyika		Makila.

II. DRAW NETS

Seines are long nets set from canoes and pulled onto shore by a rope at either end. In Northern Rhodesia they were practically confined to Lake Bangweulu, Lake Tanganyika and Lake Mweru until Nyasaland fishermen introduced them to the lower Kafue some time in this century. According to the Paramount Chief and others, Lozi men picked up the use of the net on the Kafue and carried it to Barotseland within the last two decades.

The Paramount Chief connected the Lozi word for it (*kangoni*) with the Ngoni of the Nyasa region. The Luvale *ciko-kela* appears to be little more than an ordinary tangle net adapted for dragging.

On the Kafue the nets may be as long as 400 feet, and up to 20 feet deep. As the net is pulled in this central portion billows back and retains the catch. These Kafue nets are so large that nowadays, with only small canoes available, two of these have to be used to carry the net, each canoe setting half and carrying one warp back to the bank.

The only seines with fine cods or pockets are found on Lake Tanganyika [Poll (*b*)], and in parts of the Congo [Poll (*a*)]. From Tanganyika Poll has photographs of seines without pockets, with one large pocket, and also some with multiple pockets. The latter appear to have no parallel in Africa, and have perhaps arisen because of the exceptionally steep and rocky shore. The wings and mouths of the bags, which may number from three to twelve or more, are held open by stick stretchers.

Lenge at Utinta.

Makalenge at Mpulungu.

Niavu at Kirando.

On Lake Bangweulu, and probably on Lake Mweru before draw nets were prohibited there, the normal floats were pieces of light wood pierced and strung onto the fibre head-rope. But the Kafue and Zambezi nets, originating from Lake Nyasa, are held up by wooden clappers 9-15 inches long attached at one end to the head-rope. These wave about as the net is pulled in and probably deter a proportion of fish from escaping over the top of the net while this is still in deep water. Poll (*b*) refers to similar long floats on Lake Tanganyika. In most places the weights are stones, but in Barotseland clay balls are wrapped in bark strips and secured to the foot-rope.

The shore seines of Lake Nyasa are described in detail by Bertram and by Withers. They may be as long as 1,400 feet, but such nets are exceptional, as few men can afford to construct them, and the smaller nets may be only 120 feet long, and used without pulling ropes. Withers' description of the manufacture of a net applies also to those introduced into Northern Rhodesia. The net consists of a number of panels (*zilambi*) 6 feet wide and varying in depth. In a net of 1,200 feet there would be fourteen of these panels in the belly, 122 meshes deep, and on each side of the belly twelve of 110 meshes. Towards the ends of the wings the panels would decrease in depth to 40 meshes, but the mesh size would increase from " three fingers " to " five fingers " (say from $2\frac{3}{4}$ inches stretched mesh to 5 inches). The nets seen by Withers had warps of palm fronds, each up to $1\frac{1}{2}$ miles long, but neither this material nor these dimensions are, according to Bertram, generally used on Lake Nyasa. The even pulling-in of such large nets, sometimes taking an hour and a half (Withers), is assisted by three marker floats, one on each wing and one on the belly.

The Nyasa open-water seine (*chirimila*) is worked from two canoes in deep water and in calm weather [Bertram]. It is very deep measuring 100 feet by 50 feet, the upper edge being buoyed and the lower weighted with stones. After being spread and allowed to sink several fathoms it is pulled only a short way by the 90-foot long warps and is brought up to the canoe in the form of a hollow trough. Most of the net is of 2-inch stretched mesh, but there is a central patch some 16 feet square in which the mesh is $\frac{1}{2}$ or $\frac{3}{4}$ inch. This is the bag in which the fish are removed. Sometimes a man dives in to find out whether the time is opportune for the hauling. An important point demonstrated to me by T. D. Iles, but omitted from previous accounts, is that the pulling ropes only spread the net and that a current (*mweza*) formed as a result of the lake's seiches is responsible for carrying it against the rock or projection near which the shoals of Haplochromids are lying. A similar but smaller net may be used in combination with a light (Mzumara). The *chirimila* net came to the western shore of the lake from Likoma Island, and to that place from the Wakisi living on the north-east shore [Cox]. A large-mesh deep-water seine recorded briefly from the north end of Lake Tanganyika by Poll (*b*) may be of the same type.

A form of combined lift and draw net bearing a remarkable resemblance to the *chirimila* is found on the Barotse Plain of the Zambezi (but not further north among the Luvale); and appears not to have been described previously. This *lituwa* is a large-mesh square net of native fibre, some 40 feet each way. Ropes are attached to two adjoining corners, and a single large stone to the foot-rope between them. Along three quarters of the other three sides are big floats formed by folding large pieces of grass in half and tying the middles to the net. The net is piled into two canoes which proceed together to suitable sites—deep backwaters or sections of lagoons. Casting the net into the water in a loose heap the fishermen carry the ends of the two ropes to an adjacent bank or reed bed, to which they hold on. The ropes are hauled in so that the net is extended under water and drawn a short way. Then at a signal each canoe is pulled back along its rope towards the net, while at the same time the water between the canoes is beaten with the paddles. The base of the net is then quickly lifted into the canoes so that the remainder of the net forms a complete bag. This, too, is drawn in, though at a more leisurely rate, together with the catch, and is ready for the next setting. The wide-mesh bast net which Holub in 1881 describes the Marutse and Masupias

[449]

as possessing was also certainly of this type, for he mentions a crew of four men in each canoe, and this is the number employed at the present time. It is possible, but not certain, that the Libinja had a similar device. It was the largest net on the upper Congo River, in the shape of a lidless box, over which the fish were frightened [Weeks]. There appears to be a resemblance to the deep draw net *likosso* that Sautter describes the Bolobo men setting from two canoes in the Stanley Pool. This could be closed up into a circle in deep water.

The immense royal net of the Lozi, which needed scores of men to operate, more nearly resembled the normal rectangular seine, though in addition it was equipped with a floating platform (a series of reed trays) to catch fish jumping over [Colson and Gluckman, plate II, 3]. Such platforms are arranged for leaping fish, mainly mullet, in the Mediterranean and India [Hornell].

The smaller specimens of stake nets described above with gill nets are sometimes used as draw nets in drying-up pools and river shallows, and on Lake Tanganyika Fipa fishermen have a short draw net only 30 feet long fitted with floats, weights and a stake at either end; it is drawn around fish guarding their nests in the lake shallows. Such nets were noted there by Burton in 1860, and by Weeks among the Basoko of the Congo in 1909. On Lake Nyasa a small stake net is employed to enclose fish in the shallows [G. Thompson] or as a subsidiary seine at the closing stages of hauling the large shore seines, to capture fish escaping from the latter [Bertram]. It is probably very similar to the small stake nets (mentioned above) into which fish are driven. (A length of cloth may be put to the same use [Lowe, Plate VI.F] in very shallow water.)

On Lake Nyasa, too, a cyprinid called *usipa* is caught by two divers towing a small bag net of mosquito netting between them. The bag is held open by a stake at either side, and is folded up at the end of a dive. Similar but larger nets are used on Likoma Island for other shoaling fish (Mzumara).

I Lungu ...	...	*Mkwao*; ? Lutamba.
II Nyanja ...	...	*Ukonde*; *Khoka*; *psasa*, kombe, chilimila (open water seine); *cheche* (small shore seine); *chalera* (subsidiary seine); Kawuyi (small shore seine).
Senga ...	...	Ukonde.
Nyasa-Tonga ...		*Chirimila* (open water draw and lift net); Kabelekesi (a smaller edition); *Mkwau wa pasi* (draw net); Usikiti (under water bag net).

[450]

III	Bemba ...	...	*Mkwao.*
	Ushi ...	...	*Mkwao.*
	Tabwa ...	...	*Mkwao.*
	Kaonde...	...	? Kanyandi.
	Unga ...	...	*Mkwao.*
	Shila ...	...	*Mkwao.*
	Bwile ...	...	*Mkwao.*
	Lamba ...	...	*Utombe.*
IV	Tonga ...	...	*Kombe.*
	Gowa ...	...	? Kokota.
	Ila ...	...	*Kombe.*
	We ...	...	*Busamba.*
V	Lozi ...	...	*Singoni* or *Kangoni* (*Tungoni*); *Lituwa* (*Matuwa*) (combined draw and lift net); Sikundi (Royal net).
VI	Lunda ...	...	*Mkwao.*
	Luvale ...	...	*Cikokela* (*Likokela*).
WB	Luba ...	...	*Kiamukokwa.*
	W. Tanganyika		*Mkwao;* lusuku (pocket).
	So (Basoko)	...	Makayulu.
EB	Fipa ...	...	Akankupi (shallows draw net).
SB	Ndebele ...	...	? Lukwanga.

III. Hand Nets

(a) Clap nets

Clap nets differ from the dip and scoop nets described below in that the two sticks of the frame, one held in either hand, are hinged at the outer end. Nowadays such nets, exactly similar to the bat-fowling nets of European bird-catchers, are only to be found on the peculiarly alkaline Mweru wa Ntipa, although the hand nets known to the older dwellers in the Luapula Valley were probably akin [Lammond]. In the Mweru Marsh the fishermen dip the nets downwards from the bows of a canoe, and clapping together the arms seldom fail to bring up one or more *Tilapia* in the bag. The name *mutobe* is believed to be Swahili, pointing to an introduction from the Tanganyika region.

The action of this net approximates to that of the underwater draw net, described above, and to the dip nets described below.

[451]

III Shila ...   ...   *Mutobe.*

VI Lunda ...   ...   *Mutobe.*

EB Swahili   ...   *Mutobe.*

(b) Dip and scoop nets

Apart from clap nets all other dipping and scooping nets in Central Africa appear to be either triangular in shape, with the apex towards the user, or circular, generally with the addition of long handles. Ricardo pictures the scoop nets of Lake Rukwa (figs. 7-9); they have deep pockets and are operated by men wading, or in the case of larger nets by men in canoes. Both methods are also used on Lake Nyasa [Bertram] and Lowe in addition describes migrating fish taken in scoop nets worked from platforms on the river banks (Plate VII.F). She also pictures small triangular nets, held one in either hand, with which fish are pursued in shallow water. These little paired nets seem to be identical to those of the Benue River, Nigeria [Maclaren].

Triangular dip nets are also operated from canoes on Lake Kivu [Fosbrooke *in litt.*] and on Stanley Pool [Sautter]. Poll refers to a small net among the Luba which has a pocket and which is fitted with two bamboo handles, and so does Sautter among the Libinga at Stanley Pool, while the Jaluo scoop net of Lake Victoria is also similar [Graham].

The Ndau of Mocambique have adapted the same type of net to their underwater pursuit of large Barbus [Bond]. In their case the piece of wood at the apex which holds the net apart is removable, so that the net can be rolled up for transport. Bond emphasises the importance of the curvature of the arms of the net. This curvature is upwards when the net is viewed from the side.

A variety of small circular or elliptical landing nets exists. The Rhodes-Livingstone Museum has a round net with a 12-inch cross piece acting as a handle, from the Bemba area, but most nets have handles, in keeping with their main use, which is to empty enclosures. Such a net from the Basongo of the Kasai is depicted by Matagne. Perhaps because he is so often carrying a spear, the Bantu fisherman does not employ this type of net to bring into his canoe large fish caught on long lines, as is the usual practice in West Africa.

At the upstream end of the lower gorge of the Kafue there takes place annually a run of small mormyrids, mainly *Gnathonemus*. The Tonga erect breakwaters of rocks all along the side of the ravine; the fish rest in the slack water so formed as they fight their way up at night, and are removed in huge quantities in long-handled elliptical dip nets.

[452]

BARRIER WITH ENCLOSURES, MAMBOVA (ZAMBESI).

LWANDA FISHING, NANZILA RIVER, NAMWALA.—Rev. B. D. Jinkin.

Ndjamba VALVED TRAP WITH SECTION OF BARRIER,
MONGU; FOR USE IN THE ZAMBESI.

BARRIER ACROSS THE LUAPULA RIVER AT CHEMBI; THERE ARE NO
TRAPS PRESENT.

PLATFORM SIEVE, KAFUE GORGE.

Kanyande GILL/TANGLE NETS, MONGU. NOTE THE GRASS FLOATS
AND STONE WEIGHTS.

A NEW SKILL; SEINING IN THE GWEMBE VALLEY.

Ndgaa COOP, MPULUNGU.

CLAP NET, NKATA BAY.

Mafula CONSTRICTION TRAPS, MONGU.

Makoko VALVED BASKETS, MAMBOVA.

ILA THRUST BASKET, NAMWALA.

SET RODS WITH WARNING BELLS, LUANGWA RIVER.

OTTER GUARD. USUALLY SET ROUND A SMALL *mono* TRAP INTENDED
FOR FISH MOVING LATERALLY ALONG A DAMBO BANK, FORT ROSEBERY.

KAONDE USING THREE SPEARS AT A TIME, BUSANCA FLATS.

BATWA WITH " DARK HUT " OF BLANKETS, LOWER KAFUE.

—G. J. Labuschagne.

A rather similar fishery occurs on the Luweya River, on the west shore of Lake Nyasa, during the spawning run of two species of *Barilius*, *sanjika* and *lupasa*. The Nyasa Tonga take up a few precarious stances, jealously guarded by certain families, and take the fish working up the Ciwandama Rapids in large triangular dip nets at the ends of poles 12 feet long [Hoole]. Much the same type of net is found on the Luapula [Matagne], while on Lake Tanganyika a light form of elliptical net at the end of a pole serves to scoop out individuals of *Cyathopharynx* attracted to one of their species, generally a female, attached to a float [Poll (*b*)].

On Lake Tanganyika is also a most important fishery for a small shoaling clupeid called *ndgaa* or *ndagala* which has been photographed and described in detail by Collart (*a*). The shoals are lured into shallow water by the glare of lights, and the little whitebait are scooped out in immense round dip nets. Catches of several hundred pounds have been made on moonless nights by single canoes, although according to Collart the average throughout the year is nearer 30 kilograms. The scores of flares scattered over the surface of the lake make a most picturesque scene. In their original form, even before the arrival of the Arabs on the lake [Collart], the long-handled nets were constructed of *inondo* fibre and the lights of wood or reed bundles. An assiduous worker could roll the fibre and weave a net in five to six months, there being, of course, a vast amount of labour in a net 5 to 6 metres round and 1.5 to 2 metres deep.

But modern developments have affected the fishery more than most. In 1925 mosquito netting came into use, and about 1953 kerosene pressure lamps bade fair to oust the wood braziers, while a year or two later nylon netting was introduced in the Congo. The last step in the ladder of progress is likely to be the adoption of electric lights, possibly submerged.

Burton in 1860 described a net on a circular lathe frame 6 feet in diameter, also lowered from the bows of a canoe to catch fish attracted by a glaring torch, but it is not clear whether he refers to the *ndgaa* net above or to the similar but larger meshed net Poll (*b*) reports still being used for large *Barbus* and *Distichodus*.

It is interesting to note that on the western shore of Lake Nyasa a cyprinid called *usipa* is similarly lured into the shallows with torch flares, and taken out in large triangular mosquito-netting scoops [Fryer].

I Lungu ...	...	Nsenga; *Cimuri* (*vimuri*) (large, circular).
II Chewa ...	...	Pyasa (triangular).
Nyasa-Tonga	...	*Chiwu, ciu* (*viu*) (triangular).

III	Tabwa	...	Lusenga (large, circular).
	? Shila ...	...	Luela (triangular, long-handled).
IV	Tonga ...	...	Lutele; Kansabo (small, elliptical, long-handled).
	Ila ...	...	Lutele; Iwanga (small, elliptical).
	We ...	...	Kasabwe (small, elliptical).
WB	Luba ...	...	Luelo.
	W. Tanganyika		*Kasogo* (large-mesh); *Lusenga* (large, circular or elliptical).

(c) Drop nets

A peculiar net (*imbwa*) has been brought by Fipa fishermen to the south-west corner of Lake Tanganyika. It is shaped like a curtain, 12 feet deep, with a 3-foot stick at the top and a 12-foot one at the bottom, to which is tied a stone. The stretched mesh is 8 inches. When predatory fish are attracted to the lights of the *ndgaa* fishers this curtain net is quickly dropped in their path and they are entangled. According to Poll (*b*) this net (bukila) is in the Bay of Edith trailed from a slowly moving canoe to catch *Dinopterus*.

(d) Cast nets

An exhaustive search of the literature in connection with the preparation of a monograph on the world distribution of the cast net has served only to amplify the information in Leth and Lindblom's work concerning Central and Southern Africa. The net arrived at the mouth of the Congo during the last two centuries and spread up that river with the earliest travellers and their West African followers at about the beginning of this century [Weeks and Boulenger]. It is now widely used on the Congo and its tributaries around Stanleyville [Gosse]. It does not purse, and is hemless, so that small fish are gilled and larger ones removed by hand.

To the coast of East Africa cast nets were brought by Arabs, Indians or the Portuguese. At least some of those on the Mocambique coast are pursing [Costa], as are all those employed on the southern and eastern shores of South Africa by Indians in the surf and by Europeans after bait for angling. On the lower stretches of the Zambezi and the Shire the Bantu have adopted the net, for a hemless and non-pursing type is found at Tete, and on the lower Shire among the Sena and Manganja, to whom it was introduced by the Coastal Aphodzo [Borley]. Livingstone's reference to a cast net among the Badima above Tete (*b*), p. 57, is a little dubious as he might have been employing the word in the biblical sense of " shooting " a seine.

[462]

In addition to the spread of the device up the Congo and the Zambezi among the Bantu, it has been taken on a small scale to Lake Victoria by Goans [Graham], and to the southern Sudan by Nilotes [Stubbs].

No hoop or lifting nets other than those described above are found in the region, and though a variety of small nets have been noted in the Congo the published accounts do not make clear their exact nature.

C. THRUSTING AND DRAGGING IMPLEMENTS
I. DRAG FENCES

The same type of screen used in barriers may occasionally be dragged through pools and backwaters; the Balumba, for instance, annually spend a week in dragging a 4-mile stretch of Nanzila River (Namwála District), a party working from either end and converging on the middle, at which point one screen is dragged around the other with the aid of ropes [Jinkin]. Crocodiles, which cannot hurt the fishermen because of a special pot of medicine pushed in front of the screens, are speared out, and fish removed in baskets. A supplementary mat floating in the water prevents the fish from jumping.

The Hlengwe of the Sabi fix weights and sometimes floats on their drag fences, presumably for operation in deep water. They do not now use nets, probably having lost the ability through repeated slaving raids removing their skilled workers [J. B. Thompson].

The Lala near Serenje once used a two-man dredge of grass and reeds [Madocks], and in unspecified parts of Southern Rhodesia pools are dragged with barriers of leafy sticks for barbel *Clarias* [Cockcroft]. On the Luangwa River Nsenga women still drag a 10-foot roll of grass in the shallows for fry.* An old Barotseland method was to drag pieces of floating grass (*matindi*) into the shallows [Zwahler]. These dredges (hardly to be termed drag fences) do not anywhere reach the size of the *ngogo*, the 250-yard long papyrus wall dragged through the shallows of Lake Victoria by the Nilotic Jaluo [Graham].

There is no record of drag screens with inserted traps such as the *usango* of the Baganda nor of drag lines (ropes with attached leaves), such as the Bantu Watoro on Lake George have [Worthington (*c*)]. Nor is the canoe lift screen known. This is a rectangular mat hinged on the side of the canoe, worked in towards a bank or patch of weeds and lifted so that fish fall into the canoe, which is widely used on the upper Congo [Goffin *et al.*] and in Nigeria [Maclaren].

On the lower Shire River in Nyasaland a drag fence of reeds (*nsilo*) is set around a clump of papyrus and is steadily advanced towards the bank as the papyrus is removed [Borley].

---

* This method was formerly used in Gwembe also, not necessarily by women.—EDITOR.

II Nsenga ...	...	Chikoko.

III Bemba ...	...	*Lwando*; Uluangwa.
Ushi ...	...	? Mkekwe.
Kaonde...	...	*Luando.*
Lala ...	...	*Lukulu* (grass dredge).
Lamba ...	...	*Ulwando.*

IV Tonga ...	...	*Lwando*; *Mukwesho.*
Lumbu	...	*Lwando.*
Ila ...	...	*Lwando* (with *Masambala*, supplementary mats to prevent jumping).

V Lozi ...	...	*Lwando*; Kakuko; bukoka (to pull floating grass matindi into shallows).

II. Drag Baskets

These are closely woven, with an elongated oval mouth measuring up to 7 feet by 2 feet and with one or more cross struts. The larger specimens are pulled by two women, the smaller ones pulled or pushed by one, and often a number are worked together in lines or circles. The baskets may be pushed up to a bank or reed bed, or held stationary, and the small fish driven in. They are essentially a tool for subsistence fishing, and the communal parties are occasions of much merriment. On the upper Zambezi flood plains every household seems to possess a drag basket. I have never seen these baskets, the distribution of which is exceptionally widespread, used by men, and all the accounts in the literature, with the exception of Bertram's from Lake Nyasa, Johnston's from the upper Congo and a photograph of Barotseland fishing in the Rhodes-Livingstone Museum, confirm this sex-linked usage.

There are no definite records south of the Zambezi Tonga except for the Shona *kukukura* referring to the dragging of a sack or skin (Matedza), but the Mayombe, in the Cabinda enclave north of the Congo mouth, used similar baskets [Troesch]; these are the property of the women, but are used also by the men at communal fishing parties. Enormous examples are still to be seen on the Stanley Pool. Mary Kingsley found these baskets on Corisco Island in the Gulf of Guinea and apparently that is as far north as baskets of this shape are known.

NOTE.—Plateau Tonga women near Mapanza Mission, Choma, use large baskets of this type both for drawing and thrusting in the nearby rivers. Fish trapped by the latter method are removed through a hole in the spine of the basket. When the basket is drawn the hole is lashed shut with string.—EDITOR.

I	Lungu ...	...	*Luanga* (small); Ntende (large).
II	? Nyanja	...	Cisako.
III	Bemba ...	...	*Luanga*; *ntende*.
	Ushi ...	...	*Luanga*.
	Kaonde...	...	? Chiko.
	Unga ...	...	*Lwanga*; Cipopo (fipopo); *Kusaya* (to use).
	Shile ...	...	*Ntende*.
	Lala ...	...	*Inanga*.
	Bwile ...	...	*Luanga*; *ntende*.
	Lamba ...	...	Inwanga.
IV	Tonga ...	...	*Izubo* (*Mazubo*).
	We ...	...	*Izubo* (*Mazubo*).
V	Lozi ...	...	*Lishing'o* (*Mashing'o*); Kushua (to use).
VI	Luvale ...	...	*Liïyanga* (Maiyanga); Kuswinga (to use).
	Mbunda	...	? I-sakala.
WB	Luba ...	...	Kiamba.
	So (Basoko)	...	Liemba.
	Chokwe	...	Tambi.
	Mbundu	...	Isakala; Kutamba (to use).
	Yombe ...	...	*Ndizi*.
SB	Shona ...	...	Kukukura (dragging sack or skin).

III. SCOOP BASKETS

Smaller versions of the above are used in baling out fish concentrated in pools or behind screens, or poisoned, and again mainly by women. During the annual run of *chitaka* (mixed mormyrids) the Magoye River near Mazabuka presents an amazing spectacle as several hundred vociferous Tonga women crowd into the swollen waters to place their scoop baskets in the flow, mouth downstream. Long bell-mouthed scoop baskets, such as the Jaluo women use on Lake Victoria [Worthington (*b*)], are replaced in Central Africa by the drag baskets described above.

IV	Tonga ...	...	Isiko; *Isingo*; Binda.
	Ila ...	...	Isiko.
	Toka ...	...	Cikinga.
V	Lozi ...	...	*Lukunda* (*Makunda*).
SB	Hlengwe	...	Ciranga.

IV. THRUST BASKETS

Basically cones of sticks or reeds, they have a small hole at or near the apex, through which any fish are removed after having been trapped when the basket is thrust down into mud or shallow water. Optimum catches depend on the concerted efforts of many persons, who for the most part are women. Leth and Lindblom's study of the occurrence of the thrust basket in Africa and elsewhere shows that the implement is among the most widespread of all basketwork implements. There are, however, considerable gaps in its distribution in the area under consideration.

It is found on the upper Zambezi among the Lozi and Luvale, on the Kafue among the Tonga as well as the Ila, and also perhaps among the Hlengwe on the Sabi [Bullock, although J. B. Thompson makes no mention of it].* The Lozi baskets have a long apical handle, resembling the Luimbi examples from Angola described by Baumann and also those used by the Teso on Lake Kyoga [Uganda (b)]; but the Ila baskets are without this handle, although the smaller hole is sub-apical instead of apical, as in most baskets elsewhere. A long-handled basket in the Rhodes-Livingstone Museum labelled of Tonga origin may well be Lozi, for the latter do much fishing in the Tonga area.

Apart from a record from the Fipa on Lake Tanganyika [Leth and Lindblom quoting White Fathers] thrust baskets are not found on this lake nor on lakes Bangweulu, Nyasa or Mweru. They are absent too from the eastern and south-eastern parts of the Congo Basin, and from South Africa except among the Thonga on the Mocambique border.

III	Bemba ...	... Lutendo.
IV	Tonga ...	... Ivumbu; Nzinzi.
	Ila ...	... *Ivhumbo*; Izhizhi.
	We ...	... Insompo.
V	Lozi ...	... *Ling'unge* (*Mang'unde*).
VI	Lunda ...	... ? Kisubu.
	Luvale ...	... *Chongo* (*Vyongo*); *Kutavika* (to use).
WB	Luimbi	... *Tsongo* (with prolonged apical handle).
SB	Thonga...	... Shiranga.

D. HOOKS

Lagercrantz has covered in detail the distribution of fish hooks in Africa, but his records from the southern part of the continent are relatively sparse. The primitive gorge, a straight piece of wood, is

* And on the middle Zambezi.

found among the Bakongo on the lower Congo [Johnston], while a similar implement is fashioned by the Ovimbundu of Angola out of pieces of stiff grass ½ inch long [Hambly], and by the inhabitants of the Mocambique coast and the islands of Basaruto and Santa Carolina out of acacia thorns [Ritty]. The Belingwe (Southern Rhodesia) rock shelter paintings may depict seven fish attracted to a gorge [Summers], but the interpretation is not definite.

The Lovale fish with a bunch of cords baited with worms [White], jerking out the bait as soon as a bite is felt, and so do the Lamba women [Doke] and Konde boys [MacKenzie]. The method is comparable to the " patting " or bobbing for eels in Britain with worms threaded on wool. The Hlengwe in ancient times made hooks (or more probably gorges) from fish bones [J. B. Thompson], the Ubangi and Mayombe fishermen of spines gummed to pieces of wood [Goffin and Troesch] and the Luba of curved spines. The Hottentots used hooks of teeth or bone [Schapera (a)]. In the lower and middle Congo area hooks have been found of wood, developments of the gorge. Such examples are the flexible wooden stick of the Basoko, the curved wooden hooks of the Babwende, and the " raphia-hooks " of the Kasai [Lagercrantz quoting Johnston 1908, Hammar 1907, and Maes 1924]. An unusual variation was noted by Stayt among the BaVenda, where an individual had cut off all the thorns except the last from a branch and had used the whole as a rod, line and hook combined.

Lagercrantz knew of no archaeological discoveries of hooks in Africa. There is in the National Museum, Bulawayo, a copper hook from a pre-Matabele level in the Khami ruins [Summers], and a very similar copper hook, with a shaft 2 inches long and a very slight barbless curve, in the Rhodes-Livingstone Museum, from the We of the middle Zambezi, along with the same type of hook in iron. This type of hook could only serve to take shy species of fish which could be whipped out of the water as soon as the bait was nibbled.

Accounts [Smith and Dale, and Doke, among others] show that barbless iron hooks were being made by native blacksmiths throughout the area at the time of their first arrival, but it is not possible to say how ancient the practice is. The prevailing type is so recurved as to form almost a complete ring, a shape which is well adapted to taking hold in the mouth folds of silurids; von Rosen found it particularly abundant among the Batwa and Baushi of Lake Bangweulu and, as Lagercrantz has shown, it was made also by the Luvale and Lunda on the upper Zambezi, as well as around Lake Nyasa and Lake Tanganyika, where in fact such hooks are still made [Poll (b)]. Lagercrantz depicts a number of hooks of the Baushi, including one of copper, with more open mouths; some of these are attached to lines, and their shape will only permit their use on hand lines, by which a constant strain can be kept on the fish after it is hooked. The recurved hooks, on the other hand, will hold a struggling fish and can therefore be left unattended.

All accounts agree that no barbed hook was ever fashioned in Southern or Central Africa until imported hooks of European origin were available to be copied. Such importation took place at a much later date in this region than in those parts of West Africa which were open to commerce from an earlier date.

I. SINGLE HOOKS AND HANDLINES

Single baited hooks are more often fished from a rod than on a handline, as might be expected in view of the prevailing shallow waters and the fact that the users are more often than not women and children.

Rigs, the world-wide spreading devices on handlines which keep the hooks away from the main line, are only found on Lake Nyasa [Mzumara].

An ancient custom of the Batwa on Lake Bangweulu was to fish with a tough reed to which were tied three lines, one with two recurved barbless hooks and two with one hook each [von Rosen].

The Luvale and Lozi also attach baited hooks to free floats, as do the Kiluba [Poll (a)], and other tribes of the Congo, where such floats are generally banana-shaped and act as tell-tales to the fishermen by turning over when the bait is taken [Weeks and others]. A tell-tale of another kind on the Luangwa consists of a little cluster of hand-made bells tied to a rod which itself is stuck into the river bank.

Although the habit of fastening a snare by means of a trigger release to a bent pole is common in the region generally, the technique has not been modified to the capture of fish with hooks on the end of resilient rods, as is the case in Nigeria.

I Lungu ...	...	*Ndobo; Ndobani.*
Nyasa-Tonga ...		*Mbeja;* Kuweja (to hook); Nchingama (hooks on spreaders).
II Nyanja ...	...	*Mbedza;* Kuedza (to use).
Nsenga	...	*Mbezu.*
III Bemba ...	...	Bulobo (Amalobo); Dobani.
Ushi ...	...	*Ndobani.*
Tabwa ...	...	*Ndobo.*
Kaonde...	...	*Kanda (Twanda).*
Unga ...	...	*Buloba (Amalobo).*
Shila ...	...	*Ndobani.*

[468]

Bwile ...	...	*Ndobani*; *Ndobo*; *Akalobo* (*Amalobo*); Ukulobo (to use).
Lamba ...	...	Ndowa; ukulowa (to use).
IV Tonga ...	...	*Ndobyo.*
Ila ...	...	*Kalobo* (*Tulobo*); Mavwehyi (barbless).
We ...	...	Kalobyo (barbless).
V Lozi ...	...	*Kashuto* (*Tushuto*); Kushuta ka tushuto (to use).
VI Lunda ...	...	*Ndobani*; *Lowe sabi* (to use).
Luvale ...	...	*Liyumba* (large barbless); Ulowo (Malowo) (barbed); Kuta ulovo or *Kulowa* (to use); *Linata* (unattended hook); *Kanyangapelu* (to fish with a bunch of worms).
Mbunda ...	...	Ku-loua (to use).
WB Luba ...	...	*Dowani ya mutafu* (light hook on float).
So (Basoko) ...	...	Inango.
Bayanyi ...	...	Lilobo.
Chokwe ...	...	Kayambu (tuyambu); mamina (European hooks).
EB Swahili ...	...	Ndoana.
Baganda ...	...	*Mulobi.*
SB Shona ...	...	Kuraura.
Hlengwe ...	...	Kuvedja (to use).

II. Long Lines

The habit of setting overnight a number of baited hooks attached by short snoods to a long line is not well established, for in most cases the name used is the same as that for single hooks. The Banyoro on Lake Kyoga, however, set long lines, placing heavy unbarbed hooks on to sisal lines with papyrus fibre snoods, which tends to show that the device is of long standing there, and fishers on Stanley Pool make wide use of long lines [Sautter]. The practice of dragging a series of unbaited hooks through the water in the hopes of foul-hooking fish has not been adopted.

I Lungu ...	...	*Utuwamba.*
II Nyanja ...	...	Ntambaliko.
III Bemba ...	...	*Ntanti*; Goshi; Kabamba; Mwando Wamalobo.

Ushi ...	...	*Ntanti.*
Tabwa ...	...	*Utuwamba.*
Unga ...	...	*Ntanti*; Kuteya (to use).
Shila ...	...	*Akabamba.*
Bwile ...	...	*Akabamba*; *Utubamba.*
IV Tonga ...	...	*Chiombo*; *Ndobiyo* (hook).
Ila ...	...	Tulobo.
V Lozi ...	...	*Tushuto.*
VI Lunda ...	...	*Ngoshi*; *Ntanti.*
Luvale ...	...	*Manata.*
Likoma Island		*Ntambaliko.*

III. LURES

While not indigenous, spinners have been widely adopted by enter-prising fishermen who have copied those of European anglers. On Lake Tanganyika and the Kafue near the Meshi-Teshi Gorge such spinners are trolled on handlines behind slowly paddled canoes, and on the Kafue near Kafue town and on the Zambezi at Mambova Africans have attached European spoons, or imitations of them, to long poles on 15 to 20-foot lines. These baits are cast forward and then moved back through the water with a steady sweep of the rod, together with any pike *Sarcodaces* or tiger fish *Hydrocyon* which seize the lure. Similarly, wooden and tin spinners have been adopted on Lake Nyasa [Bertram]. Some, described by Mzumara, for Likoma are exact copies of English mackerel spinners. Poll (*a*) records Tanganyika fishermen casting out baited hooks and retrieving them by hand. On the west side of Lake Tanganyika numbers of two-armed whippy sticks close to the ends of which three pointed hooks are tied are taken out to deep water. Thrashing the surface of the water with them attracts shoals of *m'volo* (*Luciolates*). Near Albertville the water is similarly thrashed with small bundles of dry pointed sticks to attract *Limnothrissa* which are impaled on the points [Poll (*a*)].

I Lungu ...	...	Mbeli-mbeli.
II Tabwa ...	...	Meli-Meli.

E. PROJECTILES

I. SPEARS AND HARPOONS

Fish spears are widely used throughout the region in a variety of circumstances. Commonly they are employed in drying pools and trap enclosures in which fish are concentrated, but their use at night with flares seems to be rarer than the attraction of fish to nets by means of lights. Macquarie indeed reports that the specialist fisherman of the Malagarasi River in Tanganyika ridiculed such a method, although it is well known to the Luvale [White]. On the Zambezi the Lozi move along the grass edge in a canoe and stab at random, and obtain surprisingly good catches. Such casual prodding is also profitable in overgrown weedy pools.* The Twa and Ila spear from rafts made of reed bundles, one such raft being in the Rhodes-Livingstone Museum. The fullest use of spears is made in the vast collective hunts for lung fish (Protopterus) among the grassy swamps around Stanley Pool [Sautter].

Most spears have a single head, with many small barbs (both forward and reverse) raised in the soft iron, securely bound to a shaft of light wood or reed. More rarely, as in the Lukanga area, there may be one or more large barbs. In their simplest form these heads are nowadays made from pieces of fencing wire, but originally the implements may have been plain pointed sticks,† for there is such a tool in the Rhodes-Livingstone Museum from the We of the Zambezi, and also barbless metal spears from the Unga and Twa on Bangweulu. There are scattered records of multident spearheads in the region particularly among the Twa and Unga of Bangweulu [von Rosen and Brelsford] and the Twa of the Lukanga and Kafue flats, and the Rhodes-Livingstone Museum has one from Siachelaba's in the middle Zambezi Valley. The Twa spears have one, two or three points, each with numerous raised barbs, or as in the case of a specimen from Bangweulu and the Lukanga in the Rhodes-Livingstone Museum they may also be barbless. Elsewhere the same effect is achieved by blind stabbing with two or more light spears at one time. The Lozi throw as many as six in a bundle! The Luba also have three- or four-pointed spears [Poll and Renson] as do Stanley Pool fishers [Sautter] and the Ovimbundu of Angola have a spear to which ten sharp prongs of palm stem are attached [Hambly]. On Likoma Island, Lake Nyasa, a barbed trident is fitted on a short thick pole which is recovered by means of a fibre rope; a light may be used to attract fish [Cox]. In the same area single-headed spears are darted at fish without being let go. Canon Cox adds the information that this *lakati* trident was brought to Likoma from the north about the end of the last century, and the recognised price was then three dogs or two goats.

The records of true fish harpoons in which the head is detachable and secured to a float, generally the spear shaft, are sparse, although there is a hippopotamus harpoon in the Rhodes-Livingstone Museum from Lake Bangweulu. The Kiluba have harpoons [Poll (*a*)], the

---

* C. N. Lawrence states that the Luvale use single-headed fish spears with a scoop action " pitchfork " fashion.—EDITOR.

† Thorn points set in reed shafts are used by Gwembe children.—EDITOR.

Bangala [Weeks], and the Stanley Pool fishers [Sautter], while the Nyasas (mentioned above) and the Banyoro tie a line to their spears [Worthington (*a*)]. Livingstone (*b*) illustrates a hippopotamus harpoon and describes a group of hunters living at Niamatobsi Island upstream from Sena (Mocambique).* Harpoons were also once used on Lake Tanganyika [Clark].

The spearing technique of the Batwa river-dwellers of the Kafue Flats is apparently unique in Africa, and resembles only the " dark-hut " method of the North American Indian [Rostlund]. At one time Europeans acquainted with the area considered it to be a recent innovation, but present users have assured me that this is not so. Where the Twa live, the Kafue runs in a well-defined deep channel, onto which a thick mat of swamp vegetation spreads. The fishermen choose a site at the edge of this mat and erect a hollow reed platform some 9 feet square, in the centre of which they place a semi-cylindrical frame sloping down towards the open water. Bringing their canoes alongside the platform, on the landward side, they look down through the 4-foot wide mouth of the funnel to a patch of open water. By covering the platform, the funnel and themselves with blankets all light is excluded, and there being no surface refraction fish swimming by are shown up with startling clarity. Their bident or trident spears are fitted with handles up to 20 feet long, according to the depth of water, and sometimes two shafts are spliced together. There were at least 250 of these " swans " nests in the Twa region in June, 1955, and catches are considerable. On one occasion an old man had a bag of 81 fish (80 of them cichlids) weighing about 75 pounds, for a day's work, and he averred that when the fish were running, a catch of 200-300 a day was not exceptional. A photograph taken in the Lukanga Swamp in 1912 shows a Twa crouching over a canoe with a spear and shading his face with a raised lily leaf [Bruce Miller]. From such a beginning might the " dark-hut " technique have evolved.

II Nyanja ...	... Momba (barbless); Chikolongwe (barbed).
III Bemba ...	... Ukuela; Ukusoe cenga (to use torches); Musumbu.
Ushi ...	... *Musumbu* (*Misumbu*).
Kaonde...	... *Musumbo* (*Misumbo*); *Mungele* (*Mingele*).
Unga ...	... *Bwela* (*Mela*).
Shila ...	... *Musumbu* (*Misumbu*).
Bwile ...	... *Musumbu* (*Misumbu*); Ukwipai sabi no Musombo.

* The Gwembe Valley Tonga formerly used hippopotamus harpoons with detachable heads, but nowadays owing to the ban on hippopotamus hunting and to the danger of such a pursuit they are not used and only rarely to be found.—EDITOR.

	Lamba …	…	Umusumba; Ukusumba (to use); Umondo (Imyondo).
IV	Tonga …	…	*Mumba* (*Miyumba*) (all fish spears); *Namako* (two-pointed); *Muingo* (three-pointed); Mbulu (from hide).
	Ila	…	*Mumba* (*Miyumba*); Ikwa (to use torches).
	We	…	*Mumba*.
V	Lozi	…	*Muwayo* (*Miwayo*); Ku waya (to use).
VI	Lunda …	…	*Isumbu* (*Masumbu*) (barbless); Cisolo (Fisolo) (two-pointed); Ukulasi sabi (to use).
	Luvale …	…	*Mumba*; Kuwaya (to use); Kumunyika (to use torches).
SB	Hlengwe	…	Njungwa.

II. Bows and Arrows

These weapons of the hunter are nowhere adapted on a large scale for fishing,* and except for the Luvale and the Hlengwe of the Sabi River their use seems to be confined to youths as a form of sport. Retrieving lines tied to the arrows are not employed.

III	Bemba …	…	Mifwi.
	Ushi	…	Katamfundo.
V	Lozi	…	Kushonda.
VI	Lunda …	…	Katamfundu.
EB	Swahili	…	Mishiali.
SB	Shona …	…	Kufura.

F. POISONS

Because the poisoning of fish has been frowned upon since the advent of the Europeans it is difficult to judge the extent of the practice to-day. Certainly it is still carried on in secluded waterways, though not as much as in the past. It was probably combined with the erection of barriers and drag-screens, and fish were actually caught by spear, scoop basket or hand.

I personally feel that the damage caused by the method was greatly exaggerated. Considerable effort had to be expended to collect and prepare enough of the various poisons to treat even small stretches of

---

* E. H. Lane Poole in an article in the *Northern Rhodesia Journal* (Vol. III, No. 2, 1956) records that he has seen fishing with bow and arrow carried on in the Luwumbu tributary of the Luangwa River—" a most dexterous performance ".

water; by no means all the fish were killed (clarias being relatively unaffected); and once caught the fish had to be eaten quickly, on account of the rapid putrefaction which appears to take place in poisoned fish, so that only local subsistence fishing was possible.

The bark, leaves and pods of a great variety of shrubs and trees provide poisonous extracts, most of which appear to suffocate the fish by restricting the action of their gills. It is for this reason that the air-breathing *Clarias* are less affected. An account of the actual poisonous plants used to kill fish is beyond the scope of this paper.

I	Lungu ...	...	? Utupa.
III	Bemba ...	...	*Ukusungila* (to mix); *Buba*; *Ububa*; *Imitungalupa*.
	Ushi ...	...	*Ukusungila*; *Buba*.
	Kaonde...	...	? *Ubululu*; *Buba*.
	Unga ...	...	*Ukukwela*.
	Shila ...	...	*Ukusungico Buba*.
	Bwile ...	...	*Ukusungico Buba*.
	Lamba ...	...	*Ukutwila Uwuwa*.
IV	Ila ...	...	*Kutwila*.
	Toka ...	...	*Kutwida*.
	Tonga ...	...	*Bu uba*.
V	Lozi ...	...	*Kuyumbela* (to use); *Siumbeliso*.
VI	Lunda ...	...	*Ukusungilo Ububa*.
	Luvale ...	...	*Kusuuila* (to use): *Usungu*.
WB	Luba ...	...	Buba.
SB	Shona ...	...	Kurovera.

G. MISCELLANEOUS

A number of minor catching methods are not susceptible to classification. Drying pools are sometimes bailed out, and fish caught in baskets, by spear or by hand and this method is a favourite among those who are not fisherfolk. What Gluckman terms " lake-hoeing " in Barotseland is the cutting up of swamp vegetation and the removal of the fish by hand, and Brelsford mentions the actual digging-up of fish aestivating in the Bangweulu Swamp mud.

Fish in small pools may be partially asphyxiated by muddying the water, and are then speared or clubbed as they gasp on the surface. This muddying is often produced by driving a herd of cattle to and fro in the pool.

[474]

The digging of artificial channels to attract fish, as on Lake Edward [Uganda (a)], and among the Bashongo [Torday] is not practised. Nor is the Baluba method recorded by Colle of diving down to large fish armed with hooks or knives.

Stunning clubs are only mentioned specifically by Brelsford among the Unga, although it is a regular practice for fishermen to knock fish on the head as soon as they are brought into the canoes, and on Lake Nyasa to contain them in special parts of the canoes by bundles of grass.

On the Shire River, which runs into the lower Zambezi, sawfish (*Prisiis*) are said to be induced by children splashing in the shallows to make a sufficient rush towards the bank that their saws become embedded in the soft mud, allowing them to be killed [Jubb].

III Bemba ...	...	Kufundawila (muddying water); Miambo (digging).
Ushi ...	...	Kupika (to dig).
Lamba ...	...	Ukusasa (muddying water); Ukupila (to bail).
Shila ...	...	Ukukata (to dig).
Unga ...	...	*Kampompolo* (club).
V Lozi ...	...	*Kucikisa* (muddying water); Kuyuba (to bail); Kuyepa (to dig).
VI Luvale ...	...	Ku kwata wa makovu (hand catching); Kusuwa (to bail).
SB Shona ...	...	Mabemba (to hit with stick).

Devices of Adjoining Areas

EASTERN BANTU REGION

The Bantu around Lake Victoria and Lake Albert termed Lacustrian by Seligman contain many fishing communities, a detailed study of which is beyond the scope of this work. Resemblances between this region and Central Africa have been discussed above; the differences are largely attributable to different aquatic conditions. The East Coast Bantu, following Seligman's classification of the Eastern Bantu, do not appear to have important fisheries. Swahili on Zanzibar have locally made hooks and lines, spears, thrust baskets, barriers and valved traps, and poison [Ingrams], and only their *mgono* (cf. *mono*), a conical trap with its entrance fitted with a spring release, is foreign to Central Africa (though not to the Congo and West Africa). Further south the Mafia Island methods include long lines, valved and baited

[475]

traps, tidal enclosures, drag nets with bags, set nets, and cast nets [Stubbings]. The last is undoubtedly an Arab or Indian introduction, while the bag on the drag nets may have been carried by the Swahili to Lake Tanganyika on their slaving incursions.

The East-Central or Nyasa Bantu cover the remainder of the Eastern Bantu area. They have fishing methods better adapted to cropping the deeper waters of Lake Nyasa, but on the whole the differences between the fishing techniques of this region and those of the Rhodesias are small. For instance, the Tonga of the western shore of Lake Nyasa excel in the underwater manipulation of a variety of nets, but such skill is unlikely to develop in murkier waters elsewhere which can be fished with less effort and danger.

WESTERN BANTU REGION

The fishing methods of the Congo Basin call for a study on their own, and reference is here made only to features of special interest.

The Luba fishing techniques on the Lualaba River are well covered by Colle and by Poll and Renson. They differ only in detail from the methods prevalent in the adjoining areas of Rhodesia, as might be expected in view of the close historical connection. The fishermen dive down to lance fish, and make hooks of curved thorns [Colle]; they set their gill nets (*maliba* or *mukonde*) singly or in batteries to form circles, and to drive the fish they strike the water with a plunger, *kitumpa*, which should be compared with the *Kutumbula* driving method of the Luapula Valley. Their seines were introduced as late as 1943 [Poll and Renson] and being equipped with a pocket, *lusuku*, they probably came from the region of Lake Tanganyika. The name of the seine (*kiamukokwa*) is akin to the *mukwao* of the Bemba area. Women use elongated drag baskets, *kiamba*, similar to those of Rhodesia and Angola.

Poll (*b*) deals fully with Lake Tanganyika, where there are numerous peculiar and specialised methods for the capture of fish in this, the deepest of African waters, where so many species are semi-pelagic. The curved silurid hooks, the many pocketed and staked seines, the luring of fish to jigs, to bundles of pointed grass or to little gleaming nets, the application of dip nets to flare-fishing (which elsewhere is only developed on Lake Nyasa) and the many chambered deepwater traps have all been referred to above. Much of Poll's information refers to the Albertville area, among the Holoholo. Other tribes on the western shore are Bembe, Bwari, Goma, Buye Tumbwe and Tabwa.

The Bushongo in the centre of the southern part of the Belgian Congo dig artificial channels in the swamps to attract fish, and set traps with trigger-released doors [Torday].

The northern bend of the Congo River, between Coquilhatville and Stanleyville, is well documented. The Poto have canoe lift-screens [Goffin and Weeks]. The Basoko have seines, round nets kept open by creepers, baited, in which fish are gilled (possibly constriction traps), nets in the form of lidless boxes over which fish are driven (possibly drag baskets or deepwater seines), round lift nets, and " sweep " nets [Goffin, Weeks and Johnston]. They have banana-shaped floats which overturn when the attached baited hooks are seized; trigger-released doors on traps and oblong baskets, *liemba* (*cf.* the *kiamba* of the Luba) operated by *men* [Johnston]. They have shelter enclosures which are baited, and their fish hooks are believed to have been introduced by white men [Weeks].

In the Cabinda enclave just north of the Congo mouth, the Mayombe are forest dwellers with many cultural affinities with the Ovimbundu of Angola [Hambly]. Most of their fishing methods [Troesch] are similar to those of Central Africa—unvalved baskets in barriers, poisoning, drag baskets, spearing, swamp bailing, and long lines in which the hooks are sharp spines tied with fibre. Line fishing with single hooks is practised only by small boys; the term is *ku loba*, similar to names used much further south, while long lining is *likamba*, also similar. But the Mayombe also use valved traps with two compartments, and traps with trigger-released doors. These, together with round lift nets and canoe screens, are devices found as far west as Southern Nigeria [Maclaren] and typical of West rather than Central Africa.

Baumann's study of the Lunda and associated groups in Angola, referred to in the sections above, shows that their fishing is very much on the same lines as that of the present dwellers in the Zambezi plains, and the same can be said of the Ovimbundu, who on Hambly's detailed evidence have much greater cultural affinities with the Western Bantu of the Congo and Rhodesia than with the Southern Bantu, with whom Seligman groups them. The Ovimbundu have gorges of stiff grass, and ten-pronged spears, and also weirs, weighted baskets of an un-specified type, and poison [Hambly]. Pairs of Vachukwe women drag long baskets against the current, and near Cangamba the Vachukwe, Luchazi and Babunda tribes fish from small bark canoes in the Kwando River. They carry small conical string nets, which are attached to stakes so that the openings face upstream. Like the nets on triangular frames reported from the Limpopo-Sibasi region [Hewitt-Ivy] these may in fact be constricting traps of a pliant fibre.

SOUTHERN BANTU REGION

The relative absence of fishable waters south of Ngamiland and the middle and lower sections of the Zambezi explains the marked paucity of references in the literature of Southern Rhodesia and South Africa to fishing practices. But it does not account for the widespread dislike

[477]

of fish as a food among the Southern Bantu. Most of these consider, or at least used to consider, that fish are unclean [Marquard and Standing], though they sometimes catch them on the coast, and also occasionally inland with basket traps, by spearing and by draining pools. The taboo is most marked among the Ndebele and the Kalanga particularly in respect of unscaled fish [Summers *in litt.*) and these, too, are avoided by many tribes in Central Africa which readily eat other fish.

J. B. Thompson's account of the Hlengwe on the Lundi and Sabi rivers is the most detailed, and has been quoted in the body of the paper above. To summarise, he mentions reed barriers and basket traps coupled with drives, drag fences, baited enclosures, spears, bows and arrows, rods (anciently with fish-bone hooks), small scoop baskets, and poison. No nets are now made, but there is a faint tradition of their use in the past. Floating screens are also attached to the drag fences in the same region, as is clearly illustrated in an excellent series of photographs of drag-fence fishing [Mockford]. A survey of the Mashona and Matabele by Bullock quotes only the BaHlengwe driving into shallows, and entrapping them in specially made open baskets forced onto the sandy floor, and adds that the Makorekore do the same type of fishing with nets. The Shona group are reported to be fish eaters, and to use nets and open baskets, and their women to catch poisoned fish by hand, while among the Ndebele fishing is spasmodic and traps are unknown, and there is a lack of organised fishing activities in their traditional culture [Kuper, Hughes and Velsen]. The Vakaranga have a valved basket trap [Franklin] which seems much the same as a Shona specimen in the National Museum, Bulawayo.

A Shona employee of this museum (Paul Matedza) provided me with much useful information about the rivers flowing to the Mazoe, information probably applicable also to the Rusape and Sabi rivers. The Shona eat only scaled fish, and catch them in barriers and valved baskets. They used a poisonous bark, and possibly in connection with this a staked net, weighted with stones on the bottom, for fish were definitely not driven into the net. They had small scoop baskets, and a sack or skin (not a net) dragged in shallows. Single barbless hooks were made out of wire, and the water was beaten beforehand to attract the fish. Small boys shot fish with arrows, and clubbed fish actually seen, particularly after muddying the pools. A drag barrier of leafy sticks has already been mentioned. The Ndau on the Haroni and Lusitu in Portuguese East Africa dive for large *Barbus* holding in one hand a V-shaped net 6-8 feet long [Bond]. It is probably the same technique referred to by Kidd in 1906, who mentions boys in Gazaland diving into the river and frightening fish into hand nets. The nets are triangular, hinged at the apex, with a spreader-crosspiece (removable for carrying) and are similar to those found on Lake Rukwa and Lake Nyasa. Bond describes the divers as retaining their catch in their teeth or a fold of the net until the completion of the dive.

The BaVenda of Northern Transvaal had fish fences with valved basket traps *mhorna* (*cf.* the *mono* of the peoples north of the Zambezi), bows and arrows, of which the heads had one or more thorns on a reed, rods with baited thorns for hooks, and rudimentary drag " nets " of thick bushy branches [Stayt]. In the Limpopo-Sibasi region, presumably also among the BaVenda, Hewitt-Ivy describes valved baskets in barriers, thrust baskets, drag nets and nets on triangular frames lifted every half-hour (into which fish force their way and are gilled), as well as the scooping-up of fry in sheets of cloth.

The Thonga, on the east coast between the Sabi River and St. Lucia, had no restriction on the use of hooks [Junod]. They erected triangular stick enclosures (*nhangu*) on the shore, closing the entrance at high tide, and placed traps of woven reeds (shibera) on the banks of the tidal rivers. The exact nature of these traps is not clear from Junod's description. Communal fishing in drying lakes (*ku tjeba*) took place, with the use of conical thrust baskets (shiringa). Recent correspondence in South African angling journals shows that elaborate barriers " extending miles " are still maintained in this region, at Kosi Bay, as well as at Port St. Johns, far to the south in Pondoland, although in the latter case they may well have been erected by strangers to the area. These Port St. Johns barriers are reported to be mere stick barriers in which the apertures were closed after the fish had entered [Hammond-Tooke].

The coastal Mpondo are the only fishermen among the south-eastern of the Southern Bantu [Shaw]. Their present-day spear consists of two iron points on a wooden shaft, but the name, *igefu*, may point to a modern origin if it is derived from the word gaff. The Mpondo also use an open basket-scoop for shrimps. From diagrams kindly made by Miss Shaw it is clear that this does not resemble the drag-baskets described above, for the Mpondo scoop is a non-rigid implement $17\frac{1}{2}$ inches deep by $21\frac{1}{2}$ inches broad, held open in a current for shrimps.

A number of small mesh dip, shove and drag nets are licensed annually on the Natal coast by prawners and bait catchers, but these devices are of recent origin [von Puttkamer].

Of the western section of the Southern Bantu, the Herero apparently did no fishing, there being no mention of such activities in Irle's account, though in Ovamboland the inhabitants had barriers (*ouluva*) with valved traps, wooden spears with iron barbs and retrieving cords, and conical thrust baskets [Tonjes]. The Mbunda, at times grouped with the Southern Bantu, are grouped with the Western Bantu.

HOTTENTOTS AND BUSHMEN

The fifteenth century Hottentots had neither boats nor hooks, and those on the sea threw assegais with lines attached, and built stone weirs [Theal], but by the early twentieth century they had come to be skilled fishermen with lines, spears and introduced trek (seine), stake and drift nets [W. W. Thompson]. According to Schapera (a) they employed hooks of teeth or bone, nets of fibre, reed baskets and pointed sticks for spears, as well as stone weirs in the sea. They later adopted iron hooks and sinew lines. The stone weirs of the Hottentots are described by Goodwin (a) as dry-stone walls covered by normal tides. His photographs show that the weirs (vywers) are semi-circular, sometimes in pairs, but have no collecting chambers or corners. They extend from the Berg River over a thousand miles of coastline to Kosi Bay, where they are used by the Bantu who have been in the area for 300 years. Elsewhere these weirs are associated with midden deposits dating to early Neolithic times, though around Agulhas some weirs are still maintained. The "mermaid scene" cave painting from George District, depicted on the cover of Vol. II, No. 7, of the *South African Archaeological Bulletin*, may perhaps represent the fishing of such a weir [Clark].

The Bushmen of the Kalahari erected stone weirs in the few river pools, and drove fish into lines of baskets [Dornan, and Schapera (a)]. They made a poison from *Euphorbia* but had no hooks. The Makobos of the Okavango River were the most skilled, having rafts, spears and nets of rushes [Dornan]. Anderson in 1861 (b) confirmed that the Ovaquangari of the Okavango had no nets, but only reed screens and beehive-shaped traps. The same author (a) found none of the Bechuanas fishing in Lake Ngami, though the conquered Bayeye did so with spears and also fibre nets, which Livingstone (a) also noted when he discovered the lake in 1849. This Ngami region, however, is the home of such a welter of tribes and mixed races and cultures that little direct comparison between peoples and environment is possible [Schapera (b), 40]. By 1955 the river Bushmen, as an organised community, had ceased to exist [van der Post].

A rock painting from the Mpongweni Mountain, Natal, tentatively ascribed to "very late" Bushmen, depicts nine canoes (?) in a semi-circle, with one man in each spearing fish [Batiss]. Either paddles or extra spears project over the other ends of the canoes. Another man on foot holds a spear. No prong or barb is shown. A very similar cave painting in Griqualand East is ascribed by Goodwin (b) to the same artist.

Discussion

It is a fact clearly demonstrated in a general study such as Hornell's that there is a relative lack of variety in the fishing devices of most Central African tribes or areas when comparison is made with similar peoples and environments elsewhere in Africa or Asia. But I feel that this merely signifies that except on lakes such as Nyasa and Tanganyika, the indigenous population has never, at least until very recent years, had to exercise much ingenuity to catch all the fish it needed. The region has always been thinly peopled, and in the absence of settled communities and organised trade, fishing was naturally conducted only for local subsistence. Simple methods such as spearing, poisoning, trapping and the dragging of drying pools were quite adequate to provide the necessary amount of fish, even for communities such as the Twa of the Kafue, Lukanga and Bangweulu, who by force of circumstances were driven to depend heavily on their fishing. Only of late years has the demand for greater catches, linked, of course, with a growing cash economy, led to a cropping of the open waters of the three lakes Mweru, Bangweulu and Nyasa, and of the Kafue River. Lake Tanganyika, on account of its tremendous depth and relative paucity of easily caught fish, cannot be compared with the other three waters. This trend towards the individual enterprise of commercialised fishing is linked with a corresponding decrease in the importance of the collective and often primitive methods of fish cropping which in the past were such a feature of the rural calendar.

Some implements and devices described above are so widespread that a study of their distribution is fruitless. For instance, spears, hooks and poison are so general in their world occurrence that their origin is quite obscure. In the case of others, such as the thrust basket, the valved basket and the constricting cone, all of which are found throughout Africa and Asia, it is just as likely that similar evolution took place separately (at least in a number of major regions) as that they were derived from a common origin. Worthington (c) also concludes that many similar devices have been evolved separately by the various peoples as a reaction to their similar wants and environments. Hornell agrees that parallel development has taken place in Asia and Africa, but argues that the similarity in basic ideas points to a long-standing culture contact between East Africa and India, a conclusion with which not all will concur.

However, there is sufficient evidence to show that a considerable amount of diffusion has taken place, and also that present-day fishing communities in the region are far from conservative in adopting strange techniques. The case of the large valved basket called *ntumba* on Lake Victoria, and *itumba* on the Luapula, has already been quoted. In this connection it is interesting that the device (still with the same name) became of first importance throughout much of Barotseland within a decade of its introduction.

Several other instances of recent transfers have been recorded, such as that of the Luchaze borrowing techniques from the Luena at Balo-

[481]

vale [McCulloch], and of the Old Mbunda bringing drag baskets to Loziland [Gluckman].

The far from simple *chirimila* net of the Nyasa-Tonga, too, is so similar to the *lituwa* of the upper Zambezi Lozi that a connection almost certainly exists. In the past the tide of conquest must have transferred knowledge and experience from one people to another, though it must be remembered that newcomers are likely to have learnt as much from those they mingled with as the converse. An example of this happening would appear to be afforded by the southern invaders of the Luyi country on the Zambezi about the beginning of the nineteenth century [J. M. Thompson]. It is unlikely, in view of the present habits of the Southern Bantu, that they had much previous experience of fishing, and yet the population still contains some of the most efficient fishermen in the Territory, just as it did in 1854 when Livingstone passed through.

In this case the invading Makololo, whom Jalla describes as being of mixed Basuto and Bechwana origin, were a minority and later in the century were assimilated, together with much of their original language, without having had any noticeable effect on either the names or the types of fishing devices.

Consequent upon settled administration there is now a considerable peaceful expansion taking place. The thriving gill-net fishery on Lake Mweru has attracted strangers to swell the numbers of the local Bwile and Shila fishermen, while on the Kafue Flats the 400-odd draw nets are operated largely by Nyasalanders in the lower reaches and Lozi in the upper, as well as by a variety of other strangers. The resident tribes supply some of the labour for the net owners, but only to a limited extent have they adopted their methods. The Nyasa-landers are becoming more and more settled, but the Lozi are still largely annual visitors. As their own waters are still relatively unfished it is possible that their migrations are partially designed to escape the obligations of family life. Fosbrooke mentions that on the south of Lake Victoria a number of overlapping migrations were attributable to this reason, and I noted exactly the same situation in the Niger delta.

Whatever the cause of these movements, the result is a diffusion and intermingling of techniques which is becoming increasingly difficult to record and interpret.

It has already been pointed out how poorly off the region is for nets, and how absolutely deficient in the basic net-making tools (the shuttle and the gauge). This is largely due to the previous lack of need for them, elaborated above. It is fairly certain that draw nets are a very recent introduction to most of the area, but coarse gill nets may be older. Graham and Worthington (c) both considered that the scoop

[482]

net of the Nilotic Jaluo was the only type strictly indigenous to the East African lakes, seines having been probably introduced to Lake Victoria about 1910. However, Livingstone (b) saw seine nets on Lake Nyasa in 1869.

The coarse tangle net of the Lozi and their peculiar lifting draw net may well be indigenous, the type of twine and the method of knotting being the same as for the widespread game nets. Further, they are only fitted with grass floats and stone weights.

Appendix

NATIVE TRIBES OF NORTHERN RHODESIA

GROUP I.—MAMBWE-SPEAKING TRIBES:

Mambwe.	*Lungu.*	Inamwanga.	Iwa.
Tambo.			

GROUP II.—TUMBUKA-NYANJA-SPEAKING TRIBES:

Tumbuka.	Yombe.	Fungwe.	Wandya.
Wenya.	Lambya.	Nyika.	Kamanga.
Senga.	*Chewa.*	Ngoni.	Ambo.
Chikunda.	*Nyasa-Tonga.*		

GROUP III.—WEMBA AND LALA-LAMBA-SPEAKING TRIBES:

Wemba (Bemba).	Mukulu.	Ngubu.	Chishinga.
Ushi.	Kawendi.	*Shila.*	*Bwile.*
Tabwa.	*Unga.*	Lala.	*Lamba.*
Lima.	Swaka.	Wisa.	Sewa.
Kaonde.	*Luano.*		

GROUP IV.—TONGA-ILA-SPEAKING TRIBES:

Tonga (including *Twa*).	*Ila.*	Sala.	Lundwi.
Lumbu.	*Soli.*	*Lenje.*	*We.* ⋆
Gowa.	Leya.	Toka.	Subya.
Totela.			

GROUP V.—SIKOLOLO-SPEAKING TRIBES:

Rozi (Lozi).	Kwangwa.	Shanjo.	Mashi.
Simaa.	Nyengo.	Mwenyi.	Makoma.
Ndundulu.	Kwandi.		

GROUP VI.—LUNDA-LUBA-SPEAKING TRIBES:

Lunda.	Luba.	Ndembo.	Nkoya.
Mashasha.	*Luchaze.*	Lushange.	Mbowe.
Luvale.	*Mbunda.*	Lukolwe.	Mbwera.

NATIVE TRIBES OF ADJOINING AREAS

EB	*Eastern Bantu* ...	*Baganda.*	*Swahili.*	*Fipa.*
WB	*Western Bantu* ...	*Yombe.* *Luimbi.*	*So (Basoko).* *Chokwe.*	*Luba.*
SB	*Southern Bantu* ...	*Shona.* *Venda.*	*Karanga.* *Hlengwe.*	*Ndebele.* *Tonga.*

⋆ The We should more correctly be called the Valley Tonga. Throughout the text of this paper, however, the former name has been used in accordance with the intentions of the Author.—EDITOR.

References

ANDERSSON, D. J. (*a*). *Lake Ngami*. 1856.

ANDERSSON, D. J. (*b*). *The Okavango River*. 1861.

BATTISS, W. W. Addendum on "Prehistoric Fishing Scenes", Vol. XCI, *South African Journal of Science*. 1944.

BAUMANN, H. VON. *Lunda: bei Bauern und Jagern in Inner Angola*. 1935.

BERTRAM, C. K. R., etc. *Report on the Fish and Fisheries of Lake Nyasa*. 1942.

BOONE, O. *Carte ethnique du Congo Belge et du Ruanda-Urundi*, Zaire VIII, No. 5. 1954.

BOULENGER, G. A. *Les Poissons du Bassin du Congo*. 1901.

BRELSFORD, W. V. *Fishermen of the Bangweulu Swamps*. 1946.

BULLOCK, C. *The Mashona and the Matabele*. 1950.

BURTON, R. F. *The Lake Regions of Central Africa*. 1860.

CHATELAIN, H. *Folk Tales of Angola*. 1894.

COCKROFT, I. G. "Hunting", *Nada*, XII. 1934.

COLLART, A. (*a*). "La Peche au Ndagala au lac Tanganyika", *Bull. Agricole Congo Belge*. 1954.

COLLE, R. P. *Les Balubas*. 1913.

COLSON, E., and GLUCKMAN, M. *Seven tribes of British Central Africa*. 1951.

DEBENHAM, F. *Study of an African Swamp*. 1952.

DOKE, C. M. *The Lambas of Northern Rhodesia*. 1931.

DORNAN, S. S. *Pygmies and Bushmen of the Kalahari*. 1925.

FOSBROOKE, H. A. "Some Aspects of Kimwami Fishing Culture", *Journal of the Royal Anthropological Institute*, LXV. 1934.

FRANKLIN, H. "Traps in common use among the Vakaranga", *Nada*, IX. 1931.

GLUCKMAN, M. *Economy of the Central Barotse Plain*. 1941.

GOFFIN, A. *Les Pecheries et les poissons du Congo*. 1909.

GOODWIN, A. J. (*a*). "Prehistoric Fishing Methods in South Africa", *Antiquity*, Vol. 20. 1946.

GOODWIN, A. J. (*b*). "A Fishing Scene from East Griqualand", *South African Archaeological Bulletin*, IV/14. 1949.

GRAHAM, M. *The Victoria Nyanza and its Fisheries*. 1929.

HAMBLY, W. D. *The Ovimbundu of Angola*. 1934.

HEWITT-IVY, R. "Extermination of Fish in Native Areas", *Veld and Vlei*, I/27. 1955.

HOLUB, E. *Seven Years in South Africa (Trans.)*. 1881.

HOOLE, M. C. *Nyasaland Journal*, 8. 1955.

HORNELL, J. *Fishing in Many Waters*. 1950.

HUGHES, J. E. *Eighteen Years on Lake Bangweulu*. 1932.

INGRAMS, W. H.   *Zanzibar, its History and Peoples.*   1931.

IRLE, J.   *Die Herero: ein Beitrag zur Landes-Volksund Missionskunde.*   1906.

JALLA, A.   *Litaba za Sichaba sa Malozi.*   1922.

JASPAN, M. A.   *The Ila Tonga Peoples of North-Western Rhodesia.*   1953.

JOHNSTON, SIR H. H.   *George Grenfell and the Congo.*   1908.

JUNOD, H. A.   *The Life of a South African Tribe.*   1927.

KIDD, D.   *Savage Childhood.*   1906.

KINGSLEY, M.   *West African Studies.*   1899.

KOMA KOMA, W. P.   *Ukonde Wophera Nsomba.*   1950.

KUPER, H., etc.   *The Shona and Ndebele of Southern Rhodesia.*   1955.

LAGERCRANTZ, S.   *Fish hooks in Africa and their Distribution.*   1934.

LETH, T., and LINDBLOM, K. G.   *Two kinds of Fishing Implements.*   1933.

LIVINGSTONE, D. (*a*).   *Missionary Travels in South Africa.*   1857.

LIVINGSTONE, D. and C. (*b*).   *Narrative of an Expedition to the Zambesi and its Tributaries.*   1865.

LOWE, R.   *Report on the Tilapia and other Fish and Fisheries of Lake Nyasa.*   1952.

MACKENZIE, D. R.   *The Spirit Ridden Konde.*   1925.

MACLAREN, P. I. R.   " Netting knots and Needles ", *Man*, LV.   1955.

MARQUARD, L., and STANDING, T. G.   *The Southern Bantu.*   1939.

McCULLOCH, G. M.   *The Southern Lunda and Related Peoples.*   1951.

MELLAND, F. H.   *In Witchbound Africa.*   1923.

MOCKFORD, H. H.   " Netting Party in Lundi and Sabi Rivers ", *South African Angler*, No. V/10.   1951.

MOORE, R. J.   *Industry and Trade on the Shores of Lake Mweru, Africa.*   1937.

POLL, M., and RENSON, H.   *Les Poissons, leur milieu et leur peche au bief superieur du Lualaba.*   1948.

POLL, M. (*a*).   *Bulletin Agricole du Congo-Belge*, XXXIX.   1948.

RICHARDS, A. I.   *Land, Labour and Diet in Northern Rhodesia.*   1939.

RICARDO, C. K.   *Report on Fish and Fisheries of Rukwa and Lake Bangweulu.*   1939.

ROSCOE, J.   *The Baganda.*   1911.

ROSEN, E. VON.   *Trasfolket.*   1916.

ROSTLUND, E.   " Freshwater Fish and Fishing in Native North America ", *Univ. Calif. Pub. Geog.*, Vol. IX.   1952.

SAUTTER.   *Les Pecheurs du Stanley Pool.*

SCHAPERA, I. (*a*).   *The Khoisan Peoples of South Africa.*   1930.

SCHAPERA, I. (*b*).   *The Bantu Speaking Tribes of South Africa.*   1946.

SELIGMANN, C. G.   *Races of Africa.*   1930.

SILISHEBO, D. L. *Bundui mwa Bulozi.* 1952.

SMITH, E. W., and DALE, A. M. *The Ila Speaking Peoples of Northern Rhodesia.* 1920.

South African Archaeological Bulletin, Vol. II, No. 7 (cover).

STAYT, H. A. *The Ba Venda.* 1931.

STUBBINGS, B. J. J. " Notes on Native Methods of Fishing in the Mafia Islands ", *Tanganyika Notes and Records.* 1945.

STUBBS, J. M. " Fresh Water Fisheries in the Northern Bahr-el-Ghazal Waters ", *Sudan Notes and Records,* XXX. 1949.

SUMMERS, R. F. H. " Imbahuru Hill, Belingwe ", *Nada* XXIX. 1952.

THEAL, G. M. *Ethnography and Condition of Africa before 1505.* 1919.

THOMPSON, J. M. (*a*). *Report of the Native Fishing Industry.* 1930.

THOMPSON, J. M. (*b*). *Memorandum on the Native Tribes and Tribal Areas of Northern Rhodesia.* 1934.

TONJES, H. *Ovamboland: Land, Leute, Mission.* 1911.

TORDAY, E. *On the Trail of the Bushongo.* 1925.

UGANDA (*a*). *Report of the Department of Game and Tsetse Control.* 1950.

UGANDA (*b*). *Report of the Department of Game and Tsetse Control.* 1951.

WEEKS, J. H. " Bangala of the Upper Congo River ", *Journal of the Royal Anthropological Institute,* XXXIX. 1909.

WHITE, C. M. N. " The Role of Hunting and Fishing in Luvale Society ", *African Studies,* 15. 1956.

WORTHINGTON, E. B. (*a*). *A Report on the Fishing Survey of Lakes Albert and Kioga.* 1929.

WORTHINGTON, E. B. (*b*). *A Report on the Fisheries of Uganda.* 1932.

WORTHINGTON, E. B. (*c*). *Inland Waters of Africa.* 1933.

MAPS: 1:3,000,000 Tribal Maps of East Africa, 1943.

The Editor regrets that he has been unable to trace full references for the ollowing:

BLACHE, etc., in press.

BURDON, T. W. 1951.

COLLART, A. (*b*). 1956.

DEPASSE, P. 1956.

MATAGNE, F. 1950.

MATHIEU, Y. 1956.

POLL, M. (*a*). 1952.

POLL, M. (*b*). 1955.

THOMPSON, W. W. 1913.

TROESCH, J. 1955.

WITHERS, F. M. 1952.

Informants

BOND, DR. G.

BONT, DR. A. F. DE.

BORLEY, H. J. H.

BRUCE MILLER, W. F., M.B.E.

BURDON, —.

BURGER, REV. J. P.

CLARK, DR. J. D.

COSTA, M. S. DA.

COX, CANON H. A. M.

FOSBROOKE, H. A.

FRYER, G.

GOSSE, J. D.

HAMMOND-TOOKE, DR. W. G.

ILES, T. D.

JACKSON, P. B. N.

JINKIN, REV. B. D.

JUBB, R. A.

LABUSCHAGNE, G. J.

LAMMOND, W., M.B.E.

LAWRENCE, C. N.

MADOCKS, J. E.

MATEDZA, P.

MITCHELL-HEGGS, M.

MZUMARA, A. J. P.

RITTY, DR. D. A. W.

SHAW, MISS E. M.

SUMMERS, R. F. H.

THOMPSON, J. B.

THOMPSON, MAJOR G.

VAN DER POST, L.

VON PUTTKAMER, E. C.

ZWAHLER, REV. J. L.

The above-mentioned people very kindly supplied information which has been incorporated in this paper.

13

RUBBER

A FOOTNOTE TO
NORTHERN RHODESIAN HISTORY

R. H. HOBSON

1960

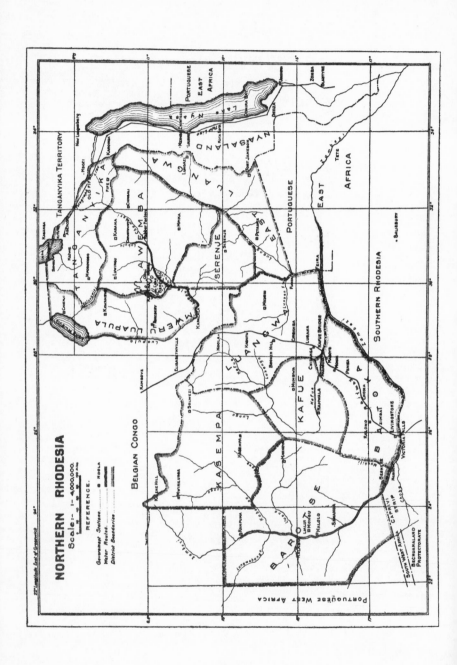

NORTHERN RHODESIA

Scale:- 1- 4,000,000.

REFERENCE.

Government Stations........ ● Ndola
Water Routes..................
District Boundaries...........

BELGIAN CONGO

TANGANYIKA TERRITORY

PORTUGUESE EAST AFRICA

NYASALAND

PORTUGUESE EAST AFRICA

SOUTHERN RHODESIA

PORTUGUESE WEST AFRICA

I. INTRODUCTION

Rubber—India rubber or Caoutchouc—is the milky juice found in several kinds of trees and shrubs, and is so called because one of its earliest European uses was for erasing. The juice or *latex* consists of rubber hydrocarbon mixed with various other substances (differing according to the source) and dispersed in water. This latex can be dried and coagulated by various methods to provide the raw rubber of commerce. The properties of rubber were known in South America from early times, and Columbus is said to have seen the natives of Haiti playing with a rubber ball. It did not reach Europe, however, until early in the nineteenth century, when small quantities were exported from trees growing wild in Brazil and used in the manufacture of waterproof overshoes and MacIntosh's raincoat and similar articles. These all suffered, however, from the instability of rubber in varying temperatures which made it hard in winter and sticky in summer. In 1844, Charles Goodyear, the Connecticut inventor, patented the mixture of rubber and sulphur now known as vulcanisation, which revolutionised the industry.

The wild sources of rubber were the only ones for many years, but in 1876, Sir Henry Wickham smuggled seeds of the Brazilian tree *Hevea braziliensis* to Kew Gardens, and from these grew all the trees on the enormous Asian plantations of to-day. Wild rubber, however, continued to be a major source of supply for many years, and it was not until 1910 that any considerable quantity of plantation rubber was put on the market. In 1916, 33 per cent. of world production (54,000 tons) still came from wild sources: but by 1940, nearly 99 per cent. of all rubber was provided by the plantations. The price of rubber fluctuated from 12s. per lb. in 1910 to 7½d. in 1921.

The wild sources of rubber besides *H. braziliensis* were *Funtumia* in the Gold Coast and other parts of Africa, *Manihot* from the Ceara Province of Brazil, and the *Landolphia* vine of several species. In Northern Rhodesia, these *Landolphia* species, together with the roots of *Carpodinus*, formed the chief sources of supply. Experiments with plantation rubber in the form of *H. braziliensis* (*Para*, as it is also called from a Brazilian province where it was formerly particularly rich) and *Ceara*, were totally unsuccessful.

The export of wild rubber from Central and East Africa probably reached its peak about 1910, and of all these territories, Northern Rhodesia was (with the exception of Zanzibar) the least important.

P. J. Greenway, in his *Wild Rubber in East Africa* notes that about the year 1910, Uganda and Kenya each supplied about 100,000 lb. of wild rubber, Tanganyika 300,000, Zanzibar 4,000, and Nyasaland nearly 60,000. The official return for Northern Rhodesia in 1912—the best year—was 15,708 lb. Nyasaland, richer in *Landolphia* than Northern Rhodesia, was also the home of the only successful attempt at plantation rubber, and the lakeshore Vizara Estate is still happily in production, since it has the very wet tropical conditions essential for *Para*. (The failure of *Para* in Northern Rhodesia is thus understandable: that *Ceara* was equally unsuitable there is not so clear, and Mr. C. G. Trapnell, formerly Government Ecologist in Northern Rhodesia, believes its failure may have been connected with lack of knowledge of a special tapping technique rather than with lack of rainfall).

Botanically, *Landolphia* have been described by Greenway as " hairy or glabrous shrubs, often of large size, usually climbing by branched terminal or false-axillary tendrils (modified flowering branches) or by sensitive flowering branches; their leaves are opposite of varying size; flowers usually white, tubular, sweetly scented, rarely up to two inches long in bud, sessile or stalked in few- or many-flowered corymbs or panicles which are sensitive and often act as hooks or tendrils; fruit a globular or pear-shaped berry, sometimes of a large size; seeds few to many embedded in a juicy pulp. The fruits of some species are edible." The main sources of *Landolphia* are the Northern, North-Western and Western Provinces together with the northern parts of the Central Province.

The other source of rubber in Northern Rhodesia, *Carpodinus gracilis**, is peculiar to the Kalahari sand areas of Barotseland and the North-Western Province. This is a small shrub of about knee-height which is common in the woodlands of this region, although it also assumes a climbing habit in dense thicket areas. Its general appearance is very similar to that of the *Landolphia* species, to which it is, in fact, closely related.†

---

*A French botanist has recently classified *Carpodinus gracilis* as a species of *Landolphia* under the name of *L. camptoloba*.

† Mr. C. G. Trapnell has provided the following list of the main sources of wild rubber in Northern Rhodesia:

    (*A*) *Tapping vines, also capable of bark extraction from stems and roots.*

        (1) *Landolphia buchananii*. *Mushitu* vine, in quantity only in Western and North-Western Provinces. Rarer in Northern and Luapula Provinces.

        (2) *Landolphia kirkii*. Vine or bush of woodlands and thickets; Northern, Luapula, Central, Western and North-Western Provinces.

    (*B*) *Root rubbers, suitable only for bark extraction from roots.*

        (1) *Carpodinus gracilis*. Small vine or ground shrub of the Kalahari sands of Barotseland, Balovale and Mwinilunga.

        (2) *Landolphia parvifolia*. Of very little use and in certain strains only. Northern, Central, Western and North-Western Provinces: locally in Western Barotseland and the Southern Province. (Certain other tapping vines exist in *mushitus*, but are rarer.)

In the Second World War, when the Far Eastern plantations were overrun by the Japanese, wild rubber in Northern Rhodesia emerged from the obscurity of twenty years, and very considerable research into sources and methods of production were undertaken by Mr. Trapnell and embodied in such publications as his *Interim Report on Methods of Extraction of Landolphia Rubber.* (Government Printer, Lusaka, May, 1942); *The Purchase of Raw Rubber* (Government Printer, Lusaka, July, 1942); and *Further Methods for the Preparation of Wild Rubber* (Government Printer, Lusaka, November, 1943). In brief, the methods evolved dealt with two methods of extraction—the tapping of vines with a liberal flow of latex, and the extraction of coagulated rubber from the stems of larger vines and the roots generally. The extraction of root rubber, unlike tapping, is laborious, and involves the removal of the bark, the beating of it to pulverise it, and finally a washing treatment which may be accompanied by further beating. In traditional methods of production, tapped rubber was produced in the form of balls, while root rubber was mainly in the form of bars or rolls. Improved methods required the preparation of both types in the form of thin sheets.

Research now being carried out at the Rhodes-Livingstone Museum by Mr. Clayton Holliday is obtaining interesting results towards a theory that wild latex in the fresh state may have been used as a base for prehistoric rock paintings. It is also quite certain that Africans did not need European influence to discover simple uses for wild rubber such as in the manufacture of drums and drumsticks (the latter were noted by C. Molyneux in the Gwembe Valley in 1914), and as rubber balls for children's play. Livingstone, on his journeys in the 1850s, collected a ball of wild rubber which is now in the Rhodes-Livingstone Museum, and there appears to have been a steady traffic in wild rubber in the Barotseland area through to Angola dating back to the earliest days of any demand from the European market. But the trade could only survive while the price was high because of the inordinate amount of labour involved in the extraction of trivial amounts of rubber. Captain K. R. Paterson observed at Mwinilunga in the early years of the Second World War that two native workers put in 124 man-hours to produce two " chitotas " (the usual quantity worked at one time). The area was one of the richest in Northern Rhodesia: the richest vines were chosen and collected not more than a mile away, and the weight of each chitota (a roll of about fourteen inches by one and a half inches) was 2½ lb. Its value then was four square yards of cloth. Mr. G. S. Jones, writing at the same period, quoted a Balovale method of production in which about forty sticks about a foot long by two inches in diameter were worth 10*s.* about the year 1908. In the Northern

Province, a Lungu messenger told Mr. C. G. Trapnell, the Government ecologist, that he could recall Swahili traders dealing in sticks of rubber (the adulteration of balls with stones and other foreign matter was not unknown) in his youth in the Mporokoso and Abercorn districts.

There is considerable evidence of rubber gathering before any extensive European visit to Central Africa, but it is probable that there was no European-controlled and organised exploitation until the opening of the Congo area by Stanley in the 1870s, which was followed by the administration of the International Association for the Exploration and Civilisation of Africa in 1876; and, most important, the period after 1885 in which King Leopold of Belgium transformed the Congo into an estate of private ownership. Of this period, Roger Casement, later to achieve fame of another kind, reported (he was H.M. Consul at Boma) as late as 1903 the most brutal exploitation: " Each time the corporal goes out to get rubber, cartridges are given to him. He must bring back all not used, and for every one used he must bring back a right hand. . . ." It was this report which brought about the formation of the Congo Reform Association in 1904 by E. D. Morel, the reformer and author of the book *Red Rubber*.

In this connection, there is a curious sidelight recalled by Mr. G. Stokes, of Abercorn, who relates that he heard the following story. The late H. W. Sheane relieved a capable Swede, named Leyer, as District Commissioner, Fife, and Leyer told Sheane that Casement had written to him at the time of his campaign against the Belgians asking for any photographs he might have of mutilated natives.

By this time, of course, the administrations of both North-Western and North-Eastern Rhodesia had for some while been casting about for any natural resources which might profitably be exported, and the currently high price of rubber brought about a wave of enthusiasm for it which indirectly—for rubber itself was a dream which vanished—contributed to the romance of the development of Northern Rhodesia.

In North-Western Rhodesia, Government interest in rubber production seems to have taken practical effect with the appointment as Rubber Conservator in 1901 or 1902 of Louis de Fries, a German, a trained naturalist and keen sportsman who was at one time (according to the accounts of the late D. Gordon Lancaster and the late Chirupula Stephenson) a goat buyer in Nyasaland; and at other times at the Chifumbaze Mine and an agent of the North Charterland Company. As Rubber Conservator, de Fries built himself a house on the rise just to the north of the present Rutland Hotel at Ndola, and planted the eucalyptus trees which still stand there. According to Chirupula, however, the results of his rubber investigations were so meagre that the Deputy Administrator gave it up, and de Fries left for England to study mineralogy following the discovery of Bwana Mkubwa.

Although there was wild rubber to be found round Ndola, conditions were perhaps more favourable in North-Eastern Rhodesia, where there was the additional accident of the presence of one of the chief heroes of this story: Johan Cornelius (or Cornelis) de Josselin (or de Josselyn) de Jong, who ultimately became the first Secretary for Agriculture in the government of the combined territories. He was a Hollander of good family: Sir Stewart Gore-Browne recalls that in 1920, when he was on his way back from the army at Cologne, he stayed with de Jong in Haarlem to discuss his plans for essential oils, and met a younger brother, Major de Jong, who was an equerry to Queen Wilhelmina. Mr. H. J. R. Hatchwell, of Livingstone, a long-time colleague of de Jong in the Agriculture Department, remembers a second brother who was a Court physician.

Mr Hatchwell believes that de Jong was not a trained agriculturist, but had possibly been connected with vanilla-growing in the Dutch East Indies (vanilla he tried in Northern Rhodesia, but it failed). However, Richard Sampson's researches have shown that de Jong entered North-Eastern Rhodesia from the east in 1896. The exact date on which he joined the administration as a probationer is obscured by contradictions in various editions of the British South Africa Company's Civil Service List, but it is more probable that the date was May rather than August of 1901, and in the same year the Mirongo district notebook shows that he was Assistant Native Commissioner at Katumbi Station. His occupation between the time of entering North-Eastern Rhodesia and of joining the Administration is no more known than his previous history: but that he had agricultural experience is borne out not only by the recollections of Mr. Hatchwell (and a similar recollection from the late Sir Tom Page) but by the fact that he was placed in charge of agricultural experiments on April 1, 1905, a date of less than happy choice in the light of future events.

But it would be less than fair to lay at de Jong's doorstep the failure of rubber to bear out the high hopes once held; or to suggest that his ignorance was to blame for the failure of some of his projects. Sir Stewart Gore-Browne recalls an unkind legend that he had failed in farming in Nyasaland—which qualified him for teaching others. To Sir Stewart's own knowledge, and nowhere contradicted, de Jong was an optimist: and in a new country where, in Mr. Hatchwell's words, " We tried all and sundry " in the hope of finding economic crops, this was no bad thing.

He was ingenious as well as optimistic, according to the late Sir Tom Page, who recalled de Jong's invention of some elaborate machinery for silk-worm culture and silk production, which unfortunately came to nothing. Coffee was a favourite of de Jong's, and in later years, says Mr. Hatchwell, the most successful was a high veld coffee " Blue Mountain ", imported from Jamaica and grown at Abercorn. The company, says Mr. Hatchwell, proudly served Abercorn coffee at their official luncheons in the Broad Street Offices in London. He started a scheme to encourage the production of sunflowers, linseed and castor oils in later years.

Quinine was another experimental failure, but apparently setbacks left de Jong undismayed.

Socially, de Jong seems to have been one of the most popular men of his day, and perhaps the best introductory sketch is provided by Mr. E. S. Eagland, who retired from the post of Government Printer in 1932: " He was a Hollander whom I first met in Livingstone about 1912. He was a well set-up and groomed fellow who posed a nicely trimmed beard, wore pince-nez glasses, and gave the impression of being a genial ' clubman ' who had travelled around and much enjoyed life in North-Eastern Rhodesia in the early days there . . .".

Mr. R. B. Dean remembers him as a portly six-footer, and many remember his strong Dutch accent (which occasionally revealed itself in un-English locutions in his official reports). Mr. B. L. Hunt describes him as a " Captain Kettle " type, whose usual invitation to a sundowner was " coom along and hellip yoursellif ".

His occupation compelled him to travel extensively (possibly accounting for the trend of such nicknames as " JOGALONG " and " JOSTLINGALONG "), and this was accomplished in a certain amount of state: he was always impeccably dressed, and his camp was established and transported with the aid of forty-four carriers. (" I can remember the actual number", writes Mr. T. C. Moore, who came to Northern Rhodesia as cotton expert six months after de Jong retired, " because many people told me about his leisurely journeyings in the farming areas with his forty-four carriers, and because I was told it was presumed that forty-four would be my entitlement." When Mr. Moore asked what on earth he would do with forty-four carriers, the remark was " received with rather pained and shocked surprise.")

Mrs. Walter Harvey recalls not only de Jong's charm and neatness (he changed for dinner every night whether in or out of camp), but his compendious camping kit, which included a silver set for his dressing table and a portrait of his wife (an occasional visitor: she could not stand the country according to Mr. Hatchwell, whose children were playmates of de Jong's small boy).

Mr Hatchwell tells a pleasant story of de Jong's attention to details of his personal comfort. Staying with him at Chilanga, de Jong was kept awake by the rattling of loose sheets of corrugated iron on the roof. He got up, called his carriers, and posted them on the roof to sleep there and hold the sheets down.

Mr. Hatchwell also tells the tale of de Jong's servant (probably Goleti, his cook for twenty-five years) who had "a dreadful vice". It appears that every time de Jong stayed with Mr. Hatchwell at Chilanga, the chamber-pot was unaccountably found to be missing on his departure. After some time, when Mr. Hatchwell was taking over de Jong's Livingstone house while de Jong went on leave, he was shown the pantry—which contained a large collection of chamber-pots. De Jong confessed that this unmentionable disgrace was the fault of his servant. "Wherever I go, he has one hidden away somewhere. I get them down here, I can't advertise them, and this is all I could do." He offered Mr. Hatchwell his pick, or even the lot: however, Mr. Hatchwell accepted only his own, but took the subsequent precaution on de Jong's visit to Chilanga of attaching it with a padlock and chain to the bedpost.

However, we must leave our "big blond Dutch *gentleman*" (Mr. V. D. Browne's phrase) for an earlier period—to the time, indeed, before he appeared on the official scene—and to an outline of the first interest in the collection of wild rubber by the Government and the production of plantation rubber.

It appears from the *Rhodesia Agricultural Journal* (Vol. I, No. 3) that in Southern Rhodesia experiments with plantation rubber had begun as early as 1900 (with extremely disappointing results from *Ceara* trees). In Northern Rhodesia, an investigation of the rubber resources of at least part of North-Eastern Rhodesia was carried out and resulted in the imposition of an export duty of 9d. a pound on rubber in September, 1902. This duty was imposed, according to Gouldsbury and Sheane's *Great Plateau of Northern Rhodesia* (1911), because of "the discovery that unscrupulous traders, not content with cutting down the vines, were digging up and boiling the roots". The duty was followed in February, 1903, by declaring the possession of root rubber illegal, and on July 1, 1903, a wide area of the North Luangwa District bounded by the Kalonga Stream, the Chambeshi River, the Lovu (Lobvu) River and the Malalo River was declared as the Maruli Rubber Reserve, where vine-cutting or latex collection was prohibited.

These actions followed a report by the Administrator, Robert Codrington, to the Directors of the British South Africa Company in terms of restrained optimism on the rubber resources of the Territory, and the reserve was declared on the basis of experience in the Mwaruli area, the sacred burial ground of the Bemba kings, where untouched ground showed considerable resources.

" Formerly," stated Codrington's report, " considerable amounts of rubber had been exported from these districts (the eastern watershed of the Luangwa, the Luapula, Luansenshi, Liposhoshi, etc.) and the usual barbarous methods of extraction and digging of the roots had done much to impoverish the resources of the country."

Very little is known of the early individual rubber traders—the men who, according to Codrington, dug up and boiled the roots, and who, he noted as being of significance, did not in any instance bear a British name, and who with very few exceptions were not even naturalised British subjects. One of these was very probably the subject of an unfortunately limited reference by Frank Melland in his *Elephants in Africa:* ". . . It was after the arrest and death of the ' rubber king ', Rabinek, and the cancellation of his fabulous concession in which Norton and Maurice Green were partners . . .". Another, less distinguished, came curiously and posthumously to light during a tour by a District Officer, Mr. P. L. Lindsell, in the Serenje District in 1958. He found that the headman of Mangani Village was tending a grave about half a mile away which proved to be that of one Fernandes " who was living out in the bush tapping rubber and died there of fever in 1907". For his attentions to the grave of " Bwana Flanganda ", the headman still receives a small annual honorarium.

In North-Western Rhodesia, there are slight records of John Lanegan O'Keefe (brother of the better-known Stephen), who was described as a " rubber and ivory trader " in Barotseland, and of Dennis Eden in the same area, of whom it has been said that when he attempted to export rubber about 1910, was frustrated by the " impossibly high " 1902 tax. Eden died of blackwater on May 18, 1913.

The Government's interest in rubber progressed from the protection of natural resources and the taxation of exports to proposals for rationalisation of the industry by cultivation of the wild plant and the introduction of exotic rubber-bearing plants and trees.

De Jong was one of, if not the only pioneer of rubber experiments in Northern Rhodesia. The Mirongo district notebook records that by 1903, he had left Katumbi and become Assistant Native Commissioner to the famous " Bobo " Young at Mirongo.

The notebook records the prohibition of rubber collection in March, 1904, and adds that " the vines are recovering " after destruction by the traders. " Good strong vines " were found at Cacheshi near Chewe's Village and along the banks of the Mulimuzi River, and at Chikanda Matipas about nine miles north-west of Mirongo.

[498]

Most interesting, however, is the note: " Some rubber seeds were planted on a stream near the station by way of experiment." Four years later, in 1908, Young gloomily records: " Spent a day at Mirongo looking over rubber plantations. The rubber trees do not look well. They all look as if dying from the tops."

The trees were probably *Ceara*, a rubber-bearing plant related to cassava. C. F. M. Swynnerton had experimented with them in Southern Rhodesia from about 1900. He got seed from the Durban botanical gardens, but found that to make them germinate he had to employ piccanins to grind the ends on grindstones. Locusts ate many of the transplants, and wild pigs and porcupine ate others. By September, 1902, he was tapping from trees thirteen to fourteen feet in height which had been planted in January, 1900. Result: a little ball of rubber three-quarters of an inch in diameter; and he records Portuguese experience of an average of ten ounce per tree in five years. *Landolphia* —also found in Southern Rhodesia—he recommended as an intercrop which would use the *Ceara* as a support.

De Jong evidently copied these experiments (and others: the *Gazette* for April 30, 1904, publishes a report from the Imperial Institute on various agricultural samples, including tobacco grown by de Jong at Mirongo), and spread some propaganda in the district over the next few years: James B. Yule, a famous pioneer elephant hunter, gave up his store at Mirongo in 1905, and took over an 1,100-acre farm, Scotsdale, in the Chinsali District.

The Mirongo notebook records that most of his stock soon died from tsetse infestation, but he grew tobacco, rice and native foodstuffs " and has planted *Ceara* rubber. During the rainy season 1909-10 he planted 1,000 *Para* rubber seeds. During the rainy season 1910-11, Yule planted out some 700 *Para* rubber trees grown from seed."

The establishment of experiments with cultivated rubber and the rubber export tax were followed by the *Rubber Trade Prohibition Regulations* (which in the event it was not found necessary to repeal until the Second World War). These made it an offence to cut any rubber plant, tree or vine, or to collect rubber latex, or to deal in, sell or offer for sale or for export any rubber (except rubber extracted from cultivated trees or vines).

Of the original cultivators of *Ceara* and *Para*. one at least remains: Mr. Gordon H. Lobb, now of Broken Hill, who, half a century ago, found himself bored by the Stock Exchange after the excitements of the Boer War, and leapt at the suggestion of a young man called Cleaver, whom he met at a Yeomanry dinner, that they should join forces and go to Abercorn, where Charles Blyth was " growing rubber ".

[499]

Lobb and Cleaver got off the train at Salisbury, and went on cycle and foot through Sipolilo, Feira, Fort Jameson, Mpika and Kasama to arrive in Abercorn in 1905. Blyth, who had come to Abercorn straight from the war in 1902, had a farm in the Saisi Valley. Cleaver (who was killed by lightning within months of his arrival) and Lobb became partners with Blyth. Charles Blyth at this time had just furnished the Administration with what Gouldsbury and Sheane described as " an exciting report on the agricultural possibilities of the plateau, in which he states that, in the Saisi Valley, *Ceara* was doing remarkably well. About 75 per cent. of seeds planted germinated, and plants which were not three months old stood about two and a half feet high and looked absolutely healthy."

The Administrator, Codrington, who had in 1903 presented the report on the rubber resources of North-Eastern Rhodesia referred to earlier, had not the same enthusiasm for *Ceara* as he had for wild rubber. A few months after Lobb's arrival, he visited the farm and " in his usual forthright way" declared they were "wasting their time" and that it was " no good trying to grow rubber ".

Codrington evidently knew better than de Jong and many others. Gouldsbury and Sheane, whose *Great Plateau* was published in 1911, quote an early report by a director (later chairman) of the British South Africa Company, Mr. Lyttelton Gell, who, after outlining the great hopes for the careful exploitation of natural rubber, goes on to propose "the introduction of superior species in cultivated areas ".

Many early settlers tried it out. Mr. Geoffrey Stokes, of Abercorn, recalls that Forsyth, owner of Dell Farm, near Isoka, had planted some *Para* or *Ceara* trees at de Jong's suggestion, and Mr. Stokes also saw them at Mpika. Mr. R. W. Dean recalls a rubber tree at Mazabuka station, and Captain John Brown recalls that some time after amalgamation in 1911, de Jong still had seeds in his possession, for Captain Brown got them in error for coffee seeds. The extent of the spread of plantation rubber is indicated in the company's annual report 1912-13, which shows that the total area under cultivation was about 2,102 acres. " The principal variety", states de Jong—by this time Secretary for Agriculture—"was *Ceara* (*Manihot glaziovii*). Other kinds such as *Para castilloa* and *Ficus elastica* are under culti-vation at Mr. Macdonald's plantation in the Luapula District. Tapping has been done so far only on a small experimental scale and no definite results have been recorded. Owing to the long dry season, the tapping season can only be very short and it is doubtful whether this will prove a paying proposition. *Ceara* rubber is only suitable for areas with a rainfall of not less than forty inches, and where the soil is rich in humus and highly retentive of moisture." Had de Jong read *The Great Plateau*? He had probably seen the report quoted in it of his colleague

Mr. McCall of the Nyasaland Agricultural and Forest Department for the year 1909-10: " I cannot advise planters to enter into *Ceara* on a large scale, as we have little or no data regarding the life of the trees, and how they stand tapping. The experiment so far is successful when *Ceara* is cultivated and planted in suitable soil, but a failure when planted in exhausted soil or left to battle against weeds without cultivation." Gouldsbury and Sheane note that this applies equally to the Nyasa-Tanganyika Plateau, and that it is probable that cultivated *Landolphia* would do better.

At this point, it may be of interest to touch briefly on the general situation in Northern Rhodesia. In March, 1912, less than a year after the amalgamation of the two territories, the permanent European population was 1,500 (including 270 women and 287 children). The native population was estimated to be nearly 900,000. The deficit on the country's balance of revenue against expenditure was £66,188. The total revenue of the country for that year was £107,558, a pathetic enough figure by present-day standards, though a considerable advance over 1910's figure of £30,260. The advance was accounted for by " the increase in the value of exports of oxen (£13,912), copper ore (£33,989), cereals (£9,023), India rubber—raw (£1,347) and railway material (£8,831). . . ."

It is clear from de Jong's reports that the rubber exports must have been wild rubber: the spread of *Ceara* and *Para* experiments had not detracted from the parallel interest in wild rubber. Gouldsbury and Sheane reported in 1911 that, though the results of the early protection of wild rubber had been disappointing, some of Codrington's prophecies had been justified, and they quoted the 1910 annual report to the British South Africa Company:

" The vast extent of Northern Rhodesia renders it impossible at present to estimate even approximately the extent of the rubber areas, but such evidence as is available points to the great prospective value of this asset. The indigenous rubber of Northern Rhodesia has been strictly protected since 1903, with the result that the number of young vines shows a great increase. This is particularly the case in North-Eastern Rhodesia, where the *Landolphia*, being a natural product of the soil and very vigorous, spreads rapidly when protected. A comparatively small portion of North-Eastern Rhodesia has recently been inspected by Mr. de Josselin de Jong, an officer of the Agricultural Department, who estimates that the five rubber forests which he visited covered, in the aggregate, upwards of 21,000 acres, and that the number of existing vines was approximately 800,000. He reports that each of the five areas would make a complete estate capable of carrying 200 vines to the acre under cultivation. Samples of Rhodesian rubber have been favourably reported upon in London, and tests are being made of the roots and stems of different varieties of the rubber-yielding plants found in Northern Rhodesia, with a view to the purchase of the most suitable machinery."

Lyttelton Gell, whose qualified optimism about " the introduction of superior species " has already been quoted, envisaged the formation of a small department of forest science to advise on the best methods of extraction and preparation of wild rubber, and the encouragement of the investment of capital in systematic cultivation. East African rubber sold in London at 2s. 6d. per lb., but native methods of preparation were faulty and impaired the market value.

" In the indigenous stage, the rubber industry does not require any outlay upon plant or large capital. It is not speculative; the settlement of the country diminishes the traders' risks, transport is comparatively cheap for an article so highly valuable in proportion to its bulk, and no expensive management is involved.

" The control of forest areas by native chiefs or headmen appears to be almost impracticable. To encourage careful preparation, rubber of unimpeachable quality might be accepted in payment of hut tax. The Lagos system, based upon a British conception of tribal property in forests, proves ineffectual, and it is questionable whether in North-Eastern Rhodesia a tribal chief possesses sufficient authority. The native who extracts the rubber is, however, the man who gives negotiable value to the company's property, and so long as he obeys regulations, he might be encouraged in every way."

Gouldsbury and Sheane go on to suggest that " it is probable that *Landolphia*, planted out between trees upon which it would climb, would do best in North-Eastern Rhodesia, more especially as vines are known to flourish. A man who obtained a concession of good ground where *Landolphia* vines flourish would do well, provided he had the capital to support himself for, say, *five years without return*.

" Root-rubber (so called) is most valuable, and flourishes in many parts of the plateau. There are good areas on the Chambesi River alone, and plenty in the Luwingu division. In the opinion of Mr. Harger, who, until recently, was engaged in reporting upon rubber, this underground stem rubber is really *Landolphia*, of which the stems, through want of suitable support and good trees, have spread aterally instead of ' aerially ' and have burrowed into the earth. The greater part of the stem can be cut and, provided the tap root is left, will grow again. A machine is in use in the Congo Free State for extracting root rubber, and it is possible that the Guiguet machine would serve the same purpose."

Much of this optimism was based on the tour by de Jong mentioned by Gouldsbury and Sheane. Mr. C. G. Trapnell, former Government

Ecologist in Northern Rhodesia, and through experience in the Second World War probably the best authority on Rhodesian wild rubber, points out that de Jong's estimate of about 800,000 rubber-bearing vines in a small portion of North-Eastern Rhodesia is probably misleading. " There is a point which may or may not have affected the early assessments ", he writes. " *L. kirkii* is a source both of tapped and bark (stem or root) rubber. *L. parvifolia* is not a tapping vine owing to resinous latex, and contains a number of forms or varieties, only one or two of which would be suitable for root rubber: the rest are too resinous. When not in fruit, the two species resemble each other so closely that even an experienced botanist can have difficulty in distinguishing them. While one can only guess now, in Mateshi full of ' rubber vine ' tangles, this could have been a misleading factor. . . ."

Physically, however, de Jong's tour was an impressive one as recorded in *The Livingstone Mail* of April 4, 1911. He left in October, 1910, and in the ensuing six months covered an estimated 5,202 miles. This was his second journey to " Kapopo, Kasempa, the Lunda country, to the sources of the Zambesi, through Balovale country, the Barotse valley and back by river . . . Mr. de Jong speaks favourably of the possibility of profitably establishing the root rubber industry. Particularly is he pleased with the Lunda and Balovale districts. "

The *Mail* followed this story up on April 15, when " Mr. Josselin de Jong . . . kindly showed our representative round his little museum last Tuesday afternoon. A map is pinned on the wall on which are delineated the various areas he located suitable for the cultivation of cotton and other textiles, and those thickly and thinly covered with root rubber plants . . . Samples of native rubber in the various stages of preparation contrasted with those he had himself prepared, and his own rubber, prepared in accordance with his example and directions, was obviously far superior to that the natives produce. They have hitherto used hot water, whereas cold water is used by Mr. de Jong. Heat greatly reduces the value of the latex. The native rubber, beaten out of the bark, washed and again beaten, is in thick sheets, known as crepe rubber. It is full of bits of bark, stones, sand, etc. . . . To produce a clean rubber, thereby reducing the export duty (4*d.* per lb.), freight and royalty (also 4*d.*)—but the latter may be abolished shortly— machinery is indispensable. Machines can be obtained for from £40 f.o.b. London to £600. Two are now working very successfully at Bandawe in Nyasaland, and one large washing and crushing machine has been installed at Benguella.

" Rubber, that is, the native product, which is very dirty, is now purchased from the natives in Barotseland at 8*d.* per lb. Export duty, royalty and freight, bring it up to 2*s.* The price of this quality on the market to-day is 2*s.* 6*d.* to 3*s.* 6*d.*, but with machinery a cleaner article will be obtainable, with a corresponding reduction in the above charges, and cleaning and drying in.

" Mr. de Jong will, on the arrival of Mr. J. M. Hayman (late Deputy Director of Agriculture of the United Province of Agra and Oudh), who has been appointed to superintend the development of the agricultural interests of the Chartered Company in Northern Rhodesia, confer with him as to the best method of attempting the commercial exploitation of the huge areas recently located in the course of the extensive journey recently undertaken by the former. In the Balovale, Barotse and Lunda districts these will at once repay enterprise. Some areas were absolutely impenetrable, and the undergrowth consisted to a very large extent of the species enumerated. Some difficulty may be encountered in procuring enough labour as these regions are sparsely inhabited.

" In a previous article we described the method of dealing with a fraction of an area each year, crushing the bulk of the root while leaving sufficient for the plant to grow again, and also planting cuttings, so that in three or four years, the area may again be worked. Thus, each successive season will better repay enterprise and a large and profitable industry be speedily built up.

" The Lunda country, with its exceptionally heavy rainfall of fifty-five inches, spread over eight months of the year, has great possibilities, and *Funtumia elastica* and vine rubbers grow splendidly, but the altitude is probably too great for *Ceara* or *Para*. Transport, which will be mainly by water, presents no difficulties, and by the time the Lunda District has been developed, it is hoped that the Benguella Railway will be within a distance of from fifty to 100 miles, which will greatly facilitate the transport of machinery and the prepared article.

" The industry, it is understood, will be exploited by private capital. The company is quite prepared to issue licences to those who have the necessary capital for the provision of adequate machinery and to tide over initial expenses. . . ."

Rubber experts such as Harger and Hayman probably account for the cryptic note in the 1911-12 annual report, which includes £2,041 spent " in connection with cotton and rubber investigation and Tropical Adviser", and £1,000 spent the following year for "agriculture, including rubber expenses ".

Certainly, rubber hopes had never risen higher than between 1911 and 1913. Exports in 1911 were 12,695 lb. worth £1,572, and in 1912, 15,708 lb. worth £1,134. De Jong's annual report for 1912-13 could report, as already noted, that over 2,000 acres were under plantation rubber, even if prospects for it were doubtful. It went on to make a momentous statement: "An important development in wild rubber will take place next year in the exploiting by machinery of the *Landolphia parvifolia* (root rubber) and the *Landolphia kirkii* (vine rubber) in the areas in the north-eastern part of the Territory."

(It should be noted that enthusiasm for the rubber industry was not universal in the Northern Rhodesia of 1913. *The Livingstone Mail* of September 9 of that year carries lengthy reports of a meeting of the North-Western Rhodesia Farmers' Association at Kafue, at which harsh words were spoken about the agricultural policy of the Administration. Mr. A. A. Willis, secretary of the association, pointed out that the Agricultural Department consisted of one man—de Jong. " He has a clerk and two little rooms. He is an excellent gentleman who tries to make bricks without straw, and spends the greater part of his time travelling between Livingstone and North-Eastern Rhodesia. Unless we create a disturbance and make ourselves objectionable nothing will be done. There have been piteous appeals for an expert, and many enquire to know when one was coming." The report added that an expert had come to the country two years before (Hayman ?) " since when there had been no one to give us advice or assistance. Unless we become objectionable we shall get nothing. A large amount of money has been invested in the country, and it is absolutely essential that something in the nature of an advisory department be formed at once. . . ."

Tom King, chairman of the association, pointed out that the Agricultural Department was really a commercial department, and agricultural in name only. " It has now been turned into an institution for growing mealies in opposition to the farmers. They don't begrudge the 1,100 bags the department has grown, but had they grown a little seed we should have been grateful. There is another department at Chilanga " (experimental gardens) " and we appreciate Mr. Wood's services, but he is not an expert. Mr. Josselin de Jong has been away on an expedition connected with the rubber industry, and we have not had much of his services. . . ."

Dougal Malcolm, then a visiting director of the company, pointed out that the company was still £80,000 a year short of making ends meet, and could not possibly afford an advisory agricultural department. Willis pointed out that de Jong was away two-thirds of the time, and the argument between Tom King and Dougal Malcolm became somewhat heated, concluding with King rejecting de Jong as an agricultural expert. " I know as much about farming as Mr. de Jong does! ")

The reasons for the choice of the north-eastern part of the Territory for the rubber factory are not clear. As de Jong himself had told the

Mail, the Lunda and Balovale districts were most pleasing of all: the Benguella Railway was coming. There were the rivers for transport: only a labour shortage could be feared. Whatever the reasons, the area on which de Jong finally decided was the Chambeshi River. Of this area, Mr. Trapnell comments with authority: "Certainly I should say that the Chambeshi area of the Northern Province was far from being the best region in the Territory. It lacked the abundant *Carpodinus* sources of Mwinilunga and Barotseland and the quantity of high-yielding *Mushitu* vines found in the north-western region. Suitable *Mushitus* were scarce in the vicinity of the rubber factory. The Chambeshi was possibly chosen, among other reasons, for a liberal water supply for washing out bark rubber."

II. THE FACTORY

The events following the decision to exploit wild rubber by machinery were to a large extent controlled by one Charles Duncan Simpson, born in Glasgow about 1870, trained as a fitter, and recruited in the 1890s by the African Lakes Corporation to develop and maintain its steamship transport system from Chinde on the Zambezi Delta to Karonga at the northern end of Lake Nyasa.

In this capacity, according to Captain R. W. M. Langham, he assembled such famous craft as the gunboat *H.M.S. Gwendolen*, the *Chauncey Maples* and the *Dunera*, finally commanding the latter (which meant, says Captain Langham, that he was "captain, first mate, engineer and cabin-boy with a native crew". Simpson himself had tales of these days, according to Sir Stewart Gore-Browne: one of them against a fellow captain. The veteran sailor was in his cabin with his boon companions when the African steersman came down to ask for the course. "Pita ku right", said the captain. "Kwambere mabwe ku right", said the steersman, referring to the shoals. "Oh, then pita ku left", said the captain, returning to his potions.)

On September 15, 1900, the *Central African Times* was able to report one of Simpson's earlier adventures, and his first visit to Northern Rhodesia: "We are able to chronicle the fact that the first steamer to disturb the hitherto restful waters of far distant Mweru has just been launched and completed her trials most successfully . . .". The vessel was the *Scotia*, built for the Lakes Corporation. The materials for it left Fort Johnston in Nyasaland on May 23 and the first consignments began to arrive at the corporation's station on Mweru on July 5. Transport arrangements were "under the direction of Mr. W. B. Chamberlain, the corporation's Assistant Manager on the Nyasa-Tanganyika Plateau" and the construction was by C. D. Simpson and George Buchanan.

According to an article by W. V. Brelsford written in 1937, Simpson then sailed the *Scotia* round the shores of Lake Mweru buying rubber from the natives. By 1910, according to Brelsford, Simpson was " (a ?) Nyasaland Superintendent of the corporation (though Chirupula Stephenson, in an obituary notice of the same year, refers to him as " Chief Engineer of the Mandala Fleet ") and was sent to England " to study the methods of extracting rubber from such African commodities as the sweet potato, and learning also how to obtain commercial rubber from the wild African rubber trees ".

By 1912, Simpson was back in Nyasaland, and his experience and training evidently came to the ears of de Jong, who journeyed to Nyasaland as newly appointed Secretary for Agriculture to offer Simpson terms under which he would be released from his contract with the corporation on receipt of a sum of money and a grant of land in British South Africa Company territory.

Mr. Geoffrey Stokes, of Abercorn, recalls de Jong's journey to Nyasaland, and that on his return, he was due to visit Chinsali on his way to Fife, but that de Jong's European companion died of blackwater in the Fife sub-district, and the visit never materialised.

Duly engaged, Simpson spent much of the year 1913 searching for a suitable site for the proposed rubber factory, and finally decided on the point where the present Great North Road crosses the Chambeshi River (according to Brelsford, " approximately Lat. 10.9 S., Long. 31.9 E. ").

Mr. Stokes, then District Commissioner, Kasama, recalls that in 1913 the Administrator, Lawrence Wallace, held an indaba there. He spoke to the assembled chiefs about the early establishment of a factory to process root rubber. Simpson was present at this meeting, at which the natives were told they would be encouraged to dig the rubber and take it for sale to the factory.

This left the question of building the factory and getting the machinery to it. At that time, the only connection between the " line of rail " and the northern and eastern parts of the country was the system of mail paths and tracks which could not support anything larger than a motor cycle. The solution arrived at was to build a special road, and to send up it a traction engine which could haul the mills and vats for the factory, and then be used as a stationary engine to drive them.

Mr. J. H. Chaplin, of Livingstone, compiled in 1958 with the help of Sir Stewart Gore-Browne some details about this traction engine, which had a long and interesting career: the article was in honour of its golden jubilee year and its presentation by Sir Stewart to the National Monuments Commission as a national relic.

" On October 6, 1908," records Mr. Chaplin, " the drawings were completed in the Leeds office of Messrs. John Fowler and Co. Ltd., engineers, for a Class B6 Compound Road Locomotive. Their catalogue of a few years later shows varieties of these engines in use throughout the world, but it seems likely that few have lasted so long as No. 13053. . . ."

Fowler's catalogue contains a testimonial from the Rhodesia-Katanga Junction Railway and Mineral Co. Ltd., reporting that in the four and a half months of the dry season, four similar engines conveyed 1,479 tons of copper from Kansanshi Mine to Baya station, a distance of seventy-five miles. " The average time for the four trains was nine days, this time including one day for overhauling, washing out, etc. The road on which the trains travelled is cut through bush country. The fuel used is wood cut from the forest en route. Water is available at streams and water holes along the road. . . ."

The gross weight of the traction engine, it transpired in correspondence years later, was eighteen tons fifteen cwt.: and the cost of a similar engine then (1921) was estimated to be £2,535 f.o.b. Sea freight, insurance, landing and rail charges to Kashitu " would probably amount to a further £750 ".

The enormous engine was duly ordered, and the route chosen for it after its " detraining " at Kashitu was to Chiwefwe, Ika, Chansa (near Chitambo Mission) and Mpika. The Administrator put out to contract the cutting of a suitable track as far as Chansa, and to have the rest built by the District Commissioner at Mpika.

The contractor was Chirupula, who had at this time just returned from a year in the Congo. In the dry season of 1913, at Wallace's request, he and James Moffat Thompson completed a survey of the contract section. Recalling this period in an interview only a week or two before his death, Chirupula said that Moffat Thompson always claimed after their return that water had been so short they had been obliged to drink elephant's urine.

As a result of the survey, the contract to build the road was awarded at " just under £4 a mile ". (In 1937, Brelsford quotes the figure as £8 a mile, but in a letter of 1942, Stephenson gave the figure as " something under £700 ", which for 180 miles works out at about £3 17s.).

The contract was for a road—or track—eighteen feet wide. Wallace asked Stephenson to begin from the Kashitu end as the traction engine would be following close behind them. But Stephenson had trimmed his tender to such a point that after paying his labour 10s. a month and feeding them, he was losing money; and when Wallace visited him with Cookson and congratulated him on the excellence of the work, Chirupula asked permission to go to the north end and work back—from an area where he could get labour at 5s. a month.

Wallace finally agreed, and Stephenson completed the road from the north end, but only after considerable recruiting troubles solved by taking his African father-in-law, Chiwali, with him, and giving out the story that he had kidnapped him. He was ransomed by the labour of his subjects.

The building of the road was completed in pioneer fashion. Writes Brelsford: " The capitaos in charge of the gangs of labour were given a rope eighteen feet wide and told to clear the bush to that width along a marked line. Of course, the ropes were lost, but the capitaos were inclined to be generous with their labour, and one stretch a mile long was found by Mr. Simpson to have been cleared to a width of about twenty yards.

" It must have been fascinating work. There were no surveyors on the work, and theoretical alignment often had to be abandoned in order to deviate the road to a stream, for the engine needed water as well as wood. For example, there was an old mail path going round the south side of the Ika Hills, but the gradient and the demands of the steam engine in the way of fuel caused the new road to lead round the north of these hills . . . Is there any other part of Central Africa that has a main road development founded on such an extraordinary beginning ? "

Before starting up the trail of the newly cut road, Simpson himself had problems. The traction engine and its three three-ton trailers arrived at Kashitu station in their component parts. There was no platform, no crane—no method of unloading. Simpson and his " Chief engineer "—the driver of the engine, Dick Quincey—pondered the problem. It was solved, according to Jim Kitchin, by enrolling Africans to collect brushwood, which was then piled at the side of the railway trucks, and the components simply pushed out on to it.

Then with sheerlegs, the engine and trailers were assembled on the spot—imaginably a considerable undertaking before the wood and water and box of matches completed the preparations for setting out on the pursuit of Chirupula's road-builders.

The journey proved long and hard for *Chitukutuku*—the generic Bemba name for traction engines with which it was immediately christened. " Owing to the very sandy nature of the greater part of the road", gloomed de Jong in his annual report, " and the general un-suitability of the engine and trailers, transport to the factory has taken over a year to accomplish . . . On one or two occasions, delay was caused by the breakdown of wire cables which had to be replaced from Bulawayo." (" What a beastly nuisance old Charlie Simpson was! "

recalls H. J. R. Hatchwell of this period. " The traction engine kept breaking down, and I had to get all the spares from Bulawayo and elsewhere, and the job, of course, was to find out exactly where he was, because there were hundreds of miles to break down in and nobody to tell you where.") De Jong continued: " The rainy season, which set in very early this year, also prevented good progress being made. I beg to mention that throughout the very great difficulties encountered, the manager, Mr. Simpson, and the engineer, Mr. Quincey, have always overcome all obstacles with great credit to themselves, and it is due to their untiring energy that everything arrived at the factory site on the 18th May." This was 1915.

De Jong's expression " over a year " was slightly euphemistic. The journey probably began about October or November of 1913. *The Livingstone Mail* of January 2, 1914, quoted its Kashitu correspondent (almost certainly identifiable from both style and origin as Chirupula) as saying that " a new Fowler traction engine recently arrived to convey stores and material for working this plantation. The engine with three trailers put together under the supervision of Messrs. Simpson and Quincey have been unable to get far on account of the rains. Consequently it has been left on the road with a couple of natives in charge, until the rains are over." (The correspondent made some sarcastic comparisons with Captain Kelsey's Cape-to-Cairo motor expedition, whose car was bogged down at Broken Hill while an advance party reconnoitred the road).

This report bears out the accurate recollections—more accurate than the Kashitu correspondent's references to rubber " plantations "— of Mr. Geoffrey Stokes that he was posted to Mpika in December, 1913, and that at that time the traction engine was bogged down not far from its starting point for the wet season.

When it was finally able to move, de Jong reported that it trundled up to Serenje with a load, came back to Kashitu for another load (to save the cost of carriers) and then battled on to the Chambeshi. Bogged down in the mud, winching out of water courses with unreliable cables—the difficulties must have been great enough to try the patience of even what the late Mr. Stanley Hillier in a 1937 obituary tribute to Simpson called " one of those Scottish engineers, famous the whole world over, who can make anything go which was made to go".

And while this heart-breaking trek was in progress, Mr. H. Wilson Fox was compiling in London for the edification of the directors of the British South Africa Company a memorandum on the *Development of Estates and Other Industries* which included an interesting set of figures showing the estimated revenue and expenditure on the rubber

[510]

LANDOLPHIA GROWING NEAR MWINILUNGA

[*Photograph by the Author*

LANDOLPHIA (HERBARIUM SPECIMEN)

STAGES IN EXTRACTION PROCESS—FRONT PILE (ON MAT), STRIPPED BARK READY FOR CRUSHING; HEAP (BACK CENTRE), TREATED BUNDLES OF CARPODINUS ROOTS READY FOR STRIPPING; MAN ON LEFT IS HOLDING CRUSHED BARK MAT IN PREPARATION FOR WATER TREATMENT; ON RIGHT, FINISHED SHEETS

CHITUKUTUKU AND YORAM IN LATER LIFE AT SHIWA NGANDU

EARLY DAYS ON THE GREAT NORTH ROAD. EXTREME LEFT: J. E. STEPHENSON WHO BUILT THE KASHITU-CHANSA SECTION FOR THE TRACTION ENGINE

THE DUKE OF GLOUCESTER AT CHARLIE SIMPSON'S HOUSE. ON THE RIGHT: MR. AND MRS. SIMPSON

THE FINAL FLOODING OF THE CHAMBESHI FACTORY. SOON AFTER THIS PHOTOGRAPH WAS TAKEN THE BUILDING COLLAPSED factory for the year ended March 31, 1915—a year which ended with the engine still on its way:

SALARIES

		£
Manager		500
Engineer		300
Accountant (proportion of salary)		75
Transport of machinery and stores from Kashitu to factory		250
Manager's travelling expenses		50
Factory wages and food		120
Office expenses		25
Tools, equipment, etc.		175
Purchase of root and cutting of vines, including transport to factory		500
Transport of rubber		267
		£2,632

Rubber manufactured: 12,000 lb. at 2s. 6d. per
lb. (London price) £1,500

These calculations did not, of course, include the cost of the road or engine and trailers, or of building the factory—a problem which Simpson was facing at much the same time: it is probable he and Quincey had to divide their time between keeping the engine on the road and building not only the factory, but offices and homes for himself and Quincey. And by March, 1915—as if he had not enough to do—he was out in the bush exploring new rubber areas. He was able to report to de Jong " very favourably on the richness and quantity of the vines and roots". He had also engaged a few skilled rubber diggers in Nyasaland to initiate the local natives into the processes of preparing root and vine rubber. De Jong reported to the Administration that he intended to visit the factory and working area about August, 1915, " when I hope to find the factory in full working order ". He was obliged, however, to note some dark clouds building up. " Experiments with the growing of exotic rubber have been discontinued for reasons given in former reports. *Ceara* rubber is being grown in the Fort Jameson District but, as predicted, results have been far from encouraging. Acreage under cultivation, 960 acres. Export nil." (The acreage was down from 2,102 in 1912-13). "At Chinsali, the late Mr. J. B. Yule started some five years ago a small plantation of *Para* rubber. This will be visited by me and a report submitted. The fall in the price of rubber in the home market has given rise to great anxiety, but I understand from letters received from the commercial branch of

[519]

the London Office that there is an increase in prices, and that owing to the war the demand is increasing." (Mr. Stokes recalls that Yule was killed in June, 1914, by an elephant while hunting in a sleeping sickness area. " On learning of his death, relatives who had been supporting him for years on the strength of his reports of his promising rubber estates were disappointed to learn that little had been done, and that the deceased's reports were largely moonshine.")

"African rubbers have almost entirely disappeared from the home markets", de Jong continued. " It is true that the output of rubber from the East is increasing, but it must be taken into consideration that the supply of African and other ' wild ' rubbers has entirely ceased and that this deficiency cannot be met in the very near future by the plantation rubber.

" The indigenous rubber prepared at the factory will be equal, if not superior in quality, to the same rubber which is being prepared by the factory of the African Lakes Corporation in Nyasaland. The rubber manufactured by this firm realises on the home market 2d. or 2½d. less than the best hard *Para*. With the home price at 3s. to 3s. 6d., a fairly good return should be realised. Every effort will be made to make up for unavoidable delay, and it is hoped to be able to forward the first consignment of rubber towards the end of this year (1915). The journey to the factory will be made via Luapula River, Lake Bangweolo and the Chambezi River in order to find out whether it is possible to transport rubber by this route and so save an expensive and long overland journey. By this route, rubber can be brought to within sixty or seventy miles of the railway."

More will be said of the water route to the north later on, but it is interesting to note at this point that de Jong's journey along it was almost certainly the first serious consideration of it as a means of transporting goods. De Jong left as he promised during August, and travelled from Ndola to Sekontwe through Belgian territory, from thence up the Luapula River, across Lake Bangweulu and up the Chambeshi River. After visiting the factory and touring the north-east generally, he returned to Livingstone in January, where he reported " most favourably " on the suitability of the water transport route.

(The North-Western Rhodesia Farmers' Association, which seems to have suspected that de Jong's extended tours were undertaken with the object of keeping out of the farmers' way, called another angry meeting in September, 1915, while de Jong was exploring the water route. At this meeting, a committee member, Mr. H. Ilsley, put forward a motion stating that " the money spent on the Agriculture Department is thrown away", that its cost was wholly disproportionate to the services rendered, and that it should be abolished. The motion was carried unanimously, drawing from Lawrence Wallace a sour inquiry as to the reasons for this care for the company's finances.)

At the factory, Simpson had established his family—his wife, the former Margaret Campbell McCliment of Scotland, and his two small daughters, Margaret Elinor and Elinor Mary. They had trekked many hundreds of miles down from Nyasaland attended only by African servants, but the journey was without incident. They reached the factory only to find themselves left often again as Simpson searched the countryside for rubber, and probably went down to aid the engine on its way. (Mrs. Simpson and the children evidently arrived before the outbreak of war, since Mr. Stokes recalls setting up a " refugee camp " at Mpika for women and children from the north at the first alarm of war. The inmates were Mrs. Blyth and children; Mrs. Lobb and children from Jericho and Mula farms on the Saisi River; Mrs. Munro and child from Fife, a sister of the well-known " Ropesole " Jones; Mrs. Bobo Young and child from Chinsali; and Mrs. Simpson and the children from the factory.)

However, when Charlie Simpson was obliged to leave his family, they were left in good hands. They were attended by two Africans who had accompanied them on the journey from Nyasaland, Chamveka " a man amongst men and a great gentleman ", and Chiwaya, the mechanic. At the factory, Simpson had another stalwart servant, Yoram Pia, who lives to this day not far from the factory, on the estate of Colonel Sir Stewart Gore-Browne, Shiwa Ngandu.

The children particularly led an enviable life. Their schooling was given them by their mother, and wide-ranging Charlie Simpson brought back pets from his tours: two lion cubs, a buck, an owl, an eagle and a wild cat. The little girl who was Elinor Simpson (now Mrs. W. K. Hudson) remembers not so much the long journey down to the Chambeshi from Nyasaland as the factory's " pièce de résistance "— a steam whistle. She recalls that " an Awemba chief was invited up the ladder to the top of the boiler. The whistle was blown. The chief fell off the ladder. The whistle had made local history."

Of the working methods of the factory little is known: Mr. Trapnell points out that it would be of great interest to know more of the process intended. " It must have been a curious one, for the traditional African extraction methods would be very difficult to reproduce mechanically." The evidence is somewhat slim. Yoram recalls that the rubber roots were dug up and brought in bundles to temporary camps where the bark was knocked off and dried and then packed in bags for sending to the factory. Vines were cut down in lengths, left to dry for a few weeks, and then collected. At the factory, according to notes compiled by Mr. O. Kerfoot, of the Northern Rhodesia Forest Department, largely from information provided by Sir Stewart Gore-Browne, the bark was boiled for some hours, being transferred to another drum for final separation. The refined product was put in buckets and then into a machine and rolled out. It was then dried on wire racks, crated and despatched.

It is most probable that the machines were either the *Guiguet* or *Valour*. The Guiguet is mentioned by Gouldsbury and Sheane as being in use in the Congo about 1910, and both Guiguet and Valour machines were in use in Nyasaland in 1913. It must be presumed that they simulated in some way the beating and washing processes. Of the machines, Harold Brown's handbook for the Imperial Institute on *Rubber and its Sources, Cultivation and Preparation* states that " very large supplies of bark are required to run them for any length of time ". This theory is borne out by *The Livingstone Mail* report quoted earlier which refers to two machines working very successfully at Bandawe in Nyasaland " and one large washing and crushing machine has been installed at Benguella ".

Mr. J. Millar, manager of the African Lakes Corporation in Ndola in 1942, recalled early Nyasaland experience of buying root rubber which in his recollection was chopped up and treated with caustic soda to remove the bark, and then coagulated with acetic acid. This fits in with a 1923 note (when the factory was being sold up) that " further endeavours are being made to find a buyer for the caustic soda ". Chirupula, in an obituary notice of Simpson in 1937, said: " Splendid crepe rubber, in sheets broad and thin, were turned out as soon as the machinery was moving . . .".

There was of course, not much time in which the process could become familiar to outsiders. The falling price of rubber and the demands of war soon halted production. Labour, which may well have been a problem from the beginning, became acutely scarce when the war opened up a new source of employment as carriers to the troops on the northern border.

The economic incentive to work was not strong among the Africans of those days. Hut tax was raised from 3s. to 5s. a year in 1914, and did not become 10s. until after the war. The African social system did not include, according to Captain R. W. M. Langham, much in the way of manual labour except fitemene and garden fencing: the rest was done by women. Fields of employment were not extensive. The porterage of stores was one of the most important: there were the mines of North-Western Rhodesia. After that, there were the half-dozen farmers in the Saisi Valley, the District Officers and storekeepers. Pay averaged about 3s. a month with 5s. 6d. ration money.

Mr. Stokes points out that competition for the services of those who wished to work was also provided by the Rhodesian Native Labour Board, which recruited for service in Southern Rhodesia.

Then came the war. The 1915-16 report for Northern Rhodesia states that the calculated monthly consumption of the troops on the northern border was 335,000 lb., and General Northey wanted a six-month reserve on top of it. The lines of communication, commanded by Colonel Hodson of the Northern Rhodesia Police, were the Broken Hill-Serenje-Mpika-Kasama Road of 429 miles, used only by carriers; the Kashitu-Kasama Road, originally in part the road cut by Chirupula, but improved by Mr. C. Briggs of the Southern Rhodesia Roads Department so that it could take motor transport; and the Ndola-Kabunda-Lukulu-Kasama route on which carriers, canoes and motor transport were used over 700 miles—the route originally surveyed by de Jong. On this route, the Chambeshi factory was an important staging post.

There were thus several factors militating against any possibility of the success of the factory: there was not so much rubber as had been expected; labour was scarce and inefficient; the price of rubber was falling; the war made more urgent demands.

Mr. J. H. Venning of Abercorn says that the only product of the factory he can recall was a rubber bath mat which Charlie Simpson made for his wife's use in the house. Mrs. Simpson, a small, rotund lady (affectionately christened " Rum Mum " by Walter Cowie, an early resident of Abercorn) stuck firmly to the bath mat and had to be rescued.

The actual production of the factory was slightly greater than one bath mat—but on the evidence available, not much greater. The export statistics are succinct, but revealing. In 1914, 20 lb. of rubber, valued at £1, were exported. In 1915, 159 lb., valued at £13, were exported. In 1916, production was 3,000 lb.—valued at £131, or a little over 10d. per lb. The mountainous labour had produced a very small mouse.

Early in 1916, de Jong, Simpson and Quincey all went on leave, and work at the factory ceased until their return. When they got back (says de Jong's report for 1916-17), they found the factory and machinery had been taken over by the military authorities, and the mills that once rolled out " splendid crepe rubber in sheets broad and thin " were grinding corn.

" Labour continues to be very scarce owing to the requirements for war transport", wrote de Jong. " Mr. Simpson, however, succeeded to get all the rubber bark cut last year transported to the factory. An extraordinary heavy flood caused the factory to be flooded but no material damage was done to the machinery or factory." (This flood foreshadowed another in the 1935-6 rainy season, when the gaunt, abandoned old building finally collapsed.)

Still optimistic, de Jong concluded by saying that until the factory was no longer needed by the Army, no rubber manufacture could be undertaken, but that as soon as labour became available, Simpson would start cutting vines and " prepare a large stock to work on ". This plan was evidently carried out, since during the year 1918, 3,872 lb. of rubber (worth £388, or 2s. per lb.—the price having risen no doubt due to the exigencies of war) were exported from the Territory, while during 1917, there were no exports of rubber at all. At this point, when the factory's total production could not have been more than 7,000 lb. of rubber (on the assumption that total exports from the country between 1915 and 1918 came from the factory alone, and not from other sources), and which in value represented only a fraction of the cost of the traction engine alone, de Jong, surely with a heavy heart, journeyed up to the factory to prepare " a detailed report on the present position and future work ". This report was submitted to the Administration in November, 1918—a time when other matters were on the minds of both the Administrator and the directors, which may account for the fact that a search of possible sources has failed to reveal it. However, it is not assuming too much to suggest that it was unfavourable and that all hope of the economic production of rubber in Northern Rhodesia had been abandoned. It was a subject seldom mentioned for some years.

The war, which had so largely been responsible for the death of the factory, now almost resulted in its destruction—but gave it also its most enduring claim to a place in history as the point at which the German commander, General von Lettow-Vorbeck, was informed of the Armistice.

Mrs. Simpson and the children had been evacuated on the Administration's orders to England in 1915, but it was not until November, 1918 (when de Jong was penning his gloomy report), that the fears which had led to the evacuation became fact, and von Lettow was advancing southwards virtually unopposed towards Broken Hill.

The then District Commissioner, Awemba District, the late Hector Croad, abandoned his headquarters at Kasama and retired with his staff to the factory on November 8. Jim Kitchin, quoting the recollections of Charlie Simpson, says that Croad brought with him to the factory about £10,000 in tax money: and with the Germans evidently hard on their heels, there was some discussion on where to hide it. Chamveka was called into the discussion, and on his recommendation it was buried in the Simpsons' goat pen, where the goats were returned to trample and hide the traces of digging.

Croad was asked by the military to " establish an intelligence department to keep in touch with the enemy's movement", and courageously scouted round the hills overlooking Kasama on November

10 to confirm that von Lettow was in occupation, and preparing to advance to Lukulu, twenty miles north of the factory, which was the terminal depot of the water transport, and the scene of frenzied activity as the defenders sought to evacuate stores down-river to hiding places in the swamps. Croad and his party returned to the factory, reaching it at 6 a.m. on November 12. The Administrator, Wallace, reporting to the company afterwards, said that the local natives had fled their villages into the bush, and it was impossible to keep enough carriers to save the stores: priority was given to food and the unlucky Europeans lost practically everything. Stores were still being evacuated from the factory when von Lettow's advance guard arrived at the river bank and were reported to be seeking a crossing at 8 a.m. on November 13.

Wallace, in Livingstone, had heard of the Armistice " by Reuter's cable " on the evening of November 11—but there was a break in the telegraph line to the north. This was unfortunate, but nothing new. The old A.T.T. line which had been put up by Rhodes from Salisbury through Nyasaland to Karonga, Fife, Abercorn, Bismarcksburg and to Ujiji in German East Africa, had, of course, been cut by the Germans, and had to be replaced. When Major Boyd A. Cuninghame led the Northern Rhodesia Rifles from Broken Hill to the northern border in December, 1914, his wagon train carried among its general cargo the materials for the new telegraph line. Mr. F. Rushforth, now of Fort Jameson, was in charge of the construction with Eric Pullon as his assistant. " The line, a light copper, was strung from tree to tree, using bush poles where trees were not provided by nature. The job (from Kashitu to Kasama) took three months, distance roughly 400 miles. Elements and elephants, not to mention the indigenous human population whose love for copper wire was being so well and cheaply stimulated, caused such frequent interruptions that a system of twenty-mile patrols had to be instituted to get any degree of continuity of communication worth while.

" On reaching Kasama, I was instructed to proceed to Abercorn and renew the section Abercorn-Karonga through Fife, which had been well and truly demolished in many places by the Germans. This section—Abercorn-Karonga—followed the old Stephenson Road, famous for the suppression of the slave trade, through the Saisi Valley, famous for the siege of Saisi. . . ."

Thus, at Chambeshi, the war was over, and no one knew it. Von Lettow was heading happily southward with his 155 Europeans, 1,300 askari, and 3,000 porters: among the defenders of the Chambeshi there was considerable confusion. Thornton's party, crossing the river, gave Sibold's askari the impression of Germans: they fled, abandoning and damaging the precious machine gun. The askari were

[525]

rounded up; Sergeant Frank Rumsey, D.C.M., mended the machine-gun with a fusee spring from a Mauser. Then a rumour that the Germans had crossed the river caused a stampede among the carriers.

No shots were fired, however, until 8 a.m. on November 13, according to Croad's report. Less authentically (a memory from Charlie Simpson, via Jim Kitchin) Yoram was nearly hit in the leg. From the same source, it is reported that von Lettow told Simpson later on that the echoing of shots under the factory's tin roof convinced the German scouts that a much larger force was present, and that a full-scale assault crossing of the river would have to be planned. (J. H. Venning recalls that it was a bitter disappointment to Wallace that the Germans failed to destroy the factory: and that it was the one thing for which he could never forgive them . . . Had they done so, the company could have claimed compensation from the British Government and thereby recouped some of the losses.)

Shots were exchanged for about a quarter of an hour—the Germans firing into the factory with Lewis guns and rifles, the defending askari firing blindly in reply. (Thornton's askari, who were not fired on, heard the shots and bolted again—and again abandoned the machine gun in the bush).

Then, at 11 a.m. on November 13, the official wire at last arrived. Jim Kitchin quotes the story that Simpson, linked to the telegraph line in his office, ran from the factory to answer the bell, and nearly became the last casualty of the First World War: a bullet hit the doorpost as he entered. The problem arose of conveying the news to von Lettow.

At 7.30 on the morning of November 14, Croad set off in a canoe to cross the river under cover of a white flag* and accompanied by Lieutenants E. J. Leslie, F. Davey and D. Barraclough, together with Sergeant Mechanic Frank Rumsey, of the Mechanical Transport Company. (Douglas Barraclough was a telegraphist; Frank Davey was in charge of police; Richard Thornton—mentioned earlier—was a farmer turned scout; Sergeant Rumsey lives to this day at Mbesuma Ranch, Chinsali.)

Across the river, the party picked up Croad's lorry (left there after his scouting expedition to Kasama) and went up the road with a white flag. An important additional member of the party was Yoram Pia, who could speak Swahili, the language of von Lettow's askari. Yoram's recently written account compares favourably with Croad's contemporary report, and here it is, slightly paraphrased:

---

* Mr. A. M. Alexander, who was present, wrote recently: "As we had all fed in Simpson's dining room, I ran in and grabbed some of his table napkins and gave them to natives to tie on sticks to put along the river bank and other places. Meanwhile I seized the lovely table cloth and got it tied to a pole and sent a native up the roof and had the pole tied to the chimney. . . ."

" When we crossed the river, we passed German soldiers on the east side of the road and, a few miles further on, we saw a German askari in front of us. When we drew near, Lieutenant Davey told me to take his weapons. I took his gun and twelve cartridges and a knife. The gun I handed to Lieutenant Davey in the lorry, and the cartridges and the knife went into Yoram's pocket. We took him about a mile in the lorry when Mr. Davey gave the askari a note to take to the German camp at Chandumukulu. Then we turned back, and met on the way the askari who had been firing at the factory, and who now turned their guns on us. We stopped and called to the white officer and told him the armistice had been signed, and then returned with him to Chandumukulu, where we handed the telegram to von Lettow's adjutant (Hauptmann von Spangenberg, in fact) and then returned to the factory. By five o'clock that day, the Germans had camped under a big tree on the Kasama side, and the following day, von Lettow came and talked with Mr. Croad. . . ."

Croad's report includes the text of a telegram which von Lettow requested should be sent to the Kaiser, and it was later a favourite story of Simpson's that the word for "Armistice " in German contained sixty-four letters, but in fact " Waffenstillstand " contains exactly a quarter of that number. But it was a good story. Von Lettow went to Kasama on November 16, and left for Abercorn on the 17th. Croad himself had returned to his headquarters at Kasama on November 15, to find only his own house and those of the Assistant Native Commissioner and the Medical Officer still standing, and only the mess and a cottage remaining in the police camp. The rest had been destroyed. (Not, according to Chirupula, by the Germans, but by one Jack Merry, who had set fire to the place after distributing the stores among the local Africans to prevent anything useful falling into German hands). Croad noted that there was " no military order about von Lettow's command—the whole thing looking like a typical Arab caravan of the old days. No attempt at any sanitary arrangements were made. . . ."

Von Lettow, evidently entertained by Simpson for his night at the Chambeshi, sent the old Scot a copy of his memoirs long afterwards.

III. END OF THE DREAM

With the departure of von Lettow to his surrender, the excitement was over; rubber was a dream that had vanished—and in 1919 Simpson found himself transferred to the Public Works Department to supervise the cutting of native timber and the preparation thereof (on a power saw-bench sent up from Livingstone and driven by the old traction engine) for making doors, windows and roofing for the new Government buildings at Kasama, Fife and Abercorn. One thousand two hundred and thirty trees were felled and brought in for sawing, but the plan was abandoned the following year because of the high cost of transporting the timber from Chambeshi.

There was, however, still the river—still the most efficient and reliable and economical method of supplying the Northern Province from the line of rail. The original survey by de Jong had been supplemented by more detailed investigation when the question of war transport arose.

An obvious choice for surveying the route was one Joseph Edward Hughes, author of *Eighteen Years on Lake Bangweulu*, who left the Administration several years before the outbreak of war, and lived at Sokontwe on the right bank of the Luapula, whence he catered for hunting parties. He had at one time been an assistant to Croad, and they remained lifelong friends, according to Mr. Stokes. Captain Langham tells a story that Hughes was a bank clerk in the Union; became engaged to a girl whose father declined permission to marry unless he could produce £10,000; and that Hughes settled on Bangweulu as hunter and otter skin trader to make his fortune. Mr. Stokes throws some cold water on this: he recalls that Hughes went to Caledon Baths for his health—possibly rheumatism—and there met his wife-to-be: and that her father did not altogether approve of Hughes' financial state.

However, Hughes had an intimate knowledge of the waterways, and he and E. B. H. Goodall, the Provincial Commissioner at Ndola, duly surveyed the route (Goodall's Channel is a present reminder of the trip). The job of organising and running the transport, hiring paddlers and canoes, was not unnaturally offered to Hughes. The latter suggested (according to Captain R. W. M. Langham) that to reinforce his authority he should be given a commission. He meant, of course, a temporary military commission as an officer. This was absent-mindedly interpreted in Livingstone as a commission of the monetary kind, and Hughes was duly awarded a commission of a shilling a load, an arrangement he thought it best not to query. Major E. C. Dunn relates that he thereby made the fortune that hunting and trading had failed to provide. The amount of stores carried to the north during the war made this more than likely.

The route provided for rail transport to Ndola, then carriers across the pedicle to Kapalala, then up the Luapula to Nsumbu in Lake Bangweulu. From Nsumbu, river craft entered the Chambeshi, and goods and passengers joined the motor road to Kasama at the old factory (on this route during the war was stationed Gordon H. Lobb, noted earlier in this tale as a pioneer rubber planter at Abercorn. And another hero of the war transport service—the motor transport from Kashitu to Kasama—was Major Cecil Duly).

[528]

The river route, though the longest, was proved the most reliable in war-time, and after the first year of operation it was pronounced " undoubtedly the chief factor in the maintenance of the troop supply system". Eventually, about 900 canoes were used on it. The motor road in Major Duly's charge was used mainly for forwarding urgent needs and for bringing down the sick and wounded from the border.

After the war was over, the river service was continued as an essential one for the supply and development of the Northern Province. Government forwarding agents were employed at Kapalala (" Kapalala " Clarke), and Chambeshi, where Simpson became forwarding agent. Headquarters of the service were at Nsumbu, where the District Commissioner was in charge. In 1920, Sir Stewart Gore-Browne recalls, two Belgians, Joos and Bourgeois, " did extremely good work " running a canoe transport service. Joos subsequently committed suicide over financial difficulties, and Bourgeois remained to straighten matters out " which he succeeded in doing very creditably".

Simpson as Government agent now had to battle with the practical problems of running such a service with African canoes, barges and paddlers. Some of the difficulties are mentioned by the headquarters stores superintendent at Livingstone in 1922, who reported bitterly that " considerable accounting has to be done in connection with these ulendoes and agents' accounts. During the year, the African Lakes Corporation made an offer to undertake the whole of this transport at a figure less than what it costs this department, but later withdrew the offer, presumably finding it could not be done at the price.

" There is not sufficient transport by this water route to warrant a regular service and some delay is experienced in the transport of goods to the northern stations. Paddlers have to be recruited at Nsumbu at which an official only resides for a portion of the year; consequently the canoes have to be stationed at Chambesi and paddlers recruited from there. Advice is sent to the Government agent at Chambesi via Kasama from here by telegram when goods are despatched which entails considerable time. . . ."

By March, 1923, the head storekeeper had recovered his good temper and reported that his department was still running the service, that there were few if any complaints, and that the mails were now taken over the river route, which, he said, proved its usefulness. (Sir Stewart Gore-Browne, commenting on the irregularity of mails in 1958, recalled Simpson's claim that " you could set your watch by the appearance of the canoes round the bend of the Chambeshi ".)

Meanwhile, there had been continuing for some time between Sir Stewart and de Jong and others various negotiations on the painful subject of disposing of the factory machinery. " I have been told ", de Jong wrote to Shiwa Ngandu, in 1921 " that you have made enquiries re the traction engine which is for sale at the Chambesi rubber factory and that you think of buying same. I enclose herewith a description of the engine which is a very good one made by the well known firm of Robey and Sons. " (It was a Fowler, of course.) " It is in excellent condition as no doubt Simpson has told you and it is of course available for inspection any day. With the engine is one truck which I believe is at Mpika, that truck could go with the engine. Wheels and axles of two other trucks if required are at the factory and are also for sale. Now with regard to price. We ask £1,000 (one thousand pounds) for the engine and spares at the factory and as mentioned the truck will go with it, provided you take that away from Mpika. The price is very fair as such an engine if bought at home now would cost three times the amount, if one could get one delivered at a short notice, which is doubtful. The price has been put low for the reason that the engine is so far away from the line and that has been taken into consideration. We have another enquiry about the engine but do not think this will come off. . . ."

This mixture of candour and salesmanship was followed within a few weeks by a communication from the commercial department of the company in London to Sir Stewart's brother in Kimberley. " I shall be pleased", said this letter, " to give you an option to purchase the engine until the 31st January, 1922 . . . for the sum of £1,500 (fifteen hundred pounds) and if desired arrangements could be made with regard to payment. . . ." This upward trend was checked by a note from Mr. Gore-Browne which received a reply suggesting that " in the circumstances perhaps you are prepared to make us an offer. . . ." Mr. Gore-Browne was pleased to make an offer: " I now find I can obtain a Tangye tubular boiler which will meet my requirements for steam distillation " (for the extraction of essential oils at Shiwa Ngandu) " for £175 delivered at Port Elizabeth. Under these circumstances, it would not be worth my while to pay more than £300 for the engine at the factory, especially as I should have to make forty miles of road to get the engine to Shiwa Ngandu. This sum is much less than the figure mentioned by the Secretary for Agriculture, but should you be prepared to consider it I will at once communicate with my brother up at Shiwa Ngandu who should shortly know whether a road between the factory and Shiwa Ngandu is a possibility. Otherwise I propose to order the Tangye boiler, and as I am anxious in that case to get the boiler out in time to take advantage of this year's high water in the Chambezi I should be most grateful if you would send me a telegram at my expense. . . ."

The bluff was called, but the commercial branch went down fighting: " Do not think company will accept £300 for traction engine what is the highest figure you can offer ? " they wired. " Fear cannot offer more than price of Tangye boiler, viz., £300", went the reply. And the company, no doubt well aware that they were lucky to get any offer at all for nearly nineteen tons of white elephant stuck 400 miles from practically anywhere, accepted with good grace.

The truck at Mpika referred to by de Jong is probably the subject of one of the best stories of all. " Croad, the District Commissioner at Kasama, thought he could use one of them at Kasama", writes Sir Stewart, " and recruited a gang to pull the thing from the Chambezi. After several days' hard work, the bantu thought it was beyond a joke and bolted. But before they left, so Croad told me, they tied the bloody great thing to a tree with a bit of bark string, *lushishi*, lest anyone should steal it! A pleasant ironical gesture."

The road needed to get the engine to Shiwa Ngandu was duly built. " My brother, who was with me then," writes Sir Stewart, " made a road from Shiwa Ngandu to join the main Mpika-Kasama Road, and you will see the road still in existence and marked on all the maps. A good many people prefer to travel that way from Kasama to the south in the rains as it avoids what is always a very bad stretch to the north of Mpika on the main road.

" It was a bit tricky as one has to go through some fairly formidable hills. I had been reconnoitring a line before finally deciding to buy the traction engine. I had practically given up all hope, and I was due to catch train and steamer for England on a date which left me no margin, when on the last night of the ulendo, the old headman, who was acting as guide, said as we sat round the camp fire, ' You aren't looking for a pass through the mountains, are you? There's a beauty about two days' journey back. . . .' I could only pass on the information to my brother, who went out and found the Kapilinkwale Pass, which he said had been specially put there by the Almighty for the required purpose."

The Class B6 Compound Road Locomotive reached Shiwa Ngandu at last: Chiwaya was again the driver, and the seventy-one-mile journey took, according to Mr. Chaplin's note, twenty-eight days, night-stopping at watering places.

" It began useful work again as a source of power and steam generator for the Shiwa essential oil distillery, and continued to do so for fifteen years", writes Mr. Chaplin, " until the fire-box burned out. The shortage of metal after the outbreak of war in 1939 caused it to be stripped of many parts, although there is no reason to suppose it might not have been repaired and be still working in normal times, instead of celebrating its golden jubilee by being repainted and set up as a national monument." Mr. Chaplin notes that one of the spare axles for the trucks is still working as part of a water wheel on a White Fathers' mission.

Sir Stewart also bought one of the huge vats in which the root rubber was boiled up, and solved the problem of getting it home by rolling it up the road. It was then converted into a still for the distillation of eucalyptus oil.

Meanwhile, Charlie Simpson, the Nyasaland pioneer of old, was establishing himself not only as an invaluable intermediary between the south and the north, but as one of the best-known characters of the old school in Northern Rhodesia. The longer he stayed in the country, as Chirupula once said, the broader became his Scots accent. He became known as " Chambeshi Simpson", as " Charlie " to his old friends, and " Butty " (in the late Mr. Hillier's phrase) " to an irreverent few". His obituary in *East Africa and Rhodesia* in September, 1937, was sub-headed " Shem-Shem of the Chambezi " (really " Semu-Sem ", the African version of Simpson, says Sir Stewart Gore-Browne) and there were probably still other names.

Mr. Hillier, who followed up Chirupula's obituary notice in *East Africa and Rhodesia* with an appreciation, said that Simpson's " yarns of the early days on the Shire and in Karonga were worth listening to" and doubtless they included the one about the assembly of the *Scotia* on Lake Mweru: the work attracted the amused interest of the local fishermen, who kindly demonstrated the worthlessness of the white men's endeavours to float a steel ship by dropping their axes in the water.

There was his story, too, of the White Father he had known in the early Northern Province days who, armed only with a Bible, rounded the bend of a bush path and came face to face with a lion. They stared at each other for some time. Eventually the lion could stand it no longer and made off into the bush.

He told of the time he was searching the Luangwa Valley for rubber when his carriers refused to follow him through dense bush which they said led to the "elephants' graveyard". And there was his story of a man-eating lion, a young animal, which was seen on the road on the north bank of the Chambeshi. It was pursued and lost in the bush. Finally it was killed on the opposite bank of the river by a young native with an axe when it was actually on top of the girl he intended to marry.

But one of his best stories concerned the visit of the Duke of Gloucester in 1928. By this time, the Great North Road had been opened to motor traffic (Simpson was an early motorist himself: Dr. R. R. Murray, Medical Officer at Kasama, reported in 1923 that on urgent calls to Luwingu, Serenje and Chinsali, " some of these journeys were made in the cars of the District Commissioner, Kasama, and of Mr. Simpson, Chambezi, proving the utility of good roads and motor transport. The great necessity for the upkeep of roads in this very wide district is obvious . . .").

Major E. C. Dunn, now of Lusaka, opened a motor service to the north, and was commissioned to meet the Duke at the Tanganyika border. However, the visit started badly: the Duke had come to Dar-es-Salaam with the Prince of Wales, but the Prince was hastily recalled on the illness of his father, and Major Dunn's motor convoy waited for days at Mwanza Mission before the Duke arrived.

The Duke came down with the Administrator, Sir Lawrence Wallace, and the road, of course, led straight to the rubber factory, where (so Major Dunn recalls) Charlie Simpson's daughters were tempted to a mild lese-majeste by playing on the gramophone a hit of the period entitled " I'm the Girl for You, You're the Boy for Me ".

From Simpson's hospitable bungalow (still in use, as a road foreman's house: the old office is a sub-post office), where the Duke stayed two or three days, he was sent off down to Ndola by the river route with two white hunters from Kenya who were in the royal party, and the famous Chamveka (who, it is said, had been with Simpson so long that he spoke English with a Glasgow accent). On the way through the swamps and down the Luapula, the Duke shot a lion, an event considered by the Duke to be the highlight of the tour, and due to the eagle eye of Chamveka.

On arrival at Ndola, however, there was no one who knew the way to the Provincial Commissioner (Goodall, pioneer of the river route) except Chamveka. And Chamveka, so Jim Kitchin tells the story, had already argued with Simpson that " Bwana " was an inadequate title for a Royal Duke: and, finding Goodall, introduced the distinguished visitor with a flourish as " His Royal Lord Highship the Duke of Gloucester ".

Except for occasional tourists, the arrival of motor transport meant the end of the river route, and the old factory was of no use even for the storage of goods in transit. But to quote Mr. Hillier again, " his cosy bungalow, situated on the banks of the Chambeshi—that placid stately stream which becomes later on the Congo—was an oasis for tired and thirsty travellers on the long dusty road from the railway to Lake Tanganyika.

" There, prince, peer or prospector—it did not matter which—were all welcome at his hospitable board." Recalling his skill as an engineer, and his capacity for conjuring spare parts from old bits of scrap iron, he goes on: " Many a broken-down motorist on the Great North Road has had cause to bless Charlie Simpson. But woe betide any young spark of a lorry-driver who might take these ministrations for

[533]

granted. He would be received with a cold stare from under those sandy, bushy eyebrows, and a few apt and caustic remarks delivered with a strong Scots accent would inform the aggressor exactly where he got off. . . ."

(And not only " young sparks of lorry drivers ". Sir Stewart Gore-Browne recalls a certain well-known cleric demanding repairs to his car, and saying: " It isn't everyone I let touch my car", to which Simpson replied: "And it isn't everyone whose car I'll touch " as he turned on his heel.)

As his years mounted up, Simpson's main occupation became the maintenance and operation of the ferry across the Chambeshi. Although during the boom years of 1930 and 1931 steel bridges and culverts were built across most of the streams and rivers of the 1,000 miles of the Great North Road the one major exception was (and remained until 1958, when work at last began on a concrete bridge) the Chambeshi.

The 1930s came in, and Simpson remained at Chambeshi, still dispensing hospitality to all who came through. At last, his achievements in the opening up of both Northern Rhodesia and Nyasaland were recognised by the award of the M.B.E. Thanks to the personal intervention of Sir Stewart Gore-Browne, he was also awarded a small civil list pension during the last ailing months of his life.

Of this period, Sir Stewart writes: " He was a wonderful fellow. Only a very short time before he died, he came over here to advise me as to whether the traction engine was repairable (the fire-box had burnt out). He was so ill that I was ashamed to have bothered him to come: but he bucked up, climbed all over the engine, and into the boiler, and took all the interest in the world, finally saying that it was too big a job to fit a fresh fire-box with the tools available."

When his illness became serious, he was taken to Lusaka Hospital for X-ray treatment, but did not benefit, and returned to the Chambeshi. But before he could reach Mr. R. W. Yule's farm, Chibwa, for a few weeks' rest, his condition deteriorated, and he went into hospital at Kasama, and died there peacefully. He was about sixty-seven years of age. His widow moved to Abercorn and remained there for some years. She died at the home of her daughter, Mrs. Elinor Hudson, in Basutoland.

(A few months before she died, she gave to an old friend, Mr. H. J. R. Hatchwell, now of Livingstone, a chest of drawers which he still has in his bedroom, and which Rum Mum told him had been damaged by a bullet from von Lettow's scouts in 1918: unfortunately, Margaret Simpson had the historic wound repaired.)

And John Cornelius de Josselin de Jong—what of him? Little is known. He retired in 1923, and it is thought that the courtly, kindly old gentleman retired to Holland, but did not long survive to enjoy his leisure and relive those fabulous tours and the tragi-comedy of Chambeshi. Mr. T. C. Moore, who arrived in Livingstone in September, 1923, a few months after de Jong's departure, to take up the post of cotton expert, found he was the only full-time member of the Department of Agriculture. . . . " Piles of documents, wrapped in brown paper, the old records of the department, were stacked in a small store-room. . . . From time to time, I delved into those piles when trying to find out what had been found out about various crops in the past. I filed some of the information which seemed most valuable in the current files of the department. I was not interested in the *Ceara* rubber documents, as it had been proved a failure. . . ."

Many more tales might have been added to this chronicle had those brown paper parcels survived the discriminatory eye of Mr. Moore and the subsequent vicissitudes of the Department of Agriculture. Instead, the curtain came down and the characters one by one have left the stage, until now there is only one left who was with Charlie Simpson when the first bricks of the factory were laid—the faithful Yoram Pia. He stayed on in the Government service at Chambeshi to operate the ferry. (He was there, he remembers well, during the last war, when the ferry plied back and forth for two and a half days to carry the 152 trucks of the Northern Rhodesia Regiment under Colonel Dimoline. He eventually retired to Nyasaland, but became homesick after his long exile, and wrote to Sir Stewart Gore-Browne, who gladly gave him employment in the estate office at Shiwa Ngandu some six years ago.)

IV. EPILOGUE

The darkness which descended might have lasted until now but for the pressure of the Second World War. Mr. Neil Clothier, formerly Chief Conservation Officer, recalls that Mr. C. G. Trapnell's ecological survey of Northern Rhodesia from 1932 onwards noted the areas where indigenous vegetation included rubber, but that it was not then considered an economic industry for the Africans of Northern Rhodesia. It was not finally mentioned in either report, though the establishment of suitable local industries from indigenous resources was one of the objects of the survey: it was considered, in fact, well after beeswax.

The old files of the Department of Agriculture are silent on the subject until January, 1937, when there came to Lusaka an inquiry forwarded from Salisbury on the prospects of obtaining native rubber from Northern Rhodesia. The inquirer, whose name and ambitions (and the reasons for them) are equally unknown, got short shrift from the then Director of Agriculture, Mr. C. J. Lewin, who pointed out

that when world rubber prices rose sufficiently, many African territories had put rubber on the market, but that at the 1936 price of 9*d*. a
pound there was little hope of Northern Rhodesia competing " without
a good deal of propaganda and instruction for Africans ". (This was a
curiously accurate prophecy of what happened during the war years.)
Mr. Lewin added that there were no exports of rubber from the
country in 1923-7, though the world price in 1925 touched 4*s*. 6*d*. per lb.
He concluded that " all thought of exporting rubber from this Territory
has been abandoned (I think rightly) for so long that I can give very
little definite information on the subject ". He commended the inquirer
to Charlie Simpson: and that was the end of it until the Second World
War, when the loss of Malaya, Burma and other Far Eastern plantations
led to a resurgence of interest in native rubber in Africa among those
with long memories. (It also led, according to the late D. Gordon
Lancaster, to the break-up of much of the old machinery at the
Chambeshi factory for the making of axes and hoes.)

In those dark days, every conceivable source of rubber latex was
eagerly pursued, from the Russian dandelion to the vast derelict *Ceara*
plantations of Tanganyika dating back to the 1900s, to which experienced
planters were hastily recalled.

In Northern Rhodesia, the first thought of rubber production was at
Abercorn. Mr. E. C. G. Hausser, of the Abercorn Trading Company,
wrote to the Government on December 8, 1942, that towards the end
of the previous year, " some experiments were made in extracting
rubber from the roots of a common shrub growing wild around
Abercorn. These were discontinued as local rubber production was
not at that time apparently desired. "

It soon was, and the first claim to reminding the Government of its
possible value thereafter must be shared almost exactly between two
men. Mr. Harry Franklin, at that time Chief Information Officer,
noted the possibilities on January 28, 1942. Four days previously, a
letter had been posted by Mr. W. A. Kaye, then operating the Sachenga
mica mine in the Mazabuka district. He asked the Government the
possibilities of or legal restrictions on gathering wild rubber in the
Chambeshi Valley, and evidently this followed an inquiry to Mr. Kaye
from a London firm.

The flow of correspondence increased, and by March, 1942, it was
established that the Dunlop factory in South Africa were prepared to
study samples of wild rubber. The British Government confirmed
that all types of rubber would be urgently needed. On May 8, 1942,
the long-forgotten Rubber Ordinance was dusted off and suspended
so that rubber could be collected anywhere, except on private land,
without permission, and soon afterwards there appeared an interim
report by the Government Ecologist, Mr. Trapnell, and an official

notice from the Agriculture Department on *The Purchase of Raw Rubber*. In this, prices ranging from 1s. 6d. to 9d. were offered for various grades of rubber, and advice was given on the collection and packing of rubber, on the types, quality, treatment of it, and the licences for it, and loans (up to £150) for the development of collection. By the end of August, about a month after publication of the notice, about two and a half tons had been received, most of it from the North-Western Province.

As the months went by, it became only too clear to anyone who cared to remember that it was indeed the North-Western Province and Barotseland rather than the Northern Province which should have been chosen for the factory thirty years before. By February, 1944, Mr. Trapnell could report on the basis of an assessment of resources and manpower that the estimated potential from Barotseland was 350 tons a year, and from the rest of the country, 150 tons.

But production was, not unexpectedly, miserably low. The price was raised to a maximum of 2s. 6d., but without a great deal of effect. The fact remained that while rubber existed in unlimited supply in the western areas, it was extremely laborious to extract, and the rate of yield was extremely low in proportion to the labour involved. The rural African was understandably remote from the pressures of a world war, and only in a few districts, most notably Balovale, did the combined exertions of Government officials and traders obtain a really adequate response.

The difficulties were appreciated even by the Ministry of Supply in Britain. In February, 1945, in a survey of the work of the African territories in the rubber field during the previous year, it was stated: "Among the outstanding increases in production is that of Northern Rhodesia, which shows, according to the Colonial Office records, an increase in export figures from 34½ tons in 1943 to 107 tons in 1944. .... Although we realise that, where rubber is collected from forest vines, there must be an increasing difficulty due to the exhaustion of the nearer areas, we feel confident that, in view of the continued urgent need for rubber, you will do everything possible to ensure that production during the present year will be at least maintained at the present level."

But the enthusiasm—which had been whipped up by 1944 to the point where a touring medical officer in the Balovale-Mwinilunga area could report that his rest was disturbed by the beating of rubber which ceased at midnight only to be resumed before dawn—began to tail off in 1945. On September 18 of that year, Mr. Lewin reported to the Chief Secretary that he found it difficult to believe that it was " necessary or desirable to continue with the hopelessly uneconomic production of relatively low-grade rubber in this Territory. The price paid to native collectors, although fantastic by pre-war standards, is equivalent, on an average, of less than 6*d*. per working day. As a consequence, the bulk of the rubber has been produced under pressure and has given an already overburdened Provincial Administration much additional work. . . ." The Ministry of Supply concurred, and by April, 1946, all stocks of rubber at the depot at Mazabuka had been cleared, and a final telegram was sent to the Secretary of State on April 10. This stated that the forty-fourth and last consignment, comprising 7.71 tons of rubber, had been sent to Durban. The total production then stood at rather less than 280 tons.

The last telegram was filed, the last of the fat files was closed, and the rubber trade, which had been born in the days of the earliest pioneers, had died in the arms of Josselin de Jong, had been reborn in the stress of a second world war, only to die for a second time. There is not likely to be a third life, for if anything has been learnt from this tale, it is that rubber was fated to failure in Northern Rhodesia. Time is a ruthless censor of failure, and the power of Codrington, the charm of de Jong, the character of Charlie Simpson—the enthusiasm of them all—cannot alter the fact that it is a wryly humorous tale of failure, disappointment and anti-climax, and for this it was consigned to oblivion.

It has been called back through the chance acquisition of a faded picture of the factory at the Chambeshi: from that picture has been built up a larger picture—a picture which provides a flash of illumination to a corner of the broad canvas of a country's history, nothing more.

But the corners and footnotes of history are sometimes the most entertaining, and it is hoped that this will have served, like a fly in amber, to amuse if not to instruct.

April, 1957–October, 1959.

14

DRAGONFLIES (*ODONATA*) OF CENTRAL AFRICA

ELLIOT PINHEY

1961

This survey is primarily concerned with the dragonflies of Northern Rhodesia but some records are included for the neighbouring territories of Katanga (Southern Congo) and Nyasaland. It is a preliminary list for this area, since only in parts of Northern Rhodesia has extensive collecting been carried out, but it may help to bridge the gap between rather more comprehensive books by the Author on the species south of the Zambezi (*Dragonflies of Southern Africa*) and those in eastern Africa, Tanganyika northwards (*Survey of the Dragonflies of Eastern Africa*). Northern Rhodesia as here delineated includes *both* banks of the Zambezi River. Dragonflies, being aquatic by nature but not influenced by political boundaries, will not favour one side of the river more than another, except where limited local conditions—current, shade on the banks and so on—may suit their purposes. Many species, of course, depend on running water for their oviposition and life cycle, whilst others prefer quiet waters. The salinity and temperature and the presence or absence of vegetation in the water has a marked effect on population and species, as well as the nature of other living organisms, friend or foe; and the state of the banks is of importance in the case of species which prefer the shade of thick bush, or merely some perches for rest and surveillance, or bare, unhampered banks. Others prefer the presence of some rocks for camouflage and others, again, will haunt the bush or scrub at some distance from water. Northern Rhodesia, with its extensive lakes, swamps, rivers, and thickly forested streams (the " litus " of the north-west) provides a very wide range of habitats, lacking only the more extremes in altitude. A very few Odonata of those not present in this area would only favour coastal levels, whilst in East Africa (and probably on the peaks in Nyasaland) a few are confined to the higher altitudes. Nevertheless, this territory has a wide range of species, both with southern affinities and also some with tropical African, even equatorial connections.

The Author has not collected personally in Nyasaland, but he has visited certain parts of the other territories; the Zambezi River at various points between Kazungulu (and Katambora) and Chirundu

Bridge; the Copperbelt; Abercorn and Kalambo Falls; Mwinilunga District from Kabompo River westwards and northwards to Ikelenge. This latter area was visited in February–March, 1960, in the company of Mr. Peter Lascelles and an African assistant, Mr. Rafael Mpala, both of whom assisted in the collecting. On this expedition a brief excursion was made into Katanga, via Elizabethville and Jadotville to Lubudi, where the principal habitats were the waterfalls on the road to the Upembe National Park and patches of forest to the north of Lubudi. In January 1958, some collecting was also done in Katanga by the Author with the assistance of Mr. T. Coffin-Grey, during a rapid expedition through the Congo and equatorial Africa to the eastern border of Nigeria. The route lay through Jadotville but then turned north-east via the Mitwaba Escarpment and the Lufua River to Albertville; then northwards to Fizi, Uvira and the northern Congo. Only brief stops could be made for collecting, except where progress was delayed by storms, mud, fallen bridges and ferries.

Much of the acquired knowledge of the Northern Rhodesian dragon-flies is due to Lascelles' enthusiasm. But other collectors have helped very considerably indeed: most of the Ndola records are due to extensive collecting by Mr. R. A. G. Green. Samfya and Lake Bangweulu have been collected mainly by Mr. R. C. Dening, who has since been active around Lusaka. Dr. P. Johnsen also assisted with valuable collections from Samfya and the Copperbelt. Mr. R. Watmough sent his records from Samfya and Lake Bangweulu. Extensive collections have been received from Mr. R. M. Kitchingman, formerly of Mwinilunga. Abercorn, Ufipa Plateau and Mweru records are largely due to Mr. L. D. E. F. Vesey Fitzgerald, particularly the Abercorn area, which thanks to his efforts must now be fairly well known for Odonata adult fauna. From Fort Jameson and elsewhere a few dragonflies were submitted by members of the Tsetse Control Unit.

Nyasaland records are chiefly due to Messrs. R. Wood, W. J. Gray and D. Eccles. A few were taken in the past by the late Mr. C. Smee.

The Author feels deeply appreciative of the assistance received from all these sources. It is to be hoped that the publication of this preliminary survey will stimulate further collecting. It is certain that many more interesting records are to be found and probably a number of further new species; particularly from Nyasaland.

A few general remarks may be made here on certain localities known to the Author.

[541]

Victoria Falls

Apart from the Falls themselves, the bush-covered islands, the rapids upstream and the nearby rocks, rock-pools and banks (with or without trees and shrubs) there is the thick fringe of bush receiving much of the spray (the so-called " rain forest "), which harbours certain species, in particular *Lestes amicus*. The thicker bush nearby and the bush near the Maramba River may have interesting Lestids, *Parazyxomma* and *Lestinogomphus*. In the rains isolated pools add to the variety of habitats.

Katambora Forest Reserve

Thick bush on the banks of the Zambezi, which is here notable for rapids, and small streams emptying into the river are productive of interesting species, notably in the genus *Neurogomphus*.

Copperbelt

The more interesting species are found at bush-fringed streams, reedy pools and extensive dambos or swamps.

Kabompo River

The collecting area was at the point where this river crosses the road from Solwezi to Mwinilunga. Besides the river species there are a few of interest in nearby swamps.

Mwinilunga

The most productive areas are the forested streams or litus. But the open streams, the Zambezi torrents, the small swamps and the larger " dambos " are all highly productive. It is evidently a relic forest area with equatorial affinities.

Abercorn

By far the richest collecting area is the shallow peat-bottomed Lake Chila which terminates in swamp; it has a fast river running out of it; it is fringed with *Brachystegia* woodland and is further varied by a patch of swamp forest. Nearby are other pools and streams as well as swamps. A short distance away are the Kalambo Falls and a forest of tall *Brachystegia*.

Jadotville

Collecting was mainly in the woodlands in the Jadotville–Elizabethville road. Here and at the swamps Odonata life was poor.

Lubudi

Just off the main road to the north of this town there is a turning to the right leading to Upembe National Park. On the way there are several large waterfalls and forested gorges which are rich in Odonata. Also on the main road to the north there are forested streams.

Mitwaba Escarpment

A few minutes collecting only on a very small stream running down the escarpment on the road.

La Manda River

Where this crosses the road beyond the escarpment: an interesting selection of species.

Lufua River

Collecting was mainly a little way from either bank, at streams and floodwaters.

In the descriptive section of this paper keys are given to families, genera and species, the last chiefly for males. Females are often less adaptable to working keys but, at least in *Zygoptera*, mating pairs are usually readily obtainable in the field. Further descriptions and references may be obtained in the book on the Southern African species (Pinhey, 1951). Larvae are not described nor recorded in this paper but a short summary is available on them in the paper on Odonata nymphs (Pinhey, 1959).

Special acknowledgements are due to those who assisted the 1960 expedition: in Lusaka, the Bensons and Denings; in Ndola, the Greens; near Solwezi, the Staff of the R.S.T. Camp; and at Mwinilunga, the Fishers, Waugh and Chief Mwinimalamba. Lastly, for the publication of this paper the Author is indebted to Dr. Desmond Clark, of the Rhodes-Livingstone Museum.

INTRODUCTION

A very brief introduction to the study of dragonflies may be of some help to those readers not well acquainted with this group of insects.

Characteristics

Dragonflies are variously known also as " Horse Stingers ", " Devil's Darning Needles " or, more appropriately, the more slender species are referred to as " Damsel Flies ". Belonging to a distinctive order of the insect world known as **ODONATA**, they are predaceous insects, with mouthparts adapted for biting their food (they are not capable of stinging). Their compound eyes (i.e., the many-faceted eyes common to insects in general) are very large and prominent: in fact dragonflies are amongst the most alert of the insects (and so are Praying Mantids). They also have three small simple eyes or ocelli (Fig. H.42) on the top of the head or vertex. The antennae are always *very short*, scarcely visible to the naked eye; slender or filiform. The parts of the face include a *labium* (a sort of lower lip) and *labrum* or upper lip, with curved mandibles in between these lips; an epistome, consisting of two parts, the ante- and the post-clypeus; to the side of these portions are the " cheeks " or genae; and the forehead or frons forms the top of the face.

The thorax is separated into two portions by a flexible joint; the front or *prothorax* and the *synthorax* (or pterothorax). The prothorax bears the front or first pair of legs. The synthorax really consists of two segments, the meso- and the meta-thorax and these in turn give rise to the names of thoracic plates which are mentioned below. This portion bears the second and third pair of legs. The synthorax is, however, elongated obliquely forwards, so that the legs, instead of being directly under the wings as in other insects, are situated far forward, close to the head. The great advantage of this to the possessor is that the dragonfly can use all its legs to hold food between the lips and, moreover, it enables it to do so even in flight. In contrast the two pairs of wings are necessarily far back on the upper or dorsal surface of this thorax. The more important sections into which this synthorax is divided are firstly a pair of *mesepisterna* on the front, which often bear pale or dark markings known as *antehumeral stripes;* then, at each side there is a *mesepimeron* (separated from mesepisternum by a fusion line known as the humeral suture), the *metepisternum* and the *metepimeron*, these last three plates being separated by the first and second lateral sutures. On the metepisternum there is one of the two pairs of thoracic breathing pores.

The abdomen is usually elongate, often very slender, and consists of ten segments. Ridges visible on the upper surface or along the sides of these segments are the transverse and lateral carinae. In the male, the last or tenth segment (denoted, simply, 10) bears appendages used for attaching on to the head or the prothorax of the other sex prior to mating. Dragonflies can carry out extraordinary aerial acrobatics, forwards, backwards, hovering or looping; and they will link up even in rapid flight, the pair flying thus in tandem for quite a while, with little apparent effect on their flying ability. The terminal or *anal appendages* of the male are on two levels, the upper or superior appendages and the inferior. In the female the terminal appendages are merely a pair of stylets or cerci. On the lower or ventral surface of the second segment in the male there are the actual mating appendages or accessory genitalia. After the tandem link-up the female connects the tip of her abdomen to this segment by curving her body upwards. The detailed study of the accessory appendages are beyond the scope of a brief introduction, although the comparative differences in the " hamules " and other organs are often essentially important in distinguishing species (c.f. the diagrams of male accessory genitalia of *Macromia*, Fig. C, D, and *Orthetrum*, Fig. E). However, the *sex* of a dragonfly can always be determined by the presence (male) or absence (female) of any appendages on the underside of segment 2: in the female the surface of this segment is quite smooth below.

The leg of a dragonfly, slender and spiny, consists, as in other insects, of several parts, the small coxae and trochanters at the base, a robust *femur*, a still longer *tibia* and the tarsal segments, the last of which bears a pair of claws. Near the tip of each claw there is a minute tooth or claw-hook.

The wings are provided with various strengthening features, apart from the " veins ", and these include a notch or *nodus* on the forward or costal margin and a thickened spot or *pterostigma* near the apex of the wing. The venational arrangement is very complicated and only the essential features (Fig. I.43) will be discussed here. Examining a wing from base outwards towards apex there is, firstly, the *costal vein* (c) on the anterior margin, followed by two radial veins, R_1 and R_2. Then, at the base, there is a gap closed by an angled vein, the *arculus*, from which is subtended the radial sector, RS. RS divides into R_3 and the combined vein R_{4+5} and in the outer part of the wing there are further short vein

[545]

sectors, such as IR_2, IR_3, Rspl. Then there is the median vein, MA, followed by the cubital, Cu and the anal vein 1A. The actual notation of these veins is derived from a study of more primitive wings in insects. The reason, for instance, that there is a Cu_2 but no Cu_1 is because it is regarded that the latter has become obsolete in the modern dragonfly wing.

A few more features are of special importance. At or near the bases of Cu_2 and 1A there is an enclosed space, the *discoidal cell* (d.c.), which may be a quadrilateral or a triangle in shape. To the outer side of the triangle in *Anisoptera* (see below) there are one, two or three rows of cells stretching to the margin, a region called the discoidal field (d.f.). Below the costal margin, the short transverse veins are known as *antenodal* cross-veins (Ax) between base and nodus, and postnodals (Px) beyond this notch. On the hindwing in *Anisoptera* the anal vein normally forms an extra loop (a.l.). And at the base of the anal margin there may be a supporting structure called the membranule.

Such, briefly, are the structural characters of the adult dragonfly. In certain features, such as the obliquely elongated thorax, the accessory genitalia on segment 2 of the male and some of the wing characters dragonflies are unique. But the layman sometimes confuses them with *Antlions*. Dragonflies always breed in water, their aquatic nymphs or larvae being totally unlike the adult in appearance. They may be squat and robust in *Anisoptera*, or slender and provided with broad tails in *Zygoptera*. They undergo no pupal state but when the adults are ready to emerge the adults crawl up any convenient object, tree-trunk at water's edge, a reed or rock, split down the back and, after an exhausting struggle, the adult emerges. The body and wings have to stretch and dry and the insect may then be ready for flight.

Antlions differ in many respects. Adults of one of the commoner species are illustrated at Plate 5. They are purely terrestrial creatures, belonging to the insect order *Neuroptera*. Their sickle-jawed larvae often make the familiar little pits in sandy soil to way-lay the unwary ant or other small insect. The adult has well-developed, conspicuous antennae, which are often knobbed (clavate) at the apices; the thorax is *not* elongated and the shortish legs are situated directly below the wings (as they are also in most insects). There are other notable differences but those already given will suffice to tell whether an insect is a dragonfly or an antlion. In habits, it might be added, adult antlions fold their wings, when at rest, roof-wise along their abdomen. They are frequently attracted to lights. In the damselfly the wings are usually *held together above their backs* (as in resting butterflies) or occasionally (in *Lestes*)

[546]

half-open. In other dragonflies the resting insect spreads its wings open, more or less horizontally. Dragonflies are only sometimes attracted to light, usually only when disturbed. There are a few nocturnal or crepuscular species but even these are not readily attracted.

In female dragonflies of the groups *Zygoptera* and *Aeshnidae* eggs are laid by means of an ovipositor which can pierce a hole in a reed or twig under or above the water surface, the eggs being inserted in the slit. Other dragonflies usually just select a stretch of water suitable to their species and drop eggs haphazardly, as their abdomen touches the water surface. Some species like still waters (the ubiquitous *Brachythemis leucosticta* and others will often carelessly distribute theirs in a temporary rain puddle); others prefer running water, or even rapids and waterfalls (*Zygonyx*). The presence or absence of shade or of reeds to act as perches; the degree of concentration of solutes in the water and the temperature will influence some species, although a few (like *Ischnura senegalensis*) are either much less particular or else more tolerant. The larvae hatching from these eggs move about by a swimming or wriggling motion in *Zygoptera* (the tailed larvae) or by a form of jet propulsion in others. Like the adults they are carnivorous, capturing any other creatures and devouring them. They catch their prey by means of a unique development of the labium, which, in the larva, is a hinged implement with jaws at the end which can be projected forward suddenly to seize the victim. The newly emerged adult is soft, often very pallid, with glistening wings. After a short period in this teneral state the insect gradually hardens and matures. In doing so it may undergo various colour changes. Consequently, a brief indication of the colour of a dragonfly will often be of little use in identifying the species unless supplementary details can be given. Moreover, being carnivorous, the food in the body decays rapidly after death and in the dried insect the surface colours may be altered by postmortem discolouration. Rapid drying or cleaning out the abdomen of the larger species is advisable to try and preserve original colours and if a fine piece of wire or other similar object is thrust right through thorax and abdomen it usually helps to prevent the body falling to pieces.

Dragonflies are harmless insects, as a whole, incapable of stinging. The adults may be considered moderately useful creatures in that they feed on flies and other insects. But they are not averse to eating other dragonflies. The larvae, on the other hand, are very important in fish dietary problems and may affect the balance of aquatic life in their own depradations on water insects. The larger species may also at times attack the smaller fish fry.

[547]

Classification

Dragonflies are easily separated into the two suborders, *Zygoptera* (damselflies) and *Anisoptera*. The former are usually slender-bodied, with widely separated eyes (Fig. H.42); their wings are all of the same shape and normally stalked or petioled at the base. In venation, the discoidal cell is always a quadrilateral. And there are numerous other characteristics. *Anisoptera* are more robust insects; their eyes usually touching one another (except in family *Gomphidae*); the hindwing is broader at the base than the forewing; the wings are not petioled; and the discoidal cell is nearly always a triangle (except *Tetrathemis* of the Central African fauna). Family divisions can be found in the following key; generic and specific separations are given on the respective pages of this survey. *Zygoptera* families considered here are *Lestidae*, *Protoneuridae*, *Platycnemididae*, *Coenagriidae*, *Agriidae* and *Chlorocyphidae*. Anisoptera consist of *Gomphidae*, *Aeshnidae*, *Corduliidae* and *Libellulidae*.

KEY TO FAMILIES OF DRAGONFLIES

1   Forewing and hindwing of same shape, usually stalked (petiolate); discoidal cell a quadrilateral.

                                   Suborder *Zygoptera*   2

      Forewing and hindwing dissimilar in shape, hindwing always broader in anal field. Discoidal cell triangular (diamond-shaped, quadrangular in *Tetrathemis*).

                                   Suborder *Anisoptera*   7

2 (1) With five or more antenodal cross-veins. Nodus remote from base (at least two-fifths wing length from base). Discoidal cell elongate, crossed . . . . Superfamily *Agrioidea*   3

        With two antenodal cross-veins. Nodus close to base (at one-third or less). Discoidal cell free 4

3 (2) Wings petiolate. Pterostigma long and narrow. Epistome enlarged, snout-like . . . Family *CHLOROCYPHIDAE*

        Wings unstalked. Pterostigma small or absent. Epistome not enlarged . . . . Family *AGRIIDAE*

4 (2) Pterostigma elongate, rectangular. An oblique cross-vein connecting R_3 to IR_3 . . . . . Superfamily *Lestoidea*
                                     Family *LESTIDAE*

        Pterostigma rhomboidal or a parallelogram. Without the oblique vein . . . . . Superfamily *Coenagrioidea* 5

5 (4) 1A absent or not more than one cell long.
                            Family *PROTONEURIDAE*

        1A well developed 6

6 (5) Discoidal cell practically rectangular.
                          Family *PLATYCNEMIDIDAE*

        This cell with lower distal angle very acute.
                          Family *COENAGRIIDAE*

7 (1) Antenodal cross-veins not normally coincident in costal and subcostal spaces. Triangles (discoidal cells) very similar in all wings and well distal to arculus.
                       Superfamily *Aeshnoidea*   8

Antenodal cross-veins mainly coincident in costal and subcostal spaces. Triangles markedly dissimilar in forewing and hindwing and at or adjacent to arculus.

Superfamily *Libelluloidea* 9

8 (7) Eyes widely separated . . . . . Family *GOMPHIDAE*

Eyes in contact with each other . . Family *AESHNIDAE*

9 (7) Primary antenodal cross-veins present. Males with auricles at base of abdomen and with keels along the tibiae.

Family *CORDULIIDAE*

No primary antenodals, auricles or tibial keels.

Family *LIBELLULIDAE*

Suborder ZYGOPTERA

Family LESTIDAE

Key to males of the genus *Lestes* Leach

1   Superior appendages bent distinctly downwards in apical half 2

Superior appendages forcipate, scarcely bent down . . . 4

2 (1) Thoracic dorsum in immature examples with slender, regular green stripes, in mature male largely pruinosed.

plagiatus

Thoracic dorsum with irregular stripes or spots, or entirely metallic green; but the dorsum non-pruinose 3

3 (2) Abdomen 37 mm. or more. Superior appendage curved downwards before apex, tapering, very hirsute . . . *uncifer*

Abdomen less than 33 mm. Superior angled downwards; not tapering and less hirsute . . . . *pinheyi*

4 (1) Thorax with regular bright green dorsal bands. Wings yellowish 5

Thorax without stripes, or these darker and irregular . . 6

5 (4) Wings yellowish with golden brown apices . . . . *amicus*

Wings usually yellowish, but without darkening at apices.

virgatus

[550]

6 (4) Thorax blackish; or brown with dark or metallic bands or
 spots 7
 Thorax uniformly brownish or greenish 9

7 (6) Thorax mainly black, without bands or spots. Abdominal
 segment 9 without yellow annulus . . . . . *wahlbergi,*
     which may be a melanic form of *pallidus*
 Thorax brown, with irregular bands and spots. Segment 9
 usually with yellow annulus 8

8 (7) Superior appendage with medial acute sub-basal tooth . *tridens*
 Superior appendage with medial, rounded sub-basal
 swelling . . . . *simulans*

9 (6) Superior appendage much paler than the body and without
 sub-basal tooth . . . . *disarmata*
 Superior appendage not markedly paler than body and provided with sub-basal tooth . . . . *pallidus*

Lestes amicus Martin, 1910, *Ann. Soc. ent. Fr.* **79**: 85, 91

This species (Plate 1, fig. *a*) is restricted in distribution in Africa and
the records are chiefly from Central Africa, where it may be locally
abundant. Northern Rhodesia: Victoria Falls (in the " Rain Forest"
during the dry months, July to October); Abercorn (in swamps);
Mwinilunga (only one example taken). Katanga: Elizabethville.

Lestes ? disarmata Fraser, 1961, in Pinhey, *Brit. Mus. (Nat. Hist.).* 11

One female collected in the so-called " Rain Forest " at the Victoria
Falls, in July, 1955, may perhaps be this little-known species, of which
only the male has been described. [The identification has since been
confirmed by the discovery of further examples—AUTHOR.]

It is a small light brown insect, abdomen 29.5 mm., hindwing 19 mm.,
similar in colour and markings and in the short, broad pterostigma to
the male *disarmata*. Moreover, the mid-dorsal black line is reduced
on the subterminal abdominal segments, and segment 10 and the cerci
are yellow, corresponding to the pallid terminalia of that species. It
cannot be described as an allotype until a male is found in that area
which can confirm the identification. One of the more pallid female
forms *pallidus* found in the same locality is larger, with the pterostigma
longer and narrower and with well marked dorsal line on terminal segments.

Lestes pallidus Rambur, 1842, *Névr.* 252 (Senegal)

Forms of this very variable and widespread species may overlap in
distribution at the Victoria Falls, as elsewhere. Northern Rhodesia:
Victoria Falls and Katambora; Kalambo Falls. Katanga: Albertville.

Lestes pinheyi Fraser, 1955, Mission de Witte, *Parc. Nat. Upemba* **38**: 10 ff.

A smaller insect than *uncifer*, for which it was mistaken by the present author (1951, *Transv. Mus. Mem.* **5**: 48). Northern Rhodesia: Victoria Falls; Samfya and Lake Bangweulu; Mwinilunga; Abercorn.

A very teneral female taken south of Ndola may also be this species.

Lestes plagiatus (Burmeister). *Agrion plagiatum* Burmeister, 1839, *Handb.* **2**: 824 (Natal)

Widespread. Northern Rhodesia: Ndola; Kabompo River; Kasempa; and on Tanganyika border at Ufipa Plateau (V. Fitzgerald). Katanga: La Manda River.

Lestes simulans Martin, 1910, loc. cit. 85, 88

The form taken at the Victoria Falls differs from those of Uganda in having the wings more fumose and in the form of the superior appendages which, in particular, are more curved in the Falls examples. It is possible that two species or subspecies are involved here, but since Martin's description was not illustrated it is difficult to decide which is the more typical.

Lestes tridens MacLachlan, 1895, *Ann. Mag. nat. Hist.* **6** (16): 24 (Moçambique)

A local species, mainly coastal. Northern Rhodesia: Abercorn.

Lestes uncifer Karsch, 1899, *Ent. Nachr.* **25**: 381 (Tanganyika)

A very local species. At the Victoria Falls the Author has only seen it in the undergrowth amongst thick bush near the Maramba River. Northern Rhodesia: Victoria Falls; Abercorn; Kalambo Falls. Katanga: Mubale.

Lestes virgatus (Burmeister). *Agrion virgatum* Burmeister, 1839, *Handb.* **2**: 824 (Natal)

Generally widespread in bush or forest. Northern Rhodesia: Ndola; Mwinilunga; Abercorn. Katanga: Upembe Nat. Park.

In addition females of two species too teneral for identification were found at Mwinilunga in March, 1960, evidently too early for mature examples. One was of the size of *pallidus;* the other larger with traces of green antehumerals, but with the pterostigma too small for *amicus*, *plagiatus* or *virgatus*.

Family **PROTONEURIDAE**

Key to genera

1 1A developed but only 1 cell long. Wings in male yellow.

Chlorocnemis

   1A absent. Wings uncoloured . . . . . . *Elattoneura*

Key to *Chlorocnemis* Selys

1 Labrum pale blue. Frons and vertex with broad blue band.
   Superior appendage of male black . . . . . *marshalli*
   Labrum black. Frontal blue band narrow 2

2 (1) Superior appendage black . . . . *lascellesi*
   Superior appendage yellow . . . . *wittei*

CHLOROCNEMIS LASCELLESI n.sp.
(Fig. 5)

Holotype male (mature). Labium creamy white, black on anterior third (including moving parts); the rest of the face and head, dorsally and ventrally, jet black, except for a pale blue transverse band across the frons in front and extending to the compound eyes. Prothorax jet black, the anterior and lateral margins pale blue and a minute lateral dot on posterior lobe whitish. Synthorax jet black dorsally and down to first lateral suture; with a broad pale blue antehumeral, not quite reaching upper dorsal limit of mesepisternum and tapering at its upper end; this stripe at its widest very slightly more than half the breadth of a mesepisternum. Lower sides of thorax pale blue, with a short black streak at upper end of second lateral suture; ventral surface pale yellowish.

Legs black; cream-coloured on coxae, trochanters and bases of femora; on meso- and meta-thoracic legs also a cream stripe on flexor surface of each femur. Wings with greenish yellow tint. Pterostigma and venation black. Forewing with 16–17 Px. Abdomen and anal appendages black, with pale markings. On 1–2 whitish lateral bands. Sky blue markings: a broad band covering proximal three-quarters of 2, tapering to a dorsal point in distal quarter; 3 with basal annulus which, on dorsum, extends posteriad for nearly one-third of this segment as an attenuate triangle; 4 with a small basal triangle; 5–7 with small rounded basal spot; 8–9 all black; 10 with dorsal patch as in the figure; and a small pale dorsal triangle near base of each superior appendage.

Appendages of the usual Chlorocnemine form; extended inwardly and broadly near bases. Pale colours in life: eye above brown, blue-green below; body markings deep sky blue with a tinge of green in some areas.

Abd. 38.5 mm., hw. 24 mm.

Paratype males. There is slight variation in size, the abdomen being almost 40 mm. in one example. Teneral males, as in others of the genus, have hyaline, uncoloured wings. This, incidentally, differs from some of the higher *Anisoptera* which have yellow on the wings, for in certain species at least this colour is brighter in the juveniles and may become less intense as the insect matures. In old males of *lascellesi* the pale dorsal spot on 10 is narrower, and that on the superior has vanished. In tenerals, again, the blue colour tends to be more violet, becoming sky blue with maturation. In these younger ones the appendages are pale brown at first.

Allotype female (almost mature). Head, thorax and legs as in male but the pale markings pale greenish instead of sky blue. Wings hyaline, untinted. Abdomen black, with similar lateral white bands, but the dorsal markings, which are bluish white, are reduced; a narrow sagittal mark on proximal half of 2; 3–5 with traces of basal annuli, with an even smaller trace on 6; 7–10 and the very short cerci black.

Abd. 38 mm., hw. 24 mm.

Paratype females. An old female is slightly larger, abdomen 39 mm., hindwing 25 mm., and the wings are faintly greenish yellow.

Remarks. A series of both sexes was collected in the Mwinilunga District, February–March, 1960, at the sources of the Zambezi and Sakeshi as well as on the latter river in Hillwood Farm. I take pleasure in naming the species after Mr. Peter Lascelles for his part in collecting some of these and for his enthusiastic support during the expedition. The species is nearest to *pauli* Longfield and *wittei* Fraser, but both those have yellow superior appendages. From *marshalli* Ris and the more tropical *superba* Schmidt *lascellesi* differs in several respects: the labrum is black instead of blue and the frontal band is narrower (in *marshalli* it is wide enough to cover part of the frons dorsally as well as anteriorly); and the abdominal markings are different.

The very teneral male captured on the Mitwaba escarpment, in company with *Allocnemis mitwabae*, in January, 1958, proves to be an example of *lascellesi*.

[554]

This species favours the edges of dense forest patches and evidently breeds in very small, quiet forest streams. Types and paratypes are in the National Museum, but one paratype male will be sent to the British Museum (Natural History).

Northern Rhodesia: Mwinilunga. Katanga: Mitwaba Escarpment.

Chlorocnemis marshalli Ris, 1921, *Ann. S. Afr. Mus.* **18**: 291 (S. Rhodesia)

This Southern Rhodesian species has been recorded from Nyasaland. It is probably to be found there in forested streams on the mountains.

Chlorocnemis wittei Fraser, 1955, *Parc Nat. Upemba, Mission de Witte* **38**: 7

Katanga: Kamitungulu (Upemba Nat. Park).

Key to males of *Elattoneura* Cowley

1   Superior appendage with two teeth, one long, one short, on a broad flange . . . . *glauca*

     Superior appendage with only one tooth, on a broad flange   2

2 (1) Larger species, abdomen 29 mm. or more. The tooth on the superior appendage like a small hook . . . . . *acuta*

     Smaller species, abdomen 27 mm. or less. The tooth a robust continuation of the broad flange . . . *frenulata*

Elattoneura acuta Kimmins, 1938, *Ann. Mag. nat. Hist.* (11) **1**: 300, f (Nigeria)

A few speciments of this large species were taken at Lubudi (Katanga) in forested gorges near waterfalls.

Elattoneura frenulata (Hagen). *Disparoneura frenulata* Hagen, in Selys, 1860, *Bull. Acad. Belg.* **2** (10): 444 (17 Sep.) (Cape)

A widespread species. Northern Rhodesia: Victoria Falls and Katambora; Ndola; Lusaka; Kasempa; Kabompo River; Mwinilunga; Abercorn. Katanga: Lubudi; La Manda River; Bunkeya; Albertville. Nyasaland: Cholo.

Elattoneura glauca Selys. *Disparoneura glauca* Selys, 1860, *Bull. Acad. Belg.* **2** (10): 443

This appears to be less common in Northern Rhodesia than south of the Zambezi or in East Africa. (Plate 1, fig. *c*.) Northern Rhodesia: Victoria Falls (uncommon); Ndola; Kabompo River; Abercorn; Chongwe River, Lusaka (Dening).

Family **PLATYCNEMIDIDAE**

Key to genera in Northern Rhodesia

1   Origin of anal vein distinctly proximal to Ac. Wings hyaline . . . . *Metacnemis*
Origin of anal vein at or almost at Ac. Wings, at least in male, distinctly yellow . . . . *Allocnemis*

Metacnemis singularis (Karsch). *Mesocnemis singularis* Karsch, 1891, *Ent. Nachr.* **17**: 67

Generally common at rocky streams, the pruinosed male conspicuous by its extensively pale blue coloration. Northern Rhodesia: Victoria Falls and Katambora.

Allocnemis mitwabae Pinhey, 1960, *Ent. Mon. Mag.* **96**: 258. ? *Allocnemis* sp. Schouteden, 1934: 79 (Lubilash, Katanga)

Males (Plate 1, fig. *b*). Superficially like a very elongate *Chlorocnemis* until the venation is examined. Labrum, genae and a broad transverse band in frontal region yellow, the whole face appearing alternately striped: yellow, on labrum and laterally to the pale bluish ventral surface of the eye; black, on epistome, laterally to the eye, surrounding this as a black band; broad yellow frontal band, continuing as a pale bluish band around the eye; and a black vertex, extending as a black dorsal patch on the eye. Antehumeral stripes narrow, yellow. Legs yellow on flexor surfaces, black on extensor, except coxae and bases of femora; tarsi black. Wings greenish yellow to deep smoky yellow. Pterostigma black, framed with yellow.

In life the eye is blue with black rings; antehumeral yellow; sides of thorax pale bluish green; 9–10 and superior appendages bright orange red. Inferiors black.

In one male variety there is a tendency to a reduction in the black: legs, including tarsi, mainly yellow; abdominal segments 3–5 *broadly* yellowish above, suffused with black; inferior appendages partly yellow. In another male variety the left antehumeral is broken dorsally.

Abd. 42.5 mm., hw. 24 mm.

Allotype female (Mature; Lubudi). Head black, with two facial bands; a grey-yellow band at labrum, laterally extended, and a broad yellow frontal band. Trace of yellow at back of occipital plate. Prothorax black, broadly yellow anteriorly and laterally. Posterior lobe appearing laterally as a procumbent black flap, medially this lobe greatly reduced, but supporting a pair of vertical, rounded, cream-coloured, flattened stylets (Fig. 9).

Synthorax black to first lateral suture, with faintly greenish tinge. Slender antehumerals not reaching dorsum and expanding ventrally; a yellow lateral dot on mesothorax collar, and yellow dots just below upper end of humeral suture. Sides of thorax greenish to whitish blue; a broad black stripe on second lateral suture. Femora cream with black stripe on extensor surfaces; tibiae cream externally, black on flexor surfaces; tarsi black. Wings somewhat greenish-fumose; pterostigma dark brown, framed with yellow. Abdomen black, with continuous yellow sublateral stripe and some yellow dorsal markings: yellow mid-dorsal line on 1–4, progressively thinner; incomplete basal annuli on 3–6; 8 all yellow dorsally; 9 with yellow median band which expands distally as a saddle; 10 and the short cerci all black. Ovipositor yellowish, black ventrally. Abd. 43 mm., hw. 28 mm. In life, the eye was blue and black as in the male; sides of thorax whitish; 9–10 dull orange-red.

Paratype female. Abd. 41.5 mm., hw. 27 mm.

Remarks. The original series of this Katanga species consisted of a few males collected on the Mitwaba Escarpment at a small trickling stream. In February, 1960, several more specimens of both sexes were collected at forested streams and waterfalls and also in shade on a broad-ish river near Lubudi. It is a larger insect than the South African *A. leucosticta* Selys (1863) with darker and smaller pterostigma. The prothoracic stylets of the female are very similar but they are black in the latter species.

Family COENAGRIIDAE

Key to genera

1   Anal vein leaves margin at Ac or less than the length of Ac before this cross-vein 2

      Anal vein leaves margin more than the length of Ac before this cross-vein 4

2 (1) Frons with well developed transverse crest. Abdominal colour yellow to red. Female without vulvar scale on 8th sternite . . . . *Ceriagrion*

      Frons without a very prominent crest. Abdomen not yellow or red (at least dorsally) 3

3 (2) Female without vulvar scale on 8th sternite . . *Pseudagrion*

      Female with this scale . . . . *Aciagrion*

4 (1) Arculus far distal to second Ax. Female without vulvar spine. Very small species, abdomen about 20 mm. or less . 5

      Arculus at second Ax or barely distal to it. Female normally with vulvar spine. Abdomen generally more than 20 mm. . 6

[557]

5 (4) Anal vein angled at its junction with Ac. . . *Agriocnemis*
Anal vein merely slightly curved at its junction with Ac.
Mortonagrion

6 (4) Pterostigma of male dissimilar in forewing and hindwing.
Postclypeus strongly metallic (in Ethiopian species).
Female polychroic . . . . *Ischnura*
Pterostigma similar in all wings. Postclypeus dull. Female
not polychroic . . . . *Enallagma*

Key to males of genus *Ceriagrion* Selys

1 Thorax in front distinctly green 2
Thorax orange or red 3

2 (1) Smaller species, with basal half of wings yellowish. Arculus
at or scarcely distal to second Ax. . . . . . *whellani*
Larger species, with wings not saffronated. Arculus well
distal to second Ax. . . . . *bidentatum*

3 (1) Tenth segment of abdomen with raised spines on distal
margin . . . . *glabrum*
Tenth segment without these raised spines 4

4 (3) Superior appendage considerably longer than inferior and
armed with large median tooth; abdomen deep red.
katamborae n. sp.
Superior appendage not or barely longer than inferior . 5

5 (4) Abdomen orange red to light red. Superior appendage
slightly longer than inferior . . . . *suave*
Abdomen deep red 6

6 (5) Small species, abdomen about 24 mm. Pterostigma
elongate . . . . *ignitum*
Large species, abdomen 35 mm. or more. Pterostigma
rhomboidal, almost square . . . . *platystigma*

Ceriagrion bidentatum Fraser, 1941, *Proc. R. ent. Soc. Lond.* B. **10**: 61, f
(Uganda)

A local species favouring thick bush or tropical forest. Northern
Rhodesia: Samfya (Dening); Lake Mweru (Johnsen).

Ceriagrion glabrum (Burmeister).   *Agrion glabrum* Burmeister, 1839,
   Handb. **2**: 821

Abundant nearly throughout Africa but very variable in colour and
size. Northern Rhodesia: Victoria Falls; Ndola; Kasempa; Samfya;
Mwinilunga. Katanga: Jadotville (under trees in savannah); Albertville. Nyasaland: Port Herald (Gray); Bua River mouth, Kota Kota;
Nkata Bay.

Ceriagrion ignitum Campion, 1914, *Ann. Mag. nat. Hist.* **14**:   281
   (Ghana)

A series of males taken at swampy streams, chiefly at Sakeshi River
source, are probably this species, but Campion's article is not illustrated.
Thorax of the male deep reddish brown above, green laterally; abdomen
crimson. Northern Rhodesia: Mwinilunga.

Ceriagrion platystigma Fraser, 1941, loc. cit. 63, ff. (Uganda)

Easily recognizable by its almost square pterostigma this large species
has only so far been taken sparsely in the Federation at Abercorn,
Northern Rhodesia, in the swamp forest and on the Lucheche River.

CERIAGRION KATAMBORAE n. sp.

(Fig. 41)

Holotype male (mature).   Labium and lower surface of occiput
creamy white; labrum and anteclypeus pale brown; rest of head above
ferruginous; back of occiput pale brown, bordering a ferruginous area.
Basal segment of antenna yellowish brown, blackish distally; flagellar
segments blackish.   Thorax pale brown, tinted with ferruginous
dorsally; without any black markings. Legs pale brown, ungues amber
but their apices and the claw-hooks black. Wings without any amber;
venation grey-brown, the main radial vein pale brown; pterostigma
elongate, reddish violet, between pale brown veins.

Forewing with 11–12 Px, hindwing with 10 Px. Arculus just distal
to second Ax. Ac nearer to first than to second Ax and situated at end
of petiole.   In right forewing of type there is an abnormal cross-vein
linking the anal vein to the margin.

Abdomen dorsally light crimson on distal end of 1, on dorsum of 2–3
and the proximal half of 4; rest of abdomen light brown, but tinged with
red dorsally.   Near distal ends of 4–6 there is a small black dorsal
crescent, and a trace of one on 3. Superior appendage very distinctive,

[559]

porrect, about two-thirds as long as 10; with strong medial tooth half-way along its shaft. Inferior much shorter, broad and somewhat curved in lateral view; the apex black; posteriorly swollen almost as a tumour. Abdomen 27.5 mm., hindwing 17 mm.

Remarks. One male only taken on a stream leading into the Zambezi River at Katambora, 7th October, 1960. This type is in the National Museum, Bulawayo. This is a smallish species, coloured like a dwarf *C. platystigma* Fraser; but with an elongate pterostigma. The anal appendages are quite unlike those of other African species of the genus, in most of which the superior is somewhat curved, very short and without the medial tooth.

Ceriagrion suave Ris, 1921, *Ann. S. Afr. Mus.* **18**: 316 ff. (Katanga)

Northern Rhodesia: Victoria Falls; Ndola; Ngoma; Luanshya; Abercorn and Ufipa Plateau (V. Fitzgerald). Katanga: Lufua River; Elizabethville; Kapiri; Kanonga.

Ceriagrion whellani Longfield, 1952, *Proc. R. ent. Soc. Lond.* B. **21**: 42, ff. (S. Rhodesia)

This small species is abundant in the few swampy, bush localities where it has been found. In life, the lips of the male are yellow; eye and thorax green above, yellowish green below; abdomen orange-red above, paler below. Northern Rhodesia: Ndola (swamps at pool's edge); Mwinilunga (swampy streams, Sakeshi etc.); Abercorn (amongst *Brachystegia* bush at swamp-end of Lake Chila); Samfya ?

? Ceriagrion corallinum Campion, 1914, *Ann. Mag. nat. Hist.* (8) **14**: 279 (S. Leone)

Schouteden (1934: 82) records this from Albertville but this may be open to doubt ? *C. corallinum* is allied to *whellani* but has longer superior appendages; and less amber on the wings.

Key to males of genus *Aciagrion* Selys

1 Abdomen 25 mm. long or less, hw. 17.5 mm. or less. Abdomen with broad black dorsal band on third to seventh
   segments. Superior appendage much shorter than tenth
   segment and branched . . . . *steeleae*

   Abdomen 28 mm. or more. Abdomen without broad black
   dorsal band on third to seventh segments 2

2 (1) Abdomen 32 mm. or less, hindwing 18–22 mm. Superior appendage very large, longer than tenth segment, provided with inner basal spine . . . . *africanum*

Abdomen 35 mm. or more 3

3 (2) Abdomen exceedingly long and slender, at least 38 mm. Superior and inferior appendages of about the same length, both much shorter than tenth segment . . . *heterosticta*

Abdomen about 35 mm. long. Inferior appendage longer than superior . . . . *attenuatum*

Examples of this genus appear to be very local or distinctly scarce.

Aciagrion africanum Martin, 1908, *Ann. Mus. Stor. nat. Genova* **43**: 659 (Port. Guinea)

Northern Rhodesia: 1 ♂ in swamp, Ikelenge, Mwinilunga; 1 ♂ in large swamp or " dambo " near Solwezi (March, 1960); Samfya (Dening).

Aciagrion attenuatum Fraser, 1928, *Trans. Ent. Soc. Lond.* **1**: 126 (Nyasaland)

Ufipa Plateau, Rhodesia—Tanganyika border (V. Fitzgerald). It was described from Zomba, Nyasaland, where the type male was collected by the late Mr. Colin Smee. Nkata Bay (Eccles).

Aciagrion heterosticta Fraser, 1955, *Rev. Zool. Bot. afr.* **52**: 19 (Katanga)

A number of very teneral examples of this long, slender insect were taken at a swampy pool near a river 25 miles south of Ndola, March, 1960. In the field they were at first thought to be a species of *Teinobasis*, because of their attenuated shape. In life, the oldest example: thorax green, abdomen pink to pinkish red. Northern Rhodesia: Ndola; Ngoma (Kafue National Park). Katanga: Lubumbashi.

Aciagrion steeleae Kimmins, 1955, *Entomolgist* **88**: 109 ff (L. Bangweulu)

This small species is, in the field, easy to mistake for an *Enallagma* or a *Pseudagrion*. It is somewhat variable and the Author's *abercornensis* (Pinhey, 1958, *Occ. Pap. Nat. Mus. S. Rhod.* **22** B: 103, ff.) appears to be no more than the commoner form of this insect, at least in some localities. The anal appendages are very short, almost like certain *Enallagma*. In one example the anal vein leaves the petiole well distal to Ac, instead of at Ac as in the normal position. In life the eye is dark blue above, green laterally, yellowish green ventrally; pale body colours cobalt. Northern Rhodesia: Mwinilunga (at swampy pool near Zambezi River); Lake Bangweulu (only the original types); Abercorn.

Key to mature males of the genus *Pseudagrion* **Selys**

In order to simplify this key a little it is divided into two main sections:

A. in which the thorax is more or less black, the antehumerals, if present, being not more than half the width of each mesepisternum. Sometimes strongly pruinosed.

B. in which the thorax dorsally is mainly pale coloured (red, blue, green), the medial and humeral black being narrow. Without pruinosity on the dorsum, except in *pseudomassaicum*.

Section A

1   Synthoracic dorsum all black in adult, without any ante-humerals; if pruinosity is present it is scanty   2

Antehumerals visible or else masked by dense pruinosity .   6

2 (1) Labrum, tibiae, tarsi all black. Pt. blackish   3

Labrum, tibiae, tarsi not mainly black. Pt. more reddish .   4

3 (2) Synthoracic dorsum with pruinosed antehumerals. Superior appendage bifurcate, the lower branch the longer (like *kersteni*) . . . . *inconspicuum*

Synthoracic dorsum black, without pruinosed antehumerals. Superior appendage short, not bifurcate . . *nigerrimum*

4 (2) Labrum red. Superior appendage unbranched and without interior tooth . . . . *whellani*

Labrum green or greenish 5

5 (4) Superior appendage branched above (like *salisburyense*).
chongwe n. sp.

Superior appendage unbranched but massive . *deningi* n. sp.

6 (1) Mature examples extensively pruinosed on thorax and abdomen 7

Mature examples with very little dorsal pruinosity or none.   11

7 (6) Superior appendage of *kersteni* form, with lower branch the longer and this branch angled below its origin . . .   8

Superior appendage not like *kersteni*   9

[562]

8 (7) Antehumerals broad. Labrum black . . . . . *kersteni*

Antehumerals very narrow. Labrum greenish . . *inconspicuum*

9 (7) Branches of superior appendage of equal length (the upper being downcurved), with fairly wide gap in between. Labrum blackish . . . . *makabusiensis*

Branches of superior with the gap v-shaped or very narrow. Labrum greenish or brown 10

10 (9) Superior appendage not robust, the lower branch parallel to the upper . . . . . . *gerstaeckeri* and *salisburyense*

Superior appendage robust; lower branch lying obliquely across broad end of the upper . . . . . . *natalense*

11 (6) Superior appendage short, unbranched 12

Superior appendage distinctly branched 14

12 (11) Face bluish; antehumerals slender, bluish or greenish. An elongate blue spot on segment 2. Superior appendage with median lobe . . . . *rubroviridis*

Face bluish; antehumerals very broad, blue. A black arrowhead on segment 2. Superior appendage without median lobe . . . . *assegaii*

Face and antehumerals red. Without pale dorsal marking on 2. Superior appendage without median lobe . . . 13

13 (12) Antehumeral broad (but often in older examples obscured by black ground colour), of even width. Apex of superior appendage broad . . . . *whellani*

Antehumeral narrow dorsally, expanding ventrally. Superior appendage narrowing apically and therefore conical . . . . *jacksoni*

14 (11) Upper branch of superior appendage much longer than lower branch, the entire superior enormous, pincer-like. Labrum conspicuously yellow . . . . *greeni*

Upper branch not longer than lower branch, the appendage not abnormally large 15

15 (14) Lower branch of superior the longer and usually more robust than the upper branch 16

Branches of superior of equal length, or the upper branch curls down slightly so that it does not extend further than the lower one 17

[563]

16 (15) Abdomen less than 35 mm. in length. Superior appendage of
kersteni form. Labrum black or green . . . *inconspicuum*

Abdomen about 38 mm. The pincer-like superior with its
lower branch not angled and thus not of *kersteni* pattern.
Labrum yellow . . . . *gigas*

17 (15) Superior appendage with narrow or v-shaped excision
between the branches. Smaller species, abdomen 27 mm.
or less 18

Branch of superior wide apart. Abdomen usually 28 mm.
or more 20

18 (17) Antehumeral stripes almost absent, only represented as
vestigial pruinosed traces . . . . *chongwe* n. sp.

Antehumerals well developed 19

19 (18) Antehumerals blue or green. Labrum green. Abdomen 2
above with a black u-shaped mark . . . . . *nubicum*

Antehumerals and labrum red. Abdomen 2 above mainly
black and without a black u . . . . *rufostigma*

20 (17) Dorsum of thorax often thinly pruinosed, labrum blackish.
The gap between the branches of the superior appendage
not broadly rounded . . . . *makabusiensis*

Dorsum not pruinosed. Labrum not blackish. The gap in
the superior broadly rounded 21

21 (20) Labrum dull-coloured, not of a yellowish hue. Pterostigma
blackish. Branches of superior appendage of equal width.
melanicterum

Labrum and face bright orange. Pterostigma reddish.
Lower branch of superior thicker than upper branch . . 22

22 (21) Branches of superior with deep incision between; lower
branch not angled below origin . . . . . . *angolense*

Branches of superior with shallow incision; lower branch
broadly angled. Inferior appendage abnormally long.
fisheri n. sp.

Section B

1   Face and thoracic dorsum red 2

    Face and thoracic dorsum blue or green 5

2 (1) Humeral black stripe slender, almost linear. Inferior appendage conical 3

    Humeral black thick. Inferior hatchet-shaped . . . 4

3 (2) Abdomen 2 all black above. Superior appendage shorter than inferior . . . . *sjoestedti*

    Abdomen 2 with black u-shaped mark above. Superior appendage at least as long as inferior . . . . . *acaciae*

4 (2) Superior appendage longer than inferior. Dorsum of thorax normally pruinosed voilet . . . *pseudomassaicum*

    Superior appendage not longer than inferior. Dorsum of thorax without pruinosity and thus appearing red . *massaicum*

5 (1) Smallish species, abdomen about 26 mm. A black mark like a cat's head on segment 2 . . . . *coelestis*

    Larger, abdomen over 30 mm. Segment 2 with a black u-shaped mark 6

6 (5) Black thoracic marking vestigial. Branches of superior appendage of equal length . . . . *glaucescens*

    Black thoracic stripes on sutures developed, although slender. Lower branch of superior appendage longer than upper.
                           glaucoideum

PSEUDAGRION·CHONGWE n. sp.

(Fig. 1)

Holotype male (mature). One of the blacker species. Labrum, genae and epistome greenish white (might be bluish in life ?); base of postclypeus, the frons and head above black; with trace of yellow on posterior edge of occiput and with small round, greenish postocular spots. Prothorax dull black, with traces of yellow, laterally, on anterior and posterior lobes. Synthorax dull black above and down sides almost to first lateral suture, in fact in dorsal third coalescing with a short stripe on this seam; rest of sides greenish yellow, with a rather broad black band on second

[565]

lateral suture. Legs black, with mere trace of white pruinosity on femora; tibiae pale brown on outer (extensor) surfaces; tarsi light brown with distal black annuli, claws also brown with black apices. Venation black. Pterostigma elongate, dark reddish brown, with pale edging. Arculus very slightly distal to second Ax, Ac at or almost at commencement of anal vein. 13–14 Px in forewing, 12–13 in hindwing. Abdomen blackish to metallic green above, yellowish below; faint trace of white pruinosity on 1–2; 8–9 pale bluish above. Appendages short, narrowly forked, resembling those of *P. salisburyense* Ris, particularly in sideview, but with the upper branch of the superior perhaps less blunt. In dorsal view it is seen that the end of an inner ventral ridge slightly projects inwards from the superior; inferiors somewhat saucer-shaped.

Abd. 33 mm., hw. 23 mm.

Paratype male 1. Smaller, abd. 29 mm., hw. 21 mm. Pruinosity developed a stage further, so that faint whitish antehumerals appear on the black thorax, each less than half the width of a mesepisternum. *Paratype* 2 is of the same size as the last but has only a trace of the antehumeral in the dorsal portion of the thorax.

Female ? A *teneral* female *Pseudagrion*, together with a mature male of this species were sent from Fort Jameson. It is not certain that the female belongs to the same species, but a brief description may be of interest. Lips, face and frons dull orange brown; a black line at extreme lateral edge of labrum and a black basal line on postclypeus; rest of head above black except for the pale brown, elongate postocular spots which are connected together across the back of the occiput. Prothorax black above, pale orange brown on anterior lobe, also laterally and with sublateral spot and median dashes of this colour; prothoracic stylets entirely orange brown, over one third as long as middle lobe. Synthorax very like *salisburyense* but with black line on first lateral suture. Legs yellowish, with black external streak on femora.

Pterostigma light brown. Abdomen metallic bronze green above; distal end of 8 with a pale (? bluish) spot; 9 pale, except for a black latero-basal patch; 10 all pale; cerci short, pale.

Abd. 28 mm., hw. 22 mm.

Remarks. Males, including the types, were collected by Mr. R. C. Dening at Chongwe, in Northern Rhodesia. A further male, slightly blacker on sides of thorax than the Chongwe types, was caught by Mr. J. Clarke (?) at Fort Jameson, in a " fishpond, surrounded by grasses and Brachystegia Woodland ", 27th December, 1957; and he collected the teneral female described above at the " margin of a dam, over reeds and grass ", at Fort Jameson, on the 31st of that month.

[566]

This species is closest to *salisburyense*, but is blacker, with the appendages differing as stated above. The mature male does not develop the extensive blue pruinosity of *salisburyense*. In less mature *salisburyense* the thorax is metallic instead of dull black. Holotype and paratype No. 1 will be in the National Museum, paratype No. 2 will be sent to the British Museum (Natural History).

PSEUDAGRION DENINGI n. sp.
(Fig. 2)

Holotype male (mature). Lips, anteclypeus, sides of face and front of frons greenish white to yellowish, with trace of black on labrum. Postclypeus, rest of frons and entire head above black, without postocular spots; in fact even ventrally the occiput is mainly black. Prothorax all dull black except for a minute whitish lateral dot and fine white lateral edge to posterior lobe. Synthorax dull black to first lateral suture; rest of sides whitish (probably pale blue-green in life) except for a continuous black stripe on second lateral suture. Femora black, posterior femora pale brown on inner (flexor) surfaces; tibiae and tarsi brown, with narrow black streak on the tibiae.

Venation dark brown. Pterostigma elongate, reddish brown. Ac at commencement of anal vein in hindwings, but slightly distad to it in forewings; 12 Px in forewings, 10–11 in hindwings. Abdomen black above, pale greenish yellow below (1–2 with blue lateral spots), with only the merest trace of white pruinosity on 1–2; 8–9 entirely pale blue except for a minute black baso-lateral dot on 8; 10 black with pale blue lateral patch, widening distally. Superior appendages black and extraordinarily robust; knotched but not branched at apex and bearing apical spines. In lateral view the ventral portion of this massive appendage is seen to slope inwards to meet the corresponding appendage of the other side. Consequently, in dorsal view the inferior appendage cannot be seen. In dorsal aspect it is seen that the superior is hollowed out along its middle portion, the lining of this hollow being only thinly chitinized. Inferior appendage much smaller, tinged with bluish.

Abd. 26 mm., hw. 19 mm.

Remarks. The holotype male in the National Museum, Bulawayo, was presented by Mr. R. C. Dening, who collected this and others at Lake Chali, Bangweulu Swamps, on the 16th October, 1959. He stated this species was very common there at the time but being unaware that it would prove to be new he did not take further specimens. A single male from Lake Chila (Abercorn) is evidently a form of the same species. The face is distinctly yellow. The thorax above is metallic bronze-green; laterally and ventrally, as well as on base of abdomen there is some white

[567]

pruinosity. There are slight differences in the shape of the blue lateral patch on 10; but the appendages are similar. It seems inadvisable to call this a paratype in case it should eventually prove to be a separate race, although it is more likely that it is merely an older example.

A smaller species than the last, this is one of the blackest *Pseudagrion* yet examined by the Author. It is evidently near *whellani* Pinhey in general features, but the superior appendages, although also unbranched in the latter, are not nearly so robust.

PSEUDAGRION FISHERI n. sp.

(Fig. 3)

Holotype male (mature). Labium and ventral surface of occiput pale yellowish. Face in front deep orange; mere traces of three black basal dots on labrum; postclypeus entirely glossy bronze-black; frons above and entire vertex bronze-black except for a trace of orange on back of occiput and for the very small greenish yellow postucular spots. Antennae black.

Prothorax bronze-black, each lobe edged laterally with orange and with a small orange lateral triangle on the median lobe. Synthorax bronze-black dorsally and to below humeral suture (covering about half the mesepimeron); with very slender, but complete, yellow ante-humerals; sides greenish yellow with rather narrow bronze-black stripes on the upper portions of the two lateral sutures. Legs pale brown, the femora entirely black on the outside, tibiae with black stripe on flexor surfaces, traces of black on tarsi; claw-hooks very short. Wings slightly fumose. Venation blackish brown, pterostigma dark reddish brown, rhomboidal. Ac at commencement of anal vein in hindwings but somewhat distad in forewings. Arculus a little beyond second Ax in forewings (by as much as the upper segment of the arculus). 14–15 Px in forewing, 12 in hindwing. Abdomen bronze-black above, with strong greenish tinge. 9–10 with blue lateral patch. Superior appendages black, very robust with broad anvil-like lower branch; the lower branch with prominent teeth before the apex and an inner flange along the stem. Inferior appendage light brown, exceptionally large, as long as the superior, and provided with a hirsute inner basal flap.

Abd. 33.5 mm., hw. 23 mm.

In life the face is bright orange, the side of the thorax green, the lower surface of the abdomen and the inferior appendages very pale ochreous.

[568]

Paratype males. The prothoracic orange triangles are larger in some individuals; and in rather less mature specimens the pterostigma is pale brown, while the legs have rather less black. Variation in size not appreciable. In tenerals the wings are slightly more fumose.

Allotype female (mature). Face greenish ochreous, the frons in front more brownish; postclypeus and head above black, scarcely with any bronze sheen; postocular spots as in male. Thorax entirely as in male, but the prothoracic triangles are slightly larger and the antehumerals a little broader, yet barely one third the width of the mesepisternum. Prothoracic stylets entirely absent. Legs greyish ochreous, with the black reduced to traces on the exterior surfaces. Wings also slightly fumose, pterostigma pale brown. Abdomen bronze-green above, strongly greenish; 10 pale laterally. Cerci black dorsally, two-thirds the length of 10.

Abd. 31 mm., hw. 22.5 mm.

Paratype females. These have more external black on femora and tibiae.

Remarks. A longish series, from which the types were selected, was taken at Ikelenge, Mwinilunga, chiefly on the Sakeshi stream at Hillwood Farm, in February and March, 1960. The Author would like to acknowledge the invaluable assistance received from the owner of the farm, Mr. A. Fisher, by naming this species after him. The species flies near the banks in the open, but near shading trees and shrubs. A few examples were taken on the Lucheche River, Abercorn, by Vesey Fitzgerald, February–March, 1957. The conspicuous orange face distinguishes this insect in the field from the yellow-faced *greeni*, of similar size. Types, three male and two female paratypes in the National Museum; one male and one female paratype will be sent to the British Museum (Natural History).

This species, in colour and markings, is near *angolense*, from which the male differs by the smaller postocular spots, the black leg markings and the peculiar appendages, with the two branches of the superior more massive and only moderately separated (widely so in *angolense*). The female is distinctive in lacking prothoracic stylets and in its narrow antehumerals. From *monardi* Longfield, of Angola, *fisheri* differs in its smaller postocular spots, the darker vertex, narrower antehumeral stripe; the appendages more massive and differing in shape. The female is close to *monardi* in many respects, particularly in having no stylets, but differs in the rather narrower antehumerals.

[569]

PSEUDAGRION GREENI Pinhey

(Fig. 4)

Pseudagrion greeni Pinhey, 1960, *Ent. Mon. Mag.* **96**: 260 (♂ Ndola)

Allotype female (Ndola). More examples of both sexes of this species which was first collected to the south of Ndola, in January, 1958, were found during the 1960 expedition to Northern Rhodesia and it can now be stated that the solitary female tentatively described with the original description of the male *greeni* can be taken as the allotype. An additional observation is that the cerci are very large, about one and a quarter times as long as 10.

Males. In life, the pale colours of males (Kabompo River): labrum pale lemon yellow to bright yellow; anteclypeus, genae, lower surface of eye greenish yellow, the rest of the eye dark brown; antehumeral pale green, sides and ventral surface of thorax pale blue-green; 8–9 violet blue above. In a teneral male the wings are slightly fumose, the labrum more ochreous; dorsum of 8–9 blue without violet tinge.

Remarks. In the field the male of this large species, like *gigas*, is distinguished by its yellow face, whereas in the superficially similar *fisheri* it is orange. *Greeni* is a much darker species, with very reduced antehumerals; and the superior appendages are enormous, pincer-like, and more akin to certain Madagascar species. The inferiors are far shorter and being flattened appear slender in sideview. The females, in size and in the possession of only vestigial prothoracic stylets, are allied to *monardi* Longfield and *superbum* Fraser, but with the ante-humerals less yellowish, more reddish to violaceous. The exceptionally long cerci are distinctive and perhaps correlated in development with the long appendages of the male *greeni*.

The original short series was collected on the swampy banks of a small river to the south of Ndola in January, 1958. A further example was taken at the same stream in March, 1960, and others in February, 1960, at a swampy stream running into the Kabompo River, east of Mwinilunga, and others in similar situations on the Sakeshi stream. The allotype female is in the National Museum.

Pseudagrion acaciae Foerster, 1906, *Jber. Ver. Naturk. Mannheim* **71-72**: (56 sep.) (Transvaal)

An apparently uncommon species. Northern Rhodesia: Chirundu Bridge (Zambezi River), Victoria Falls and Katambora; Ndola.

Pseudagrion angolense Selys, 1876, *Bull. Acad. Belg.* (2) **42**: 493 (Angola)

A very common sciaphilous species in many parts of Africa. Northern Rhodesia: Ndola; Abercorn; Mwinilunga. Katanga: La Manda River; Lubudi; Lufua River; Fizi; Upemba nat. Park.

Pseudagrion assegaii Pinhey, 1950, *Ann. Transv. Mus.* **21**: 261, ff. (Transvaal and Southern Rhodesia)

An uncommon species taken by Dening (September 1960) at Mumbwa in Northern Rhodesia.

Pseudagrion coelestis Longfield, 1945, *Arch. Mus. Bocage* **16**: 9, 28, ff (Angola)

A rather sparsely scattered species. Northern Rhodesia: Victoria Falls and Katambora; Abercorn.

Pseudagrion gerstaeckeri Karsch, 1899, *Ent. Nachr.* **25**: 379, f. (Zanzibar)

Katanga: Lusinga. Nyasaland: Mzimba. Very closely allied to *salisburyense* but with distinct antehumeral stripes in mature examples.

Pseudagrion gigas Ris, 1936, *Abh. Senckenb. naturf. Ges.* **433**: 33 (Sikasso)

A local species, preferring the larger streams or rivers. Northern Rhodesia: Ndola; Kabompo River; Mwinilunga. Nyasaland: Cholo.

Pseudagrion glaucescens Selys, 1876, *Bull. Acad. Belg.* (2) **42**: 498 (Sierra Leone)

Another local species. Northern Rhodesia: Victoria Falls; Ndola; Samfya; Luanshya; Kasempa. Katanga: Kiambi and Lufua River. It has been recorded (under the name *zumbense* Návas, 1917) in Moçambique and it seems certain that the species occurs in Nyasaland.

Pseudagrion glaucoideum Ris, 1936, *Abh. Senckenb. naturf. Ges.* **433**: 66 (B. Congo)

Not a well known species. Katanga: Lufua River.

Pseudagrion inconspicuum Ris, 1931, *Rev. suisse Zool.* 98, f. (Angola)

There appear to be two distinct forms of this insect in Northern Rhodesia, with rather similar markings, and without clear distinctions in pterostigma or appendages. It is hoped that further material will be obtained, since it is locally common.

[571]

(*a*) Large form, similar to an example in the National Museum from Cazombo, Angola, November 1955. Labrum black; thorax very black, without antehumerals or with only a trace of pruinosed blue ones in older examples. Abd. 32–34 mm. Kabompo River, March 1960; Ndola (Green) May 1959; Kigwishi (Dening) July 1959; Chongwe River, Lusaka, March 1960 (Dening); Fort Rosebery (Dening).

(*b*) Small form. Labrum green, Antehumerals normally present, often pruinosed. Abd. 24–26 mm. Ndola (Green) May 1959; Luanshya December 1957; Abercorn (Vesey Fitzgerald) February, March, May, November, 1957; Mwinilunga February, March, 1960.

Pseudagrion jacksoni Pinhey, 1961, *Publications Brit. Mus.* (*Nat. Hist.*) 37

Hitherto only known from the type male and female from Northern Uganda, a single male was captured in March, 1960, on the Kabompo River. It belongs to the *whellani* group. Slightly larger than *rufostigma*, which is similar in general appearance, *jacksoni* has club-shaped antehumerals, unlike *rufostigma* and *whellani;* and the short superior appendage is unbranched and pointed (blunt, unbranched in *whellani*, branched in *rufostigma*).

Pseudagrion kersteni (Gerstaecker). *Agrion kersteni* Gerstaecker, 1869, *Arch. Naturgesch.* **35** (1): 222 (East Africa)

Perhaps the commonest Damselfly in most parts of Africa. Males (Plate 1, fig. *d*) are distinguishable in the field by the strongly pruinosed head and antehumerals and the green eyes. Northern Rhodesia: Victoria Falls; Ndola; Kasemba; Mwinilunga; Fort Rosebery; Lusaka; Abercorn. Katanga: Lubudi; Elizabethville; Albertville. Nyasaland: Mzimba; Fort Hill; Cholo; Nkata Bay.

Pseudagrion makabusiensis Pinhey, 1950, *Ann. Transv. Mus.* **21**: 263 (S. Rhodesia)

So far only known from the two Rhodesias. Abundant at Ndola and Mwinilunga; variable in size, males, abd. 28–33 mm. Northern Rhodesia: Ndola; Mwinilunga; Abercorn; Chongwe River, Lusaka.

Pseudagrion massaicum Sjoestedt. *Ps. punctum massaicum* Sjoestedt, 1909, *Kilim.–Meru Exp.* **2**: 48 (Kilimanjaro)

Certainly much more widespread in these territories than the records indicate. Northern Rhodesia: Ndola; Kabompo River (Johnsen). Katanga: Upemba Nat. Park. Nyasaland: Bua River mouth, Kota Kota.

Pseudagrion melanicterum Selys, 1876, *Bull. Acad. Belg.* (2) **42**: 492
(W. Africa)

Although Northern Rhodesia seems to be the southern limit of its range, it is abundant wherever it occurs in these territories, in rather dense bush or in forest. Pairs in copula were taken in Mwinilunga and other localities. One male was captured with a Tineoid moth as prey, another with a Jassid. The antehumerals of the male *melanicterum* may be slender and normal, as in West African examples, or slightly wider in some specimens from Mwinilunga. The size is variable: males, abd. 27–34 mm., hw. 18–23 mm. Northern Rhodesia: Ndola; Mufulira; Mwinilunga; Samfya; Abercorn (in swamp forest). Katanga: La Manda River; Lufua River; Upemba Nat. Park.

Pseudagrion natalense Ris, 1921, *Ann. S. Afr. Mus.* **18**: 307 (S. Africa)

Some of the larger males (abd. c. 35 mm.) seem indistinguishable from *spernatum* Selys (1881, *Ann. Mus. Stor. nat. Gènova* **16**: 223) from further north. Northern Rhodesia: Victoria Falls; Ndola; Mwinilunga; Abercorn. Katanga: Lubudi.

Pseudagrion nigerrimum Pinhey, 1950, *Ann. Transv. Mus.* **21**: 265
(S. Rhodesia)

Northern Rhodesia: Victoria Falls.

Pseudagrion nubicum Selys, 1876, *Bull. Acad. Belg.* (2) **42**: 501 (Nubia)

A local species, Rhodesian examples are larger than the form which is abundant in Uganda on the reedy fringes of Lake Victoria. Northern Rhodesia: Victoria Falls; Kafue River; Samfya (common, according to Watmough). Katanga: Lufua River.

Pseudagrion pseudomassaicum Pinhey, 1951, *Transv. Mus. Mem.* **5**: 93, ff.
(S. Africa)

A widespread species, preferring running water. Northern Rhodesia: Victoria Falls; Ndola; Mwinilunga. Katanga: Lufua River.

Pseudagrion rubroviridis Pinhey, 1956, *Occ. Pap. Coryndon. Mus.* **4**: 23, ff. (V. Falls)

A local insect. Northern Rhodesia: Victoria Falls.

Pseudagrion rufostigma Longfield, 1945, *Arch. Mus. Bocage* **16**: 11, 28, ff. (Angola)

Locally common in some parts of Northern Rhodesia and many were seen in copula. The face and antehumerals are vermillion, as in the rarer *jacksoni*. Pale colours of female in life: eye yellow, brown above; face pale yellow; antehumerals yellowish brown. Northern Rhodesia: Katambora; South of Ndola; Kabompo River; Mwinilunga.

[573]

Pseudagrion salisburyense Ris, 1921, *Ann. S. Afr. Mus.* **18**: 306 (S. Rhodesia, S. Africa)

A common insect in the southern part of the continent. Very like *gerstaeckeri* but with the narrow antehumerals quite obscured by pruinosity. Northern Rhodesia: Victoria Falls and Katambora; Ndola; Abercorn. Katanga: Lubudi. Nyasaland: Mzimba.

Pseudagrion sjoestedti Foerster, 1906, *Jber. Ver. Naturk. Mannheim* **71-72**: (62 sep.) (Cameroons)

A very local species. Northern Rhodesia: Victoria Falls; Chongwe River, Lusaka (Dening). Katanga: Albertville; Elizabethville (*vide* Schouteden).

Pseudagrion whellani Pinhey, 1956, loc. cit. 18, ff.

Widespread. Northern Rhodesia: Victoria Falls; Kapiri Mposhi; Ndola; Kasempa; Abercorn. Katanga: Bunkeya; Lufua River.

Key to males of *Agriocnemis* Selys and *Mortonagrion* Fraser

1   Superior appendage forcipate and much longer than inferior . . . . *forcipata*

    Superior appendage not forcipate, not or scacely longer than inferior 2

2 (1) Superior appendage deeply bifid, with its lower branch the longer and sloping steeply downwards . . . . *gratiosa*

    Superior appendage not deeply bifid, but broad and curled downwards 3

3 (2) Superior with a long medio-ventral spine. Postocular spots normally present . . . . *exilis*

    Superior without ventral spine. A darker insect, normally without postocular spots . . . . . *Mortonagrion stygium*

Agriocnemis exilis Selys, 1872, *Rev. Mag. Zool.* (182 sep.) (Madagascar etc.)

· A very widespread insect, despite its minute size (Plate 1, fig. *e*). Generally gregarious at swampy pools and easy to collect by sweeping. Northern Rhodesia: Victoria Falls; Ndola; Mwinilunga; Abercorn; Samfya (Watmough: common in " dambos "). Nyasaland: Nkata Bay.

[574]

Agriocnemis forcipata Le Roi, 1915, *Ergebn. zte Z. Afr. Exp.* **1**: 341, pl. (Sudan). *A. victoria* Fraser, 1928, *Trans. Ent. Soc. Lond.* 123, f. (Uganda)

The common form in the Mwinilunga District, in swamps near Sakeshi River and at the source of that river, is the smaller form *victoria*. In the Northern Congo the Author has found the larger *forcipata* dominant. Northern Rhodesia: Mwinilunga.

Agriocnemis gratiosa Gerstaecker, 1891, *Jb. Hamburg. wiss. Anst.* **9**: 190 (Zanzibar)

Uncommon in Southern Africa. The Author has taken this at Vila Paiva in Portuguese East Africa but not in Rhodesia. Northern Rhodesia: Lake Mweru (V. Fitzgerald); Samfya (Dening).

Mortonagrion stygium (Fraser). *Agriocnemis stygia* Fraser, 1954, *Rev. Zool. bot. Afr.* **50**: 274, ff. (B. Congo)

Northern Rhodesia: Victoria Falls; Abercorn. Katanga: Bunkeya.

Key to males of *Enallagma* Charpentier

Records in Northern Rhodesia and Katanga for *Enallagma* are scarce.

1   Distal end of 10th segment raised and bifurcate, dorsally. Lower end of mesepisternum with rounded lappets.
                           subfurcatum
    Distal end of 10 not markedly raised nor bifurcate. Thorax without lappets 2

2 (1) Abdomen normally 21 mm. or less 3
      Abdomen normally 23 mm. or more 4

3 (2) Pterostigma a pale rhombus, framed in rounded veins. Ac usually nearer sécond, than to first, Ax . . . . *minutum*
      Pterostigma elongate at upper distal angle, framed in straight veins. Ac nearer first Ax or midway between the two . . . . *nigridorsum*

4 (2) Superior appendages directed horizontally 5
      Superior appendages bent downwards or sharply angled . 6

5 (4) Pale species with reduced dark markings. Pterostigma yellow . . . . *subtile*
      With dark markings on thorax and abdomen. Pterostigma brown or grey . . . . *glaucum*

[575]

6 (4) Superior appendage sloping down for half its length, then
bent anteriad at right angles: laterally, appearing like head
and neck of a bird . . . . *longfieldae*

Superior appendage bent straight down, or sinuously . 7

7 (6) Inferior appendage with long, slender spine. Abdomen
23–26 mm. . . . . *elongatum*

Inferior with short spine. Abdomen 28–30 mm. . *sinuatum*

Enallagma elongatum (Martin). *Ischnura elongata* Martin, 1906, *Bull. Mus. Hist. nat. Paris* **12**: 513

Probably more widespread than available records indicate. Northern Rhodesia: Ndola, February 1960. Katanga: Lualaba; Mubale.

Enallagma glaucum (Burmeister). *Agrion glaucum* Burmeister, 1839, *Handb.* **2**: 821 (Cape)

This species is rather less common north of the Zambezi than in Southern Africa. Northern Rhodesia: Ndola.

Enallagma longfieldae Fraser, 1947, *Proc. R. ent. Soc. Lond.* B**16**: 146, ff. (Uganda)

The Katanga records may be the southern limit of this Uganda species. Katanga: La Manda River; Kabambare.

Enallagma minutum Ris, 1931, *Rev. suisse Zool.* **38**: 102, f. (Angola)

A minute, uncommon insect. Northern Rhodesia: Abercorn.

Enallagma nigridorsum Selys, 1876, *Bull Acad. Belg.* (2) **41**: 531 (114 sep.) (Zanzibar)

No records from this area yet, although found in Tanganyika and south of the Zambesi. New records in Southern Rhodesia: Bulawayo and Balla Balla.

Enallagma sinuatum Ris, 1921, *Ann. S. Afr. Mus.* **18**: 330 f.

Apparently an uncommon insect. Northern Rhodesia: 35 miles north of Kapiri Mposhi; Milambo, Fort Rosebery; Abercorn and Ufipa Plateau (V. Fitzgerald).

Enallagma subfurcatum Selys, 1876, *Bull. Acad. Belg.* (2) **41**: 534 (117 sep.) (Abyssinia)

Normally a high altitude species. Northern Rhodesia: Fort Jameson.

Enallagma subtile Ris, 1921, *Ann. S. Afr. Mus.* **18**: 332 (Katanga).
Libyagrion decoloratum Fraser, 1928, *Trans. Ent. Soc. Lond.* **76**: 126
(Nyasal.)

Taken on Ufipa Plateau (V. Fitzgerald) and Northern Rhodesia:
Abercorn. Southern Rhodesia, on the Vumba and in South Melsetter.
Also Katanga. Nyasaland: Zomba (described as *decoloratum* and
originally captured by the late Mr. Colin Smee).

Ischnura senegalensis (Rambur). *Agrion senegalense* Rambur, 1842,
Névr. 276

This widespread, abundant insect may appear in most dragonfly
habitats. Northern Rhodesia: Victoria Falls; Abercorn. And
certainly elsewhere. Katanga: Chembe.

Family AGRIIDAE

Key to genera

1   MA straight until nodus. Pterostigma small or absent .   *Phaon*

    MA curved before nodus. Pterostigma normally developed.

                     Umma

Phaon iridipennis (Burmeister). *Calopteryx iridipennis* Burmeister, 1839,
Handb. **2**: 827 (Durban)

A common shade-loving insect. Some examples from Northern
Rhodesia have the thorax plain brown without the iridescent green
bands, but they are otherwise normal. Northern Rhodesia: Victoria
Falls; Ndola; Lusaka; Mwinilunga; Kasempe; Abercorn (in swamp
forest). Katanga: Kanonga; Lufua River; Elizabethville etc. (*vide*
Schouteden). Nyasaland: Mzimba; Njakwa Gorge; Nkata Bay.

Key to *Umma* Kirby

1   Pterostigma 1.5 mm. or less. Margins of wings densely
    black . . . . *mesostigma*

    Pterostigma 2 mm. or more. Wing margins not outlined in
    black 2

2 (1) Abdomen 38 mm. or less. Wings strongly greenish yellow.
    Pterostigma green or pale blue . . . . . . *distincta*

    Abdomen 45 mm. or more. Wings hyaline. Pterostigma
    lilac or violet . . . . *electa*

[577]

Umma distincta Longfield, 1933, *Stylops* **2**: 139 (Kambove, Congo)

A beautiful insect, the male (Plate 1, fig. *h*) with metallic green body, the head, front of thorax and, in juvenile males, the dorsum of the abdomen royal blue; wings fumose; pterostigma metallic green, occasionally sprinkled with shimmering pale blue or violet (showing an apparent resemblance to *electa* Longfield). In the female the body is duller metallic green, only the face royal blue. The Pterostigma in this sex varies from 1.5 to 3 mm. The size is very variable. Abercorn specimens generally, and some Kabompo–Mwinilunga males having abdomens of 33.5–35.5 mm.; other Mwinilunga and the Ndola males having abdomens of 42–43 mm. Despite such variations there appear to be no valid distinctions: body coloration, wings, pterostigma, and appendages and the accessory organs are all similar. It is possible that the Abercorn specimens, being consistently small in a very long series, even at different times of the year, might be separated as a different race. On the other hand at the Kabompo River, examples of large and small forms were found in the same short stretch of semi-shaded, sandy-banked river. Northern Rhodesia: Ndola; Kabompo River; Mwinilunga (Sakeshi River, Zambezi River, Zambezi source and elsewhere, in or on edges of riverine bush or forest); Abercorn (swamp forest). Katanga: Kambove; Kamina.

Umma electa Longfield, 1933, ibid. 139 (Kambove)

The Author has not seen this species. Katanga: Kambove; Upembe National Park; Lubumbashi (*vide* Schouteden); Kapiri.

Umma mesostigma (Selys). *Cleis mesostigma* Selys, 1879, *Bull. Acad. Belg.* (2) **47**: 358 (Cameroons). Katanga: Kafukumba) *vide* Schouteden, as *fuscipleuris* (err. pro *fuscimarginis* Sjoest.)

Family **CHLOROCYPHIDAE**

Key to genera

1   Tibiae of male expanded, flattened and coloured . *Platycypha*

     Tibiae of male not expanded, blackish . . . *Chlorocypha*

Platycypha caligata (Selys). *Libellago caligata* Selys, 1853, *Bull. Acad. Belg.* **20** *Suppl.:* 57 (Natal)

This widespread species (Plate 1, fig. *f*, *g*) the male with sky blue abdomen, red, basally, at the sides, the tibiae red and white (yellow and white in immature examples) is common in the Territory as elsewhere.

Occasionally, the investigator may be fortunate in seeing the court-ship dance of the male (Pinhey, 1951: 133), although this is not always performed. Northern Rhodesia: Victoria Falls and Katambora; Ndola; Kasempa; Mwinilunga; Lusaka; Kabompo River; Solwezi; Abercorn. Katanga: Albertville; Fizi; Elizabethville; Kanonga. Nyasaland: Mzimbə; Njakwa Gorge; Cholo.

CHLOROCYPHA Fraser

Apart from the well-known, crimson-bodied *luminosa* two new species of red-bodied *Chlorocypha* were collected in February–March, 1960, in the Ikelenge region of Mwinilunga. Unfortunately, although long series were collected, many were attacked by mould in their triangular envelopes, largely because of the excessively damp conditions.

Key to males

1 Second abdominal segment mainly black above, with pale central spot. The pale, branched antehumerals well developed or, in older specimens, entirely obscured by black. Epistome blackish in front, at least in mature examples . . . . *luminosa*

Second abdominal segment mainly red, with black spots attached to distal margin. Antehumerals not obscured in the older examples 2

2 (1) Epistome dark in front or with white vertical lines. Branches of antehumerals slender. The distal spots on segment 2 large and bean-shaped 3

Epistome blue in front. Branches of antehumerals well-developed. Distal spots on segment 2 small and divergent
frigida n. sp.

3 (2) Distal spots on segment 3–4 in the form of minute isolated dashes . . . . *wittei*

Distal spots on 3–4 like small wedges joined to posterior margin . . . . *fabamacula* n. sp.

Key to females

1 Second segment broadly black above, with pale central spot. Black U-shaped marks on third and fourth segments . 2

Second abdominal segment largely pale above, with small black spot attached to distal margin. Black dorsal markings on third and fourth segments slender, divergent . . . 3

2 (1) The black on second segment very broad, its lateral edge straight or concave. The U-marks on third and fourth broad and regular . . . . *luminosa*

The black on second segment less broad, its lateral edge angular. The U on fourth broad and regular, but that on third tapering and incurved posteriorly . . *fabamacula* n. sp.

3 (1) Epistome blue . . . . *frigida* n. sp.

Epistome black . . . . *wittei*

Chlorocypha luminosa (Karsch). *Libellago luminosa* Karsch, 1893, *Berl. ent. Z.* **38**: 33 (Togo)

Libellago consueta Karsch, 1899, *Ent. Nachr.* **25**: 376 (Nyassa)

(Fig. 6). Central African specimens of this species might generally be referred to the form *consueta;* yet occasional examples similar to typical *luminosa,* which was described from West Africa, occur amongst the darker *consueta.* This may indicate that the slight differences are due to maturation changes.

The species, with its crimson-bodied male, is locally common in the warmer and moister parts of the Federation, more often in riverine bush. One very large female taken at Lubudi, with hindwing slightly over 29 mm., is more or less of the dimensions of *lacuselephantum* (Karsch, 1899, *Ent. Nachr.* **25**: 165) which was described from a female taken in the Cameroons.

Northern Rhodesia: Chirundu Bridge (Zambezi); Ndola; Fort Rosebery; Kabompo River; Mwinilunga (especially on the Zambezi River); Abercorn (swamp forest). Katanga: Lubudi (forested gorges); Lufua River; Fizi; Elizabethville. Nyasaland: The form *consueta* was described from the north of that territory. Nkata Bay.

CHLOROCYPHA FABAMACULA n. sp.

(Fig. 8)

Holotype male. (Solwezi). Face black in front, labrum with pale lateral spot. Head above with pale spots on epistome and frons; slender lateral stripes on vertex, pale postocular spots and a pale line on back of occiput. Prothorax with pale angular lateral spots. Synthorax greenish black almost down to first lateral suture; with fine yellowish median line; slender, branched antehumerals, the outer branch almost or quite broken near dorsal end; a stripe below humeral suture. Sides greenish, with short black dorsal stripe on first lateral suture and continuous stripe on second suture. Legs black, tibiae white on flexor surfaces. Wings hyaline, with amber at bases, almost to arculus. Pterostigma dark brown. Quadrilateral in forewings with 1–2 cross-veins, in hindwings with 2–3 cross-veins.

Abdomen orange-red on basal segments, more brick red on terminal segments; with sparse black markings: broad spot on 1; two large, stalked bean-shaped markings (after which the name is chosen) on 2; 3–4 with smaller distal spots on margins; 5–6 or 5–7 with mere traces of hyphens. A black basal band on 10; appendages black.

Abd. 19 mm., hw. 21.5 mm. pt. 2 mm.

Paratypes (all Mwinilunga). Essentially similar. In one male the distal spots on 2nd segment are free.

Allotype female (Mwinilunga). Face in front orange brown with black central patches on labrum and epistome. Head above as in male. Thorax with the stripe below humeral suture branched, but in opposite direction to the branched antehumeral: thus the thorax is paler laterally than in the male. Legs entirely black. Wings with the basal amber extending diffusely below costa to apex. Pterostigma with pale central spot. One cross-vein in all quadrilaterals. Abdomen: 1 with black central patch: 2 with central pale spot ringed with black, which is angular on lateral edges; 3–7 with broad black u-marks. 8–10 and cerci all black.

Abd. 18.5 mm., hw. 24 mm., pt. 2 mm.

Paratype female. Similar.

Remarks. This is a smaller species than *luminosa*, with the abdomen generally orange-red, but sometimes almost crimson. Both sexes have the saffron traces on the wings. It was noticeable in close inspection that, in life, there were fine white lines down the epistome of the male. The species is near to *basilewskyi* Fraser (1955, *Ann. Mus. Tervuren* 8. *Zool.* **36**: 23) but differs in having the antehumerals more complete and the spots on second segment joined to distal margin. From the incomplete type male of *wittei* it differs in pattern on the third segment. Types will be in the National Museum; one paratype of each sex (regrettably stained) will be sent to the British Museum (Nat. Hist.). All were collected in the Mwinilunga District at bush-fringed streams, except the Solwezi type.

CHLOROCYPHA FRIGIDA n. sp.

(Fig. 7)

Holotype male. Distinguished from its allies in Northern Rhodesia by the blue " nose ", i.e., the front of the face; hence the suggested name. Entire face in front pale greenish blue. Head above black with the usual pale spots, the lateral stripes on the vertex being joined to the pale stripe at back of occiput. Prothorax with pale anterior, posterior and lateral spots. Synthorax greenish black only to humeral suture, with broad, branched antehumerals, and pale median line. Sides greenish; with black streak on mesepimeron, a trace of black at upper end of first suture and a continuous stripe below second lateral suture. Legs entirely black, with trace of pruinosity. Wings with only the merest trace of basal amber and a tinge of apical fumosity. Pterostigma black.

Abdomen crimson above, with sparse black markings: central spot on 1; distal spots joined to margin on 2–5; hyphen traces on 6–7; basal band on 9. Appendages black.

Abd. 20 mm., hw. 26 mm., pt. 2.5 mm.

Paratypes. The distal hyphens may show also on segment 8.

Allotype female (mature). Face pale brownish. Head above with larger pale areas than male. Thorax and legs as in male. Wings faintly saffronated in anterior portion to pterostigma. Pterostigma with pale central spot. Abdomen with sparse black dorsal markings: central spot on 1; distal spots joined to margin on 2; a rectangular distal patch with lateral extensions directed posteriad on 3–5; on 6 this becomes a thin-limbed U; 7–8 with broad black dorso-lateral bands, incomplete on 7; 9 black with pale lateral patch and two small distal, dorsal dots; 10 and cerci black.

Abd. 18.5 mm., hw. 27 mm., pt. 2.5 mm.

Paratype (more teneral). Face in front greenish. Amber on wings a little more intense.

Remarks. With its blue face this species is distinct from other Central African species, but similar, in this feature, to other species taken by Gambles in Nigeria. It is comparable in size and abdominal coloration to *luminosa*, which, however, is dark on the two basal segments of the abdomen, in both sexes. In life, the labrum and epistome in front are pale blue-green; spots on dorsum of head pale grey-green; abdomen crimson. In the female, the " nose " is also pale bluish in life. The specimens were taken, from March 2nd–5th, 1960, in Mwinilunga:

streams chiefly in the Ikelenge area. They were shy insects, appearing in sunlit spots at forested streams. Examples were also taken at a water-fall. Types will be in the National Museum; one paratype of each sex will go to the British Museum (Nat. Hist.).

Chlorocypha wittei Fraser, 1955, *Parc Nat. Upemba* **38**: 10, ff. (Katanga)
  Katanga: Mubale

In the genus *Chlorocypha* the pale dorsal markings on the head must not be considered too important in distinguishing species since they all seem to have them at sometime during the development. It is true, however, that in fully mature examples of certain species, such as *straeleni, cyanifrons* and *rubida*, these markings are more vivid, sky blue.

Other Chlorocypha are recorded by Fraser from Upembe National Park (Fraser, 1955: 12–13), such as *rubida* Selys, *dispar* Beauv., etc. It seems a little doubtful if these actually occur in this region of the Congo.

Suborder **ANISOPTERA**

Family **GOMPHIDAE**

Key to genera

1　　All triangles and hypertriangles with more than one cross-vein 2

　　　Triangles and hypertriangles normally free　. . . . 4

2　(1) Foliations developed on 8th (but not 9th) segment in both sexes . . . . *Ictinogomphus*

　　　Foliations absent on 8 and 9: or present in female on 8 and 9 3

3　(2) Subpterostigmatal cells smaller than those just below them. Superior appendage of male bifurcate . . . *Diastatomma*

　　　Subpterostigmatal cells of about same size as those below them. Superior appendage unbranched . . . *Gomphidia*

4　(1) Forewing with 3–4 cross-veins between RS and MA proxi-mad to bifurcation of RS 5

　　　Forewing with 1–2 cross-veins in this area　. . . . 6

5　(4) 10th abdominal segment normal . . . . *Microgomphus*

　　　10th segment exceedingly long, cylindrical . *Lestinogomphus*

6 (4) Hindfemur reaching to or beyond middle of segment 2.

Notogomphus

    Hindfemur not reaching beyond base of segment 2 . . 7

7 (6) Frons rounded in front . . . . . . *Neurogomphus*

    Frons with well-developed crest 8

8 (7) Hindwing with anal loop 9

    Hindwing without anal loop 10

9 (8) Abdomen with foliations on 8 and 9. Superior appendage of male much longer than 10 . . . . *Onychogomphus*

    Abdomen with narrow foliations on 8, none on 9. Superior appendage much shorter than 10 . . . . *Ceratogomphus*

10 (9) Pterostigma at least 4 mm. long. Superior appendage of male scarcely longer than 10; inferior as long as superior.

Crenigomphus

    Pterostigma usually less than 3.5 mm. Superior much longer than 10, but inferior much shorter than superior.

Paragomphus

Key to genus *Ictinogomphus* Cowley

1   Foliations on 8th segment very reduced. Triangles equilateral in shape . . . . *dundoensis*

    Foliations very large on 8. Triangles elongate at distal angle 2

2 (1) Labrum mainly yellowish. Frons above with or without a slender-stemmed T-mark. Thorax mainly greenish with short black stripes . . . . *ferox*

    Labrum mainly black. Frons above with broad-stemmed T. Thorax black with short yellowish stripes . . . *regisalberti*

Ictinogomphus ferox (Rambur). *Ictinus ferox* Rambur, 1842, *Névr.* 173 (Senegal)

A large, common insect (Plate 3, fig. *b*) addicted to settling on tall reeds in rivers, lakes or dams. Northern Rhodesia: Victoria Falls; Lake Bangweulu (Watmough). Katanga: Albertville.

Ictinogomphus regisalberti (Schout.). *Ictinus regisalberti* Schouteden, 1934, *Ann. Mus. Congo Belg. Zool.* Sér. **3** (1): 54, f. (Elizabethville)

Katanga: Elizabethville (Seydel).

Ictinogomphus dundoensis Pinhey 1961, *Publ. cult. Cia Diamant. Angola.*

Smaller than the common *I. ferox*, with reduced flaps on the 8th segment, this insect is only known so far in the female, which has been found in Angola and in Northern Rhodesia near Ndola.

Key to genus *Diastatomma* Burmeister

1   Thorax reddish brown with black and yellow stripes .   *soror*

       Thorax black with green stripes . . . . *bicolor*

Diastatomma bicolor Selys, 1869, *Bull. Acad. Belg.* (2) **28**: 201 (S. Nigeria)

Katanga: Sashila (leg. Overlaet: *vide* Schouteden).

Diastatomma soror Schouteden, 1934, *Ann. Mus. Congo Belg. Zool.* Sér. **3** (1): 59 (Congo)

This very handsome Gomphid is known from Northern Rhodesia: Abercorn (in *Brachystegia* bush fringing Lake Chila) and Katanga: Penge (leg. Seydel); Lualaba.

Gomphidia quarrei (Schouteden). *Diastatomma quarrei* Schouteden, 1934, ibid. 57 (Congo)

A smaller, slimmer insect than *I. ferox*. Locally common in Rhodesia at the Victoria Falls and Katambora.

Microgomphus mozambicensis Pinhey, 1959, *Occ. Pap. nat. Mus. S. Rhod.* **23** B: 340, ff.

? *Microgomphus* sp. Fraser, 1955, *Parc. Nat. Upemba* **38**: 18 (female, Upemba Park)

This species, described from the Eastern border of Southern Rhodesia and neighbouring regions of Moçambique may be the same as Fraser's record from the Upemba National Park in the Katanga. A recent record in Southern Rhodesia is from the Vumba Mountains, Umtali, January, 1960 (one male in a rocky stream in Witchwood forest).

Lestinogomphus africanus (Fraser). *Echinopterogomphus africanus* Fraser, 1926, *Trans. Ent. Soc. Lond.* **74**: 355 ff. (Sierra Leone)

Northern Rhodesia: Maramba River, near Victoria Falls (in rather dense bush); Mwinilunga (teneral female only, March 1960). The Author has also taken it in recent years on the Hunyani River near Salisbury, October, 1956.

Key to genus *Notogomphus* Selys

1   Costa yellow. Face almost entirely yellow 2
      Costa black. Face in front with black or brown markings . 3

2 (1) Inner antehumerals slender and continuous. Humeral
       stripes double . . . . *praetorius*
       Inner antehumerals short, fusiform. A single broad humeral
       stripe . . . . *zernyi*

3 (1) Markings on face jet black: hind femora black . *dendrohyrax*
       Markings on face brown. Hind femora not black . . . 4

4 (3) Superior appendage with conical, spiked apex . . *flavifrons*
       Superior appendage fist-shaped . . . . *lujai*

Notogomphus dendrohyrax (Foerster).   *Podogomphus dendrohyrax* Foerster, 1906, *Jb. nassau Ver. Naturk.* **59**: 326 (Usambara Mountains)

Not recorded from the area under consideration but mentioned here since it was collected by the Author in January, 1960, on the Vumba Mountains, Umtali (stream in Witchwood Valley) and it occurs in Tanganyika.

Notogomphus flavifrons Fraser, 1952, *Occ. Pap. Coryndon Mus.* **3**: 8, ff. (Uganda)

A few examples of both sexes were collected in grass land near forested river and waterfall gorges, in Katanga: Lubudi.

Notogomphus lujai Schouteden, 1934, *Ann. Mus. Congo Belg. Zool.* Sér. **3** (1): 62 (Kivu)

Katanga: Mubale.

Notogomphus praetorius Selys, 1878, *Bull. Acad. Belg.* (2) **46**: 447 (Transvaal)

Widespread in this part of Africa. In life the body markings are bright or pale grass green. One female at Mwinilunga was captured devouring a Bombyliid (*Exoprosopa umbrosa* Loew.). Northern Rhodesia: Ndola; Chingola; Mwinilunga; Abercorn; Kalambo Falls. Katanga: Elizabethville; Mubale.

Notogomphus zernyi (St. Quentin). *Podogomphus zernyi* St. Quentin, 1942, *Ann. naturh.* (*Mus.*) *Hofmus. Wien.* **52**: 110 (Lupembeberg); *Notogomphus* sp. Pinhey, 1951, *Transv. Mus. Mem.* **5**: 145

The species described by the present Author in 1951 was probably *zernyi*, which St. Quentin obtained from near the Nyasa–Tanganyika border, at Mount Lupembe and Ugano. More recently it has been collected again in Southern Rhodesia at Inyanga (Turnbull-Kemp), on the Vumba (Pinhey) and in Melsetter (Plowes).

Key to genus *Neurogomphus* **Karsch**

1 Thorax black, with two green antehumeral stripes. Abdomen about 35 mm. . . . . *uelensis*
Thorax brown, with one antehumeral. Abdomen about 40 mm. . . . . *fuscifrons*
Examples of this genus appear to be distinctly scarce.

Neurogomphus fuscifrons Karsch, 1890, *Ent. Nachr.* **16**: 380 (Cameroons)

This magnificent insect (Plate 2, fig. *a*) was captured at Katambora. It has also been seen on an island near the Victoria Falls, but flying persistently high.

Neurogomphus uelensis Schouteden, 1934, *Ann. Mus. Congo Belge Zool.* Sér. **3** (2) 3: 65 (Congo)

The Author captured a solitary female at Katambora, January, 1956, and has only seen one other example in the field (also a female)—in central Tanganyika.

A variety under the name of *Neurog. vicinus* Schouteden (1934: 66) was recorded from Kibombo (Katanga) by Seydel.

Key to genus *Onychogomphus* **Selys**

1 Antehumeral stripes joined to pale collar so that the stripes appear 7-shaped 7-*flavum*
Antehumerals not connected to collar 2

2 (1) Antehumerals short, rounded at ends . . . . *supinus*
Antehumerals elongate, angular at ends . . *kitchingmani*

Onychogomphus kitchingmani Pinhey, 1960, *Ent. Mon. Mag.* **96**: 265
Allotype female (unfortunately stained in preservation). (Fig. 10).

Examples were taken in copula and markings were seen, in the field, to be similar in the two sexes. In life, the eye of the male was greenish blue, grey ventrally; of the female green above, yellow below. Body markings were bluish green in the male, greener in the female. In the preserved females the face in front is more ochreous than pale greyish (of the male); frons with broad black basal band. Thoracic markings (similar to male) almost obscured by the staining. Femora brown with black exterior distal streak; tibiae and tarsi black. Wings slightly fumose, pterostigma light brown between black veins. Abdomen blackish brown with yellowish markings: somewhat obscured on 1–2 but probably very like the male holotype; 3–6 with elongate basal triangles almost reaching distal ends, and yellow lateral band, the dorsal triangles being constricted so that their distal ends are spear-shaped; 7 with yellow basal annulus and sub-basal dorsal spot connected to it; 8 with trace of dorsal yellow at base; 9 dorsally with basal and distal spots and a lateral band; 10 and cerci all yellowish.

Abd. 30 mm., hw. 29 mm., pt. 3 mm.

The type male was collected by Kitchingman in May, 1957. A series of both sexes was collected on a stream south of Ikelenge, mostly near a waterfall or over rapids in March, 1960.

Northern Rhodesia: Mwinilunga.

It is possible that the better known and slightly larger *Onychogomphus supinus* Selys (1854) may be found in these territories since it occurs south of the Zambezi as well as in East Africa.

Onychogomphus 7-flavum Fraser, 1955, *Parc Nat. Upemba* **38**: 18

Known only from two females from Mubale (Katanga).

Ceratogomphus pictus Selys, 1854, *Bull. Acad. Belg.* (2) **21**: 42 (Cape)

A common insect in Southern Rhodesia but not yet recorded north of the Zambezi except from Lusinga (Congo) (*vide* Fraser, 1955: 26).

Key to males of genus *Crenigomphus* Selys

1   Abdomen with foliations on 8–9; segment 9 shorter than 10
hartmanni
     Abdomen without foliations 2

2 (1) Segment 9 shorter than 10. Inferior appendage in sideview slender, ending in a long thin spine. Abdomen about 30 mm. . . . . *renei*
     Segment 9 as long as 10. Inferior in sideview very robust to apex where there are short tumours carrying teeth. Abdomen 34 mm. or more . . . . *cornutus*

Crenigomphus cornutus Pinhey, 1956, *Occ. Pap. nat. Mus. S. Rhod.*
21B: 83 f. (Zambezi)

Settles on grasses and reeds. (Plate 3, fig. *a*). Northern Rhodesia:
Victoria Falls and Katambora; Kabompo River; Mwinilunga (Ikelenge).

Crenigomphus hartmanni (Foerster). *Onychogomphus hartmanni* Foerster,
1898, *Ent. Nachr.* **24**: 166 (S. Africa)

Nyasaland: Mzimba. It occurs in Southern Rhodesia and Tanganyika and so there is no reason why it should not be found in Northern
Rhodesia.

Crenigomphus renei Fraser, 1936, *Proc. R. ent. Soc. Lond.* B.**5**: 137
(Uganda)

Katanga: Mubale (*vide* Fraser, 1955).

Key to males of *Paragomphus* **Cowley**

1   Face pale;   at most with only faint brown markings.
      Thoracic markings usually obscure (except *elpidius*) . .   2
      Face with distinct blackish bands. Thorax distinctly black
      with green markings   5

2 (1) Superior appendages diverge before apices; apices broad
      and truncate. Foliations on abdomen very broad .   *nyassicus*
      Superiors parallel in apical half and tapering   3

3 (2) Pterostigma brown. Thoracic markings distinct. Superior
      appendage tapering to a single point . . . .   *elpidius*
      Pterostigma yellow. Thoracic markings normally indistinct.
      Superior not ending merely in a single point   4

4 (3) Frons only green above. Superior terminating in a ledge
      with one point . . . .   *lacustris*
      Frons with broad brown basal band. Superior terminating
      in two or more small teeth . . . .   *hageni*

5 (1) Superior appendages parallel to apices; each superior
      strongly curved and tapering. Abdomen about 36 mm.
                                                          sabicus
      Superiors divergent before apices. Abdomen 33 mm. or
      less   6

6 (5) Superiors strongly tapering. Antehumeral stripe 7-shaped
                                                       zambeziensis
      Superiors broad. Antehumeral fusiform . . .   *cognatus*

Paragomphus cognatus (Rambur). *Gomphus cognatus* Rambur, 1842, *Névr.* 167

A common species in open, rocky streams; or, more often as its melanic form *nquelicus* Foerster, in thick bush or forest (for instance, examples of this occur at the Vumba Mountains in Southern Rhodesia). Northern Rhodesia: Ndola; Mwinilunga; Chifua River. Katanga: Albertville. Nyasaland: Fort William (Gray).

Paragomphus elpidius (Ris). *Mesogomphus elpidius* Ris, 1921, *Ann. S. Afr. Mus.* **18**: 346, ff. (S. Afr., Congo)

Zambezi River: Victoria Falls; Siachelaba; Chirundu Bridge. It has been recorded from Nyasaland and Katanga (Kapiri).

Paragomphus hageni (Selys). *Onychogomphus hageni* Selys, 1870, *Ann. Soc. ent. Belg.* **14**: 14, 15, 20 (Egypt)

Probably the commonest Gomphid in Africa. Northern Rhodesia: Chirundu Bridge; Samfya; Lake Bangweulu (sandy beaches: Watmough).

Paragomphus lacustris (Karsch). *Onychogomphus lacustris* Karsch, 1890, *Ent. Nachr.* **16**: 377 (Lake Tanganyika)

Northern Rhodesian examples of what the present Author considers to be this species: Victoria Falls and Katambora; Samfya. Katanga: Albertville (Mayné—*vide* Schouteden).

Paragomphus nyassicus Kimmins, 1955, *Entomologist* **88**: 111 (Nyasal.)

Described, as the name implies, from Nyasaland, it has been taken in that territory by Arnold at Salima Bay, November, 1943. Northern Rhodesia: Victoria Falls (Pinhey, in the dry season month of October). Nyasaland: Nkata Bay (Eccles); Salima Bay (Arnold).

Paragomphus sabicus Pinhey, 1950. *Ann. Transv. Mus.* **21**: 270 ff. (S. Rhodesia)

So far as this region is concerned, only known from the Victoria Falls.

Paragomphus zambeziensis Pinhey, 1960, *Ent. Mon. Mag.* **96**: 266

Only known from the type male, Chirundu Bridge, Zambezi River, January, 1958.

N.B.—*Notogomphus nyassicus* Gruenberg, rather inadequately described (1902) from a solitary female, is much more likely to be a *Paragomphus*. If so, and if distinct, Kimmins' *nyassicus* will prove to be a homonym.

Tragogomphus seydeli Schouteden (1934: 64, Lubumbashi, Elizabethville) may in reality be a *Paragomphus*.

Phyllogomphus sp. Eccles recently submitted a female of this genus, the first record for this area, from Monkey Bay, Nyasaland. Although possibly a new species it is too damaged for description.

Family AESHNIDAE

Key to genera

1   IR_3 forked proximally to pterostigma 2

     IR_3 forked beyond middle of pterostigma 4

2 (1) Eyes normal, in contact for scarcely more than the dorsal length of the frons. Frons and face more than one third the transverse diameter of the head 3

     Eyes enlarged, in contact for twice the dorsal length of the frons. Frons and face less than one-third the transverse diameter of the head 5

3 (2) R_3 gradually curved below pterostigma. Tornus of hind-wing angled in male . . . . *Aeshna*

     R_3 almost angled below pterostigma. Tornus rounded in male. . . . . *Anaciaeschna*

4 (1) IA in hindwing forms a loop at start and then runs parallel to Cu_2 . . . . *Hemianax*

     IA in hindwing more or less parallel to Cu_2 at start . *Anax*

5 (2) Median space free . . . . *Acanthagyna*

     Median space traversed . . . . . . *Heliaeschna*

Key to genus *Aeshna* Fabricius

1   Dorsal mark on frons a black spot and a semicircle . *rileyi*

     Dorsal mark on frons a conical spot only . . . . *wittei*

Aeshna rileyi (Calvert). *Aeschna rileyi* Calvert, 1892, *Trans. Amer. ent Soc.* **19**: 164 (Kilimanjaro)

A common shade-loving species the male with the accessory append-ages on second segment strongly projecting. Northern Rhodesia: Chifua River (Dening); Kabompo River; Mwinilunga. Katanga: Lubudi; Elizabethville. Nyasaland: Zomba.

Aeshna wittei Fraser, 1955, *Parc Nat. Upemba* **38**: 14

Very close to *rileyi*. Katanga: Kaziba.

It is very probable that *A. ellioti* Kirby may be found at the higher elevations, particularly in Nyasaland. It is a more brightly coloured insect and the appendages on second segment are not prominent.

[591]

Anaciaeschna triangulifera McLachlan, 1895, *Ann. Mag. nat. Hist.* (6) **17**: 409 (Moçambique)

Crepuscular. Northern Rhodesia: Ndola (Green). Katanga: Elizabethville (Seydel).

Hemianax ephippiger (Burmeister). *Aeschna ephippiger* Burmeister, 1839, *Handb.* **2**: 840 (Madras)

A common migrant, recognizable in the male by the blue dorsal saddle on second segment. Northern Rhodesia: Victoria Falls; Abercorn. Katanga: Elizabethville.

Key to genus *Anax* Leach

1   Abdominal segments 4–10 mainly red. Frons without black marking 2

        Segments 4–10 not red. Frons with black dorsal marking .   3

2 (1) Abdomen (without appendages) at least 50 mm. Without brown subcostal streaks, merely traces of amber . . *speratus*

        Abdomen (without appendages) 45–48 mm. Each wing with brown subcostal streak . . . . *bangweuluensis*

3 (1) Abdomen mainly blue or greenish . . . . . *imperator*

        Abdomen 4–10 mainly black 4

4 (3) Abdomen of male 78 mm. or more, female 67 mm. or more. Abdomen with yellow spots . . . . *tristis*

        Abdomen about 55 mm. Abdomen with blue or greenish spots . . . . *chloromelas*

Anax bangweuluensis Kimmins, 1955, *Entomologist* **88**: 110

Described from a single rather immature male collected at Lake Bangweulu by Miss Steele in 1946, a few mature examples have been obtained by Dening from the same locality. All were taken at light or at dusk near Samfya (Dening).

Adult male. The only points to add to Kimmins' description are that the distal ends of the femora are black; the abdomen, as in *speratus*, uniformly reddish without yellowish markings; the " yellowish brown " basal patch of the teneral example has become a dark brown subcostal streak as far as the arculus in each wing; costa and pterostigma orange. Abd. 47–48 mm., hw. 46–48 mm. " Taken at light with two others, 24 Nov. 1959 " (Dening).

An immature male shows intermediate characters between the teneral and the adult; for instance the costa is still yellow, the abdomen paler.

Ne-Allotype female (just mature) (Fig. 11 and Plate 2, fig. *b*). Similar to the mature male in most respects, including the brown subcostal streak. Thorax slightly greener; abdomen dull yellowish orange on 1–2; the rest dull reddish brown (this colour starting on 2 as a mid-dorsal dark line); laterally on 3–9 with a very indistinct yellowish band; 10 and appendages light reddish. The cerci are flattened dorso-ventrally, with acute apices and with a convex ridge down the centre; each cercus about three times the length of segment 10. Abd. 48 mm., hw. 49 mm., pt. 5 mm. This female was taken at Samfya (Lake Bangweulu), 26th November, 1959.

Remarks. As so far known this smaller relative of *speratus* is confined to Lake Bangweulu and flies at dusk. The holotype is in the British Museum (Nat. Hist.), allotype in National Museum, Bulawayo.

Anax chloromelas Ris, 1911, *Ann. Soc. ent. Belg.* **55**: 321, ff. (West Africa)

Apparently a scarce insect. It is superficially like a dark *imperator*. Northern Rhodesia: Abercorn (Vesey Fitzgerald, October, 1957).

Anax imperator Leach, 1815, in Brewster's *Edinb. Encycl.* **9**: 137 (Europe)

A cosmopolitan species recognizable in the male by its pale blue abdomen. Northern Rhodesia: Victoria Falls; Mwinilunga; Abercorn; Samfya; Luaka Lagoon, Bangweulu (Watmough); Ndola.

Anax speratus Hagen, 1867, *Verh. Zool.-bot. Ges. Wien.* Wien **17**: 46 (Cape)

The widespread, large red species (thorax often green). Northern Rhodesia: Victoria Falls; Ndola; Mwinilunga. Nyasaland: Cholo.

Anax tristis Hagen, 1867, *loc. cit.* **17**: 35 (Guinea)

The immense black species with yellow abdominal markings and green thorax. Northern Rhodesia: Victoria Falls; Mwinilunga (hawking down the more open parts of forest streams); Samfya (seen by Watmough); Abercorn and Ufipa Plateau. Katanga: Kiambi; Mabwe.

Key to genus *Acanthagyna* **Kirby**

1   Hindwing shorter than abdomen. Small species, abdomen
    and hindwing less than 47 mm. long . . . . *manderica*
    Hindwing as long as or longer than abdomen. Abdomen
    and hindwing at least 50 mm. . . . . *villosa*
    Species of this genus are crepuscular.

Acanthagyna manderica (Gruenberg). *Gynacantha manderica* Gruenberg, 1902, *S. B. Ges. Naturf. Fr. Berl.* **9**: 234 (Ukami)

Northern Rhodesia: Kafue River, Machiga, (Johnsen, April, 1958); Broken Hill (Dening); Abercorn and Ufipa Plateau. Katanga: Mubale.

Acanthagyna villosa (Gruenberg). *Gyn. villosa* Gruenberg, 1902, loc. cit. **9**: 233 (Langenberg).

This species was described from Nyassa District, but the present Author has only seen tropical African examples.

Katanga: Elizabethville (*vide* Schouteden).

Heliaeschna trinervulata Fraser, 1955, *Parc Nat. Upemba* **38**: 16 (Uganda and Katanga).

Katanga: Mubale.

Family CORDULIIDAE

The only genus so far recorded from the area under consideration is *Macromia* and despite the general scarcity and elusiveness of these insects the number of species recorded is moderately large. Certain of the species are hard to distinguish.

Key to *Macromia* **Rambur**

1	Thorax without pale antehumeral stripes	2
	Thorax with at least a partial antehumeral	3
2 (1)	Thorax without any pale lateral stripes	*reginae*
	Thorax with one golden lateral stripe	*unifasciata*
3 (1)	Thorax without pale lateral stripes	4
	Thorax with 1–2 lateral stripes	5
4 (3)	Abdomen 46–47 mm.	*bifasciata*
	Abdomen 48–51 mm.	*reginae halei*
5 (3)	Segment 6 (and often 5) all black. Superior appendage black	6
	Segments 5 and 6 with distinct yellow basal patches . .	9
6 (5)	Abdomen 38 mm., hindwing about 36 mm. . .	*overlaeti*
	Abdomen at least 42 mm.	7

7 (6) 10th segment in male with robust cone and spine. Wings of
       female fumose, but not distinctly yellow at apices (except
       in juvenile females) . . . . *monoceros*

       10th segment in male without cone or spine 8

8 (7) Hamule of male with very long hook. Female with all wings
       amber at apices . . . . *sylvatica*

       Hamule of male with short hook. Female unknown.
                                                    subtropicalis

9 (5) Abdomen over 45 mm. Male with cone and spine on 10th
       segment. Both sexes normally with two rows in discoidal
       field 10

       Abdomen 41 mm. or less. Male normally with 1 row in dis-
       coidal field 11

10 (9) 10th segment of male with one spine. Superior appendage
       black . . . . *onerata*

       10th segment of male with two well-developed spines.
       Superior appendage normally yellow . . . . *kimminsi*

11 (9) 10th segment of male flat, without cone or spine . *africana*

       10th segment of male with cone and usually a spine . . 12

12 (11) Superior appendage yellow . . . . *picta*

        Superior appendage black 13

13 (12) Costa yellow . . . . *overlaeti*

        Costa black . . . . *congolica*

Since this is rather an inadequately known genus the Author will
indicate here and in diagrams from males in the National Museum,
Bulawayo, some of the structural features that distinguish them. The
identification, however, of one or two of them is not yet certain and
further research may show changes.

Of the males of species considered here, only three have very well-
developed foliations on segment 8 (see diagrams): *africana* (Fig. 12)
subtropicalis (Fig. 14) and *sylvatica* (Fig. 17). In some species the
dorsum of the 10th segment is flat, without any spine or cone: *africana*,
sylvatica, *reginae* (Fig. 21) (and *bifasciata*); and in others this area is
convex but lacking spines: ? *overlaeti* (Fig. 13), *subtropicalis* and
congolica (Fig. 15). There are two spines in *kimminsi* (Fig. 22). In *picta*
(Fig. 16) there is a single spine on a bulbous base; whilst in *onerata*
(Fig. 18), *monoceros* (Fig. 19) and *unifasciata* (Fig. 20) the single spine

is mounted on a very prominent base. The hamules also show distinctive features but these will be considered under each species. In most species the posterior lobe and the hamule are glossy black. In *picta* the posterior lobe as well as the superior appendage are yellow. In *kimminsi* the posterior lobe is also yellow. The superior appendage in *unifasciata* has a ventro-basal ledge.

Macromia africana (Selys). *Phyllomacromia africana* Selys, 1871, *Bull. Acad. Belg.* (2) **31**: 554 (Nubia)

A small species. Hamule not very robust, hook long and slender Northern Rhodesia: Siachelaba, Zambezi River (D. Plowes).

Macromia ? bifasciata Martin. *Phyllom. bifasciata* Martin, 1912, *Feuill. jeun. Nat.* (5) **42**: 96 (W. Africa)

Except for its slightly smaller size there appears to be very little to distinguish the males of this from the large *reginae*. The accessory appendages are identical to *reginae*. The dark brown at the bases of the wings in the female is more restricted than in the latter insect. Northern Rhodesia: Samfya; Lake Mweru (V. Fitzgerald); Abercorn (Lucheche River).

Macromia congolica Fraser, 1955, *Rev. Zool. Bot. afr.* **52**: 21 (Katanga)

Described from Katanga. Not as small as *picta* and *africana*. Hamule very large and robust, angled ventro-posteriorly; with a short, broad, flattened hook. Northern Rhodesia: Kabompo River (males hovering over the river, in February and March, 1960). In life the eye was emerald; pale body markings greenish yellow.

Macromia kimminsi Fraser, 1954, ibid. **49**: 63, ff. (Sierra Leone)

A rather large species characterized by the dark crescent near the anterior edge of the frons. Hamule elongate, with a broad, stout hook. Northern Rhodesia: Mwinilunga. The single male has a well-developed metepimeral stripe. In life the eye was emerald; pale body markings greenish yellow.

Macromia monoceros Forster, 1906, *Jb. nassau. Ver. Naturk.* **59**: 319 (Somalia)

This species is found in Southern Rhodesia, Portuguese East Africa and northwards in East Africa. The hamule robust, with a moderately stout hook. Mwinilunga examples placed to this species correspond except in the hamular hook which is replaced in such examples by short

[596]

tumours. Whether they represent a separate race or species may be considered at a later date. Northern Rhodesia: Mwinilunga (forest streams); Abercorn (Lucheche River). In the Mwinilunga examples the eye, in both sexes was emerald in life; pale body markings yellow, with a faint tinge of green.

Macromia onerata Martin, 1906, *Coll. Zool. Selys* **17**: 74 (Tanganyika, S. Leone)

A fairly large species. Hamule moderate, with broad, flattened hook. Katanga: Lubudi (flying in open woodland). In life the eye of the male was emerald, yellow below; thoracic stripes greenish yellow. In the female the eye was pale dull green; pale markings on body yellow; wing apices with amber patches.

Macromia ? overlaeti Schouteden, 1934, *Ann. Mus. Congo Belg. Zool.* Sér. **3** (1): 45 (Congo)

A small example, allied to *picta*, but with very distinctive hamule and lacking a spine on the 10th segment, is tentatively placed here. There is no sub-basal spine on the superior appendage, unlike *schoutedeni* Fraser. The hamule is robust, angled ventro-posteriorly and has a prominent hook: very like the hamule in the larger species *congolica*. Katanga: Lubumbashi.

Macromia picta Selys, 1871, *Bull. Acad. Belg.* (2) **31**: 552 (Cape)

By far the commonest of the genus in Africa; a small species (Plate 2, fig. *e*). Hamule well developed but the hook rather small. Northern Rhodesia: Binga, Zambezi; Siachelaba, Zambezi; Katambora, Zambezi. Nyasaland: Njakwa Gorge.

Macromia reginae Le Roi, 1915, *Ergeb. d. Z. Afrika Exp. Zool.* **1**: 348 (Sudan)

The largest of the species occurring in the Federation; widespread in Africa. Hamule large, rounded, the hook moderate. *M. bifasciata* only seems to differ in minor characters. Northern Rhodesia: Samfya (Dening and Johnsen); Lake Bangweula and Lake Wumba (Watmough); Abercorn. The Author has also seen it at Binga, on the Zambezi River.

Macromia subtropicalis Fraser, 1954, *Rev. Zool. Bot. afr.* **49**: 60, ff. (Congo)

Larger and darker than the *picta* group. Hamule rather like *picta* but with longer hook. Northern Rhodesia: Victoria Falls.

Macromia sylvatica Fraser, 1954, ibid. 56, ff. (East Africa)

The typical form was described from Uganda. The Lubudi examples may represent a different race since they differ in certain respects: larger, the abdomen (male) with appendages 45 mm., instead of 42 mm. and with two rows in the discoidal field of the forewing instead of one. The hamule, however, is typical, with its very long curved hook and posterior inner flange. They eye of the Katanga male was emerald; thoracic stripes, greenish yellow; abdominal pale markings yellow. Katanga: Lubudi (forested gorge, near waterfall, February, 1960).

Macromia unifasciata Fraser, 1954, ibid. **49**: 67, ff. (Congo)

Described from Mubale, in the Congo, by Fraser, a single male of this magnificent insect, which eluded the Author, was captured by his assistant, Raphael Mpala, on the Sakeshi River, Hillwood Farm, February, 1960. In flight the unusual golden eyes and the single broad golden thoracic band are very distinctive, in this fairly large species. The other pale body markings are bright yellow. In all other living *Macromia* seen by the Author the eyes are emerald or greenish. The hamule is is moderately robust with broad, flattened hook. Northern Rhodesia: Mwinilunga (hawking occasionally up and down the river). Katanga: Mubale, Upemba Nat. Park.

Family LIBELLULIDAE
Key to genera

1   Triangle of forewing very broad, its costal edge more than half as long as the basal edge; or it is quadrangular. Hindwing with more than 1 Ac. Last Ax in forewing always complete 2

       Triangle of forewing narrower (never quadrangular), its costal edge less than half the basal edge 5

2 (1) Discoidal cell in forewing obviously quadrangular. Discoidal field in forewing of one row right to termen.

                                                    Tetrathemis

       Discoidal cell in forewing triangular (although its costal edge may be broken towards one end) 3

3 (2) Discoidal field of one row, not expanding until beyond nodus. Anal loop 3–4 cells . . . . . . *Allorhizucha*

       Discoidal field of one row, but expanding before nodus. Anal loop more than 4 cells 4

4 (3) With 1–2 accessory bridge veins. Triangle in hindwing
     normally crossed . . . . *Neodythemis*
     Without accessory bridge veins. Triangle in hindwing free.

                                                     Notiothemis

 5 (1) Arculus at or distal to second Ax 6
     Arculus distinctly proximal to second Ax 15

 6 (5) Last Ax in forewing complete 7
     Last Ax in forewing incomplete 12

 7 (6) Hindwing with 2 Ac 8
     Hindwing with 1 Ac 9

 8 (7) Discoidal field in forewing of 3–5 rows . . *Hadrothemis*
     Discoidal field in forewing of 2 rows . . . *Atoconeura*

 9 (7) Discoidal field of 3 rows 10
     Discoidal field of 2 rows (or with 3 cells at triangle) . . 11

10 (9) Vertex grooved; clypeus narrower than frons . . *Orthetrum*
     Vertex rounded; clypeus broader than frons . *Nesciothemis*
                              and some examples of *Hadrothemis*

11 (9) Triangle in forewing narrow. Cu_2 weakly curved. Anal
     loop elongate . . . . *Oxythemis*
     Triangle in forewing broadish. Cu_2 strongly curved. Anal
     loop blunt . . . . *Aethiothemis*

12 (6) Hindwing with 3–4 Ac. Accessory bridge veins present.
                                                    Thermochoria
     Hindwing with 2–3 Ac. No accessory bridge veins . *Porpax*
     Hindwing with 1 Ac. No accessory bridge veins . . . 13

13 (12) Discoidal field in forewing of 3 rows, expanding. Ptero-
     stigma bicolorous . . . . *Hemistigma*
     Discoidal field forewing of 2 rows 14

14 (13) Triangle in forewing broad. Discoidal field expanding.
     $8\frac{1}{2}$ Ax . . . . *Eleuthemis*
     Triangle forewing not broad. Discoidal field not expanding.
     $10–10\frac{1}{2}$ Ax . . . . *Porpacithemis*

15 (5) Costa with infraction before nodus . . . . *Palpopleura*
     Costa evenly curved or straightish to nodus 16

16 (15) Last Ax in forewing complete 17

Last Ax in forewing incomplete 22

17 (16) Discoidal field in forewing of 2 rows (but may start with
3 cells at triangle) 18

Discoidal field in forewing of 3 rows . . . . . . *Trithemis*

18 (17) Discoidal field expanding distally 19

Discoidal field in forewing parallel or convergent . . . 20

19 (18) Abdomen triquetral or cylindrical. Triangle crossed in
forewing . . . . *Aethiothemis*

Abdomen swollen on basal 4 or 6 segments, the rest slender.
Triangle free in forewing . . . . *Acisoma*

20 (18) Forewing with 8 Ax or more . . . . . *Lokithemis*

Forewing with 6–7 Ax 21

21 (20) Large insects; forewing with 7 Ax . . . . . *Urothemis*

Small insects; forewing with 6 Ax . . . . *Aethriamanta*

22 (16) Discoidal field forewing at least slightly expanding . . 23

Discoidal field forewing contracting or parallel. . . . 30

23 (22) Hindwing with 2 Ac. Small insects (abdomen under
20 mm.) . . . . *Porpax*

Hindwing with 1 Ac 24

24 (23) Abdomen swollen on basal 4 or 6 segments, then slender.
Forewing with $6\frac{1}{2}$–$8\frac{1}{2}$ Ax. Small insects . . . *Acisoma*

Abdomen normal, or only swollen on segments 1–3 . . 25

25 (24) Discoidal field in forewing starts 2 rows 26

Discoidal field in forewing starts 3 rows 27

26 (25) Cu_2 in forewing slightly curved, in hindwing it is at anal
angle of triangle . . . . *Chalcostephia*

Cu_2 in forewing strongly curved, in hindwing it is well
distal to anal angle of triangle . . . . . . *Diplacodes*

27 (25) Anal loop in hindwing short, not extending far distal to
triangle . . . . *Crocothemis*

Anal loop extending 2–4 cells beyond level of triangle . 28

28 (27) Forewing with $6\frac{1}{2}$–$7\frac{1}{2}$ Ax . . . . *Brachythemis*

Forewing with at least $10\frac{1}{2}$ Ax 29

29 (28) Rspl. loop of 1 row. Eyes in contact for short distance.
Pterostigma bicolorous . . . . *Hemistigma*
Rspl. loop of 2–3 rows. Eyes in contact for long distance.
Pterostigma unicolorous . . . . *Bradinopyga*

30 (22) Discoidal field in forewing 2 rows (but may show 3 cells at
triangle) 31
Discoidal field in forewing of 3–4 rows 33

31 (30) Forewing with less than 8 Ax. Prothoracic hindlobe large.
(small examples) *Sympetrum*
Forewing with 8½ or more Ax. Prothoracic hindlobe small . 32

32 (31) Pterostigma longer, 2.5 mm. Eye contact long.
Porpacithemis
Pterostigma shorter, 2 mm. Eye contact short . . *Lokithemis*

33 (30) Forewing with 6½–7½ Ax 34
Forewing with 8½ or more Ax 36

34 (33) Hindlobe of prothorax small. Abdomen short and broad.
Pterostigma usually bicolorous . . . . . *Brachythemis*
Hindlobe of prothorax large. Abdomen slender. Ptero-
stigma unicolorous 35

35 (34) Triangle crossed in forewing . . . . . *Sympetrum*
Triangle free in forewing . . . . . *Philonomon*

36 (33) Triangle in forewing and hindwing almost on the same level 37
Triangle in forewing 3 or more cells distal to triangle in
hindwing 42

37 (36) Anal loop in hindwing open at margin . . . . *Tholymis*
Anal loop closed before margin 38

38 (37) Anal loop reaching 1–2 cells beyond triangle in hindwing.
Trithemis
Anal loop reaching 3–4 cells beyond triangle 39

39 (38) Rspl. loop of 1 row. R3 in forewing slightly curved. Body
non-metallic . . . . *Parazyxomma*
Rspl. loop normally of 2 rows. R3 in forewing strongly
sinuous. Body metallic 40

40 (39) Pterostigma usually 4 mm. or less. Tibial spines slender
Zygonyx
Pterostigma usually over 4 mm. Tibial spines robust . . 41

41 (40) Abdomen very swollen at base, then very slender.

Olpogastra s.g. *Olpogastra*

Abdomen swollen at base, then of average width.

Olpogastra s.g. *Zygonoides*

42 (36) Pterostigma of same size in forewing and hindwing. Body
blackish, metallic . . . . *Rhyothemis*
Pterostigma distinctly longer in forewing than in hindwing.
Body not nearly all black and non-metallic 43

43 (42) R_3 strongly sinuous. Hindwing with 2 Ac . . .   *Pantala*
R_3 almost straight. Hindwing with 1 Ac . *Trapezostigma*

Tetrathemis polleni (Selys). *Neophlebia polleni* Selys, 1869, *Pollen et van
Dam, Madag. Ins.* 18, pl.

Very few records yet from this area. The mature male is easily
recognized in the field by its narrow, broadly blackened wings and its
characteristic flight, slowly flapping its wings. Northern Rhodesia:
Victoria Falls. Katanga: Lubudi (a muddy, forested stream).

Key to *Allorhizucha* **Karsch**

1   Labium broadly black in middle. Thorax without green
humeral stripe . . . . *klingi*
Labium all yellow. Thorax with broad green humeral band.

preussi

Allorhizucha klingi Karsch, 1890, *Berl. ent. Z.* **33**: 390 (Togo)

In the Rhodesian examples the pale thoracic markings are much
greener than normal: in equatorial Africa these areas are more strongly
yellowish. In life, eye all blue-green, face pale green; pale body markings
blue green. Northern Rhodesia: Mwinilunga (in dense forest).

Allorhizucha preussi Karsch, 1891, *Ent. Nachr.* 17: 80 (Cameroons)

Both sexes were fairly common at forest streams and at the Zambezi
Source in Mwinilunga District. In life, eye of male grey-blue to blue-
green, paler below; labium whitish; pale markings on the body
grey-blue. In an immature male the eye was grey-green, brown above;
labium yellow; body markings bright yellowish green. The black
lateral stripes on the thorax, on first and second lateral sutures, are
much better developed than in examples from equatorial Africa and
it is probable that Rhodesian examples represent a distinctive race.
However, series from the Northern Congo and Nigeria show a little
variation in this respect.

Northern Rhodesia: Mwinilunga. Katanga: Kamina (Schouteden).

NEODYTHEMIS FITZGERALDI n. sp.

(Fig. 38)

The examples are juvenile but not teneral.

Holotype male. Labium bright yellow with black median band, broadened posteriorly. Face bright yellow; labrum with narrow black free border; frons and vertex steely blue, the latter with yellow dorsal " bow-tie " mark. Prothorax yellow on anterior and posterior lobes; middle lobe black with yellow median and lateral spots. Thorax black, with dark green tinge, to below humeral suture: with yellow median stripe and somewhat sinuous antehumeral; sides yellow, with irregular black bands on the sutures and a trace of black on the metepimeron. Legs black, with yellow areas on coxae and trochanters; claws ferruginous, hooks short. Venation black; pterostigma blackish, short, slightly convex, on inner and costal edges; trace of amber at base of all cubital spaces. 1 Ac in forewing, 2 in hindwing; anal loops of 6 cells; discoidal field in forewing expanding after 4 cells. All Ht crossed; t free, but crossed in right hindwing. Forewing with 10–11 Ax. Abdomen black, with yellow marking; 1 with dorsal triangle and lateral patch; 2 with dorsal band, constricted in middle and tapering posteriorly, and an angular lateral patch; 3 with two lateral stripes the upper one severed by transverse carina; 4–7 with one lateral strip (severed on 4–5); 8–10 black, 10 with yellow ventro-lateral spot. Appendages black, normal; superiors somewhat fusiform; inferiors slightly notched apically. Accessories normal, as in the figure.

Abd. 22 mm., hw. 26 mm., pt. 2.5 mm.

Allotype female. Very similar; metallic dorsal patch on frons somewhat reduced anteriorly; dorsal mark on vertex rectangular; pterostigma and venation brown; amber basal patches on wings slightly more developed. Forewing with 11–12 Ax; t in both hindwings crossed; and loop 6–7. Fore-femur yellow laterally. Abdomen slightly stouter; cerci short, black. Paratype female similar.

Remarks. Collected by L. D. Vesey Fitzgerald, at Abercorn, in swamp forest and on Lucheche River, in months of March and December. Of the known *Neodythemis*, most of which are Malgassian, this species is nearest to *africana* Fraser in body markings. In that species the labium is largely black, labrum all black; vesicle all metallic blue. And *africana* has less black in the region of the first lateral suture. Nodal index is higher in that species.

N. gorillae Pinhey is smaller, dark on the lips and with the thoracic stripes more regular.

[603]

In *hildebrandti* the labium has a black median triangle, the labrum is yellow but more broadly edged with black; antehumeral stripe incomplete; lateral black stripes rather similar but the abdominal markings are different, particularly those on dorsum of 1–2. The other Madagascar species, *arnoulti* and *pauliani* are darker on sides of thorax; while *trinervulata* lacks the antehumeral stripe, among other differences.

Holotype male and paratype female will be in National Museum, Bulawayo, allotype female in the British Museum (Nat. Hist.).

? *NEODYTHEMIS* species indet.

A solitary, teneral female dragonfly, taken at the same forest stream in Katanga as *Tetrathemis polleni* and, in the field, mistaken for a female of that species, has proved to be rather an enigma. It does not seem to belong to any known African genus. Since, however, females of many Libellulids may show aberrant venation it does not appear desirable to erect a new genus for it and the insect is, therefore, placed temporarily under *Neodythemis* which is one of its closest Tetrathemine relatives.

The following brief description may be recorded: a Tetrathemine with eye contact long; prothoracic hindlobe large. Discoidal triangles broad, in forewing broken on costal edge, free; Ht crossed in forewing, free in hindwing. Forewing with 10 Ax, the last complete; arc between 2nd and 3rd Ax. No Bsq. Discoidal field in forewing of one row for 4–5 cells, expanding before subnodus. Anal loop of 8 cells; membranule minute; Cu_2 in hindwing originates at or distal to lower angle of triangle. Forewing with 1 Ac, hindwing with 2. Sectors of arc in all wings on very long stalk. Abdomen 21 mm., hindwing 28 mm., pterostigma 2 mm.

These characters place this female near *Neodythemis*, from which it differs in lacking accessory bridge veins and its longer anal loop; and *Notiothemis* which is venationally close but differs notably in size and general facies. In general features it is surprisingly near *Archaeophlebia* of Madagascar, but in that genus the discoidal cell is obviously quadrangular; the forewing has 2 Ac, since the distal one has not properly developed as the proximal edge of the subtriangle (a subtriangle is definite in the Katanga female although it is quadrangular, having a short costal edge); and the hypertriangles in *Archceophlebia* are free.

Katanga: Lubudi, February, 1960.

Key to genus *Notiothemis* **Ris**

1   Labrum nearly all pale. Hindwing with 2 Ac . . . *jonesi*
       Labrum black. Hindwing with 3 Ac . . . . . *robertsi*

Notiothemis robertsi Fraser, 1944, *Proc. R. ent. Soc. Lond.* B. **13**: 42, ff.
(Uganda)

Several of this Uganda-described insect where collected at pools in
and near forest streams in the Mwinilunga District, including a pair in
copula. One tortological male has a split vein at the bridge of the left
forewing. Eye in male, in life, deep cobalt with chocolate patches; body
markings green. One female was observed ovipositing, which she performed while at rest on the water, inserting her abdomen as in the
manner of insertion-ovipositor-bearing families (as in *Aeshnidae*).
Females of Tetrathemines (except *Micromacromia* and *Allorhizucha*) are,
in the Author's experience, even shier than the males. Only one female
was captured and in this the apex of the abdomen has shrunk and become
distorted on drying. It does not appear, however, that there is any marked
development of the ovipositor in this example.

Ne-Allotype female (Ikelenge, in copula). Like males except for
stouter abdomen and traces of deep amber at all wing bases. Abd. 19
mm., hw. 25 mm., pt. 2 mm. Allotype in National Museum, Bulawayo.

Northern Rhodesia: Mwinilunga.

Notiothemis jonesi Ris, 1919, *Coll. Zool. Selys* **16** (2): 1054, f. (Tanganyika)

Katanga: Elizabethville (*vide* Schouteden, "johnesi", 1934). It
occurs in Southern Rhodesia, Moçambique and East Africa.

Key to genus *Hadrothemis* **Karsch (Central African forms only)**

1   Hindwing 34 mm. or less. Abdomen of male bright red,
       frons metallic violet or violet blue. Triangle in hindwing
       normally free. All wings with dark amber basal patches.
                                                              defecta
       Hindwing 35 mm. or more. Abdomen of male normally
       blue pruinosed, frons steely blue. Triangle in hindwing
       crossed 2

2 (1) Forewing with no more than a trace of basal amber, hind-
       wing with palish amber basal patch . . . . . *camarensis*
       Forewing with basal patch reaching arculus, hindwing
       with broad dark amber or brown patch . . . . *versuta*

[605]

Hadrothemis camarensis (Kirby). *Orthetrum camarense* Kirby, 1889, *Proc. zool. Soc. Lond.* **12**: 298 (Cameroons)

Katanga: Ganza (Upemba Park).

Hadrothemis defecta (Karsch). *Thermorthemis defecta* Karsch, 1891, *Ent. Nachr.* **17**: 61 (S. Leone)

Only two males (one very old and battered) found in swamp near forested stream, settling on reeds. Eye of male, in life, dark brown, with violet sheen on top, a green sheen laterally; abdomen crimson. Northern Rhodesia: Mwinilunga. In equatorial Africa the Author has found this species in or at the edges of forest settling on dead twigs. Katanga: Kamina (Schouteden, Seydel); Kilwezi.

Hadrothemis versuta (Karsch). *Thermorth. versuta* Karsch, 1891, ibid., 62 (Cameroons)

Several taken at forest streams; the males darting about, hovering and tending to be inquisitive. Eye in male dark red-brown; the dark abdomen covered with thin blue pruinosity. In a teneral female; eye pale grey-blue, brown above; body yellow; thorax with greenish tint, the antehumerals dark blue-green.

Northern Rhodesia: Mwinilunga.

Oxythemis sp. near *carpenteri* Fraser, 1944, *Proc. R. ent. Soc. Lond.* B. **18**: 85, ff. (Uganda)

A solitary female taken near Ndola, Northern Rhodesia, in March, 1959, may be this little-known species. More material is required for certain determination. It is superficially like *Orthetrum abbotti*, differing venationally. *Oxythemis* is very near *Aethiothemis*.

Key to genus *Nesciothemis* **Longfield**

1   In male, basal half of abdomen pruinosed blue, distal half distinctly red. Wings of female not brown at apices but with distinct amber spots at bases . . . . . *fitzgeraldi*

       In male, basal half of abdomen pruinosed whitish blue, distal half not red. Wings of female usually with brown apical patches; the bases without or only faintly saffronated.
farinosum

Nesciothemis farinosum (Foerster). *Orthetrum farinosum* Foerster, 1898, *Ent. Nachr.* **24**: 169 (Transvaal)

A common insect. Both large and dwarf forms occur on the Zambezi. Henri Bertrand collected a male at Kabanga, Congo, in 1958, in which the arculus in each forewing was between 1st and 2nd Ax. Northern Rhodesia: Victoria Falls and Katambora; Ndola; Mwinilunga; Samfya; Lusaka. Nyasaland: Cholo.

Nesciothemis fitzgeraldi Longfield, 1955, *Publ. cult. Cia Diamant. Angola* **27** (1): 61 ff.

Orthetrum fitzgeraldi Pinhey, 1956, *Occ. Pap. Coryndon Mus.* **4**: 30 ff. (Abercorn)

A striking insect which lives in swamp (source of Sakeshi River) at Mwinilunga, or is common in Brachystegia woodland, fringing Lake Chila, at Abercorn. Northern Rhodesia: Abercorn; Mwinilunga; Samfya (Dening).

Key to genus *Orthetrum* Newman (partly after Longfield, 1955)

1	Thorax with distinct creamy or white lateral stripes . .	2
	Thorax without pale stripes	6
2 (1)	1 row Rspl.	3
	At least partially 2 rows Rspl.	4
3 (2)	Pterostigma 3 mm. or less; 1 pale lateral stripe on thorax.	
		chrysostigma
	Pterostigma over 3 mm.; 1–2 pale lateral stripes . . *falsum*	
4 (2)	With pale stripes on front of thorax. Abdomen very long, with heavy black stripes . . . . *trinacria*	
	Thorax with pale lateral stripes and sometimes distinct stripes also on front of thorax. Abdomen of normal dimensions, not very heavily black-striped	5
5 (4)	With distinctive stripes on front and sides of thorax . *caffrum*	
	With faint stripes on sides only . . . . . . *brachiale*	
6 (1)	Body with pruinosity	7
	Body without pruinosity	27
7 (6)	Pruinosity on thorax and abdomen	8
	Pruinosity only on abdomen	18
8 (7)	Male pale blue	9
	Male dark blue (indigo)	16
9 (8)	2 rows Rspl.	10
	1 row Rspl.	11

10 (9) Pterostigma 3 mm. or more . . . . *brachiale*

Pterostigma less than 3 mm. . . . . *caffrum*

11 (9) Abdomen 23 mm. or less. Pterostigma 2.5 mm. . *rhodesiae*

Abdomen 24 mm. or more. Pterostigma usually more than 2.5 mm. 12

12 (11) Abdomen 28 mm. or less. Pterostigma 3 mm. or more . . 13

Abdomen 29 mm. or more. Pterostigma 3 mm. or less. *chrysostigma* or *guineense*

13 (12) Abdomen 25 mm. or less. Pterostigma 3.5 –4mm. . *abbotti*

Abdomen 26 mm. or more. Pterostigma 3–3.8 mm. . 14

14 (13) Abdomen 27 mm. or less . . . . *hintzi*

Abdomen 28 mm. or more 15

15 (14) Abdomen 30 mm. or less. Pterostigma 3–3.5 mm. . *machadoi*

Abdomen 30 mm. or more. Pterostigma 3.5 mm. . . *falsum*

16 (8) Abdomen 38 mm. or more, not constricted on 3, not fusiform . . . . *trinacria*

Abdomen 30 mm. or less, constricted on 3, slightly fusiform 17

17 (16) 1 row Rspl. Pterostigma 3–3.5 mm. . . . . *machadoi*

2 rows Rspl. Pterostigma 4–5 mm. . . . . *macrostigma*

18 (7) Abdomen with blue pruinosity; thorax may be thinly pruinose 19

Abdomen with whitish pruinosity; thorax black and green only 25

19 (18) 1 row Rspl. 20

2 rows Rspl. 22

20 (19) Subcostal cross-veins and pterostigma yellow. Thorax scarcely marked at sides with black . . . . *machadoi*

Subcostal cross-veins and pterostigma blackish. Thorax heavily striped 21

21 (20) Base of hindwing with pale amber spot . . . . *falsum*

Base of hindwing with dark amber spot. . . . . *julia*

22 (19) Subcostal cross-veins black. Thorax dull green or brownish.

stemmale kalai

Subcostal cross-veins yellow. Thorax brighter green . . 23

23 (22) Thorax bright green with broad black stripes . . *icteromelas*

Thorax lighter green with slender blackish stripes . . . 24

24 (23) Abdomen about 28 mm. Pterostigma 4 mm. . *macrostigma*

Abdomen 30 mm. or more. Pterostigma 3.5 mm. . *brachiale*

25 (18) 2 rows Rspl. Pterostigma normally over 3 mm. . *stemmale kalai*

1 row Rspl. Pterostigma normally less than 3 mm. . . . 26

26 (25) Abdomen distinctly fusiform . . . . . *microstigma*

Abdomen scarcely fusiform . . . . . . *julia*

27 (6) Subcostal cross-veins black 28

Subcostal cross-veins yellow 31

28 (27) 2 rows Rspl. . . . . *stemmale kalai*

1 row Rspl. 29

29 (28) Abdomen rather slender. Pterostigma 3 mm. or more . 30

Abdomen fusiform. Pterostigma 2.5 mm. or less.

microstigma

30 (29) Base of hindwing with pale amber spot . . . . *falsum*

Base of hindwing with deep amber spot . . . . *julia*

31 (27) 1 row Rspl. almost entirely 32

2 rows Rspl. 35

32 (31) Abdomen with narrow black lateral stripe, terminal segments not broadly black . . . . *guineense*

Abdomen with broad black lateral stripe, terminal segments mainly black 33

33 (32) Humeral black stripe very reduced, and only traces of lateral stripes on thorax . . . . *abbotti*

Humeral black stripe broad 34

34 (33) Abdomen 27 mm. or less . . . . *hintzi*

Abdomen 28 mm. or more . . . . . . *machadoi*

[609]

35 (31) Thorax with several slender black stripes . . . *brachiale*

Thorax with reduced black marking or else with thick black
stripes **36**

36 (35) Thorax with broad stripes. Abdomen with broad mid-
dorsal stripe; black ventrally. . . . . . *icteromelas*

Thorax with narrow stripes. Abdomen without broad mid-
dorsal stripe; largely yellowish ventrally . . *macrostigma*

As will be seen from the above key it is not easy to separate many of
the species of this genus. In males it is advisable to refer to diagrams
of the accessory appendages on segment 2. (Fig. E, 23–37).

Certain species are generally distinguishable in the males, particularly
if the thorax is not heavily pruinosed. *O. trinacria* (Fig. 37), dark blue
when mature, is the easiest to distinguish in both sexes because of its
great size, elongate abdomen, large thorax and its hawking habit,
usually flying low down over water or over the banks. The smaller
icteromelas (Fig. 36) is also distinguishable because of its elongate
abdomen, and its vivid green body with thick black stripes. Neither of
these are forest insects. *O. caffrum* (Fig. 23), until fully pruinosed, is
characterized by its bright white stripes, one on the front of the thorax,
two on the sides, each edged by a black line. In immature *chrysostigma*
(Fig. 24) there is normally one strong white lateral stripe. In *microstigma*
(Fig. 34) the male is normally very dark on the thorax, the pterostigma
short and pale; in the female the abdomen is unusually broad for
Rhodesian species and the wings normally have extensive amber basal
areas. *O. falsum* (Fig. 33) is generally in thickish bush or in forest and
has rather bright markings: the green in the thorax or the incomplete
blue on the abdomen of the less mature individuals; black thoracic
stripes are clear-cut. *O. stemmale kalai* (Fig. 31) is a larger insect with the
colour and markings less pronounced: but it is essential to determine
this by genitalia. In *julia* (Fig. 32) the thorax is generally darker than
the similar-sized *falsum*, the pterostigma rather short and the amber
basal trace on the hindwing is deeply coloured. It is only found in or
near real forest areas.

O. brachiale (Fig. 35) may be confused with *falsum* or *stemmale kalai*
in the field. It is *usually* larger than the former and has a long pterostigma. Very often it can be distinguished at once by pale lateral stripes
on the thorax.

The remaining species are small or smallish. The largest of these is
machadoi (Fig. 26) with rather thin dark lines on the thorax. *O.
guineense* (Fig. 29) and *hintzi* (Fig. 27) are heavily marked with black and
hard to distinguish except by genitalia. *O. macrostigma* (Fig. 28) is a

small species characterized by a long, pale pterostigma. It is the scarcest of the species in Rhodesia known to the Author. *O. abbotti* (Fig. 25) is a very small species, the thorax very green due to reduction in black marking. The small *rhodesiae* (Fig. 30) is only readily separated on genitalia.

Orthetrum abbotti Calvert, 1892, *Trans. Amer. ent. Soc.* **19**: 162 (Kilimanjaro)

Common. Northern Rhodesia: Victoria Falls and Katambora; Luanshya; Mokambo (Rhodesia-Katanga border); Mwinilunga; Abercorn; Chinyunyu Hot Springs, east of Lusaka (Dening). Katanga: La Manda River; Lubumbashi; Kilwezi.

Orthetrum brachiale (Beauvois). *Libellula brachialis* Beauvois, 1805, *Ins. Afr. Amér.* 171, pl. (Nigeria)

Common. Northern Rhodesia: Victoria Falls and Zambezi River; Samfya; Abercorn. Katanga: Lufua River; Elizabethville; Albertville; Upemba Park. Nyasaland: Mzimba.

Orthetrum caffrum (Burm.). *Libellula caffra* Burmeister, 1839, *Handb.* **2**: 856 (Natal)

Common but scarcely known yet from this area. Northern Rhodesia: Abercorn. Katanga: Mubale.

Orthetrum chrysostigma (Burm.). *Libellula chrysostigma* Burmeister, 1839, id. loc. 857 (Teneriffe)

Common. Northern Rhodesia: Victoria Falls; Abercorn. Katanga: Lubudi; Kiambi; Elizabethville; Upemba Park. Nyasaland: Fort Hill.

Orthetrum falsum falsum Longfield. *Orthetrum capense falsum* Longfield, 1955, *Publ. cult. Cia Diamant. Angola* **27** (1): 26, ff. (Kenya)

Common. In one of the males taken in copula at Mwinilunga the brightly pruinosed blue abdomen was marked distinctly with yellow distal triangles on most abdominal segments. Clear-cut markings like this are rather a feature of this species. Northern Rhodesia: Victoria Falls; Solwezi; Samfya; Mwinilunga (especially Zambezi River); Abercorn; Ndola. Katanga: Lubudi; Albertville, etc.; Upemba Park. Nyasaland: Mzimba; Cholo.

Orthetrum guineense Ris. *Orth. chrysostigma guineense* Ris (pars.) 1909, *Coll. Zool. Selys.* **10**: 207 f. (Angola)

Common. Northern Rhodesia: Mwinilunga; Samfya; Abercorn; Ndola. Katanga: Upemba Nat. Park. Nyasaland: Nkata Bay.

[611]

Orthetrum hintzi hintzi Schmidt, 1949 (1951), *Arch. Mus. Bocage* **20**: 174, 178, ff. (Portug. Guinea)

Common. Northern Rhodesia: Ndola; Mwinilunga: Abercorn. Katanga: La Manda River; Fizi. Nyasaland: Mzimba.

Orthetrum icteromelas Ris, 1909, loc. cit. 197 (Madagascar)

A locally common species in Central Africa, less common further north. Northern Rhodesia: Samfya (Dening and Watmough); Abercorn. Katanga: Kongolo (*vide* Schouteden).

Orthetrum julia Kirby, 1900, *Ann. Mag. nat. Hist.* (7) **6**: 75, f. (S. Leone)

The Rhodesian examples of this common equatorial forest insect are rather less dark than their northern relatives.

Northern Rhodesia: Mwinilunga. Katanga: Lubudi.

Orthetrum machadoi Longfield, 1955, loc. cit. 35, ff. (Angola)

Less common here than in East Africa. Northern Rhodesia: Kabompo River; Abercorn.

Orthetrum macrostigma Longfield, 1945, *Arch. Mus. Bocage*, **16**: 25, 30, ff. (Angola)

An apparently scarce species of which the Author has so far only secured a single male. The hamular hook is very distinctive, almost more like a *Lokia* in appearance. Northern Rhodesia: Mwinilunga.

Orthetrum microstigma Ris, 1911, *Rev. Zool. Bot. afr.* **1**: 128, f. (Cameroons)

A very robust, local species, found at swamp-edged streams, especially at the fringes of forest patches. Some females show yellow cross-veins near anterior parts of wings, but these are not fully mature and cannot be considered to be race *imitans* Schmidt. The males all have black cross-veins. Northern Rhodesia: Mwinilunga (Sakeshi River and at its source). Katanga: Kamina; Albertville, etc.; Kilwezi; Upemba.

Orthetrum rhodesiae Pinhey, 1960, *Ent. Mon. Mag.* **96**: 269

So far known only from Kapiri M'poshi and from a river to the south of Ndola in Northern Rhodesia (Plate 2, fig. *f*).

Orthetrum stemmale kalai Longfield, 1936, *Trans. R. ent. Soc. Lond.* **85**: 487, 493 (Zambezi)

Although widespread and not uncommon in East and tropical Africa, it has so far proved elusive in the area under consideration. Northern Rhodesia: Victoria Falls (described from the island of Kalai); Samfya (Dening).

Orthetrum trinacria (Selys). *Libellula trinacria* Selys, 1841, *Rev. Zool.* 244 (Sicily)

Widespread but preferring open waters. Strong flight, of a steady, hawking nature. Northern Rhodesia: Samfya; Zambezi River; Abercorn (abundant).

Key to genus *Palpopleura* **Rambur**

1   Wings long. 1–2 black streaks below base of costa in forewing and a black spot at nodus . . . . .   *deceptor*

       Wings short and more extensively marked with black or brown 2

2 (1) Face and side of thorax mainly yellow; dark patches on each wing either confined to base (male) or in two isolated patches (female) . . . . *jucunda*

       Face and sides of thorax dark brown to blackish; sides of thorax with yellow stripes. Dark wing markings not confined to base and continuous, not in isolated patches.
                                      lucia 3

3 (2) In forewing the black covers whole wing area from base to pterostigma in male . . . . *lucia* f. *lucia*

       In forewing the black is incomplete posteriorly, invaginated (cut into) . . . . *lucia* f. *portia*

Palpopleura deceptor (Calvert). *Hemistigmoides deceptor* Calvert, 1899, *Proc. Acad. nat. Sci. Philad.* 241, f. (Somalia)

Generally somewhat uncommon and a more alert insect than other *Palpopleura*. Prefers open, reedy pools. Northern Rhodesia: Victoria Falls (at pools near the river). Katanga: Albertville; Upemba Park. Nyasaland: Mzimba.

Palpopleura jucunda Rambur, 1842, *Névr.* 134 (Cape)

Commoner in south and central than in equatorial Africa. Reedy pools. One of the prettiest dragonflies (Plate 2, fig. *c*). Northern Rhodesia: Ndola; Mwinilunga; Abercorn; Chinyunyu Hot Springs, Lusaka (Dening). Katanga: Lubumbashi, etc.; Mubale.

Palpopleura lucia (Drury). *Libellula lucia* Drury, 1773, *Ill. Exot. Ins.* **2**: 82, pl. (Sierra Leone)

Libellula portia Drury, 1773, ibid. 86, pl. (S. Leone)

Abundant in most parts of the continental ethiopian region (Plate 2, 3). In some areas the darker form *lucia* is more abundant at the lower elevations, *portia* being at higher altitudes. Where there is thick bush or forest, however, *lucia* tends to be commoner, although *portia* may appear at the fringes of the bush or in forest clearings. The suggestion, however, that they are very close but distinct *species* seems doubtful, since intermediates do occur in parts of tropical Africa, although not in the regions under consideration here.

Northern Rhodesia: Victoria Falls; Mwinilunga; Samfya (Watmough; one male only); Abercorn; Lusaka. Katanga: Albertville; Elizabethville, etc.; Upemba Park. Nyasaland: Fort Hill; Nkata Bay.

Eleuthemis buettikoferi Ris, 1910, *Coll. Zool. Selys.* **11**: 384, ff. (Liberia)

This rather beautiful insect, the male (Plate 3, fig. *f*) with pale blue, rather flattened body, the forewing tipped with chocolate brown, is a rarity in many parts of Africa, but locally common in some parts of Rhodesia. It favours twigs in sunny spots over rivers or wide streams. The apical patch and the insects themselves vary in size. Forewing in male 26–28 mm. Northern Rhodesia: Victoria Falls and Katambora; Kabompo River; Mwinilunga. Katanga: Upemba Park (Fraser 1955: 26).

Tentative key to *Aethiothemis* **Martin-Ris**

1   Abdomen slender on segments 3–10, swollen at base.

bequaerti

Abdomen somewhat flattened dorso-ventrally .   *mediofasciata*
and *solitaria*

Aethiothemis bequaerti Ris, 1919, *Coll. Zool. Selys* **16** (2): 1127 (Elizabethville)

This small, slender-bodied species is known in Rhodesia from a few males only, taken at the open swamp end of Lake Chila, Abercorn, in April. Fraser refers it to a genus *Nubiothemis* (Fraser, 1954, *Rev. Zool. bot. Afr.* **50**: 263) and it is evidently the same as Fisher's *Cirrothemis bella* (Fisher, 1939, *Notul. Nat.* **10**: 4). It was described from Elizabethville. The species *Oxythemis carpenteri* Fraser may also belong to this genus and, like *bequaerti*, it has a cylindrical abdomen.

[614]

Aethiothemis mediofasciata Ris, 1931, *Rev. suisse Zool.* **38**: 106 (Angola)

It is not quite certain yet how this species differs from *solitaria* Ris (Ris, 1908, *Ann. Mus. Stor. nat. Genova* **43**: 663), said to be a slightly smaller insect having brown wing apices. Most, if not all, Rhodesian, examples appear to be nearer *mediofasciata*, although there is a slight range in size. A few specimens amongst the very long series collected by Green near Ndola have deeply saffronated wings from base to nodus, rather like *palustris* Martin (Martin, 1912, *Feuille jeun. Nat.* (5) **42**: 95) but with general features, including wing venation, similar to the *mediofasciata* series. It does not appear that these heavily amber-tinted specimens are in any particular stage of maturity, as might be suspected in some Libellulid genera, in which less mature individuals have more amber on the wings than in mature examples. These *Aethiothemis* are confined to open swamps and it is interesting to find that they are only found in the adult state in or just after the rains. The Author collected a long series at Abercorn in April, 1954. In 1960 at Mwinilunga teneral examples (and one mature male) were just appearing in early March. Green has informed the Author that April and May are the months for this group near Ndola. In mid-March, 1960, during the return of the expedition one mature male was taken to the south of Ndola. In the immature male and female the eye is brown above, grey below; body chestnut and orange, with a broad black dorsal stripe down the abdomen. In the mature male, the abdomen is pruinosed blue above.

Northern Rhodesia: Ndola; Abercorn; Mwinilunga. Schouteden (1934) records *solitaria* from Kiambi (Katanga).

Chalcostephia flavifrons Kirby, 1889, *Trans. zool. Soc. Lond.* **12**: 337 (Angola)

Scarce in the area considered here. The male has a yellow face, a steely blue frons, and a forked process on the ventral surface of the base of the abdomen. Northern Rhodesia: Victoria Falls and Katambora; Ndola; Lufubu River mouth (southern end of Lake Tanganyika, Vesey Fitzgerald). Also recorded from Katanga (Ris.).

Lokithemis leakeyi Pinhey, 1956, *Occ. Pap. Coryndon Mus.* **4**: 34 (Abercorn)

This slender-bodied insect has so far only been taken in the type locality, Abercorn. Named after Dr. L. S. B. Leakey who sponsored the exhibition when the species was captured in 1954.

Porpacithemis dubia Fraser, 1954, *Rev. Zool. Bot. afr.* **50**: 261 (Gaboon)

Closely allied to the last insect. One male and one female were taken near the Zambezi River (Mwinilunga) 2 March, 1960, and a short series in the Katanga, January, 1958. In the male the eye was grey, dark brown on top; thorax marked with pale green; abdomen pruinosed whitish blue. In the female the eye was grey, brown on top; pale marking on thorax green.

Northern Rhodesia: Mwinilunga. Katanga: La Manda River.

Porpax asperipes risi Pinhey, 1958, *Occ. Pap. nat. Mus. S. Rhod.* 22B: 115

Smaller than the West African nominotypical race this elusive sub-species was described from the Vumba and Mount Selinda in Southern Rhodesia. One pair was collected by Lascelles at Hillwood Farm. Northern Rhodesia: Mwinilunga (February, 1960).

In the male, in life, eye pale blue, green above; labium yellow, labrum and clypeus pale green; frons and vertex pale blue; antehumeral stripe indicated by isolated blue pruinosity; other thoracic and abdominal pale markings green, the abdomen above thinly pruinosed blue. In the female the pale body markings were more yellowish green. Abdominal segments 2–7 pale blue pruinosed above.

Thermochoria equivocata Kirby, 1889, *Trans. zool. Soc. Lond.* 12: 339, f. (W. Africa)

Schouteden (1934) records this from Katanga.

Hemistigma albipuncta (Rambur). *Libellula albipuncta* Rambur, 1842, *Névr.* 93 (Senegal)

A common species (Plate 3, fig. *e*). Fraser's form *neurothemoides* (Fraser, 1954, *Rev. Zool. Bot. afr.* 50: 257) lacking the black rays, occurs amongst typical and other varieties. Wings in the female may be with or without brown apical patches. Northern Rhodesia: Victoria Falls and Katambora; Ngoma (Kafue National Park); Ndola; Samfya and Lake Bangweulu (common, according to Dening and Watmough); Mwinilunga; Abercorn. Katanga: Chembe; Mubale; Kanonga. Nyasaland: Port Herald; Bua River (Kota Kota); Nkata Bay.

Key to genus *Diplacodes* **Kirby**

1   Smaller insects, hindwing of male about 19 mm., the mature males black but coated with thin pruinosity; females and immature males reddish brown on front of thorax; black stripes on thorax and abdomen of immature males thicker.

exilis

Larger insects, hindwing of male 21 mm. or more, the mature males black without dorsal pruinosity. Immature male and female ochreous on thorax with thinner lines.

lefebvrei

Diplacodes exilis Ris, 1911, *Coll. Zool. Selys.* **12**: 464

A small local species. Northern Rhodesia: Mwinilunga; Abercorn.

Also recorded from Nyasaland, but the Author has not seen examples from there.

Diplacodes lefebvrei (Rambur). *Libellula lefebvrei* Rambur, 1842, loc. cit. 112, 117 (Egypt)

This dragonfly, very black in the mature male, is abundant in many parts of this continent. Northern Rhodesia: Victoria Falls; Broken Hill; Ndola; Mwinilunga; Samfya; Abercorn and Ufipa Plateau (V. Fitzgerald). Katanga: Elizabethville; Albertville; Upemba. Nyasaland: Salima Bay.

Key to genus *Acisoma* Kirby

1   Abdomen swollen on basal half, sharply contracted in the middle, then slender. Subtriangle on forewing free . *panorpoides*

    Abdomen gradually tapering to the end. Subtriangle on forewing crossed . . . . *trifidum*

Acisoma panorpoides ascalaphoides Rambur. *A. ascalaphoides* Rambur, 1842, *Névr.* 29, ff. (Madagascar)

A common species of quiet open waters, settling preferably on Water Lily leaves. Northern Rhodesia: Victoria Falls; Ndola; Abercorn; Samfya; Chinyunya Hot Springs, east of Lusaka (Dening).

Acisoma trifidum Kirby, 1889, *Trans. zool. Soc. Lond.* **12**: 341 (Congo)

A scarce and local forest species. Northern Rhodesia: Mwinilunga (Sakeshi River, and its source); Samfya. Katanga: Albertville (Schouteden, 1934).

Key to genus *Brachythemis* Brauer

1   Wings without basal amber. Base of frons with distinctive black band. Abdomen not markedly expanded; blackish in mature male; wings of male with black bands . *leucosticta*

    Wings with very broad basal amber. Base of frons with only a trace of black. Abdomen swollen; red in male. Wings of male without black bands. . . . . *lacustris*

[617]

Brachythemis lacustris (Kirby). *Trithemis lacustris* Kirby, 1889, *Trans. zool. Soc. Lond.* **12**: 329 (Wadelai)

Locally abundant in swampy places. Northern Rhodesia: Victoria Falls; Kafue River; Lake Wumba, Bangweulu swamps (Watmough); Mwinilunga. Katanga: Chembe; Elizabethville, etc.

Brachythemis leucosticta (Burmeister). *Libellula leucosticta* Burmeister, 1839, *Handb.* **2**: 849 (loc. varia)

This black-banded dragonfly (Plate 3, fig. *g*) which settles or flies low over cleared banks of any pool or even near a temporary puddle, is familiar in most parts of Africa. Northern Rhodesia: Chirundu Bridge; Victoria Falls; Ndola; Samfya; Abercorn. Katanga: *vide* Schouteden 1934. Nyasaland: Cholo; Nkata Bay; Lake Shirwa (Arnold).

Key to genus *Crocothemis* **Brauer**

1   Abdomen broad, triquetral; vividly red in male; hindwing with small bright amber patch not or barely reaching the arculus 2

Abdomen slender, cylindrical (if narrowly triquetral, then with no amber at wing bases) 3

2 (1) Abdomen up to 3 mm. at widest. Pterostigma usually scarlet, 3 mm. or less. Lateral carina on segment 5 with 12 small teeth or less . . . . *sanguinolenta*

Abdomen over 3 mm. at widest. Pterostigma yellow, over 3 mm. Lateral carina on segment 5 with 17 or more denticles . . . . *erythraea*

3 (1) All wings broadly amber, forewing to base of triangle, hindwing to distal end of triangle. Pterostigma only 2.5 mm. . . . . *brevistigma* n.sp.

Wings without basal amber. Pterostigma 3 mm. or more . 4

4 (3) Hindwing triangle free. Thorax and abdomen chequered with black . . . . *saxicolor*

Hindwing triangle often crossed. Thorax and abdomen only with minute traces of black . . . . *divisa*

[618]

CROCOTHEMIS BREVISTIGMA n. sp.

(Fig. 39)

Holotype male, mature. Face and frons ochreous, labium paler, vertex and occiput browner. Pro- and synthorax ochreous brown, sides pale greenish ochreous. Legs ochreous brown with black spines. Venation brown, costa and subcostal cross-veins paler; pterostigma pale brown between black veins. Wings broadly amber at base: forewing in subcostal and cubital spaces as far as proximal angle of triangle, in median and anal fields to level of subtriangle; in hindwing to just beyond distal angle of triangle, covering two-thirds of anal loop and almost reaching tornus. Forewing with $9\frac{1}{2}$ Ax, 8 Px; triangle and subtriangle crossed in forewings, free in hindwing. Venation close. Abdomen and all appendages brownish (redder in life); discontinuous black smears along lateral carina of 4–9. 11–12 denticles on this carina on segment 5. Anal appendages normal; accessories on 2 typical of the genus which is very uniform in these organs; in *erythraea* they are more obviously robust but then this is the largest known African species. Abd. 19 mm., hw. 25 mm., pt. 2.5 mm. In less mature paratypes the costa is more yellow.

Allotype female. Very similar. Abd. 18 mm., hw. 24 mm., pt. 2.5 mm.

In life the abdomen of the male was as red as *sanguinolenta;* eye in both sexes pale blue, maroon on top.

Remarks. The first example seen of this insect was a headless male taken at Abercorn in June, 1943. Its broadly amber wings, small pterostigma and slender body suggested a new species or very aberrant variety of one of the species and it was submitted to Longfield in 1953, who considered it to be *sanguinolenta* or a new subspecies of this. In April, 1957, Kitchingham collected two more males (the paratypes, unfortunately, lacking terminal 5 segments of abdomen). In February–March, 1960, at Mwinilunga, the Author collected two more males (holotype and a damaged example) and the allotype female. The species was settling on granite rocks close to the Zambezi and also, amongst typical *sanguinolenta* and *divisa* it was settling on muddy tracks near Mwinimalamba. Holotype, allotype and one male paratype in National Museum, Bulawayo, one paratype male (lacking abdomen 6–10) will be in the British Museum (Nat. Hist.). Northern Rhodesia: Abercorn; Mwinilunga.

Crocothemis divisa Baumann, 1898, *Ent. Nachr.* **24**: 242 (Togo)

Like *saxicolor* this more widespread insect particularly likes to settle on rocks, either on the banks of rivers and streams or on rocks on hills. Northern Rhodesia: Ndola; Mwinilunga; Lusaka; Abercorn. Katanga: La Manda River; Elizabethville; Albertville, etc.; Upemba Park.

Crocothemis erythraea (Brullé). *Libellula erythraea* Brullé, 1832, *Expéd. Sci. Morée* **3** (1): 102, f. (Moravia)

One of the commonest of the larger red-bodied dragonflies (Plate 3, fig. *h*), principally at open waters. Northern Rhodesia: Victoria Falls; Mwinilunga; Abercorn; Samfya; Fort Rosebery. Katanga: Chembe; Elizabethville, etc. (*vide* Schouteden, 1934); Upemba Park.

Crocothemis sanguinolenta (Burmeister). *Libellula sanguinolenta* Burmeister, 1839, *Handb.* **2**: 859 (Cape)

Very similar in appearance and distribution to the previous species but usually readily distinguished by its shorter, red pterostigma. Northern Rhodesia: Victoria Falls; Ndola; Lusaka; Mwinilunga; Abercorn and Ufipa Plateau. Katanga: Chembe; Elizabethville, etc.; Upemba Park. Nyasaland: Cholo; Zomba; Fort Hill.

Crocothemis saxicolor Ris, 1919, *Coll. Zool. Selys* **16** (2): 1164 (S. Rhodesia)

A scarcer and more local insect than the last three, this was described from Southern Rhodesia, but has been recorded from Nyasaland (Miss B. Rankine). It generally settles on rocks near water or on hill-sides. It varies in colour from a drab light brown, with black reticulation, a form blending very well with granite rocks; to a dark red form.

Bradinopyga cornuta Ris, 1911, *Coll. Zool. Selys* **13**: 547, f. (Moçambique; Tanganyika)

A local insect, favouring granite rocks, near the faster running streams or rivers. Northern Rhodesia: Mwinilunga (f. *cornuta* Ris) (Zambezi River). Katanga: Upemba National Park.

Sympterum fonscolombei (Selys). *Libellula fonscolombei* Selys, 1840, *Libell. Eur.* 29, 49, 208 (France)

No record from this area yet of this rather cosmopolitan insect, although there is little doubt that it occurs in many areas. It favours open reedy pools.

[620]

Philonomon luminans (Karsch). *Sympetrum luminans* Karsch, 1893, *Berl. ent. Z.* **38**: 22 (loc. varia)

Widespread, preferring reedy pools. Northern Rhodesia: Victoria Falls; Solwezi; Abercorn. Nyasaland: Mzimba.

Atoconeura biordinata biordinata Karsch, 1899, *Ent. Nachr.* **25**: 371 (Tanganyika)

Although the race *chirinda* Longfield occurs in Southern Rhodesia, Gray sent the larger nominotypical race from Nyasaland; this was described from Tanganyika. It will probably be found on the lower slopes of hills in the north-east of Northern Rhodesia but so far there are no records from Northern Rhodesia. Katanga: 40 miles north of Kuibo Falls; Katentania (Seydel); Upemba. Nyasaland: Mzimba.

Key to genus *Trithemis* Brauer

Males:

1   Body colour mainly red or reddish; sometimes with thin violet pruinosity 2

       Body mainly bronze-brown to black, normally with yellow markings; or adults with dense or dark blue pruinosity, at least on thorax or occasionally all black 7

2 (1) Abdomen slender, distinctly constricted at 3 3

       Abdomen broader, triquetral, scarcely constricted at 3 . 5

3 (2) Forewing without distinct basal colouring. Abdomen dull orange or red. Hindwing at least 30 mm. . . . . . *werneri*

       Forewing with basal amber. Abdomen bright red. Hindwing less than 30 mm. 4

4 (3) Basal amber in hindwing scarcely reaching proximal edge of triangle, not covering anal loop, the cellules not darkened . . . . *arteriosa arteriosa*

       Basal amber hindwing reaching beyond t., covering most of loop, the cellules usually filled in with brown.

                       monardi monardi

5 (2) Frons red, non-metallic. Amber patch on hindwing reaches beyond triangle. Pterostigma less than 2 mm.

                          kirbyi ardens

       Frons metallic or non-metallic. Amber patch hindwing not reaching beyond proximal edge of t. Pterostigma 2.5 mm. or more 6

6 (5) Pterostigma mainly black. Frons not metallic. Abdomen
always distinctly red . . . . *pluvialis*

Pterostigma yellow to brown. Frons metallic violet.
Abdomen of adult coated with pruinosity to give a reddish
violet colour . . . . *annulata*

7 (1) Abdomen broad, tapering, but not distinctly constricted . 8

Abdomen slender, distinctly constricted at 3 12

8 (7) Last Ax forewing normally complete. Black lateral bands on
thorax separate (but thoracic marking may be obscured by
dark blue pruinosity). Hamular hook small . . *dorsalis*

Last Ax forewing incomplete. Black lateral bands on thorax
linked together (but may be obscured by pale or dark
pruinosity) 9

9 (8) Frons glossy dark brown. Labium all black . . . *dichroa*

Frons metallic violet. Labium with yellow lateral spots . 10

10 (9) Hindwing about 26–27 mm. Body of adult all black . . *atra*

Hindwing normally at least 30 mm. Body not completely
black 11

11 (10) Abdomen (without appendages) four-fifth as long as hindwing. Hook of hamule very large . . . . . *ellenbecki*

Abdomen three-quarters as long as hindwing. Hook of
hamule small . . . . *pruinata*

12 (7) Adult not pruinosed, but bronze-brown. Abdomen slender.
Wings uniformly yellowish . . . . *anomala*

Adult with dark or light blue pruinosity; in less mature
condition not bronzed. Wings not uniformly yellow . . 13

13 (12) Abdomen *very* slender. Pruinosity dark blue. Hindwing
with trace of basal amber or brown 14

Abdomen not excessively slender. Pruinosity pale blue.
Hindwing without basal amber 15

14 (13) Forewing with not more than $9\frac{1}{2}$ Ax. Pterostigma whitish
on ventral surface . . . . *hecate*

Forewing with at least $10\frac{1}{2}$ Ax. Pterostigma almost as dark
ventrally as dorsally . . . . *basitincta*

15 (13) Hindwing with an isolated saffron patch in anal area. Frons
metallic blue. Pruinosity pale blue . . . . . . *stictica*

Hindwing without saffron marking 16

16 (15) Thorax in mature individual yellow at sides, pale blue in
front . . . . *parasticta*

Adult, thorax all blue 17

17 (16) Frons metallic violet. Hamule scimitar-shaped . *donaldsoni*

Frons metallic blue. Hamular hook small, curved . *nuptialis*

Females:

1   Frons with deep furrow between conical lobes. Hindwing
with small isolated yellow spot between anal loop and
tornus . . . . *kirbyi ardens*

Frontal furrow shallow, the lobes rounded. No isolated
yellow spot on hindwing 2

2 (1) Abdomen mainly yellowish to reddish brown with black
markings 3

Abdomen mainly black with short yellow streaks . . 12

3 (2) Abdomen with short black subdorsal bands on 2–3 (or 2–4)
and a lateral stripe on 4–7 4

Abdomen either with continuous black dorsal and lateral
bands on 2–10 or else with scarcely any black markings . 6

4 (3) Hindwing 30 mm. or more. Forewing hyaline at
base . . . . *werneri*

Hindwing 29 mm. or less. Forewing with basal amber . 5

5 (4) Basal amber on hindwing not reaching beyond proximal
edge of triangle . . . . *arteriosa*

Basal amber on hindwing extending beyond distal edge of
triangle . . . . *monardi*

6 (3) Pterostigma ochreous to brown or reddish . . *annulata*

Pterostigma brown to black; at most a pale posterior
edging 7

7 (6) Veins mostly red. Amber patch on hindwing nearly reaching tornus. Abdomen with narrow black lateral stripe.

pluvialis

Veins mainly black (subcostal cross-veins may be yellowish). Hindwing with, at most, only very small amber spot. Abdomen with broad black lateral band 8

8 (7) Last Ax in forewing normally complete. Lateral black lines on thorax separate . . . . *dorsalis*

Last Ax in forewing incomplete. Lateral stripes in thorax linked up 9

9 (8) Synthorax in front normally with two confluent yellow triangles. Frons above partly dark metallic blue. Pterostigma brown. Hindwing 30 mm. . . . . . *nuptialis*

Synthorax with complete yellow antehumeral stripes . . 10

10 (9) Frons with glossy black basal band. Wing apices with brown patches. Pterostigma paler posteriorly. Hindwing about 29 mm. . . . . *dichroa*

Band on frons metallic blue-black. No brown at wing apices. Hindwing usually over 30 mm. 11

11 (10) Pterostigma with pale posterior line. Lateral lobe of labium yellow at margin . . . . *ellenbecki*

Pterostigma without pale posterior line. Lateral lobe of labium black, enclosing small yellow spot . . . *pruinata*

12 (2) Hindwing over 31 mm., without basal amber. Frons with steely blue basal band . . . . *donaldsoni*

Hindwing 30 mm. or less; with trace of basal amber . 13

13 (12) Abdomen about 30 mm., with double row of pale streaks on each side 14

Abdomen 27 mm. or less, with single row of pale streaks on each side 15

14 (13) Wings strongly yellow all over . . . . . . *anomala*

Wings with patch of basal amber . . . . . *parasticta*

[624]

15 (13) Abdomen robust, 22–24 mm. Pale markings pale yellow.
Hindwing often with yellow cloud near anal loop .   . *stictica*

Abdomen more slender, 24 mm. or more, Pale markings
more ochreous. No yellow cloud on hindwing . . . 16

16 (15) Forewing with 9½ Ax or less . . . . *hecate*

Forewing with 10½ Ax or more 17

17 (16) Thorax laterally with vertical black stripe . . . *basitincta*

Thorax with broad blackish lateral horizontal stripe . . *atra*

TRITHEMIS Brauer

Subgenus *Helothemis* Karsch

T. dorsalis (Rambur). *Libellula dorsalis* Rambur, 1842, *Névr.* 89 (Cape)

Common Species. Northern Rhodesia: Kapiri M'Poshi; Ndola;
Lusaka; Mwinilunga (Sakeshi River source); Kabompo River;
Abercorn; Mokambo (on Katanga border). Katanga: Bunkeya;
Elizabethville, etc.; Upemba Park.

Subgenus *Trithemis* Brauer

Trithemis annulata (Beauvois). *Libellula annulata Beauvois*, 1805,
Ins. Afr. Amér. 69, f. (Oware)

Common. Male conspicuous by its pinkish " claret-coloured "
abdomen. Northern Rhodesia: Victoria Falls; Ndola; Mwinilunga;
Samfya. Katanga: Upemba Park.

Trithemis anomala Pinhey, 1956, *Occ. Pap. Coryndon Mus.* **4**: 38, ff.
(Abercorn)

Characterized by its bronze-brown body and yellowish wings.
Extremely local, in swamp. Northern Rhodesia: Mwinilunga (Sakeshi
River source); Abercorn (swamp-end of Lake Chila).

Trithemis arteriosa arteriosa (Burmeister). *Libellula arteriosa* Burmeister,
1839, *Handb.* **2**: 850 (Natal)

One of the commonest dragonflies in the whole African continent.
Northern Rhodesia: Victoria Falls; Ndola; Kitwe; Chingola;
Mwinilunga; Abercorn; Fort Rosebery; Lusaka. Katanga: Lufua
River; Elizabethville etc.; Upemba. Nyasaland: Cholo; Nkata Bay.

Trithemis atra Pinhey, 1961, *Publn. Brit. Mus. (Nat. Hist.).* 166

A very little-known small black species, easy to confuse with *dichroa* or, in the field, with *Diplacodes lefebvrei*. Northern Rhodesia: 30 miles south of Ndola.

Trithemis basitincta Ris. *Tr. donaldsoni basitincta* Ris, 1912, *Coll. Zool. Selys*, **14**: 784 (Cameroons)

Mwinilunga examples (Zambezi River, and at various waterfalls and rapids) are variable in size and have a distinct but small basal amber ray in cubital space and a trace of amber against the anal triangle, in hindwing: this amber is slightly more marked than in the Victoria Falls series. But the variation in Rhodesia is not nearly as great as in tropical Africa. A local species. Northern Rhodesia: Victoria Falls; Kafue River; Ndola; Mwinilunga; Abercorn. Katanga; Mubale.

Trithemis dichroa Karsch, 1893, *Berl. ent. Z.* **38**: 24 (Togo)

A scarce small black species (*vide atra*). Northern Rhodesia: Mwinilunga.

Trithemis donaldsoni (Calvert). *Pseudomacromia donaldsoni* Calvert, 1899, *Proc. Acad. nat. Sci. Philad.* 235, f. (Somalia)

This pale blue species is scarcely known yet in the territories considered here although common in Southern Rhodesia. Prefers open streams and rivers. Northern Rhodesia: Victoria Falls. Katanga: Mubali; Pelenge Gorge.

Trithemis ellenbecki Foerster, 1906, *Jb. nassau. Ver. Naturk.* **59**: 314 f. (Abysinnia)

A very common darkish blue insect (male), not very particular about habitat although less common in thicker bush. Northern Rhodesia: Victoria Falls; Mwinilunga; Abercorn; Lusaka. Katanga: Lubudi; Elizabethville; Upemba. Nyasaland: Cholo.

Trithemis hecate Ris, 1912, *Coll. Zool. Selys* **14**: 787 (Madagascar)

Rather uncommon and local, but apparently migratory, since it suddenly appeared at lakes near Salisbury (Southern Rhodesia) where it was evidently absent before. Northern Rhodesia: Samfya; Abercorn.

Trithemis kirbyi ardens Gerstaecker, *Tr. ardens* Gerstaecker, 1891, *Jb. Hamburg wiss. Anst.* **9**: (5, 9, 187 sep.) (East Africa)

The nominotypical race is Asiatic. Normally abundant, particularly on rocky streams or rivers, yet scarcely recorded yet in these areas. Northern Rhodesia: Victoria Falls. Katanga: Upemba Park.

Trithemis monardi Ris, 1931, *Rev. suisse Zool.* **38**: 108, f. (Angola)

Not uncommon in Central Africa but rare outside that region. At reedy pools. Males often adopt a fluttering flight. Northern Rhodesia: Chingali (? Kafue River); Kapiri M'Poshi; Katambora; Ndola; Kabompo River (swamp); Mwinilunga; Abercorn.

Trithemis nuptialis Karsch, 1894, *Berl. ent. Z.* **39**: 12 ff. (Cameroons)

A dark blue West African species found sparsely in Central Africa. Northern Rhodesia: Ndola; Mwinilunga. Katanga: Elizabethville.

Trithemis parasticta Pinhey, 1956, loc. cit. 35, ff. (Abercorn)

A very local Northern Rhodesian insect. Northern Rhodesia: Ndola; Abercorn; Samfya (Dening).

Trithemis pluvialis Foerster, 1906, *Jber. Ver. Naturk. Mannheim* **71-72**: (30 sep.). (Tanganyika)

A not uncommon red species which it is possible to confuse in the field with *arteriosa*. The abdomen is slightly broader and less marked with black; the wings with larger amber patch. Northern Rhodesia: Fort Rosebery; Lusaka; Ndola; Kabompo River (swamp); Mwinilunga; Abercorn. Katanga: Elizabethville; Albertville; Mubale.

Trithemis pruinata Karsch, 1898, *Ent. Nachr.* **24**: 342; idem, 1899, ibid. **25**: 369 (Togo)

This species is extraordinarily similar to *ellenbecki*, and the only way of distinguishing them in the field is to examine the hamular hook, which is so large in the latter species. The Author has examined great numbers in the field and his conclusion at present is that *pruinata* is generally scarce in most areas of Central and Eastern Africa and he has only seen few examples from West Africa. At Mwinilunga it appears to be slightly less scarce than elsewhere in Central Africa. One male captured there has two incomplete final antenodals in one forewing. Northern Rhodesia: Ndola; Mwinilunga (chiefly on the Zambezi River).

Trithemis stictica (Burmeister). *Libellula stictica* Burmeister, 1839, loc. cit. 850 (Natal)

At the Victoria Falls dwarf examples are numerous as well as the normal ones. This also applies at Mwinilunga. Common in swamps, reedy pools or rivers. Northern Rhodesia: Victoria Falls; Kapiri M'Poshi; Luanshya (dwarf); Ndola: Mwinilunga; Abercorn; Bangweulu Swamps. Katanga: La Manda River; Upemba Park. Nyasaland: Nkata Bay.

[627]

Trithemis werneri Ris, 1912, *Coll. Zool. Selys* **14**: 765, f. (Sudan)

This dull-coloured species appears to be scarce. So far only from Chirundu Bridge on the Zambezi, where it was taken by the Author in 1948 and has not been seen there since. It occurs in Southern Rhodesia (sparsely) and in the northern limits of East Africa. Katanga: Albertville (Mayné: *vide* Schouteden, 1934).

Key to genus *Zygonyx* Hagen-Selys

1   No pale transverse band on front of thorax. Abdomen not conspicuously club-shaped 2

Thorax with a broken whitish transverse band in front. Abdomen in male inflated before the end and therefore club-shaped; a broad yellow band on 7th segment 4

2 (1) Abdomen only about three-quarters the length of the hindwing. A conspicuous yellow band on segment 7, but without conspicuous spots on other segments and without pruinosity . . . . *flavicosta*

Abdomen almost the same length as the hindwing. Abdomen either pruinose or with yellow spots on most segments 3

3 (2) Labium with broad black median band. Adults without blue pruinosity. Abdomen with conspicuous rounded orange lateral spots. Pterostigma black . . . . *torrida*

Labium with median lobe black. Both sexes developing blue pruinosity. Orange abdominal spots when visible are elongate. Pterostigma reddish brown . . . . *natalensis*

4 (1) Hindwing not excessively broad, with 3–4 rows of cells between anal loop and base. Wings in both sexes hyaline . . . . *speciosa*

Hindwing very broad, with 7–8 rows between loop and base. Female with large brown fasciae on the wings (male unknown) . . . . *eusebia*

Zygonyx flavicosta (Sjoestedt). *Pseudomacromia flavicosta* Sjoestedt, 1899, *Bih. svensk. Vetensk. Akad. Handl.* **25** (4): 24 (Congo)

A series of this tropical West African insect was taken at the Kabompo River and at Mwinilunga (Sakeshi and Zambezi Rivers), all hovering over running waters. These differed slightly but consistently from examples taken in equatorial Africa.

ZYGONYX FLAVICOSTA MWINILUNGAE n. ssp.

(Fig. 40)

Holotype male. Lateral lobes of labium more broadly black on inner (medial) edges. The metallic blue colouring on the frons extending to a lesser degree down the sides than in the northerly race. In the female *Allotype* the labial black is similar to the male. The frontal metallic coloration is, however, reduced in females of both races and does not extend down the front or sides.

Remarks. Two pairs were taken in copula others singly. Holotype and allotype of this race, the latter with a male in copula, are in the National Museum, Bulawayo. A paratype male and female will go to the British Museum (Nat. Hist.). Seydel has taken the species in the Katanga at Katentania.

Zygonyx natalensis (Martin). *Pseudomacromia natalensis* Martin, 1900, *Bull. Mus. Hist. nat. Paris* 106, 107 (Natal)

Usually very common at waterfalls and rapids. The only continental African species of the genus which develops any extent of blue pruinosity. Northern Rhodesia: Victoria Falls; Ndola; Mufulira; Kabompo River; Mwinilunga. Katanga: Lubudi; Elizabethville; Upemba Park. Nyasaland: Njakwa Gorge.

Zygonyx speciosa Karsch. *Pseudom. speciosa* Karsch, 1891, *Ent. Nachr.* **17**: 74 (Cameroons)

Prefers the broader streams or rivers, hovering over the rapids or waterfalls. (Plate 4, fig. *b*). Eye in male whitish grey, pale body markings ivory white. The only female seen by the Author is in the private collection of the late Charles Seydel and was taken in Elizabethville. It has more extensive brown basal marks on the hindwing than the male. Both sexes are readily distinguished from other species from this area by the presence of the ivory transverse band on the front of the thorax. Northern Rhodesia: Mwinilunga (Zambezi River); Kabompo River (seen but not captured); Abercorn; Ndola.

Zygonyx torrida (Kirby). *Pseudom. torrida* Kirby, 1889, *Trans. zool. Soc. Lond.* **12**: 299, 340 (loc. varia)

Very widespread; conspicuous by the orange spots on the abdomen, in which it superficially resembles *Olpogastra fuelleborni*. However, the latter is not a waterfall-rapids species, nor a hoverer; and its abdomen is much more swollen at the base. Northern Rhodesia: Victoria Falls and Zambezi River. Katanga: Elizabethville.

Zygonyx eusebia (Ris). *Pseudomacromia eusebia* Ris, 1912, *Coll. Zool. Selys.* **14**: 814 (Congo)

One female of this magnificent species was taken in the Katanga by Seydel at Kamina.

Key to genus *Olpogastra* Karsch

1   Abdomen longer than hindwing, very swollen at base, the remaining segments very slender . . subgenus *Olpogastra*

lugubris

Abdomen shorter than hindwing; fusiform, not slender. subgenus *Zygonoides* . . . . *fuelleborni*

Subgenus *Olpogastra* Karsch

Olpogastra lugubris Karsch, 1895 (Ehrenberg mss), *Ent. Nachr.* **21**: 199, 201 (Dongola)

Not uncommon at reedy edges of large pools or rivers. Its peculiar abdomen and the yellow speckled, metallic black thorax readily distinguish it. Northern Rhodesia: Victoria Falls; Kapiri M'Poshi; Samfya. Katanga: Kuibo Falls; Upemba Park.

Subgenus *Zygonoides* Fraser

Olpogastra fuelleborni fuelleborni Gruenberg, 1902, *S. B. Ges. Naturf. Fr. Berl.* **9**: 235 (Nubia, Langenberg)

In this area it is so far known only from the Victoria Falls—Katambora section of the Zambezi River, where it settles on bushes overhanging the river.

Key to genus *Rhyothemis* Hagen

1   Forewing hyaline or with only the merest trace of amber at extreme base. Hindwing with large basal metallic—black area reaching from base to halfway between distal angle of discoidal cell and nodus . . . . . . *semihyalina*

Both wings coloured from base to at least the nodus . . 2

2 (1) Wings yellow at base, with intricate pattern of black bands and spots between base and nodus. Pterostigma ochreous.

mariposa

Wings largely metallic black up to the black pterostigma, with a few hyaline spots . . . . *fenestrina*

All species of this genus are conspicuous and they tend to have a fluttering flight. They generally prefer swamps or reedy pools.

Rhyothemis fenestrina (Rambur). *Libellula fenestrina* Rambur, 1842, *Névr.* 40

Although locally abundant in parts of tropical Africa (e.g. Uganda) where it is found in or at the edges of forest, in Central Africa only few examples are recorded so far, from swamps. (Plate 4, fig. *c*). Northern Rhodesia: Samfya (Watmough and Dening); Katambora; Mwinilunga; Abercorn. It has also been taken in Katanga (Lamaire).

Rhyothemis mariposa Ris, 1913, *Coll. Zool. Selys* **15**: 961, f. (South West Africa)

This attractive insect is practically only known in the area under consideration, with one or two sparse records elsewhere such as the type locality in South West Africa. Northern Rhodesia: Ndola; Chingola; Kabompo River (swamp); Mukende swamp (North-Western Province); Samfya and Lake Bangweulu; Abercorn. Katanga: Elizabethville; Kafakumba (Overlaet: *vide* Schouteden).

Rhyothemis semihyalina (Desjardins). *Libellula semihyalina* Desjardins, 1832, *Rapp. Soc. Maurice Isl.* 1; idem, 1835, *Ann. Soc. ent. Fr.* **4**: 4 (Mauritius)

The common form (Plate 4, fig. *d*) found in most parts of Africa is referable to the race *separata* Selys (Selys, 1849, in Lucas, *Algérie* **3**: 115 (Algeria)). The nominotypical race is Mauritian. Northern Rhodesia: Katambora; Broken Hill; Ndola; Samfya; Lake Bangweulu; Lusaka. Katanga: Lubumbashi; Elizabethville, etc.

Parazyxomma flavicans (Martin). *Zyxomma flavicans* Martin, 1908, *Ann. Mus. Stor. nat. Genova* **43**: 657 (Portug. Guinea)

This remarkably local and scarce insect somewhat resembling a rather large *Brachythemis leucosticta* but more retiring and crepuscular in habits, has been found in Northern Rhodesia in recent years: near Maramba River (Victoria Falls; in thick bush); Samfya (Dening).

[631]

Tholymis tillarga (Fabricius). *Libellula tillarga* Fabricius, 1798, *Suppl. Ent. Syst.* 285 (East Indies)

A cosmopolitan, crepuscular species marked in the male with a brown and milky-white patch on the hindwing near the nodus. Northern Rhodesia: Victoria Falls; Chirundu Bridge; Ndola; Samfya; Mwinilunga; Buleya-Mweru; Fort Jameson; Abercorn. Katanga: Albertville; Mubali.

The continental African form can be referred to forma *pallida* Beauvois.

Pantala flavescens (Fabr.). *Libellula flavescens* Fabricius, 1798, ibid. 285 (India)

A cosmopolitan migrant, found anywhere except in the denser forests; even at rain-puddles, like *Brachythemis leucosticta*. Northern Rhodesia: Victoria Falls; Ndola; Kabompo River; Bangweulu; Lusaka; Mwinilunga; Abercorn. Katanga: Elizabethville, etc.; Upemba Park.

Trapezostigma basilaris (Beauvois). *Libellula basilaris* Beauvois, 1805, *Ins. Afr. Amér.* 171, f. (Nigeria)

A strongly flying migrant in Africa and Asia. Examples are sometimes referrable to f. *burmeisteri* Kirby, with the red patches on the hindwing linked up, but more often they have them separate, like typical *basilaris*. (Plate 4, fig. *a*). Northern Rhodesia: Victoria Falls; Chingola; Solwezi (procured with dust shot on a swamp by Lascelles); Fort Jameson; Bangweulu; Abercorn; Lusaka. Katanga: Albertville, etc. Nyasaland: Mzimba.

Key to genus *Urothemis* Brauer

1   Abdomen with narrow blackish stripe on 4–6, broadening on 7–9; frons and abdomen of male red. Basal patch on hindwing in both sexes yellow with reddish brown marking.

assignata

Abdomen with broad black band on 4–10; frons of male metallic blue-black, abdomen in adult male coated with grey-blue pruinosity. Basal patch on hindwing blackish in male; in female more broadly amber with sparser red marking . . . . *edwardsi*

[632]

Urothemis assignata (Selys). *Libellula assignata* Selys, 1872, *Rev. Zool.*
(2) **23**: 176 (Madagascar)

Often a common red-bodied species at reedy pools, but so far, in this area, only recorded from Katambora on the Zambezi River, and in Katanga at Albertville and Mabwe (Upemba).

Urothemis edwardsi (Selys). *Lib. edwardsi* Selys, 1849, in Lucas, *Algérie*
3: 124, ff. (Algeria)

Prefers rivers or broad streams to pools. The dark blue-bodied male is a conspicuous insect. Northern Rhodesia: Victoria Falls and Katambora; Broken Hill; Samfya; Lake Bangweulu; Abercorn. Katanga: Luapula River (Chembe); Albertville; Kiambi, etc.

Aethriamanta rezia Kirby, 1889, *Trans. zool. Soc. Lond.* **12**: 298
(Madagascar)

A small red species with very open venation and short brown basal rays on the hindwing. Settles on reeds or twigs over or near water. Not very common. Northern Rhodesia: Victoria Falls; Ndola; Abercorn.

A SELECTION OF LITERATURE

BRINCK, PER. . . . 1955   In *South African Animal Life; Results of the Lund. Univ. Exped.* 1950–51. **2** *Odonata:* 191–333.

CORBET, P. S. . . 1956–7   Larvae of East African *Odonata. Entomologist.* **89**: 97, etc.; **90**: 28, etc.

FRASER, F. C. . . 1928   *Odonata* of the African Continent. *Trans. Ent. Soc. Lond.* **76**: 123–138, 6 ff.

1941   New African species of *Ceriagrion. Proc. R. ent. Soc. London.* B.**10**: 61–66, ff.

1944   A note on the genus *Notiothemis:* etc. ibid. B.**13**: 40–43, 2 ff.

1949   *Gomphidae* from the Belgian Congo. *Rev. Zool. bot. Africa* **42**: 101–138.

1952   Notes on African *Gomphidae;* etc. *Occas. Papers Corynd. Mus.* **3**: 3–12, 4 ff.

1954   New species of *Macromia* from Tropical Africa. *Rev. Zool. bot. Africa.* **49**: 41–76, ff.

1955   *Odonata: Mission de Witte, Parc Nat. Upemba.* **38** (1): 3–32, ff.

1957   A Reclassification of the Order *Odonata. Roy. Zool. Soc. N.S.W.* 133 pp., 62 ff.

1959   A note on the differentiation of *Lestes uncifer* Karsch and *L. pinheyi* Fraser. *Ent. Mon. Mag.* **95**: 88–89, pl. 7.

1959   Description of the female of *Notogomphus flavifrons* Fraser, ibid. **95**: 125, f. 1.

1960   The Crenigomphines of Tropical Africa. *Rev. Zool. bot. Africa.* **61**: 205–214.

KIMMINS, D. E. . . 1938 New African species of *Elattoneura.*
Ann. Mag. nat. Hist. (11) **1**:
294–302, ff. 1–6.

LONGFIELD, C. . . 1936 Studies on African *Odonata* with
synonymy; etc. *Trans. R. ent. Soc.
Lond.* **85** (20): 467–498, 10 ff.

1945 The *Odonata* of Angola; Missions Sci.
Suisse, 1928–9, 32–33. *Arch. Mus.
Bocage* **16**: 1–31, 11 ff. (1947).

1952 Two new species of African *Ceriagrion*; etc. *Proc. R. ent. Soc. Lond.*
B **21**: 41–48 ff.

1955 Odonata of North Angola. 1. *Publ.
Cult. Comp. Diamantes* **27** Dundo:
11–64 ff.

1959 idem., 2. ibid. **45**: 13–42, ff.

PINHEY, E. C. G. . 1951 Dragonflies of Southern Africa.
Transv. Mus. Mem. **5**, 310 pp., pls.,
ff. (with general refs., Odonata).

1956 Some Dragonflies of East and Central
Africa and a rarity from Mauritius.
Occas. Papers Corynd. Mus. **4**:
17–41, ff., pls.

1956 A new Rhodesian Dragonfly of the
family *Gomphidae. Occas. Papers
Nat. Mus.*, S. Rhod. **21**B: 83–84, ff.

1958 East African Odonata (Ergebn. D.
Zool. Ostafr. Exp. 1951–2). *Stuttg.
Beitr. Naturk.* **10**: 1–5.

1958 Records of Dragonflies from the
Zambezi and Rhodesia; etc. *Occas.
Papers Nat. Mus.*, S. Rhod. **22**B:
97–116, 7 ff.

1959 New Dragonflies of the genus *Agriocnemis* and a key to males of the
genus. *Journ. Ent. Soc. S. Africa.*
22: 465–468, ff. 1–12.

PINHEY, E. C. G.   .   1959   Notes on African *Odonata* nymphs. ibid. 469–488, ff. 1–44.

                        1959   A new dragonflv from S. Rhodesia, etc. *Occas. Papers Nat. Mus. S. Rhod.* **23**B: 340–342, ff.

                        1960   Dragonflies collected on an expedition from Rhodesia to Nigeria in 1958. *Ent. Mon. Mag.* **96**: 256–271.

                        1961   A Survey of the Dragonflies of Eastern Africa. *Brit. Mus. (Nat. Hist.)*, London.

RIS, F.   . . .   1909–19 Libellulinen monogr. bearbeitet. Cat. *Col. Zool. Selys.* **9-16**. 1278 pp., ff., pls.

                        1921   The Odonata or Dragonflies of S. Africa. *Ann. S. African Mus.* **18**: 245–445, ff., pls.

                        1931   *Odonata* aus Süd-Angola. *Rev. Suisse Zool.* Genova. **38**: 97–112, ff.

RIS, F. and   . .   1936   Afrikan. Arten, *Pseudagrion. Abh.* SCHMIDT, E.   *Senck. Naturf. Gesch.* **433**: 1–68, ff.

SAINT QUENTIN, D. .   1941   Beiträge z. Kenntniss d. Insektenf. d. D. Ostafr., Matengo-Hochl., H. Zerny. 4 *Odonata*. *Ann. Naturh. Mus. Wien.* **52**: 106–116, 2 ff.

SCHOUTEDEN, H.   .   1934   Cat. raison. d. la Faune ent. Congo Belge. Odonates. *Ann. Mus. Congo Belge. Zool. Sér.* 3 (2) **3** (1): 1–84, ff.

PLATE 1

Some damselflies, *Zygoptera*

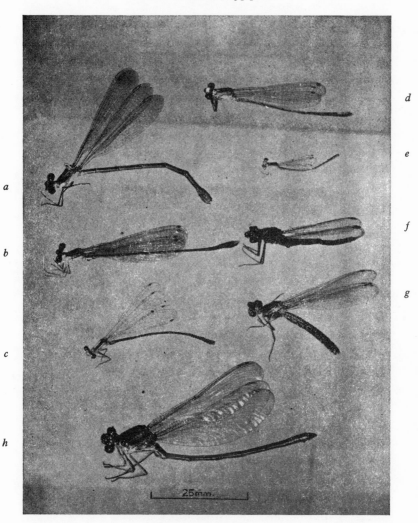

- *a.*   *Lestes amicus* Martin, ♀
- *b.*   *Allocnemis mitwabae* Pinhey, ♂
- *c.*   *Elattoneura glauca* (Selys), ♂
- *d.*   *Pseudagrion kersteni* Gerstaecker, ♂
- *e.*   *Agriocnemis exilis* Selys, ♂
- *f.*   *Platycypha caligata* (Selys), ♂
- *g.*   *P. caligata,* ♀
- *h.*   *Umma distincta* Longfield, ♂

PLATE 2

Miscellaneous Dragonflies

a. *Neurogomphus fuscifrons* Karsch, ♀
b. *Anax bangweuluensis* Kimmins, allotype ♀
c. *Palpopleura jucunda* Rambur, ♂
d. *P. lucia* form *portia* (Drury), ♂
e. *Macromia picta* Selys, ♂
f. *Orthetrum rhodesiae* Pinhey, paratype ♂

PLATE 3

Some *Anisoptera*

a. *Crenigomphus cornutus* Pinhey, ♀
b. *Ictingomphus ferox* (Rambur), ♂
c. *Palpopleura lucia* (Drury), ♂
d. *P. lucia* (Drury), ♀
e. *Hemistigma albipuncta* (Rambur), ♂
f. *Eleuthemis buettikofferi* Ris, ♂
g. *Brachythemis leucosticta* (Burmeister), ♂
h. *Crocothemis erythraea* (Brullé), ♂

[639]

PLATE 4

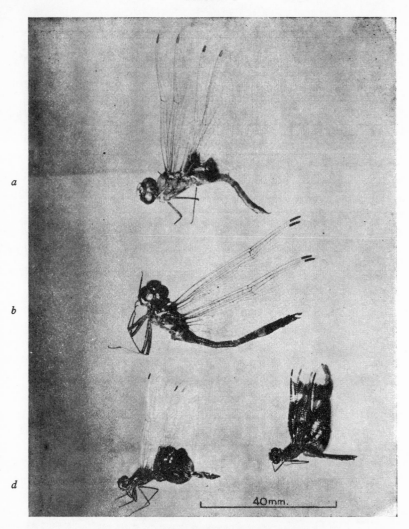

a.   *Trapezostigma basilaris* (Beauvois), ♀

b.   *Zygonyx speciosa* (Karsch), ♂

c.   *Rhyothemis fenestrina* (Rambur), ♂

d.   *Rhyothemis semihyalina* (Desjardins), ♂

[640]

PLATE 5

A typical Antlion, *Palpares sparsus* McLachlan, ♂ (Family *Myrmeleonidae*)

50 min

FIGURE A

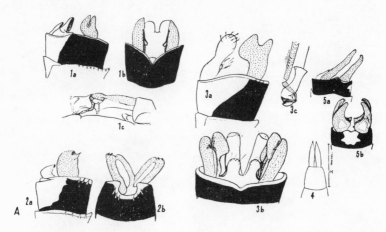

1. *Pseudagrion chongwe* n. sp.
   a. b. anal appendages of male, from right and from above.
   c. penis, from left, and left hamule.

2. *Pseudagrion deningi* n. sp.
   a, b. anal appendages, from right and from above (in dorsal view the inferiors are not visible).

3. *Pseudagrion fisheri* n. sp.
   a, b. anal appendages, from right and from above.
   c. penis, from left.

4. *Pseudagrion greeni* Pinhey. Cerci and 10th segment of female, from above.

5. *Chlorocnemis lascellesi* n. sp.
   a, b. anal appendages of male, from right and from above.

FIGURE B

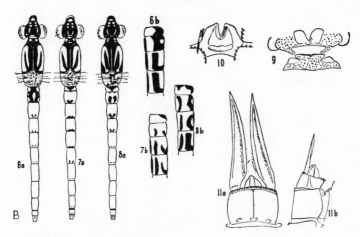

6. *Chlorocypha luminosa* (Karsch).
   a. male (not mature), from above.
   b. basal segments of female, from left.

7. *Chlorocypha frigida* n. sp.
   a. male, from above.
   b. basal segments of female, from left.

8. *Chlorocypha fabamacula* n. sp.
   a. male, from above.
   b. basal segments of female, from left.

9. *Allocnemis mitwabae* Pinhey. Posterior lobe of prothorax (with stylets) and anterior part of mesothorax, from above.

10. *Onychogomphus kitchingmani* Pinhey. Female vulvar scale.

11. *Anax bangweuluensis* Kimmins.
    a. 10th segment and cerci of female, from above.
    b. 9–10 and cerci, from left (less enlarged).

FIGURE C

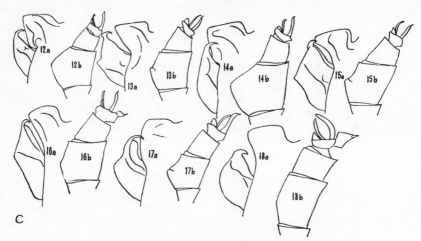

C

Macromia. Accessory genitalia of males, (*a*) from right; *b*. terminal segments and anal appendages, from right (less enlarged):

12. *africana.*
13. *? overlaeti.*
14. *subtropicalis.*
15. *congolica.*
16. *picta.*
17. ⸱ *sylvatica.*
18. *onerata.*

FIGURE D

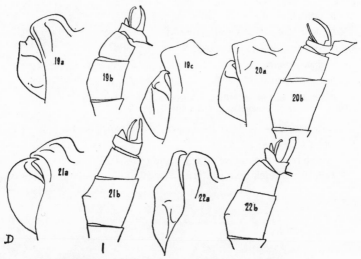

D

Macromia. Accessory genitalia of males (*a, c*), from right; *b*. terminal segments and anal appendages, from right (less enlarged):

19. *monoceros:* *a, b.* ex Mwinilunga; *c.* ex Moçambique.
20. *unifasciata.*
21. *reginae* (*bifasciata* very similar).
22. *kimminsi.*

[644]

FIGURE E

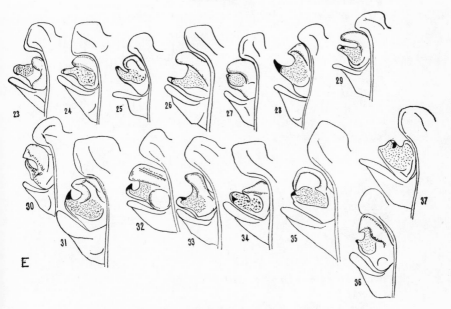

Orthetrum. Accessory genitalia of males, from right:

23. *caffrum.*	28. *macrostigma.*	33. *falsum falsum.*
24. *chrysostigma.*	29. *guineense.*	34. *microstigma.*
25. *abbotti.*	30. *rhodesiae.*	35. *brachiale.*
26. *machadoi.*	31. *stemmale kalai.*	36. *icteromelas.*
27. *hintzi.*	32. *julia.*	37. *trinacria.*

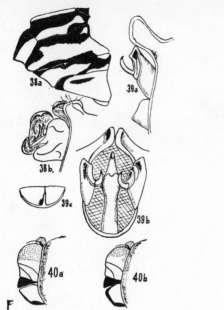

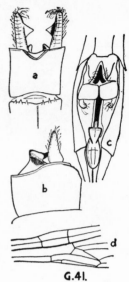

FIGURE F

38. *Neodythemis fitzgeraldi* n. sp. Male.
    a. thorax, from left.
    b. accessory genitalia, from right, latero-ventrally.

39. *Crocothemis brevistigma* n. sp.
    a, b. accessory genitalia of male, from right and from below.
    c. vulvar scale of female.

40. *Zygonyx flavicosta* (Sjoestedt). Face of male, from left:
    a. flavicosta flavicosta Sjoestedt.
    b. flavicosta mwinilungae n. ssp.

FIGURE G

41. *Ceriagrion katamborae* n. sp. Male.
    a, b. anal appendages, from above and from right.
    c. second abdominal segment, from below.
    d. base of right forewing with abnormal cross-vein.

[646]

H 42

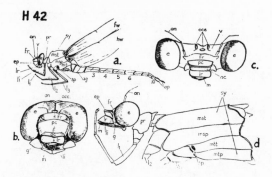

42. Structure of the dragonfly body.

   a, b. An Anisopteran dragonfly, *Anax speratus,* male and an enlarged view of its face.

   c, d. A damselfly, *Pseudagrion kersteni,* face; head and thorax.

        ac—anteclypeus.

        ag—accessory genitalia on segment 2.

        an—antenna.

        ap—anal appendages (superior and inferior).

        e—compound eye.

        ep—epistome (ante- and post-clypeus).

        fr—frons.

        fw—forewing.

        g—gena.

        hw—hindwing.

        l_1, l_2, l_3—legs.

        li—labium.

        lr—labrum.

        m—mandible.

        msp—mesepimeron.

        mst—mesepisternum.

        mtp—metepimeron.

        mtt—metepisternum.

        occ—occiput.

        oce—ocelli.

        pc—post-clypeus.

        pr—prothorax.

        sp—thoracic spiracle or breathing pore.

        sy—synthorax.

        v—vertex.

        3, 4, 5—abdominal segments.

FIGURE I

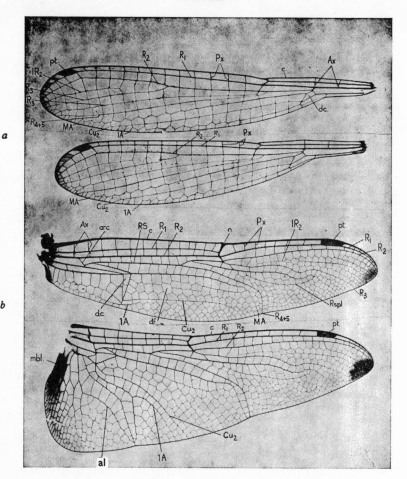

43. Wing venation.

    a. A Zygopteran dragonfly, *Pseudagrion kersteni.*

    b. An Anisopteran, *Pantala flavescens.*

        arc—arculus.

        mbl—membranule.

        n—nodus.

        pt—pterostigma.

NOTE—Other lettering in text, pp. 6-7.

15

LUNDA MEDICINE AND THE TREATMENT OF DISEASE

V. W. TURNER

1963

PREFACE

Dr. V. W. Turner, who is at present a Lecturer in the University of Manchester, is an authority on the Ndembu people of the Mwinilunga District of Northern Rhodesia among whom he worked for nearly two and a half years between 1950 and 1954 when he was a Research Officer on the staff of the Rhodes-Livingstone Institute. The monograph *Schism and Continuity in an African Society* (1957) that resulted from this field study is already well known, and has proved a valuable contribution to our knowledge of the Ndembu.

This present paper is one of a number that Dr. Turner has produced since 1957 on various aspects of Ndembu culture not fully covered in his main work. In this paper he examines not only the causes, symptoms, treatment and effects of a considerable number of ailments, both physical and otherwise, but also Ndembu concepts and explanations of these diseases.

As a detailed catalogue of Bantu diseases this paper adds considerably to our knowledge of the cultures of Central Africa. Dr. Turner's approach to the subject, however, provides more than a catalogue; it gives us an insight into the idea behind Ndembu therapy and as such is a valuable contribution to the study of Bantu medicine as a whole.

GERVAS CLAY.

LIVINGSTONE,
July, 1963.

ETHNOGRAPHIC INTRODUCTION

The people whose medical practices are described in this Paper are the Ndembu of Mwinilunga District in the extreme north-west of Northern Rhodesia.[1] They are a branch of the Southern Lunda—and indeed often speak of themselves as " Lunda "—who are thought to be descendants of seventeenth century emigrants from the North Lunda kingdom, not long after the establishment of the important Mwata Yamvo dynasty there under Luban influence. The Lunda kingdom, cradle of the Lunda peoples, is on the Bushimaie River in the present Kapanga Territory.

Today the Ndembu number about 17,000 at a density of about six per square mile. They inhabit the western portion of Mwinilunga District between the West Lunga River and the Angolan border, approximately between 11 degrees and 12 degrees south latitude. The Ndembu territory comprises woodland and grassy plain, having high rainfall and a network of rivers, many of which originate in the district on the Congo–Zambezi watershed. There is shifting hoe cultivation of cassava, millet, maize, and a variety of garden crops; more fertile streamside gardens are also used for maize. Male hunting was traditionally of great importance but has declined under modern conditions. The Ndembu have few cattle, but keep some chickens and goats. Villages have traditionally moved every four or five years to new sites, perhaps because of hunting as well as shifting cultivation, but the spread of kimberley brick housing is markedly stabilising residence.

Ndembu villages are usually small, compact and circular in shape. They are based on a core of matrilineally related kin, with spouses, small children and dependants. The village headman belongs to the nuclear matrilineage. Kanongesha is Senior Chief and he has four sub-chiefs under his authority.

---

[1] I am grateful to the Center for Advanced Studies in the Behavioral Sciences (Ford Foundation) for providing me with the opportunity to write up these notes.

I am greatly indebted to Mr. Barrie Reynolds, Keeper of Ethnography at the Rhodes-Livingstone Museum, not only for personal encouragement in a field of data marginal to my main research, but also for enlisting the generous help of Mr. D. B. Fanshawe, Principal Scientific Officer in the Northern Rhodesia Forest Department, and of Dr. D. A. Cahal, formerly Regional Scientific Director in London of the Squibb Institute for Medical Research. These specialists, by commenting on botanical and medical aspects of the paper, have considerably strengthened its presentation.

I. LUNDA MEDICINE AND THE TREATMENT OF DISEASE

In an illuminating appraisal of the literature on disease and treatment in primitive medicine,[1] Erwin Ackerknecht has pointed out that "most data on treatment, in general ethnographic monographs, consist of a list of drugs or other techniques used, of a list of the diseases in which they are applied, and of statements as to the possible objective effect that such measures have. It is obvious that such descriptions, valuable as they are, omit just the points needed for our special inquiry: *what are the ideas underlying these therapeutic acts, and under what circumstances (with or without ritual) are they performed?* "[2] Since Ackerknecht wrote, there have been several praiseworthy attempts to answer his queries,[3] directly or by implication, but by and large there have been few systematic discussions of the relationship between the treatment of disease and the religious beliefs, ideas and practices of a specific tribal society.

I am painfully aware that my own data on the treatment of disease, collected intermittently in the form of *ad hoc* observations and accounts by informants of varying intelligence and knowledge of tribal therapy, are relatively scanty and have many *lacunae*, but they are enough to demonstrate that Ndembu healing procedures are governed by the same principles and modes of classification as their religious rites and moral concepts. In this paper I am not primarily concerned with the familiar problem of the extent to which primitive medicine is magico-religious or rational, for I am not a medical man and cannot say with authority just how " effective " a given procedure has been. My aim here is to reveal the ideas implicit in the Ndembu treatment of disease and to show that these ideas pervade wider realms of belief and action.

DISEASE, MISFORTUNE AND AFFLICTION

In the first place Ndembu conceive disease or illness (*musong'u*) as a species of misfortune (*malwa, kuhalwa, kuyindama* or *kubula kutooka*— this last term signifying " to lack whiteness or luck or purity "). Misfortune is a class term of which other species include: bad luck at hunting, reproductive disorders, physical accidents and the loss of property. It might be argued that words such as " misfortune ",

---

[1] Ackerknecht, E. H., " Natural Diseases and Rational Treatment in Primitive Medicine", *Bulletin of the History of Medicine*, Vol. XIX, No. 5, May 1946, p. 471.

[2] My italics.

[3] E.g., in the field of African studies there have been analyses of tribal therapies by Monica Wilson, S. F. Nadel and Michael Gelfand.

" accident ", " bad luck ", " mischance " are erroneous translations of *malwa* and its synonyms, for there is indeed no concept of " accident " among the Ndembu, who seek to find a cause for every calamity—far from being " prelogical ", they are obsessively logical, though on the basis of mystical premises, as Evans-Pritchard showed us in his classical study of Azande systems of belief.[1] The Ndembu, like the Azande, consider that calamities and adversities of all kinds are caused by mystical forces generated or evoked and directed by conscious agents. These agents may be alive or dead, human or extra-human. They may operate directly on their victims or indirectly through mystical intermediaries. Ancestral spirits cause suffering directly; living sorcerers and witches work evil through medicines or familiars or through a combination of both. A person may also raise a " zombie " or " wraith " (*musalu*), an evil component of the personality which persists after death, by means of a curse and send it to kill someone against whom he has a grudge (*chitela*). But ancestral spirits, witches, sorcerers and utterers of curses are not regarded as the sole causes of illness. For Ndembu talk of different kinds of " *nyisong'u* ", " illnesses " or " diseases " and recognise that specific symptoms are connected with each of them. At first I assumed that the Ndembu regarded these *nyisong'u* merely as conditions of the body and that they had been influenced in this respect by European notions. But when I enquired further I found that the *nyisong'u* appeared to be endowed with independent life and that part of the therapy consisted in using " bitter ", " hot " or evil-smelling herbs to disgust and disconcert the *musong'u* and drive it away.

Yet Ndembu speak as though sorcery and witchcraft were always in the background where illness is concerned. Some sicknesses are so common that the element of the untoward which makes people immediately suspect sorcery or witchcraft is lacking. Nevertheless, if these become exceptionally severe or protracted, suspicion grows. There are certain classes of calamities which are believed *a priori* to have ancestral spirits as their probable cause. These are female reproductive troubles, including menstrual disorders, frequent miscarriage and still-birth, and lack of success at hunting. Illness may or may not be caused by ancestral spirits. If the patient dreams of dead relatives while he is sick, the probability is that he is being afflicted by an ancestral spirit. But the possibility of sorcery or witchcraft cannot be ruled out even here, for these evildoers are notorious deceivers and illusionists. Thus it is usual for the relatives of a person who has had a lengthy illness accompanied by frequent dreams to seek out a diviner. The diviner, by means

---

[1] E. E. Evans-Pritchard, *Witchcraft, Oracles and Magic among the Azande*, Oxford University Press (1937).

[653]

of one or another of various techniques,[1] diagnoses a mystical cause as responsible and a rite is performed either to propitiate a specific manifestation of an ancestral spirit or to exorcise the familiars of sorcery or witchcraft.

But consulting a diviner and sponsoring a curative rite are both costly and troublesome for marginal subsistence-cultivators, and there are many herbalists and lay-healers in the villages who claim to be able to dispel *nyisong'u*, whether these are associated with spirits and witches or not. Some Ndembu believe that *all* ailments are mystically caused but that most are brought on by " only little grudges " and can be dealt with by local herbalists in their early stages. For it is thought that the familiars of witchcraft and sorcery are activated only by sudden violent anger or by long-cherished, smouldering " grudges " (*yitela*), resulting from some affront or the product of jealousy or envy. A minor grudge or quarrel might induce a sorcerer to send a minor ailment against his rival. But in this case there is little public interest in " who did it ? " It is mainly a matter for the patient and his close kin and affines who desire the restoration of his health.

Some illnesses are believed to be caused by the breach of a ritual prohibition which is disclosed by the nature of its symptoms. For example, leprosy (*mbumba*) is thought to be the result of transgressing one of the taboos of *Mukanda*, the boys' circumcision ceremony. A form of fever, associated with foaming at the mouth and believed to attack only young children, is said to be caused by eating the meat of the hyrax (*chibatata*) or wild pig (*chombu*). Other diseases, such as elephant-iasis of the scrotum, may result, according to Ndembu ideas, from coming in contact with protective medicine against adultery—though it is conceded that the disease may not always have this cause, for a new-born child may have it.

Other diseases again, such as tuberculosis (*musong'u wantulu*, " the disease of the chest ") and dysentery (*kapokota*) are held to have been imported by the Europeans, though treatments based on traditional Ndembu pharmacological principles have been developed to cope with them, as we shall see. These may or may not be connected by Ndembu with indigenous notions of witchcraft or spirit possession. In the case of severe tuberculosis the rite of *Tukuka*, introduced from the Chokwe and Luvale territories, is often performed. Its aim is to propitiate the souls of living aliens, but principally those of Europeans, which are believed to fly about at night, to possess Ndembu, causing them to

---

[1] *See* my *Ndembu Divination: Its Symbolism and Techniques*, Rhodes-Livingstone Paper No. 31, Manchester University Press (1961).

tremble violently, and to feed on their lungs.[1] Nevertheless, before Ndembu have recourse to *Tukuka* specialists, they treat tuberculosis as if it were *musong'u* with herbal and other kinds of " medicines ".

Ackerknecht[2] has shown that of the diseases regarded as " natural " by primitives, three groups seem to stand out: " the very slight diseases (colds); the very common diseases (old age, tuberculosis, venereal diseases, malaria, filariasis, yaws, food poisoning, sun-stroke, skin diseases); and the diseases imported by the Whites ". Children's diseases are often added to group 2 (the very common diseases). The word " natural " is not apposite here, for Ndembu do not distinguish, as we do, between natural and super-natural orders. For them there is only a single cosmic order, though some parts of it are " quite clear " and others are " dark " and obscure, some things are visible and others cannot be seen. The process of therapy, as we shall see, is partly a process of making hidden and secret things visible, and thereby accessible, if they are harmful, to redressive and remedial action. But Ackerknecht's formulation would fit the Ndembu facts if we substituted for " natural diseases " the phrase " diseases in their own right ", i.e. not as brought on by spirits or witches. Perhaps the only instance of disease regarded as inexplicable in its origin, if not natural, is the influenza epidemic of 1918 which followed the First World War and swept destructively through Ndembu territory, as it did through the rest of the world.

Colour Symbolism, Medicines and Treatment

The classification of reality in terms of the tripartite colour division between white, red and black, which I have discussed elsewhere,[3] is also of crucial importance in therapeutic procedures. For among the many senses of whiteness are: strength (*wukolu*), life (*wumi*), health (*kuhanda*), making visible (*kusolola*), sweeping clean (*kukomba*) and washing (impurities from) oneself (*kuwela*). It also stands for " prosperity " and " freedom from misfortune ". Thus the state of health is a " white ", " clean " and " pure " state. The state of ill health is on the contrary a " black " state, and indeed one of the attributes of blackness is " having diseases " (*yikweti yikatu*—from the verb *kukata*,

---

[1] H. Baumann, *Lunda: Bei Bauern und Jägern in Inner-Angola*, Berlin: Würfel-Verlag (1935), pp. 205–6, mentions that the Chokwe themselves connect *Tukuka* with Europeans, and that two clay models of bellows (representing lungs ?) " are important for the cult."

[2] Ackerknecht, *op. cit.* (1946), p. 472.

[3] (*a*) " Ritual Symbolism, Morality and Social Structure among the Ndembu ", *Human Problems in British Central Africa;* Rhodes-Livingstone Journal XXX (December 1961), pp. 9–10; (*b*) " Three Symbols of Passage in Ndembu Initiation Ritual", *Essays on the Ritual of Social Relations*, Ed. M. Gluckman, Manchester University Press (1962).

" to be ill "—*yikatu* is synonymous with *musong'u*). " Black " is also to " lack luck " (*kubula kutooka*) or " purity ", to have " sufferings " (*yihung'u*) and " misfortune " (*malwa*). It also represents " darkness " (*mwidima*) and " what is secret " (*chakujinda*) or " what is hidden " (*chakusweka*). One of the aims of therapy, therefore, is to restore to the patient who is in a " black " state, his former " whiteness ". Symbolic actions directed to that end include sweeping the patient's body with a medicine broom to get rid of the " impure things " on it or in it and washing him with decoctions of pounded herbs. Some medicines are literally " white " substances, made from plants with white bark, wood, roots or fruits, or from birds or animals with white feathers or fur. Others have analogous qualities to " whiteness " or " purity ", like the tree *mukombukombu* (*Tricalysia angolensis* (*Leptactina*)), whose leaves are used in the making of a medicine broom (*chisampu*). The name of this tree is homonymous with *kukomba* (to sweep), and from the name alone, and not from any physical property of the tree—its leaves are small and unsuitable for sweeping—*mukombukombu* has acquired its ritual role as an instrument of purification.

But " to make white " (*kutookisha*) is more than these: it is to make clear and explicit, to leave nothing hidden or confused. The herbal and other " medicines " applied to the patient as potions, lotions or poultices are substances each of which has its own specific " virtue "—each reveals either some aspect of the disease or points forward to some aspect of the desired state of health or " whiteness ". The pharmacopoeia for each disease is nothing less than a description of the disease in symbolic terms and a statement of the attributes of health and wholeness. Behind the symbols and their interpretation lies the pattern of values peculiar to Ndembu, the fundamental frame of their thinking and feeling. Thus the act of treatment is itself a " white " action, directed against the " black " action of the disease.

Redness also has its part to play in therapy, its usual equivocal part. For in some respects, it represents, as we have seen, " power " (*ng'ovu*), " life " (*wumi*), the strength and joy that comes from eating the flesh of animals and the blood-tie linking together matrilineal kin and mother and child. It also stands for murder, necrophagous witchcraft and the impure blood of menstruation. Thus some diseases, in addition to being " black ", also have a " red " lethal character. Bilharzia (*kaseli kamashi*) is such a disease for one of its symptoms is blood (*mashi*) in the urine. The use of certain red medicines in its treatment is therefore appropriate, for these " reveal " the essential character of the disease.

But although this fundamental classification governs the symbolic articles and symbolic actions of Ndembu treatments, nevertheless there are other features to be considered here. Most important is the Ndembu concept of " medicines ". C. M. N. White has outlined the main features of Luvale beliefs in medicines[1] and for the most part his conclusions apply to the Ndembu, who are neighbours of the Luvale. Like the Luvale, Ndembu distinguish between two classes of medicines, *yitumbu* (Luvale *vitumbo*) and *mpelu* (Luvale *lupelo*). White describes the former as " of vegetable or inorganic nature ", and the latter as " organic material ". I would like to distinguish these classes further by the mode of association thought to exist between the symbol and its object and associated concepts. In the case of *yitumbu*, the associative link is dominantly one of sympathy, the symbol shares an aspect of the object's existence or state. For example, the root of the *kapumbwa* plant (*Ancylobothrys amoena*) secretes white gum which resembles pus (*mashina*). *Yitumbu* made from this root is used in the treatment of gonorrhea (*kaseli kamashina*), one symptom of which for Ndembu is the presence of pus in the urine. In the case of *mpelu*, the associative link is one of *contagion*—to borrow a useful term from Sir James Frazer which indicates that the symbol has in fact been part of the object it signifies or has been in close physical contact with it. Thus as part of the *materia medica* employed to cure tuberculosis we find portions of the diaphragm of an antbear (*itandantulu dachibudi*). This animal has a strong chest and *mpelu* taken from it will, so it is believed, strengthen the chest of the patient. Similarly the hair of an albino (*mwabi*) is considered " strengthening ", for an albino is a " white " or auspicious being.

Yitumbu has much the same range of senses as the East Central Bantu term *muti* which Goodall,[2] writing of the Bemba, defined as " medicine, simple, charm, drug, poison (almost entirely prepared from the bark, leaves, wood or roots of trees) ". In the present paper I shall be concerned only with its use as medicine, drug and simple, not as poison or charm.

I propose to describe a series of diseases and their treatments, just as my informants told me of them. In the course of these accounts, we shall encounter different kinds and classes of medicines and ways in which they are applied. It is in these contexts of situation that we shall get to understand their properties and uses best.

INVENTORY OF DISEASES

The following list of diseases makes no claim to completeness or even adequacy, but it represents some of the more common types which

---

[1] *Elements in Luvale Beliefs and Rituals*, Rhodes-Livingstone Paper No. 32, Manchester University Press for the Rhodes-Livingstone Institute (1961), pp. 35–38.

[2] Goodall, E. B. H., *Some Wemba Words*, Oxford University Press (1921), p. 80.

spring readily to the mind of a Kandembu. I give the vernacular term for the disease, informants' comments on its name and symptoms, (*yuma yakutiyayi muntu mumujimba hakukata*) and finally the term by which it is known in English. In this matter of translation I have followed the advice of Dr. Cahal who points out that the *chimbuki* treats symptoms and signs not specific diseases. The vernacular terms correspond to symptoms. Thus *kaseli kamashi* is haematuria, not necessarily bilharzia, although bilharzia may well be the most common cause of haematuria among the Ndembu.

LIST OF COMMON NDEMBU DISEASES

Mbumba yaluzong'a or *mbumba yachula*

" This disease causes people to lose toes and fingers. They have white spots." [Almost certainly leprosy.]

Mbumba yichinana

" Red leprosy." [Possibly yaws.]

Kaseli kamashi

" Blood is seen in the urine." [Haematuria.]

Kaseli kamashina

" There is pus in the urine." [Pyuria.]

Musong'u wantulu

" The disease of the chest; the patient spits blood." [Chest disease (haemoptysis).]

Musong'u wamesesi

" The disease of sore eyes. A cream-coloured liquid, called *mpota* comes out of the eyes. A white film covers the eyes. But only a few go blind with it." [Possibly conjunctivo-keratitis and corneal opacities.]

Musong'u wamatu

" Disease of the ears. Pus comes out of the ear, following earache. The patient may become deaf (*wajika matu*)." [Otitis media.]

Musong'u wevumu

" Disease of the stomach. There are several kinds: (1) Pains in the stomach; (2) inability to defecate; (3) a " running " stomach; (4) " *Kapokota* ", a disease which perforates the intestine. This disease comes from the Northern Rhodesian Copperbelt." [(1) Stomach ache; (2) constipation; (3) diarrhoea; (4) dysentery.]

[658]

Musong'u wakalepa

" The patient cannot move. This disease is incurable, and has been known by Ndembu from time immemorial." [Paralysis.]

Musong'u wakuzaluka

" The patient talks much, sleeps or goes away without giving warning, curses wildly. Once there was a woman called Nyasoneka of Nswana-kamawu Village in Chief Mukang'ala's area. Her illness started with a headache. Then she had great fever. Her relatives thought she had some ordinary illness. After some months she became weak and tired. This was followed by a time when she stole food. Then she grew garrulous and began to tell lies. She did not seem to take any notice of the opinions of others. She took to sleeping in different villages, a night in each. Finally she went away into the bush where she got lost and died—no one found her body. People generally reckoned her to be mad (*kuzaluka*). About four years elapsed from the beginning of her illness to her death." [Insanity.]

Musong'u wanyima

" Disease of the back. The patient feels a pain in the back which gradually grows worse. In bad cases the person's back becomes bent (*wukuheng'a nyima*)." [Backache.]

Musong'u wachinkonya

" This is to fall down in a fit (*kukonya*)." [Epilepsy.]

Musong'u wawansi

" The disease of childhood. First the child cries a lot. This is followed by shivering and fever. After one day it begins to move its limbs convulsively. If the disease started in the morning, it will do this once that day, but on the following day will do it twice or thrice. These limb movements will continue for two or three weeks and then stop. If it goes on for longer the people will think it is epilepsy. This disease is caused by eating the flesh of the hyrax or of the wild pig, for these animals make a bubbling sound and move their limbs independently of their bodies." [?]

Musong'u wakanwa

" Disease of the mouth. It starts with a pain in the gums, with small boils (*mabobela*). The gums become swollen and discharge blood and pus. Teeth drop out." [Pyorrhea.]

[659]

Musong'u wachingongu

" Disease of smallpox. *Tungongu* are small tattoo marks, the raised scars of tattooing, i.e. cheloids. The patient is isolated from the village and treated in the bush (European influence?)." [Probably smallpox with occasionally severe chickenpox being included.]

Musong'u wamutu

" Disease of the head. A person first feels very cold and his head feels very heavy. Then he has pain in his whole body. Sometimes it ends in death. Since much pain is felt in the temples, incisions are made in them and medicines are rubbed in." [Headache with fever.]

Musong'u watupepa

"A person feels sharp pains in his feet, just as when one suddenly withdraws one's feet from the neighbourhood of a hot fire in very cold weather. The pain proceeds up the leg to the hips where it stops. He cannot walk. The cure is to keep the feet warm." [Severe cramps.]

Musong'u wawunonu (also called *musong'u wakaswendi*)

" Pus flows from the genitals, and from the ears, nose and throat." [Possibly Lymphogranuloma venereum.]

Musong'u wampang'a

" It attacks the testicles and causes them to swell." [Swelling of the scrotum, it probably includes hydroceles, hernia, varicoceles as well as elephantiasis.]

Musong'u wanshing'u

"A person feels as though the inside of his neck is broken." [Stiff neck.]

Musong'u wakunong'oka

"A person often falls into a doze." [Possibly sleeping sickness, but may also include encephalitis, some forms of epilepsy and brain tumours.]

II. TREATMENT OF SPECIFIC DISEASES

I now present some accounts of treatments given to me by a number of informants, including Muchona, my best informant on ritual and medicine, Kasonda my cook, Ihembi, a famed doctor and herbalist, Sandombu, the principal " actor " in the " social dramas " of my book *Schism and Continuity*, Chakadyi, a village headman, Windson Kashinakaji, a village schoolmaster, and Winford, a young educated man.

MBUMBA YALUZONG'A, LEPROSY

" Leprosy attacks a woman if she walks in the former site of a circumcision lodge, where the men were making *nfunda* medicine (the major protective medicine of the lodge which contains cindered fore-skins, the urine of apprentice-circumcisers, the ashes of the burnt lodge and of various sacred fires and a number of other highly dangerous symbolic substances). *Mbumba* attacks people in the air where the boys were circumcised (a site known as *ifwilu*, ' the place of dying '). But if your blood can fight *mbumba* you will not be attacked."

CURATIVE PROCEDURE

" First you collect medicines (*kuhuka yitumbu*). The first thing is to go to a former circumcision site (*ifwilu*) to the *mudyi* tree[1] under which *Kambanji* (' War Leader '), the senior novice (a title) was circumcised, and take a single piece of its root.

" Next you go to the streamside evergreen forest (*itu*) where the *mbumba yachula* tree (*Landolphia rubescens*) grows. (This means ' leprosy of the frog ' and refers to the pale mottlings and spots on a frog's skin which resembles the marks of leprosy.) A branch of this tree is cut, and some bark scrapings (*nyemba*) are removed by an axe (*kazemba*) or knife (*mpoku*). These are put either in a potsherd (*chizanda*), a round, flat winnowing basket (*lwalu*) or any kind of discarded basket.

" Next a root (*muzaji* or *muji*) of *kavulawumi* (*Maprounea africana*) is collected. After this they go to the former site of the fire near which the novice *Kambanji* slept at a lodge and take a root from the ground beneath it, of any species. They also take a root of any species from the earth beneath the fire of the novice called *kajika* (' the little-one-who-closes '), who was the last to be circumcised. They then go into the bush to find the tree with white-spotted bark (called *mutondu wamabeng'a*, ' the tree of spots ') and collect bark-scrapings.

---

[1] *Diplorrhyncus condylocarpon*.

" They return, scrape the skin from the roots and burn the bark and root-scrapings they have collected. The ashes are then mixed with castor oil (*imonu*) to form an ointment.

" Now the patient is brought and the doctors (*ayimbuki* or *ayimbanda*) make circular cuts around the sores and patches or spots (*mabeng'a ambumba*) of leprosy. They rub the ointment into these incisions, then rub what is left into the patient's whole body."

COMMENTS

No explanations were given of the significance of these actions and medicines, but it is clear that the main principle underlying the treatment is to collect a number of substances which exhibit sympathetic associations with leprosy, or with boys' circumcision (of which one of the main mystical sanctions is leprosy), and to incinerate these, thereby destroying the disease (by sympathetic magic). This would be in accordance with the principle underlying the burning of the seclusion lodge (*ng'ula*) itself. It is said that " all diseases are burnt if they are thrown into the burning *ng'ula* ", presumably in symbolic guise.

It is interesting that *mudyi*, normally employed in ritual to signify such " good " things as " mother's milk ", " womanhood ", " matriliny " and " tribal custom " should here be connected with leprosy. *Mudyi* is a " white " symbol, according to Ndembu principles of classification, and leprosy is a " white " disease, so that it would appear that whiteness (*wutooka*) is ambivalent in meaning. It is said that if a novice dies during *Mukanda*, no case may be brought against the lodge officials for compensation, since " God (*Nzambi*) took him ". God is represented by white symbols, and it is likely that leprosy, a ritual sanction in other contexts also—if a Paramount Chief's *lukanu* bracelet of royalty is polluted the incumbent will become a leper—is regarded as a divine punishment, a punishment by the *Deus absconditus*.

KASELI KAMASHI, HAEMATURIA
(probably caused by bilharzia)

" Doctors begin to give medicines to the patient when they see that his urine contains blood or pus. If they see blood they know that it is *kaseli kamashi*; if pus, that it is *kaseli kamashina* (gonorrhea)."

CURATIVE PROCEDURE

" Red gum is collected from the *mupuchi* tree (*Brachystegia spiciformis*). Then some roots of the *katunya* tree (*Uvariastrom hexaloboides*) are dug up, which grows on the banks of rivers. Its roots are red.

[662]

They are cut up into small pieces, mixed with *mupuchi* gum and put in water in a clay jug (*mulondu*). The jug is then warmed on a fire and when it is warm the patient drinks this medicine. He goes on taking it at intervals from two days to a week.

" If the patient does not get better the doctor collects the roots of the *wutotu* (*Gardenia imperialis*) and *kansanying'a* shrubs, which grow near rivers or on large termite-hills (*tuwumbu*). These are cut up, mixed with water in a jug, warmed, then drunk by the patient. *Wutotu* has white roots and produces white gum. *Kansanying'a* has white roots and stinks strongly (*kanunka hama*)." Other roots are used in this treatment but the informant who told me of it had forgotten them.

COMMENTS

The beginnings of an explanation appear in this account, for the informant, unsolicited, thought it necessary to mention the colour of the roots and gums employed as medicine. The red medicines seem to refer to the blood passed in the urine. *Wutotu* is used in the treatment of *kaseli kamashina*, thought by Ndembu to be closely connected with *kaseli kamashi*. The basic principle here seems to be homoeopathic; give the patient a medicine which has similar properties to the symptoms of the disease and he will recover. It should be noted that medicine is in this instance taken internally—the *musong'u* affects the internal organs—whereas in the case of leprosy, medicines, representing spotted and discoloured skin, were applied to the body surfaces.

KASELI KAMASHINA, PYURIA

CURATIVE PROCEDURE

The doctor collects and cuts up *wutotu* and *kapumbwa* roots and puts them into an earthenware vessel (*nsaba*) or jug (*mulondu*). Water is added, the pot is warmed and the patient drinks. This is repeated every day for several weeks. If the patient does not recover, the medicines of *kaseli kamashi* are tried.

Sometimes a potion of *mudyi* (*Diplorrhyncus condylocarpon*) and *kajing'a ludi*[1] roots is given.

COMMENTS

It was explained that in the context of " *wumbuki* ", " treatment with medicines ", whitish exudations from trees and shrubs are called

---

[1] This is a creeper with small white, five-pointed starlike flowers. Possibly *Strophanthus welwitschii*. Fanshawe suggests that *Kajing'a ludi* might also be applied to a *Landolphia* or *Apocynaceae* creeper.

mashina, " pus ", while red secretions are called *mashi*, " blood ". The *kapumbwa* plant produces white gum, which drops on the ground and is said to resemble pus. *Mudyi*, of course, secretes a milky latex which in more auspicious ritual contexts represents mother's milk.

MUSONG'U WANTULU, CHEST DISEASE (HAEMOPTYSIS)

CURATIVE PROCEDURE

(a) First potion

" The doctor goes first to an old burrow where red army ants (*nsalafu*) live. He digs and finds roots in it, cuts them up, puts them in a clay jug with water, and gives this potion to the patient to drink."

COMMENTS

An abandoned burrow, now inhabited by the migratory red ants, is known as *itala dawansalafu*, " the hut of the red ants ". Roots that have come in contact with these ants share their characteristics, prominent among which is their sharp, needle-like bite. " The pain in the chest is like the bites of red ants."

CURATIVE PROCEDURE

(b) Second potion

" The doctor locates and cuts up roots of the *mukula* tree (*Pterocarpus angolensis*), and mixes them in a clay jug with (i) the diaphragm of an antbear; (ii) *muhanu* (*Ficus* sp.) roots; (iii) the scale of a pangolin. Water is added, the mixture is warmed, and the patient (*muyeji*) drinks."

INDIGENOUS EXPLANATION

" The *mukula* tree drops red gum; it is the tree of blood (indeed, it has many ritual uses with this significance[1]). It represents the spitting of blood. The diaphragm of an antbear (*itandantulu dachibudi*) is used because the antbear has a strong chest and they want the patient to have a strong chest too. The scale (*ikalu*) of a pangolin (*nkaka*) is put in because the pangolin moves slowly and curls up if it sees anyone coming. A hunter can carry it easily curled up. In the same way the disease can be caught and taken away to die. *Muhanu* roots are used because *muhanu* grows up a hole in another tree—it will break the obstruction in a patient's chest. It does not matter which of these two potions is given first."

---

[1] *See*, for example, my article " Three Symbols of Passage " in *Essays on the Ritual of Social Relations*, Ed. Gluckman, Manchester University (1962).

COMMENTS

Three of the ingredients listed above are classed as *mpelu* (pl. *jipelu*) i.e., as operating by contagious magic. These are the roots from the red ants' nest, and the portions of antbear and pangolin. It would seem logical to a European observer, once he knew that haemoptysis was likened to the biting of red ants, to suppose that the Ndembu used ant-eater medicines to destroy the disease just as ant-eaters consume ants. But no informant gave me this explanation. Moral: One should guess meanings as little as possible and collect native explanations, as Professor Monica Wilson has always urged.[1]

MUSONG'U WAMATU, DISCHARGE FROM THE EARS (OTITIS MEDIA)

CURATIVE PROCEDURE

" Yellowish fruits of the *chikoli* tree (*Strychnos spinosa*) are cut in two, the pulp is stirred up and lukewarm water is poured into the fruit. It is then left to soak in thoroughly. After a time some drops of the juice are allowed to fall into the patient's affected ear.

"Alternatively, bark is scraped from the *mushokotu* tree (*Faurea saligna*), mixed with water in a large clay pot, the mixture is warmed and drops are inserted in the patient's ear."

COMMENTS

No explanations of the use of these vegetable medicines in terms of sympathetic or contagious magic were forthcoming. I have known Ndembu, treated in this way, who asserted strongly that they experienced an improvement in their condition. It is possible that these medicines are employed because they are objectively effective.

MUSONG'U WEVUMU, DISEASE OF THE STOMACH

There are two kinds of this disease. One is for women and one is for children. The kind for women is called *Chisumi* or *Mukung'a*. It affects the stomach in a line that crosses it completely just above the navel in front. A woman may have this pain whether she is expecting a child or not. It is continuous until medicines are given.

The one for children is just called *musong'u wevumu* with no other name.

---

[1] E.g. in the first few pages of *Rituals of Kinship among the Nyakyusa*, London: Oxford University Press (1957).

(a) Chisumi or Mukung'a

" Two old potsherds (*yiząnda*) or cooking pots (*manung'u*) are found in the village and taken by the doctor to a stream. One potsherd is put on either bank of the stream at a place where an old tree has fallen across the water. Bark from the root of any species of tree is scraped off and some scrapings are placed in both potsherds. Then warm water is poured in one, and cold water in the other. After that both potsherds are put on the same side of the stream. The roots used as medicine must go right across the stream. Water must have flowed over and pushed against them.

" When all has been made ready the doctor and his helpers bring a razor (*ntewula*) and make two cuts in the woman's abdomen, one on each side of the navel. Then they fetch cupping horns (*tusumu*)[1] and the doctor (*chimbanda*) sucks (*ku-sumika*) one horn on the abdomen, and one on the woman's back immediately opposite. He waits for a short while, then grasps both horns at once, pulls them off abruptly and empties the blood into the stream.

" Next, the doctor makes an incision at the outer side of each of the two cuts on the patient's abdomen, and others on the outer side of those on her back. The horns are applied and removed as before. Afterwards the doctor takes medicine from the potsherds and rubs it into the cuts. He then tells the patient to return to her village. Meanwhile he remains at the site of the operation and makes a barrage (*kafuza*) across the stream just where he threw in the blood. Then he throws in the potsherds and the dregs of the medicine at the same place. But he does not throw the cupping horns away. When he is ready to go, he pulls the barrage away and releases the water. Everything he has thrown in is completely carried away.

---

[1] These are usually goats' horns with the tips removed. After they have been sucked on over an incision in the patient's body, the open top end is plugged with beeswax by the operator and left for a time before removal. *Tusumu* are used in several rites to suck from a patient's body substances that have been injected into it by magical or mystical means. For example, the upper middle incisor of a dead hunter is believed to " bite " (*ku-suma*) a living relative of that hunter for neglect of his memory or as a punishment for quarrelling between kin. " Biting " means that the tooth burrows beneath the victim's skin causing intolerable pain. It is extracted by the joint action of ritual and cupping. Again, sorcerers are supposed to shoot teeth, pieces of human bone and soil from graves into the bodies of those they wish to kill. They use a miniature gun carved from a human tibia and known as the " night gun " (*wuta wawufuku*).

NOTE.—A full description of night guns and the ways in which they are used may be found in the following: Barrie Reynolds, *Magic Divination and Witchcraft among the Barotse of Northern Rhodesia*, London: Chatto & Windus for the Rhodes-Livingstone Museum (1963).—*Editor*.

"After he has returned to the village with his cupping horns, the doctor goes into the bush and collects the root of the *mwala* tree (*Afzelia quanzensis*), which is very bitter in taste. One large root is taken, cut up and warmed in an earthenware vessel (*nsaba*). It is then given to the patient to drink and she takes it for about a week.

" If there is no improvement he goes to a *mutata* tree (*Securidaca longipedunculata*), digs up and removes one long root which he cuts in pieces. These he puts in a pot with water, warms the medicine and gives it to the patient to drink. This she does for several days until she gets quite better. But if she is still sick, roots of *molu wawubwang'u*[1] are cut up and mixed with the chopped roots of the *kakwema* tree (*Uvaria angolensis* or *Enneastemon schweinforthii*). These are then heated in an earthenware vessel and given to the patient until she gets better, perhaps for as long as two weeks."

INDIGENOUS EXPLANATION

" The name *Chisumi* is from *ku-suma*, ' to bite '. Its other name, *Mukung'a*, is from *ku-kung'ama*, ' to lie across, traverse '. Thus the root used for medicine lies across the stream just as the disease lies across the stomach. *Ku-kung'ika* stands for the piling up of flotsam (*ntotu jahameji*) against the traversing root. This flotsam or rubbish resembles the disease. Medicine is rubbed into the cuts to rid the woman's stomach of the rubbish. When the doctor pulls down the barrage, the disease goes away like the rubbish.

" The bitterness (*kulula*) of the *mwala* root can kill the disease. *Mutata* has a very nasty smell. The woman should drink its medicine to make her stomach smell very much. The disease will smell it and die because of its stink. *Molu wawubwang'u* also has a strong smell to kill the disease. So has *kakwema*. Medicines that are used because they stink (*ku-nunka*) are called ' *yitumbu yanunka* or *yitumbu yevumba* '.

"A disease (*musong'u*) is something which remains alive in the body. If it goes on and on the patient is *wahalwa* or *mukwakuyindama*, an inauspicious person."[2]

---

[1] A creeper found near streams. It is hung around the shoulders of the patient-candidate in the *Wubwang'u* rite performed for mothers of twins—it is supposed also to whiten the milk of a mother who has been yielding " red " or " yellow " milk—the result of some infection of the mammary glands, no doubt.

[2] Ndembu mean many things by these terms. Such a person is (*a*) in a " black ", i.e. impure and unhealthy state; he is (*b*) either afflicted by an ancestral spirit in punishment of his own or of his kin-group's transgressions or is under attack by witchcraft/sorcery. In other words, the *musong'u* has been mystically intensified and is now associated with other malignant agencies.

[667]

This treatment stands on the borderline between the taking of more or less rational therapeutic measures and the performance of a magical rite. The first part of the treatment consists almost entirely of acts in accordance with the principles of sympathetic magic. A pain " crosses " the stomach, which is like a stream in that through it fluids and solids pass, and from it (since it is thought to be continuous with the womb) flow children; hence a doctor goes to a stream with his patient and performs symbolic actions indicative of the removal of obstructions that impede the flow of the water and cause flotsam (=the disease) to pile up. The symbolism of two banks or sides is repeated in another form with the cupping horns—one in front and one at the back of the patient—and in the cutting of incisions on either side of the navel. Some informants connected the treatment with dysmenorrhea for which it was the cure. The disease was believed to hold up the normal flow of the menses and hence to cause temporary sterility, for Ndembu recognise that normal periodicity is a prerequisite of pregnancy. The pain, they feel, is connected with the damming up of the ordinary flow.

The quasi-rational aspect emerges in the second part of the treatment in which potions are given to the patient to drink. Given the premise that the disease is a living entity inhabiting the stomach it is quite rational to suppose that bitter or evil-smelling substances, disliked on the whole by human beings, animals and birds, will drive it away or kill it. I am in full agreement with Ackerknecht's strictures on Malinowski for calling " scientific " the rational elements in primitive medicine,[1] for, as he says: " Practical behaviour is not yet science. A butcher is no scientist. Science, full of disinterested curiosity, aims primarily at truth, not at practical success or psychic relaxation . . . Science is unthinkable without the experiment . . . presupposes a quality of scepticism . . . is a late invention of humanity." This is very different from acting medically, as Rivers[2] pointed out, with perfect logic and rationality, but on the basis of false, supernaturalistic premises. Yet it must be admitted that medicine in our culture relies to a certain extent on suggestion. The General Practitioner in British rural areas administers " nasty " medicines, partly on account of their curative properties and partly to satisfy the patient that they are " strong " enough to " kill " the ailment.

For all I know *mwala* root-juice may be empirically effective in curing stomach-ache, but if this is so, it is effective for the wrong reasons. It is possible that many " medicines " have been tried out by Ndembu

---

[1] *Op. Cit.*, p. 489.

[2] Rivers, W. H. R., *Medicine, Magic and Religion*, London (1924), p. 52.

doctors and some have been found to procure relief. But the next step
has not been to set up a series of carefully controlled experiments to
isolate the substance causing the beneficial effect. Rather it is to examine
the sensorily perceptible attributes of the plant to see which of them
might be regarded as an expression or embodiment of auspicious mystical
powers, or which of them exhibited some virtue opposed to the putative
properties of the disease. It is a question of allocating the item to a
pre-existent category, and not of making new discoveries by the
experimental method.

CURATIVE PROCEDURE

(b) *Musong'u wevumu watwansi*, " *Stomach disease of Children* "

" The doctor collects and cuts up long roots of *kapwipu* (*Swartzia
madagascariensis*) and *musong'asong'a* (or *lusong'wasong'wa*, *Ximenia
americana*). The root-skin (*nyemba*) of *kapwipu* is scraped off on one
day and put in two different potsherds. Hot water is put in one pot of
kapwipu medicine, cold water in the other; the *musong'asong'a* medicine
is dealt with likewise. The doctor and his child-patient then sit under
the *kapwipu* tree from which medicine was obtained and the doctor
makes incisions on the patient's stomach beside the navel and on his
back, just as for *Chisumi*, and applies *tusumu* cupping horns. When a
girdle of horn-scars has been made round the patient's waist, *kapwipu*
medicine is rubbed into them. When all is over, the doctor (*chimbuki*)
buries (*wavumbika* or *wajika*) the potsherd containers, together with the
blood sucked from the patient and kept in a small calabash, in the hole
in the ground left by the long tap root taken for medicine.

" Next day the same process is repeated under the *musong'asong'a*
tree with medicine obtained from that tree.

"Afterwards roots of the *chiputa mazala* tree (*Erythrina tomentosa*)
are cut up into pieces (*yikunku*), put into a clay pot and heated until
lukewarm (*kavuyenki*). The patient is then given this decoction to
drink.

" If the disease continues, *kanshinshi* root medicine is given lukewarm
to the patient as a draught.

" Finally, *kakung'ami* root medicine is given as a lukewarm potion."

INDIGENOUS EXPLANATION

" *Kapwipu* medicine is used because it is a hard tree. Hardness
(*ku-kola*) represents health and strength. *Musong'asong'a* is used for the
same reason. *Chiputa mazala* medicine is given because it has a strong
smell, *kanshinshi* because it has both a strong smell and a bitter taste.

[669]

" *Kakung'ami* is used not only because of its stink, but also because of its bubbling sound (*chilululu*—sounds of flatulence) which drives the disease to one side, so that it no longer lies across the stomach. The disease fears (*watiya woma*) the medicine. If the stomach cannot fight it the disease spreads right over it, but the medicine chases it into one place where it will die.

" When the doctor goes to the *kapwipu* tree, he makes an address (*ku-lang'ula*) before collecting this, the principal (*mukulumpi*) medicine of the treatment. He mentions the doctor who taught him how to administer it, the name of the patient and the circumstances leading up to the treatment."

(*c*) *When men have stomach ache—also called musong'u wevumu*

" The doctor collects, cuts up and puts in a pot with lukewarm water the roots of *katong'a* (*Strychnos cocculoides*), which are very bitter, and gives the potion to the patient to drink.

" *Mulolu* roots (*Annona nana*) may be given as a decoction—because they have a strong smell.

" If the disease continues *chikwata* roots (*Zizyphus mucronata*) may be given as above, because they are a little bitter."

COMMENTS ON (*b*) AND (*c*)

Ackerknecht[1] has observed that blood letting " is effective in some diseases although we do not know why, and have discarded it (in the West), therefore, almost entirely. In most cases its magico-religious ' purificative ' character or its objective to drive out disease demons is obvious ". The use of cupping techniques among the Ndembu would provide an example of " magico-religious " beliefs. In the case of " stomach disease " one of the main aims is to introduce substances possessing mystical power into the body of the patient. Although this was not stated by Ndembu informants, it is probable that there is here some notion of " replacement ". Blood is taken out—and in the case of (*b*) poured into the hole from which the medicine root was removed—and replaced by medicine which it is hoped will force away the disease or give toughness and health to the patient.

We meet once more in these treatments the notion that a disease is animate and vulnerable to obnoxious tastes and smells.

---

[1] *Op. cit.*, p. 482.

MUSONG'U WAMESESI, CONJUNCTIVO-KERATITIS, CORNEAL OPACITIES AND OTHER EYE DISEASES

CURATIVE PROCEDURE

Bark is scraped from the trunk of a *muhuma* tree, and mixed with warm water in a clay pot. The patient's eyes are then bathed in the lotion. If this is not enough, the tiny leaves of *lweng'eng'i* (*Dracaena reflexa*) are crushed between the fingers (a process known as *ku-chikita*), put in a leaf-funnel (*lutotu*) and allowed to drop in the patient's eyes.

Finally, steam treatment may be tried. Leaves of the *wadikalanziza* tree, sometimes known as *kayiza* (*Strychnos stuhlmannii*), are collected, put in a pot with water and heated to the boiling point. The patient covers his head with a blanket and puts his face in the rising steam (*luya*).

INDIGENOUS EXPLANATION

In the case of each of these three medicines informants told me that the efficacy (*ng'ovu*) of the herb is derived from its " bitterness ". " Bitterness " is *wukawu* or the verbal noun *kulula*. Ndembu say that " *wukawu* " can " stick to " (*ku-lamata*) the disease, " like a leach " (*neyi izambu*), until it dies.

One informant gave me a little information about *kayiza*, which might help to identify it correctly. He said, " *Kayiza* is very bitter in taste. It can grow into a big tree. Its fruits when ripe are as black as ink. They blacken your tongue when you eat them. That is why it is called also *wadikalanziza*, from *wadikala*, ' you deny ', for you can't deny eating it since it makes your tongue black ".

MUSONG'U WAKUZALUKA, INSANITY

CURATIVE PROCEDURE

" The doctor first collects old bones of a mad dog. Then he goes to a *musoli* tree (*Vangueriopsis lanciflora*) and collects a root and some leaves. Next he takes a root and leaves of *ikamba dachihamba* (or *musambanjita*) (*Cryptosepalum maraviense*) and a root of *musong'asong'a* (*Ximenia americana*), followed by leafy branches and roots of *mukombukombu* (*Tricalysia angolensis*), *mututambululu* (*Xylopia adoratissima*), and *muhotuhotu* (*Canthium venosum*). Next a root and leaves of *mukanda-china* which grows on termite-hills are collected.

" The doctor then goes to a place where a wild pig (*chombu*) was lying or trampling and there collects grasses and twigs. The doctor and his assistants go to the termite-hill from which they obtained *mukanda-china* (*Rhus longipes*, or possibly *Eriocoelum* sp.) medicine. There they cut up all the roots they have collected, mix them together well and fill two pots (*mazawu*) with the mixture. Old calabashes (*yipwepu*) can be used. Then they add any part of a dead leopard, a piece of wild pig's meat and a mad dog's bone to each pot. These portions are classed as *jipelu*. *Mpelu* from the coney or hyrax (*chibila, chibatata*), the mamba (*ntoka*), the lion (*mutupa*) and of a fish called *muvundu* are also added to the contents of each pot.

" Now water is brought and poured in each *izawu*. There is no pounding of the tree-medicines (*nyitondu*) in a mortar, as is often done. A medicine broom (*chisampu*) is made of the leafy branches of *mukombu-kombu, muhotuhotu, mututambululu* and *musoli*. Both pots contain only cold medicine—the pots must not be warmed. One pot is carried to the top of the termite-hill, the other is left at the foot of it. The patient, the crazy person, is made to kneel while the doctor gives him the medicine to drink, first from the pot at the top of the termitary, then from the one at the bottom. Then he sprinkles the patient's eyes and face with his medicine broom. He repeats this treatment twice a day until the patient is able to say that he has recovered. No drums are played at this treatment."

INDIGENOUS EXPLANATION

" The *musoli* tree is the *ishikenu*, ' the place of greeting ', where an invocation is made. It is the senior of the medicines. It has many edible fruits, yellow and purple, called *nsoli*, much eaten by duiker (*nkayi*) and other antelope from September to November. Its name is from *ku-solola*, ' to reveal '. Here it means ' to make everything clear ' for a mad person does not see things clearly.

" *Musambanjita* used to be a war medicine to make people invulnerable to bullets or spears. Here it does the eyes good, for a person suffering from this disease feels dizzy in the eyes. This medicine clears the eyes.

" *Musong'asong'a* feels bitter (*kutiya wukawu*) to the eyes. This tree produces red edible fruits—*ku-song'a* signifies ' to produce fruits '.

" *Mukandachina* is collected because it has the habit of growing on top of termite-hills. A mad person is like a person who passes above (things). (*Muntu wazaluka wudi neyi muntu wahita kwiwulu.*) He wanders about in the air (*mumpepela*), on the tops of hills and even of trees. He can do nothing in a peaceful way. It is seldom that he talks while sitting, but he talks in the air (*while standing ?*). That is also why a pot of medicine is placed on *top* of a termitary. There is a *mukishi*,[1]

---

[1] *Mukula* or *Kaluwi, see* below, p. 675.

(a manifestation of) an ancestral spirit (in the form of a hunter of long ago), who also behaves like a mad person and ascends to the tops or crests of places.

" *Mpelu* taken from a leopard (*chisumpa*) is used because a leopard is like a madman, and kills for no reason, only for sport (*nakuhema hohu*).

" *Mpelu* of a wild pig is used because it moves about just like a mad person (randomly). So does a coney.

"The *muvundu* fish may swim upside down, it changes its direction, it is a mad fish. Its name is connected with *ku-vundumuka*, ' to pack up and go away without giving any reason '.

" This disease of insanity comes in the air."

The Special Case of Rabies

" If a person has been bitten by a mad dog, he will, in the first instance, be given a medicine to make him vomit.

" The doctor goes to a *kavulawumi* tree (*Maprounea africana*), digs down and exposes the root, and cuts off a piece about six inches long.

" He then scrapes off the skin or bark of the root with the help of an old piece of calabash and puts these scrapings (*nyemba*) in the sunshine to dry. When dry they are pounded into powder (*luseng'a*) in a mortar. The doctor next brings some thin cassava porridge (*kapudyi*), to which he adds the powder, mixing it well in.

" He gives this mixture to the patient to drink. After drinking, the patient vomits very much, and has frequent motions of the bowels.

"Another treatment is to cut up the root of *mudiansefu* (possibly *Craterosiphon quarrei*), which secretes a white gum, add water to the portions in a pot and boil for about a quarter of an hour. While the water is still boiling, *kapudyi* gruel is brought and the medicine is added to it hot. The patient must then drink it while it is still very hot. The medicine stays within a short while, then the patient vomits and excretes at short intervals until his stomach is cleared out.

" These emetics and aperients, *kavulawumi* and *mudiansefu*, are equally strong. If they fail, the full medicines for *musong'u wakuzaluka* (*see* pages 671-2) are used."

INDIGENOUS EXPLANATION

"A person bitten by a mad dog froths at the mouth (*ku-tupula*), just like the dog. Such frothy saliva is called *izeng'i* (singular), while

[673]

ordinary saliva is called *mazeng'i* (plural). ' To foam at the mouth like a madman ' is *kutupula izeng'i-zeng'i*. The poison given to a man by a mad dog is just like arrow-poison (*wulembi*) taken from the *Strophanthus* plant (also *wulembi*)."

The Treatment of Madness as a Rite of Affliction[1]

" The drum (or rite) of mad ancestral spirits (*ng'oma yawakishi akuzaluka*) is ' played ' (performed) if all these medicines fail. It is then supposed that the spirits of people who died insane have ' caught ' (possessed) the patient."

CURATIVE PROCEDURE

My best informant, Muchona,[2] described the rite as follows:

" The relative responsible for the patient [literally the ' owner of the patient ' (*mwenimuyeji*)] starts the proceedings by bringing the doctor (*chimbuki*—as in herbal therapy) a cock or a goat, which may be of any colour. The doctor agrees and fetches *mpelu* made from an ' *mpompa* ' a wooden fetter used to fasten the limbs of madmen, slaves and criminals.

" Next he goes to an old site of the *Mung'ong'i* cult rites[3] and collects five or six roots from any species of tree which grows there. What is important is not the species but the place—the *izembi* shelter of the sacred mysteries. Then he goes to the site of a former circumcision lodge and collects about six roots from the *ifwilu* or ' place of dying ', where the boys are actually circumcised.

" Next, he and his assistants (an assistant or apprentice doctor is called *kadiza*, ' one who is learning ') go to a stream and collect in the gallery forest (*itu*) roots and leaves of the *kaleng'ang'ombi* thornbush.[4] Two clay pots are used, each containing the same

[1] See my *Schism and Continuity*, *op. cit.*, pp. 292–303, for a discussion of this class of rites.

[2] A character sketch of Muchona appears in " Muchona the Hornet, Interpreter of Religion," article in *In the Company of Man*, Ed. J. Casagrande, Harper Brothers, New York (1960), and his interpretations form a considerable part of *Ndembu Divination*, Rhodes-Livingstone Paper No. 31 (1961).

[3] A funerary association which performs elaborate initiation rites on the death of its members. Among the Northern Lunda, or Luunda, it appears to have been connected with male circumcision; but among the Ndembu, and other Southern Lunda and such culturally similar tribes as the Luvale, Chokwe and Luchazi, the circumcision rites, called *Mukanda*, are performed independently of *Mung'ong'i*.

[4] Used as a symbol during the rite accompanying circumcision, and explained in terms of the foundation myth of *Mukanda*. For a fuller account, *see* my " Three Symbols of Passage in Ndembu Ritual ", M. Gluckman, Ed., *Essays on the Ritual of Social Relations*, Manchester University Press (1962).

medicine. One *izawu* pot is taken to the top of a termite-hill (*kawumbu*), the other is left on the ground. Then the goat's throat is cut and its blood poured in each pot. The pots contain cut and pounded roots collected by the doctor.

" Next the patient drinks from both pots. The whole following night is spent in splashing medicine (*ku-kupula*) on the patient's body, washing it with medicine and giving him a medicine draught at intervals.

" Drums are played near the medicine pot on the ground. The site is in the bush not far from the village. They begin by singing *Mung'ong'i* songs, then *Mukanda* songs, and follow these with songs from the *Kayong'u* rite[1]—performed to propitiate an ancestral spirit which causes chest trouble and confers the power to divine by tossing symbolic objects in a basket—and from the *Kaluwi* rite,[2] performed to placate a particularly troublesome manifestation of a hunter ancestor. These spirits are regarded as ' mad ' (*akuzaluka*), for they make those possessed[3] by them jerk about convulsively (*ku-zakuka*). Both patient and doctor jerk and shiver. The doctor must treat himself with medicine along with the patient otherwise the mad spirit may possess him also. When he shivers the spirit is temporarily in him too.

"After drumming, the doctor continues to administer these medicines to the patient, for days or maybe weeks, until he is better."

COMMENTS

It is interesting to note in what respects the treatment of insanity as a " disease " (*musong'u*) resembles the *rite* of affliction, where madness is regarded as a sign and symptom of affliction by an ancestral spirit. Both procedures stress the opposition of " above " and " below " (*hewulu* as opposed to *hamaseki*, literally " in the air " and " on the ground "), both take place on and near termite-hills, both involve the splashing of the patient—although Muchona did not mention the collection of the usual components of a medicine broom, *mukombu-kombu*, *muhotuhotu* and *mututambululu* fronds, this was probably done before the affliction rite.

---

[1] *Ndembu Divination, op. cit.*, pp. 23–26.

[2] Or *Mukala* rite—mentioned in my article " Themes in the Symbolism of Ndembu Hunting Ritual", *Anthropological Quarterly*, Vol. 35, No. 2 (April, 1962), p.51.

[3] Ndembu say " *waheta mukishi*," " you have a spirit," when they wish to indicate possession by a spirit. Often, too, they speak of a spirit which " catches " (*wakwata*) a patient.

But there are also profound differences between them, for the rite deals with the spirit of a deceased kinsman as well as with a disease. Since ancestral spirits are said " to be pleased by the playing of drums ", drumming and singing must accompany the administration of medicines. Indeed, among the objects in a diviner's basket a piece of wood crudely carved to represent a drum stands for " rites to propitiate ancestral spirits."[1]

The slaughter of an animal or fowl is another recurrent feature of rites of affliction that is not found in the direct treatment of disease. It is not always easy to see such slaughters as " sacrifices ", for often the animal or chicken represents the ancestral spirit himself: If there is sacrifice, it is a sacrifice (in symbolic guise) *of* the ancestor, not *to* the ancestor; on behalf of the ritual participants and as a sign of reconciliation and communion between the spirit and his kin. Nevertheless, however it may be regarded, the slaughter of an animal is a characteristic feature of manistic rites among the Ndembu.

There may be a connection with the slaughter of a goat at this rite and at *Kayong'u*. At *Kayong'u*, too, a cock is slaughtered by the patient himself, who bites the bird's head off. About this act Muchona said:[2] " *Kayong'u* makes a person a little mad. He feels as if he were drunk or epileptic." It looks as though the spirit responsible for insanity were a species of the *Kayong'u* manifestation. The classical association between soothsaying and madness is made in a tribal milieu, for *Kayong'u* is usually regarded as the mode of affliction assumed by a dead diviner's spirit.

This comparison of treatment and rite enables us to see that a " rite of affliction " is a combination of *therapy*, aimed at treating the pathological condition (cataract, madness, reproductive disorder) and *religious service* (veneration and propitiation of ancestral spirits). There has been a considerable fusion of these procedures, so that some *medicines* have become *symbols* for modes of spirit manifestation, while something of the " law " bound character of magic has influenced the relationship held to exist between ancestral spirits and their living kin. Thus it seems to be assumed that if one collects the medicines appropriate to a rite and applies them correctly, the ancestral spirit is more or less *compelled* to stop afflicting the patient. This situation differs at any rate from invocations made to village shrine-trees, outside the rite of affliction context, in which appeals are made to ancestors to " change their livers " (i.e. " minds ") and cease causing trouble to their relatives. Here " freewill " apparently prevails over " necessity ".

---

[1] *Ndembu Divination, op. cit.*, p. 65.
[2] *Ibid.*, p. 32.

MUSONG'U WANYIMA, BACKACHE

(a) " The doctor takes part of a broken hoe blade. Then he goes to a tree that has been struck by lightning and takes a portion of the splintered wood. After that he goes to an old village site to the place where a mortar once stood for pounding cassava roots and grain. There he digs and removes the first root he finds—of any species of tree.

" He now brings the patient and makes him lie under a *mudyi* tree (*Diplorrhyncus condylocarpon*) that is naturally bent. With his knife, he scrapes off bark from underneath the bend in the tree. Then he collects some bark scrapings (*nyemba*) from the upper side. His next task is to place a pounding pole (*mwishi*) at right angles to the tree. He then adds to the medicine in his basket (*lwalu*—a flat round winnowing basket) some scrapings from the top of a tortoise's shell.

" The patient is then allowed to leave the *mudyi* site for a moment while the doctor brings a potsherd (*chizanda*) in which he puts red *ing'aji* oil (palm oil?). He scrapes some iron dust from the broken hoe on to the oil. Then he burns the piece of lightning-struck tree and adds its ash to the mixture. In go the tortoise shell scrapings and finally the *nyemba* of the *mudyi* tree. The medicine is thoroughly mixed with the oil.

" The doctor then makes two or three lines of small incisions across the small of the patient's back, where the pain is, with his razor (*ntewula*). When the blood begins to ooze, the doctor rubs the medicine into those cuts. The medicine goes into the blood right to the part where the pain is felt.

" When that is done, the doctor takes the pounding pole (*mwishi*) and presses (*ku-kanda*) it on the patient's back where the incisions are. The doctor presses the pestle lengthw'se on the back with both hands. He then puts the razor and medicines in a pot and removes them from the scene.

" Now the doctor tells the patient to hold the pounding pole up vertically and to go under the crook in the *mudyi* tree once more. The patient must then straighten himself up, with the help of the pounding pole, and push the *mudyi* up with his back (a process known as *ku-dyikanda*).

" Now he must address the tree (*ku-subwila mutondu*) as follows: ' I have already left this disease with you (*nakushiyili dehi musong'u*). I must go home feeling no more pain, because I have left it already with you.' Then the patient returns home bearing the pounding pole."

(b) *Another Treatment.* " The doctor goes in the early morning to where a mortar stands. He gets women to shift its position, digs down and removes a piece of any root he finds there. Then he scrapes some dirt from the base of the mortar itself. He mixes the scrapings from the root and the earth scrapings with castor oil (*imonu*) or palm oil (*ing'aji*) in a potsherd.

" Next he makes the patient lie across the hole where he removed the root at the former site of the mortar. Then he makes three lines of cuts with his razor across the patient's back where he felt pain, and rubs medicine into the incisions. After that, he orders the patient to pull himself upright by means of the pounding pole that usually goes with the mortar. He must then walk to his hut. He must leave the pounding pole upright[1] against a tree near his hut, and never let it lie on its side."

INDIGENOUS EXPLANATION OF (a) AND (b)

In the first of these treatments " the doctor took a broken hoe blade because hoe blades snap suddenly (*koto-o*) when people are digging. In the same way a person with backache (lumbago) feels as though he has suddenly been broken.

"A meal mortar is used because of the pounding (*ku-twa*). This represents ' hitting '. Having backache is like being hit very hard.

"A tortoise shell is used because a tortoise has a hard shell and a hard body, so he never feels backache. Its medicine strengthens the back.

" The *mudyi* tree has white gum, so it is a white or lucky tree. The patient leaves bad things with *mudyi*, and its whiteness gives him health (*wukolu*)."

In the second treatment the earth from the mortar " is a kind of *mpelu* for strengthening (*nakukolesha*) ".

NOTE ON LIGHTNING (*Nzaji*)

"A lightning-smitten tree is used because lightning gives a sudden shock (expressed by the ideophone *bele-e*). ' To strike ' is *kw-anda*. ' Thunder ' is *chivumina*, ' to thunder ' *ku-vuma* or *ku-dulumwina*. Lightning is an animal. A mole-rat (*mpumba*) makes a sound similar to that of thunder. The lightning grows jealous and tries to hit the mole-rat and kill it. That is why lightning follows the holes and ' hills ' of mole-rats all the way along."

---

[1] To lean upright is *ku-kunjika*.

This treatment appears to be almost entirely magical. In less severe cases it is possible to imagine that there may be some psychological benefit.

MUSONG'U WACHINKONYA, EPILEPSY

CURATIVE PROCEDURE

" The doctor goes first to a *museng'u* tree (*Ochna pulchra*) and collects leaves which are rolled up into a curl backward from the tip (*mafu adikonya adivung'a mafunda*) to form bundles (*mafunda*).

" Next he brings an old calabash cut across (*chipwepu*) and puts into it both pounded and unpounded *museng'u* leaves. He then adds several kinds of *mpelu*:

(1) a portion of coney or hyrax (*chibatata*);

(2) a piece of the beak of a *samunkambu* bird;

(3) the scale of a pangolin.

" The doctor then takes a reed (*iteti*) and blows into it to make the water (which contains all these ingredients) bubble (*wapepa mwiteti nakubukumwina meji*). At intervals he washes the patient's face with the bubbling, foaming water.

" If this treatment fails after several days, the doctor collects the same kinds of *jipelu*, then goes to a *mulendi* tree (*Sterculia quinqueloba*) and cuts from it a part of a root. Then he goes to a place where a lion, leopard or wild pig has scratched and collects grass scratched by their claws or hooves. He brings along another *chipwepu* calabash, cuts the *mulendi* roots into pieces and adds them to cold water in the *chipwepu*. Then he puts all the *jipelu* (including those of the previous treatment) in the medicine, adding thereto the scratched grass, and takes the *chipwepu* to the village ash pile (*izalelu*). He puts it on top of the ash pile and gives the patient medicine to drink from his cupped hand. After this, he washes the face, head and chest of the patient, and repeats the treatment for several days."

INDIGENOUS EXPLANATION

" *Museng'u* is used because the epileptic patient shoots out his arms, then folds them again like curled *museng'u* leaves.

" *Chibatata* (*mpelu*) is used because it is made animal or like an epileptic.

[679]

PLATE I

Doctors (*ayimbuki*) collect medicines in the bush. The doctor on the left holds a flat round winnowing basket (*lwalu*) in the left hand. He has just cut some bark chips with the axe on his right shoulder. The right hand is the hand of masculinity, fatherhood and authority; the left hand represents femininity, motherhood and docility. Note the lush variety of plant species. The doctor has a wide knowledge of the virtues and magical properties of plants. The doctor to the right is rubbing a stridulator (*ndamba*), a musical instrument consecrated to the veneration of the spirits of hunters

PLATE II

The paraphernalia of a curative rite. The patient is on the left; cupping horns (*tusumu*) are affixed to her back. Each is stoppered with beeswax. In the centre is a temporary shrine erected to ancestral spirits. A variety of medicine containers may be seen, ranging from locally made clay pots to store-bought mugs. The skin on a drumhead is being warmed over a ritual fire, both to make it taut for playing and to imbue it with the virtue of the fire. Notice how the patient is spattered with medicine leaves, splashed on to her by doctors with their medicine brooms. The leaf covering the pot in the foreground is of the castor oil plant, which is used in many rites

PLATE III

A patient sits on a stool during treatment. Over her shoulders is draped a
portion of the Gallery Forest creeper *moluwawubwang'u*. Traces of medicines
with which she has been splashed may be seen on her back and head, and medicine
leaves are strewn on the ground. *Moluwawubwang'u* is used to produce a good
supply of milk in an expectant mother. On the left, one doctor leaps under
another's legs, a symbolic action representing fertility. A calabash of water for
mixing with pounded leaf medicine is on the right

PLATE IV

The marks left on a patient's back by cupping horns immediately after their
removal. Medicines also adhere to the skin

" *Samunkambu* is a bird which flies up and down spasmodically, like an epileptic, making a whirring sound.

" The pangolin (*nkaka*) curls itself into a ball like an epileptic's spasm.

" The doctor blows through the reed so that the foam rises (*kulonda kafulolu[1] kanyamuki*), like the foam on an epileptic's lips.

" *Mulendi* is a very slippery or glossy (=*senena*) tree, difficult to climb. The patient's disease will slip down and fall just like the climber of *mulendi*.

" The scratched grass is used because a lion, leopard or wild pig scratches just like an epileptic in his fit.

" The ash pile is used because everything is thrown there, so the disease should be thrown there too."

COMMENTS

This is another treatment which appears to rely entirely upon the principles of contagious and sympathetic magic. It is possible that the more severe the disease the greater the recourse to magical techniques (q.v., leprosy, insanity, lumbago).

MUSONG'U WAKANWA, DISEASE OF THE MOUTH

(A variety of conditions, including Pyorrhea and Toothache)

(a) For Blisters in the Mouth (Mabobela mukanwa)

One educated informant, a mission out-school teacher, described this condition, marked by blisters and sores in the mouth, as " scurvy ", which is indeed characterised by swollen gums. It is probable that he picked up the term at the mission hospital at Kalene Hill (C.M.M.L.). Dr. Cahal writes that while some conditions under this heading may be scurvy, others may well be apthous ulcers, herpetic ulcers and so forth. For, as mentioned above, the Ndembu doctor treats symptoms not diseases.

CURATIVE PROCEDURE

" First, the doctor goes to a *mwalu* tree (also called *kalukuta*, possibly *Olax obtusifolius*), collects roots, cuts them up, puts them in a pot with water and boils them for several minutes. When he judges it hot enough he puts the pot between the patient's open legs, makes him put his

---

[1] This term is also applied to the fermentation of beer.

head over the pot, covers him entirely with a blanket, and tells him to open his mouth directly in the path of the rising steam. To cover oneself with a cloth (so that the wind will not blow the steam away) is termed *kudibutililamu* or *kudijikililamu*. When the patient's body begins to sweat, the doctor removes the blanket or skin, takes medicine from the pot and tells the patient to rinse his mouth out with it (*ku-mumika*— ' to wash out the mouth with water' is *ku-kucha*). This treatment continues for three or four days.

" If the results are not good, the doctor goes to a *mwang'alala* tree (*Paropsia brazzeana*), takes roots, cuts them up and warms them gently on a fire in a pot with water, then gives the medicine to the patient as a mouthwash.

"Another mouthwash is made by splitting large pieces (*nakusesa yibalu*) of the *musosu* plant (*Boscia corymbosa*) which grows on termite-hills. These laths are then soaked in warm water and given to the patient to rinse his mouth with. He may do this for a week.

" Finally, roots of *kambanjibanji* are cut into pieces and warmed in water. The resultant mouthwash is retained in the patient's mouth for several minutes. He repeats this at intervals for several days."

INDIGENOUS EXPLANATION

" *Mwalu* is used because it is bitter and can kill the disease.

" *Mwang'alala* is used because it sets the teeth on edge; also it is hot (*ku-yeya*).

" *Musosu* is used because it lacks saltiness, is insipid."

One doctor said, when discussing *musosu*, that doctors test out different medicines until they find one to deaden the pain—a remark which implies some degree of rational experimentation.

" *Kambanjibanji* is used because it is hot (*ku-yeya*)."[1]

(b) Kakeleketi. Toothache with Mouth Soreness (possibly from ku-kelekela, " to gnaw ")

This is a condition in which " bad teeth are left to fall out on their own ", i.e. are not extracted. It is said that the following " medicines " will remove the pain and the teeth will drop out.

---

[1] This root is also used as a female aphrodisiac for the same reason—" to heat desire ".

CURATIVE PROCEDURE

" The doctor cuts up the root of an *ipupa*, puts the pieces in a pot with warm water and gives them to the patient as a mouthwash. He must rinse his mouth in the mixture frequently for several days. *Ipupa* is used because it is rather hot (*dayeya chanti*)."

(c) Chivukuta, Pyorrhea

If the above treatment proves ineffectual, and the doctor " finds blood on the front of the gums ", he may suspect that the patient is suffering from *chivukuta*, " the disease that eats the gums " (*musong'u wadyang'a wushinshinyi*).

CURATIVE PROCEDURE

" The doctor (*chimbuki*) fetches *ileng'i* reeds and burns them into ash—often used for salt. Then he goes to the nest of a species of tiny ants called *masoha*, and takes from it a ball (of organic material) known as *isoha*. Then he burns the *isoha* into ash and mixes it with *ileng'i* ash. He brings part of a calabash and makes little holes (*walokola nyiteta*) in the calabash. Then a large leaf, such as a *mubula* leaf (*Uapaca* sp). is put into the calabash as a loose lining. The ashes are placed on top of the leaf. Next another old calabash is set beneath the first one. Water is gently poured over the ash and then strained (*ku-keleka*) through the holes of the upper calabash into the lower one. The same process is used for straining salt from grass ashes to add to food. The leaf prevents the ash itself from coming through. When the doctor estimates that enough strained liquid is in the lower calabash, he pours it off into his medicine pot. Then he goes to a *kapepi* tree (*Hymenocardia acida*), takes a root and scrapes the outside bark (*nyemba*) into an empty *chipwepu* calabash-container.

" The doctor boils the water from the strained ashes until it has all evaporated leaving only salty powder (*mung'wa*). He mixes this with the *kapepi* scrapings, then crushes the mixture very fine with a knife handle. He now adds just enough water to make the mixture into a paste.

" Taking this paste he rubs it very gently into the painful part of the patient's gums. Sometimes blood comes from the rubbing and the patient begins to spit blood and paste. After a while the patient rubs the paste on himself, resting when the pain becomes too great. He goes on rubbing until blood ceases to flow from the painful spot. This is a very good treatment."

" *Ileng'i* ash is used because it is very pungently salty (*ku-tukuma*).

" *Isoha* is used because it resembles blisters (*mabobela*) or boils (*mahuti*).

" *Kapepi* is used because of its bitterness (*wukawu*).[1] "

COMMENTS

Pyorrhea is said by the mission doctors at Kalene Hospital to be very common among the Ndembu. Some attributed its prevalence to their dependence on cassava as a staple crop—almost pure carbohydrate.

MUSONG'U WAMPANG'A, SWELLING OF THE SCROTUM

This disease is thought to be most commonly caused by *mukayu* " medicines ", used by husbands to protect their wives from adultery and by the owners of hives and gardens against thieves. White[2] discusses similar protective medicines among the Luvale and concludes that they " contain a selective power within them which enables them to function . . . medicine to keep adulterers from a wife will not injure the husband but only adulterers ". It is this selective power, so it is believed, which causes the scrotum—and in some cases the *membrum virile*—of the adulterer to swell up. But Ndembu are quick to point out that the disease is not invariably caused by *mukayu*—" for even a newborn infant may have it ".

CURATIVE PROCEDURE

" The first thing the doctor (*chimbuki*) does is to go to an *ivung'uvung'u* tree (*Kigelia pinnata*—the ' sausage tree ', with long pods) and make an address to it (*ku-shahu mpandula*). He carries his axe and hoe and says: " You, O tree, I received you from another doctor.[3] The medicine we have collected from you here must have the power of killing the diseases." (*Eyi mutondu nawutambwili kudi chimbanda mukwawu yitumbu yinukuhukaku yikali nang'ovu yakujaha nyisong'u.*)

" Then the doctor digs up a root, takes some leaves and collects fruit from the tree. He puts one piece of root in a pot, then cuts the long pod into two parts of which one is chopped up and put in the pot. Warm water is added and the patient drinks the potion repeatedly for several days.

---

[1] *See* p. 671.

[2] *Elements in Luvale Beliefs and Rituals, op. cit.,* p. 36.

[3] I.e., he learnt the properties and use of the tree as a therapy for elephantiasis from another doctor.

" The doctor next brings two potsherds, in each of which he places some *ivung'uvung'u* medicine. Then he scrapes the root and puts some scrapings in each potsherd. The leaves are pounded into pulped leaf medicine, known as *nsompu*, which is put in a third potsherd in cold water. Hot water is poured in one of the original potsherds and cold water into the other. Now the patient is taken to the village ash pile (*izalelu*). The doctor then drinks *nsompu* leaf medicine, gives some to the patient, and then makes his assistant, who will tap the patient's blood (*ku-sumuna muyeji*), have a draught. That potsherd is then removed.

" The operator makes cuts on the lower half of the patient's abdomen and applies a cupping horn (*kasumu*); makes another cut just to the right of the navel and applies a horn; applies another to the right of the stomach and another just above the right hip. The operator rubs hot medicine from one potsherd into the cuts and presses it in (*ku-kanda*). After the horns have been removed, a hole is made in the ash pile, and the patient's blood is poured into it from the cupping horns and lightly covered with ashes. During the operation the patient is made to drink medicine from the pot. Afterwards the potsherds are taken away and kept for further use. The pot goes with the patient to his hut. He must go on drinking medicine after the treatment. Next day the operator and patient come back to the ash pile with the pot and three potsherds and the treatment is repeated. This continues for two or three days and after it is over the patient must go on drinking the medicine for a long time.

" The doctor afterwards goes and collects a pumpkin vine (*molu weyang'wa*), cuts a piece off it and takes its roots. He conceals these in his hut. Then he goes to a bundle of *nsama*, used to smoke out bees. The *nsama* consists of a cone- or poke-shaped bundle of small leafy twigs (*nsonsu*) containing dry twigs and grass and tied around with bark string. A bark rope (*isosu*) is tied to its narrow top end. When a man goes to get honey, he lifts the *nsama* by this rope as he climbs the tree to the beehive or nest. He sets fire to the *nsama* and ties it to a bough above the hive so that it dangles just below the hive and smokes out the bees. Very often the rope breaks or burns through and is left hanging from the branch by the honey gatherer. It is this abandoned portion that is collected by the doctor. He then goes to a *muhwila* tree (*Strychnos spinosa*)—which produces large round fruits—and removes a fruit, a root, and some leaves.

"At his village he pounds the leaves he has collected into *nsompu* and puts it into a calabash cup (*lupanda*). Other *nsompu* is put into a small clay pot (*kanung'u*). The *isosu* rope fragment is added to this pot, also the roots of the pumpkin vine and the *muhwila* tree. This is for the patient to drink.

" Then cupping horns and medicine are applied as before, and medicine is drunk by the patient."

INDIGENOUS EXPLANATION

" *Ivung'uvung'u* is used because the fruits in its pod resemble testicles (*nyisokwa* or *makutu*).

" *Iyang'wa*, the pumpkin, is used because it is like a swollen testicle. The fruit of *muhwila* is used for the same reason.

" *Isosu dansama*, the piece of rope, is a kind of *mpelu*. It is used because the *nsama* bundle hangs from it. With elephantiasis the testicles hang down because of their weight.

MUSONG'U WAMUTU, HEADACHE

Two kinds of *musong'u wamutu* are recognised:

(a) *Musong'u wamutu* properly so-called, which begins when " a person feels that the skin of his temples is moving about (throbbing?). His head feels heavy and pain comes in his temples first, then spreads to his whole head."

(b) *Musong'u wanyembu wamutu* or *Kakenka*, which starts " with a pain just above the eyes in mid-brow and spreads till it covers the whole eye, then spreads to the ears. It gives ' ku-kena ', a word which describes the very bright light made when lightning falls on a hut—such a light comes very suddenly, it is a sharp stab of pain ".

CURATIVE PROCEDURE

(a) " The doctor (*chimbuki*) goes to a *kapwipu* tree (*Swartzia madagascariensis*) and cuts from it some large chips of bark (*yitumbu yakusesa*). He then puts these in a pot and adds either hot or cold water. After a time the patient washes his whole head with it. He may do this at any time of the day or evening, and continues with the washing for several days.

" If the *kapwipu* medicine fails, the doctor goes to a *chikoli* tree (*Strychnos spinosa*), carrying a flaming bundle of grass with which he burns some of its leaves. He collects burnt leaves and puts them in a mortar where they are pounded into *nsompu*. This is put into a pot and warm water is added. The doctor tells his patient to wash his head in the medicine. If the patient has suffered from the disease before, he can collect these medicines himself, otherwise he must seek out a doctor. This treatment continues throughout the day—the washing is known as *ku-boba*, where the water is taken in the hollowed hand and splashed vigorously on the head. *Ku-boba* strictly refers to this splashing of the head. This treatment may last for several days.

" If *chikoli* fails, the doctor collects a root of *kambanjibanji*,[1] scrapes it and puts the scrapings in an old potsherd. He then goes to a *lweng'i* or *lweng'eng'i* plant (*Dracaena reflexa*) and takes some leaves. These are mixed with the *kambanjibanji* bark scrapings, after having first been crushed in the doctor's fingers. He then takes his razor and makes incisions from the right temple along the hairline to the left temple. He rubs the medicine into the cut marks. This medicine is wanted so that it can fight the disease in order to kill it.

" If the disease still continues, two further cuts are made in each temple and horns are sucked onto them. No medicine is used with these *tusumu*."

INDIGENOUS EXPLANATION

" *Kapwipu* is used because of its bitterness (*wukawu*) and its heat (*ku-yeya*), like that of chillies or pepper. When it is mixed with water, it can enter the whole head and fight the disease.

" *Chikoli* is used for its bitterness (*wukawu*), but also because it is a ' strong ' medicine (*ku-kola*—' to be strong or well ').

" *Kambanjibanji* is used because of its heat (*ku-yeya*) and slight astringency.

" *Lweng'i* smells strongly and has ' heat '. It causes pain when rubbed in. When you burn leaves this means that you burn ' a *chisaku* '[2]. When you burn leaves you burn ' insects ' (*tububu*—an euphemism for witches' familiars here) and *ndumba* (witches' familiars), in fact everything with bad magical power; you make the *chisaku* go away (*wafumisha chisaku*).

" Headache is usually caused by a *chisaku*; if a patient has one it will be burnt with the leaves. *Chisaku* is bad luck (*malwa*) which causes death or suffering, causes someone to be beaten to death or makes a

---

[1] *See* also p. 685.

[2] According to White, *Elements in Luvale Beliefs and Rituals, op. cit.*, p. 38, the Luvale cognate term *chisako* " denotes anything afflicting a person, be it illness, bad luck or failure such as lack of success in hunting, or a troublesome spirit."

man break an arm or leg. It is the same as a ' grudge ' (*chitela*) which a man cherishes secretly against another. One kind of *chisaku* is from familiars of witchcraft, another is from ghosts (*chisaku chikwawu chawafu*).

" *Lweng'i* grows near the edge of villages, it is used in many treatments. It is also used by sorcerers (*aloji*).[1]"

CURATIVE PROCEDURE

(*b*) *Musong'u wanyembu.* " The doctor goes to a *mudyi* tree (*Diplorrhyncus condylocarpon*), and splits off a portion (*chibalu*). Then he goes to a tree smitten by lightning and takes another portion. Then one from a *kapepi* tree (*Hymenocardia acida*) and another from a *kapwipu* tree (*Swartzia madagascariensis*) and from a *chikwata* tree (*Zizyphus mucronata*) and another from a *chikoli* tree (*Strychnos spinosa*). All these *yibalu* are brought to the patient's hut. An old pot is then fetched. All the medicines are put into it. Then a piece of *mpemba* (white clay) and a piece of *ng'ula* or *mukundu* (red clay), already softened, are brought, and the doctor draws a line of white clay (*mufunda wampemba*) round the rim of the pot and a line of red clay (*mufunda wang'ula*) underneath it. The ₊pot is then suspended by bark string over the patient's doorway. Sometimes a pangolin's scale is added to the medicine. Water is added to the pot, which is now called *izawu*, a ' container of medicine '.

"At dawn one of the patient's relatives comes with two axe blades. The doctor comes too and washes the patient's head, pressing on medicine where he feels pain. As he does this the relative clinks (*ku-kenkumwina*) the axe blades together near the front of the patient's head. When he has been thoroughly washed with medicine, his relative drops the axe heads at his feet. This treatment is repeated at sunset, and at dawn and sunset for several days, until the headache is cured."

INDIGENOUS EXPLANATION

" *Mudyi* is used because it was used at *Nkang'a*, the girls' puberty rites. Also because it is bitter. *Mudyi* is a strong tree (*mutondu wakola*).

"A lightning-struck tree is used because lightning is like the stabbing pain of a headache.

" *Kapepi* is used because of its bitterness (*wukawu*).

" *Kapwipu* is used because of its bitterness and heat.

---

[1] For its use in divination, *see Ndembu Divination, op. cit.*, p. 73.

" *Chikwata* (which has strong thorns) is used because it can pierce the disease.

" *Chikoli* is used because it is strong.

" The line of *mpemba* is just for purifying (*ku-tookesha*); the line of *mukundu* means blood (*mashi*) or bad luck (*ku-halwa*). The pangolin is used because it can kill the disease. It is used in many treatments. For the pangolin lies on an *isoha* (*see* p. 31), a kind of round ants' nest, waiting for the ants to come out to eat them. The clinking axe blades represent the pain of the headache. The relative drops them suddenly at his feet so that the disease may instantly leave the patient.

" When the sun comes, it brings the proper light. The sun (*itang'wa*) comes for all things, it is the elder of the country (*itang'wa wudinakwinza nayuma yejima, diyi mukulumpi wampata*). We say that (the application of) medicines must begin early just when the sun itself begins to appear. We have all found, we Africans, that if we do this our diseases become weak (*nyisong'u yetu yifomoki*). We believe, too, that diseases must die with the sun in the evening; that is why they also treat the patient in the evening.

"A long time ago the sun was said to be ' *Nzambi* '[1] (the name now given to the Deity). *Nzambi* looks after the rain, the animals, and people. Once there was a man who came from Luunda[2] called *Mweni*, ' The Owner ', or *Mweniwamatung'a*, ' The Owner of the Realms ', an important chief. He spoke personally to *Nzambi*. If he wanted more food for his people he would ask *Nzambi* for it. He reached the Lukoji River in the Congo. Now people come together to venerate *Mweni* in the *Musolu* rite—performed by chiefs when the rains are late in coming."

COMMENTS

" Headache " is a condition that seems more clearly associated with beliefs in witchcraft and sorcery than many other diseases. Possibly this is because the head is regarded as peculiarly the seat of one's individual life. A pain in the head may be the sign of a mystical attack on one's life by a sorcerer or witch. But the treatment of headache is directed against a vague and unspecified crowd of malevolent agencies rather than a particular witch or ghost. In this respect, it falls, together with the treatment of insanity, into a borderline category between *therapy* and *ritual*. When Ndembu speak about " the bitterness ", " the heat ", " the sourness ", " the strength ", "the saltiness " or

---

[1] *See* H. Baumann's Views (*Lunda; Bei Bauern und Jägern in Inner-Angola*, pp. 104–5) on the solar concept of death and resurrection among the Chokwe.

[2] The traditional homeland of the Ndembu in the Katanga.

" the pungency " of medicines, it is clear that they think of them as having some empirically remedial effect on the patient's state, even though we would consider that the principles underlying their use are those of sympathetic, contagious and homoeopathic magic. But when they make medicine from a lightning-struck tree to cure headache, simply because they sense an analogy between lightning and sudden headache, they would be the first to admit that the medicine was used not because of its empirically verified curative effects, but because " the disease resembles lightning ", and therefore is imbued with the same sort of mystical power. Once embodied in a symbol, that power can be controlled by the doctor for the patient's benefit. A step further in the direction of ritual is exemplified by the burning of the *chikoli* leaves (pp. 689–90). This is done explicitly to destroy the harm brought on by mystical agencies. The action is directed against the malignant agency rather than against the disease. Yet the *kapwipu* medicine, which is employed because of its " heat and bitterness " and the *chikoli* medicine which is burnt " to destroy witches' familiars " are both applied in exactly the same manner—as a headwash[1]

The distinction between " medicine " as " drug " and as " ritual symbol " is a very fine one, and it is not always possible to make it clearly. All things are felt to be charged with powers of various kinds and it is the job both of the herbalist and of the ritual specialist to manipulate these for the benefit of society. The ritual specialist may be said to deal primarily with powers that have already come under the control of conscious and purposive beings, visible or invisible, alive or dead, who use them, in general, to afflict the living with illness and misfortune. " Diseases " although they are sometimes said to " think ", are certainly regarded as " alive " but are more like animals than persons, and motiveless in their malignancy. They might almost be said to come lowest in a hierarchy of afflicting agencies, and to be controlled and directed by those above them. The Ndembu theory of affliction decrees that when conscious, voluntary beings decide to afflict human beings with illness they rarely do so alone, or in their own right, but usually with the help of another conscious being, or through an inter-mediary being or power. Thus a witch has her familiar homunculi, the *tuyebela* or *andumba*, a sorcerer has his *ilomba*, the human-faced serpent, or his figurines activated by human blood, the invoker of a curse raises by it a zombie (*musalu*) to do his fell work, while an ancestral spirit, as in *Chihamba*, may afflict in association with a demigod or may

---

[1] As many investigations have pointed out, it is the theoretical basis which demarcates primitive from Western medicine most clearly. It is possible that *chikoli* ash contains an ingredient which objectively reduces headache, but the ash is not used for this reason; curative medicines are epiphenomena of mystical beliefs, not the results of scientific experiment.

assume the guise of a specific " mode of affliction " (among the Luvale known as *lihamba*[1]). The *musong'u*, the " disease ", is believed to be strengthened by these intermediaries, which act on behalf of conscious beings who desire either the death or punishment of the patient.

MUSONG'U WANSHING'U, DISEASE OF THE NECK, STIFF NECK

Ndembu say that the sufferer from this disease " feels as though the inside of his neck is broken, he has a pain in the back of his neck, and his neck is stiff and immovable ".

CURATIVE PROCEDURE

(*a*) " The doctor first goes to a *mubang'a* tree (*Afrormosia angolensis*) and breaks off a branch retaining all its twigs. He then ties a string to its broken end and to the tip to make a small bow (*kawuta*). Next he goes to collect some grass or reeds called *nteng'wiji* (*Phragmites*); he takes two individual pieces broken off at the joints. He puts blobs of wax (*ndunda*) of the small *chilundi* bee on the tips of the grass stems. With branch for bow and grass stem as arrow he approaches close to the spot where the pain is and releases the ' arrow '. Then he repeats the procedure at another part of the patient's neck. Next he puts the patient's arm between the bow and string and hangs the bow over his shoulder (*ku-pakatisha kawuta*).

" The doctor also takes some portions of the outer bark of the *mubang'a* tree, chews them and spits the juice on the painful place and also on the place where there is no pain. Then the patient lifts the bow over his head and presses (*ku-kanda*) it into his neck all the way round. Afterwards the doctor puts the bow and arrow in the overhanging thatch of the patient's hut above the verandah.

(*b*) " Should the above treatment be unsuccessful the doctor goes into the bush to look for a place where a python (*mboma*) died, leaving its bones. If he is lucky he takes three of the vertebrae and puts them on a string to form a necklace. The procedure is first to warm these bones over a fire, then to press them into the sore place, and finally to tie them on a string round the patient's neck. This treatment continues for several days."

---

[1] White, *Elements. op. cit.*, p. 47. *Mahamba* may originally have been earth-spirits which later became syncretized with ancestral spirits and now appear as the culturally standardized mode of manifestation—in terms of illness and ill luck—of the latter.

[694]

"A branch of the *mubang'a* tree stands stiffly; to bend it with a string means to make it yield to pressure. The disease pushes the patient's neck straight like the branch of the hard *mubang'a*—the tree against which novices urinate in seclusion during *Mukanda* to make their wounds heal and give them a hard erection. *Nteng'wiji* grass is used because when it hits someone it is just like the pain he feels in the neck. The beeswax is soft (*yayovu*), so the disease will become soft (supple) too.

"A python is used in the second treatment because it is strong and supple (*mamovu*); thus the neck will become flexible instead of stiff."

MUSONG'U WACHINGONGU, SMALLPOX (WITH SEVERE CHICKENPOX)

Smallpox is not considered to be the result of witchcraft/sorcery or of ancestral affliction. It is said " to come to you in the air from Europeans ". It is thought by Ndembu to be very deadly, and formerly its victims were secluded in the bush far from their villages. If a mother fell sick with smallpox, her child could accompany her, and vice versa. One of my informants, Sandombu, considered it to be the second worst disease, leprosy being the more feared. Several Ndembu know the " true " (*yalala*) medicines, but there are no great specialists, as there are for insanity and leprosy. Treatment is usually given in the bush itself.

Curative Procedure

(*a*) The doctor collects bark-scrapings from the following trees:

Mufung'u (*Anisophyllea* sp.), the " wild plum ", which has reddish bark and bears either reddish or purple plum-like edible fruits;

Mukula (*Pterocarpus angolensis*), which secretes a red gum;

Luvung'u (*Anisophyllea boehmii*), which has round, orange-coloured fruits.

These bark-scrapings (*nyemba*) are mixed with *museng'eleli* grass, and a European disinfectant, such as Jeyes Fluid, bought at the local store, is added. The mixture is rubbed on the pustules.

(*b*) When the smallpox victim shivers with fever, the pounded leaves of the *wululu* shrub (*Khaya nyassica?*) are rubbed on his body. This treatment is continued for two successive days. *Wululu* is a legume with yellow flowers and small, round, paired leaves in a spray of light green colour. The pounded leaves are also used in the preparation of fish poison. I have not been able to identify this plant: it is possibly the *mululu* of the Bemba, Yombe, Ila, Lamba, Kaonde and many other tribes, identified by the Northern Rhodesia Forest Department as *Khaya nyassica*. Fanshawe suggests it might be a species of *Cassia*.

CONCLUDING NOTE ON TREATMENTS OF DISEASES

The above makes up the full tally of my systematic accounts of the treatment of various diseases. What follows consists of the organisation of comments and remarks made to me at various times during my fieldwork by a variety of informants. Before we consider them, however, it is worth mentioning that Ndembu recognise the originators of new curative procedures under the titles " *Sayitumbu* ", Father of the Medicines, or " *Sakuuka* ", Father of Treatment. For example, it was said that Katontu of Kalema Village in Chief Kanongesha Ndembi's area was a Sayitumbu. A former Kanongesha, Chief Izemba, is declared to have introduced many curative techniques—and also the *Kaneng'a* rite against illness caused by witchcraft or sorcery. Although there is an element of standardisation in the procedures I have listed, particularly with regard to quasi-ritual acts such as straightening a bent *mudyi* tree to cure backache, yet there is considerable variation in herbalists' recommendations of medicines to be used for particular diseases. For example, some herbalists recommended that the pounded leaves and roots of the *musenzi* (*Combretum zeyheri*) plant should be steeped in cold water for two days and then given to men suffering from dysentery (*kapokota*) rather than the *chikwata* roots mentioned in the description above of the treatment of men's *musong'u wevumu* (*see* p. 670).

III. FURTHER DATA ON THE
TREATMENT OF NDEMBU DISEASES

Among the accounts I collected are data on some of the mechanical devices and " surgical procedures" of the Ndembu. Much of this material was collected in Mbamvu Village, in Chief Mwininyilamba's area. The villagers had come fairly recently—three years before—from the Lovwa River in Angola and were still relatively uninfluenced by the behaviour and values of a changing society. Their views may fairly be said to be those of traditional Ndembu.

SURVEY OF MECHANICAL DEVICES USED IN MEDICINE
(Mainly from Recent Angolan Immigrants)
MASSAGE

To cure constipation, the stomach is rubbed with castor oil and then massaged gently.

CIRCULAR BANDAGES

If muscles are displaced or joints dislocated, circular bandages, consisting of sheets of bark fibre bound round by bark strings, are tied tightly round the affected area. The bandage is called *chisesa,* a term which also denotes a split palm mat. A *chisesa* is also used in one treatment of headache. First, small incisions are made between each eye and ear, and then medicine made from the bark of the *kalayi* plant is rubbed into them. Finally, a *chisesa* is tied round the head to cover the cuts.

CURE OF BLEEDING

To prevent bleeding, cold water is quickly applied to a wound. If the nose bleeds, it is plugged with leaves.

ABSCESSES (*mahuti*)

Abscesses may be cut with a knife or pierced with a sharp stick and washed out with warm water.

SNAKE BITE

First, a ligature is tied at the nearest joint—below the knee or elbow as the case may be—then the flesh is cut out around the snake bite and medicine is applied to the wound. The medicine consists of:

  (*a*) a powder made from the dried and pounded heads of all the poisonous snakes known to the Ndembu—this powder is known as *ndakala*;

[697]

(b) powdered root-bark of the *mukeketi* (*Veptoderris nabilis*) tree—also known as *musombu*;

(c) powdered root-bark of *mupembi* (*Ekebergia arborea*);

(d) powdered root-bark of *mundoyi* (*Chrysophyllum* [*Magalismont-anum*] *bangweolense*);

(e) powdered root-bark of *mutokatoka* (*Ilex mitis*).

At the same time as medicine is applied to the wound the patient must chew the leaves of *musombu*, *mupembi*, *mundoyi*, *mutokatoka* and *mwang'alala* (*Paropsia brazzeana*), and swallow the juice mixed with his saliva.

Next, purses (*masaku*) made from the skins of three species of mongoose (*kabunshi*, *mung'eli* and *kang'amba*) are tightly bound round the ligature. Before they are tied on they are rubbed on the patient's calf and forearm. If the blood is not flowing freely from the wound as it ought to do, the doctor takes some *ndakala* medicine from a tortoise shell container (*mbachi*), chews it in his mouth, sucks the wound, then applies the medicine.

TREATMENT OF SEVERE CUTS

Bark scrapings of *mupuchi* (*Brachystegia spiciformis*), *muvuka* (*Marquesia macrova*), *mwanda* (*Julbernardia paniculata*), *mundoyi* (*Chrysophyllum* sp.), *mwang'alala* (*Paropsia brazzeana*) and *mudyi* (*Diplorrhyncus condylocarpon*) are boiled in a pot, and the hot mixture is applied in a sheet of bark fibre to the affected part and tied over it. Then a grass hut (*nkunka*) is built for the patient outside the village where he may lie quietly until he recuperates.

EMETICS

If a person has swallowed something poisonous, he is given root-scrapings of *mundoyi* which are mixed with thin warmed gruel (*kapudyi*) and eaten; root peelings of *kavulawumi* (*Maprounea africana*) are also dropped in beer which is then drunk.

If a person has drunk a large amount of beer but cannot vomit, he chews leaves of any available species and swallows the sap.

ENEMAS

Enemas are made of small calabashes (*tuswaha*) with reeds inserted through the necks. They are filled with warm water and given to the patient to administer himself. They are used in cases of dysentery (*kapokota*) and, if the patient has become very thin, of hookworm.

SPLINTS

Splints are used for broken limbs. They are made of mats of split palm (*yisesa*), split sugar cane or tough reed, tied round with bark string. The patient is segregated from the village in a grass hut, as in the treatment for severe cuts. Medicine leaves are applied to the skin under the mats. The famous *Sayitumbu*, Katontu, mentioned on p. 41, is said to have cured broken limbs by breaking the legs of a chicken and treating patient and chicken together. When the chicken starts to walk again so (in theory!) will the patient.

AMPUTATION is unknown.

STITCHES

Stitches are never made in wounds. If a cut is deep the doctor closes one eye " so that the medicine may sink in deeply ".

BURNS

" If someone has a burn the doctor brings him *chitakachi* leaves (*Phyllanthus discoideus*), which are pounded, then soaked in water. He rubs this medicine on the burn. This treatment continues for two days.

" If the burn made a severe wound, the doctor burns a wild pig's bones to ash. Then he takes the patient to a *mukula* tree, rubs *mukula* gum on the wound and finishes by rubbing bone ash (*mula*) on it. This treatment is repeated for several days.

" If the wound does not heal, the doctor goes to a *kampandi* tree (*Maytenus cymosus*), collects some pieces of bark, pounds them and puts them in the sun to dry. When dry, they are sieved so as to form a powder. The patient is brought and his wound is well washed with water. When it is clean this powder is applied while the burn is still wet. The water and powder should meet together and form a scab. This treatment goes on for as many weeks as the burn requires to be healed.

" *Chitakachi* is *wazema* or ' tacky ', it comes off in a long string, all in one piece. Its leaves are treacly like that, just like the leaves of the relish plant *wusi*, they are difficult to separate, like honey. They are used so that the wound will not spread but will remain in one piece.

" *Mukula* is used so that the burn will form a hard dry scab, like *mukula* gum. The wild pig's bone-meal, mixed with *mukula* gum, is used to make the burn hard like a dry paste.

" *Kampandi* is used to make the wound form a scab, for the bark of *kampandi* is hard."

Steam Bath

We have already noted the use of the steam bath in the treatment of eye disease (p. 671). It is also used occasionally during the *Kayong'u* rite, which may be performed for a patient who shows signs of asthma or bronchitis, thought to be the result of ancestral affliction.[1]

Scarification

Scarification, it will be remembered, is a standard Ndembu therapeutic practice.[2]

Cupping

Employed in several rites of affliction (e.g. *Ihamba*, *Kaneng'a*) with the avowed aim of removing harmful objects, mystically propelled into it, from the patient's body. Cupping is also used in several kinds of therapy.[3]

FURTHER NOTES ON TREATMENT AND MEDICINES

For Sores (*Yilonda*, sing. *chilonda*)

(*a*) The pounded leaves of *wunkomukomu* (possibly *Aphrohiza nitida*) are mixed with copper ore obtained from returned labour migrants from the Northern Rhodesian Copperbelt and are rubbed on the sores. *Wunkomukomu* is a small shrub with large lanceolate leaves.

(*b*) Either pounded *muvuka* (*Marquesia macrova*) roots mixed with salt or pounded *kapwipu* (*Swartzia madagascariensis*) leaves mixed with salt are rubbed into the sores.

For Infantile Disorders

(*a*) If an infant is very feeble his father collects leaves of *chikang'anjamba* (another name for the *chikoli* tree mentioned above in several treatments; the name *chikang'anjamba* means " (the tree) the elephant fails to (break) "; it is used because it is very tough and enduring. The name *chikoli* is from *ku-kola*, " to be strong, hard or healthy "). These are pounded and left to steep in cold water.

(*b*) If a child is slow in learning to walk, his father collects *kambanjibanji* leaves (used also as a toothache cure, *see* p. 685), pounds them, allows them to steep in cold water for three days then gives them to the child to drink.

---

[1] *See Ndembu Divination, op. cit.*, pp. 5, 23–26.
[2] *Ibid.*, pp. 14, 20, 25, 37, 38, 47, 50, 59.
[3] *Ibid., see* pp. 20, 21, 24, 25, 27, 47, 48, 50.

FOR HOOKWORM

The pounded leaves of *kavulawumi* (*Maprounea africana*) are administered in cold water to induce vomiting.

FOR LACTATION TROUBLES

" If a woman's breast milk (*mayeli*) becomes ' red ' or ' yellow ', it is called *nshidi*, ' guilt ' or ' sin '. If her baby drinks it, often it will die. If the creeper or vine *moluwawubwang'u* is twined around the breast that is not giving white milk, it will become white."

In the *Wubwang'u* rites, performed for a mother of twins, *molu wawubwang'u* is one of the principal medicines, and is regarded as the dominant symbol of the *itu*, or streamside forest.

FOR MASCULINE STERILITY

" If the colour of a man's semen is ' red ' or ' yellow ' he will become a sterile person (*nshinta*). But if he eats medicine made from the *mucheki* plant, mixed with thin gruel (*kapudyi*), his semen will become white. After he has finished eating *mucheki*, he must dig a little hole in the ground and urinate into it."

Mucheki is the dominant symbol of the *kutumbuka* or major phase of the great *Chihamba* rite,[1] where its root is regarded as epitomising the purest ' whiteness ' and all the values and ideas annexed thereto. In these two medicines, *molu wawubwang'u* and *mucheki*, we get a glimpse of the relationship between religious rite and lay treatment. Here it would seem the treatment derives from the rite, the ' magical ' practice from the ' religious ' observance.

---

[1] *See* my *Chihamba, The White Spirit*, Rhodes-Livingstone Paper, Number 33, 1962.

ALPHABETICAL LIST OF TREES AND SHRUBS USED IN TREATMENTS[1]

Prefix	Root	Botanical Name	Disease or Injury	Reason for Use
Mw-	ala	*Afzelia quanzensis*	Stomach disease	"Bitterness will kill disease" (Contains a high proportion of tannins with marked astringent effect —Cahal)
Mw-	alu or lukuta	*?Olax obtusifolius*	Blisters in mouth (Scurvy ?)	"Bitter, can kill disease"
Ka-	anda	*Julbernardia paniculata*		
Mw-	ang'alala	*Paropsia brazzeana*	Blisters in mouth (Scurvy ?)	"It is hot and sets teeth on edge"
Mw-	ang'alala	*Paropsia brazzeana*	Snake bite	
Mw-	ang'alala	*Paropsia brazzeana*	Severe cuts	"Stiff tree to bend"
Mu-	bang'a	*Afrormosia angolensis*	Stiff neck	"Has mottled bark like leper's skin"
M-	bumba yachula	*Landolphia rufescens*	Leprosy	"A 'white' medicine, makes semen white"
Mu-	cheki	*Cremaspora triflora*	Male sterility	"Bitter"
Wa-ka-	dikalanziza or yiza	(*Memecylon flavovirens*) *Strychnos stuhlmannii*	Eye disease	"Aperient"
Mu-	diansefu	*? Craterosiphon quarrei*	Rabies	Auspicious tree (here it refers also to bent specimen—like patient's back)
Mu-	dyi	*Diplorrhyncus condylo-carpon*	Backache	

[1] The identifications are based on the Northern Rhodesia Government Forest Department Check List (Vernacular/Botanical Names), 1950. They were then revised and corrected by Mr. Fanshawe.

Mu-	dyi	*Diplorrhyncus condylo-carpon*	Gonorrhea	White latex resembles pus of gonorrhea
Mu-	dyi	*Diplorrhyncus condylo-carpon*	Headache	Auspicious, bitter
Mu-	dyi	*Diplorrhyncus condylo-carpon*	Leprosy	White like leprous spots, symbolic role in *Mukanda* rites, sanctioned by leprosy
Mu-	dyi	*Diplorrhyncus condylo-carpon*	Severe cuts	
Lu-	eng'eng'i	*Draecena reflexa* var. *nitens*	Eye disease	"Bitter"
Lu-	eng'eng'i		Headache	"Strong smell and hot"
Mu-	fung'u	? *Arisophyllea boehmii*	Smallpox	"Reddish fruits"
Mu-	hanu	*Ficus* sp.	Tuberculosis	"Grows in hole in other trees; will break obstruction in chest"
Mu-	hotuhotu	*Canthium venosum*	Insanity	Traditional component of medicine broom
Mu-	huma	*Strychnos spinosa* (*Strophanthus welwitschii*) } Eye disease		"Bitter"
Mu-	hwila	? *Apocynaceae* creeper.	Gonorrhea	"Creeper with white flowers" (= pus)
Ka-	jing'a ludi	*Landolphia*		
I-	kamba daChihamba	*Cryptosepalum maraviense*	Insanity	"Clears the eyes"

Mu-	kandachina	(Eriocoelum sp.)/Rhus longipes	} Insanity	"Grows on top of termite hills; a madman goes to top of things"
Chi-	kang'anjamba (see chi-koli)	Strychnos spinosa		
Mu-	kekeiti	(Veptoderris nabilis) Syzygium guineense	Snake bite	
Chi-	koli	Strychnos spinosa	Earache	"Yellow fruits"
Chi-	koli	Strychnos spinosa	Headache	"Bitter and strong"
Chi-	koli	Strychnos spinosa	Slow infant development	"Strong tree"
Mu-	kombukombu	Tricalysia angolensis (Leptactina)	Insanity	Component of medicine broom
Mu-	kula	Pterocarpus angolensis	Burns	"Red gum dries like scab"
Mu-	kula	Pterocarpus angolensis	Smallpox	"Red gum like pustules"
Mu-	kula	Pterocarpus angolensis	Tuberculosis	"Red gum—spitting blood"
Ka-	kung'ami		Children's stomach trouble	"Stinks, bubbles, drives disease aside"
Chi-	kwata	Zizyphus mucronata	Men's stomach disease	"Bitter"
Chi-	kwata	Zizyphus mucronata	Headache	"Strong thorns pierce disease"
Ka-	kwema	(Enneastemon schwein-forthii) Uvaria ango-lensis	Stomach disease	"Its nasty smell kills disease"
Mu-	lendi	Sterculia quinqueloba	Epilepsy	"Very slippery; so disease will slip from patient"

Ka-	*leng'ang'ombi*	Thornbush of gallery forest	Insanity	"Used in *Mukanda* rites"
I-	*leng'i*	(? *Uapaca sansibarica*) *Cyperus* sp.	Pyorrhea	"Reeds from which salt is made. Saltiness can cure"
Mu-	*lolu*	*Anona nana*	Men's stomach disease	"Strong smell"
Ka-	*lukutu*	See *mwalu*	Smallpox	
Wu-	*lulu*	(*Khaya nyassica*) *Cassia* sp.		
Ka-	*mbanjibanji*		Headache	"Strong and astringent"
Ka-	*mbanjibanji*		Blisters in mouth (Scurvy?)	"Hot"
Ka-	*mbanjibanji*		Slow infant development	
Ka-	*mpandi*	*Maytenus cymosus*	Burns	"Its bark is hard and scab-like"
Mu-	*ndoyi*	*Chrysophyllum* (*Magahis montanum*)	Severe cuts	
Mu-	*ndoyi*	*bangweolense*	Snake bite	
Mu-	*ndoyi*	(? *Aphrohiza nitida*) small shrub, large lanceolate leaves	Poison in stomach	
Wu-	*nkomukomu*		Sores	Emetic
Ka-	*nsanying'a*		Bilharzia	"Has white roots and strong smell"

Ka-	nshinshi		Stomach disease of children	" Strong smell and bitter taste "
M(w)-	olu wawubwang'u		Lactation disorders	"A ' white ' creeper. Can make milk flow white "
(Mu-	Lu wawubwang'u)			
Mu-	pembi	Ekebergia arborea	Stomach disease	" Strong smell kills disease "
Ka-	pepi	Hymenocardia acida	Snake bite	
Ka-	pepi	Hymenocardia acida	Headache	" Bitter "
Mu-	puchi	Brachystegia spiciformis	Pyorrhea	" Bitter "
Mu-	puchi	Brachystegia spiciformis	Bilharzia	" Red gum, like blood of bilharzia "
Ka-	pumbwa	Ancylobothrys amoena	Severe cuts	
Chi-	puta mazala	Erythrina tomentosa	Gonorrhea	" Its white gum drops on the ground, resembles pus of gonorrhea "
Ka-	pwipu	Swartzia madagascariensis	Stomach disease of children	" Strong smell "
Ka-	pwipu	Swartzia madagascariensis	Headache	" Bitter and hot "
Ka-	pwipu	Swartzia madagascariensis }	Sores	
Mu-	sambanjita	Cryptosepalum maravense }	Stomach disease of children	" Hardness of tree=health and strength "
Mu-	seng'u	Ochna pulchra	Epilepsy	" Its leaves are curled like someone in an epileptic fit "

Mu-	senzi	Combretum zeyheri	Dysentery	
Mu-	shokotu	Faurea saligna	Earache	
Mu-	soli	Vangueriopsis lanciflora	Insanity	"To clear madman's mind"
Mu-	sombu	Syzygium guineense		
Mu-	song'asong'a	Ximenia americana	Stomach disease of children	"Has hard wood, makes strong and healthy"
Mu-	song'asong'a	(Olax obtusifolius)	Insanity	"Bitter for the eyes. Clears them"
Mu-	sosu	Boscia corymbosa	Blisters in mouth (Scurvy?)	"Lacks salt, mild"
Chi-	takachi	(Phyllanthus discoideus)	Burns	"Stickiness of leaves coagulates burn"
Mu-	tata	Securidaca longipedunculata	Stomach disease	"Its nasty smell will kill disease"
Mu-	tokatoka	Ilex mitis	Snake bite	
Ka-	tong'a	Strychnos cocculoides	Stomach disease of men	"Very bitter"
Wu-	totu	Gardenia imperialis/	Bilharzia	"White roots and gum resemble pus"
Wu-	totu	Tabernaemontana angolensis	Gonorrhea	"White roots and gum resemble pus of gonorrhea"
Ka-	tunya	(Uvariastrom hexaloboides) Harungana madagascariensis	Bilharzia	"Red roots like blood of bilharzia"

Mu-	tutambululu	*Xylopia adoratissima*	Insanity	Component of medicine broom
Mu-	vuka	*Marquesia macrova*	Severe cuts	
Mu-	vuka	*Marquesia macrova*	Sores	
Ka-	vulavumi	*Maprounea africana*	Hookworm	"Brings on vomiting"
Ka-	vulavumi	*Maprounea africana*	Leprosy	
Ka-	vulavumi	*Maprounea africana*	Poison in stomach	Emetic
Ka-	vulavumi	*Maprounea africana*	Rabies	Emetic
Lu-	vung'u	*Anisophyllea boehmii*	Smallpox	"Round orange fruits" (like pustules?)
I-	vung'uvung'u	*Kigelia pinnata*	Elephantiasis of scrotum	"Fruits resemble testicles"
I-	yang'eva	? *Agauria salicifolia*	Elephantiasis of scrotum	"Resembles swollen testicles"
Ka-	yiza	(*Memecylon flavovirens*) *strychnos stuhlmannii*		

IV. ANALYSIS AND CONCLUSIONS

It has been said[1] that in the primitive treatment of disease, " an invisible force is dealt with visibly by means that are meant and understood to be symbolic ". This formulation would account for much that goes on at Ndembu curative procedures. It seems to be the case, however, that some scope is permitted for experiment,[2] but in the main it is held that to make visible by symbolic means is to make a disease accessible to therapeutic action, also of a symbolic character. A glance at the Alphabetical List of Trees and Plants Used in Treatments illustrates this point sufficiently. Sympathetic, contagious and homeopathic magic appear to account for the employment of the majority of the " medicines ". All the senses—sight, hearing, taste, smell and touch—are enlisted in the service of association and analogy. *Mucheki* is used because its wood is white and its medicine will hence make " red " semen " white " and fruitful. The " sound " of *kung'ami* as it bubbles in a child's stomach will " drive the disease to one side ". The bitter taste of *kapepi* or *mwalu* will " kill diseases of the mouth ". The " nasty smell " of *mutata* will " kill stomach disease in women ". The " stiffness " of *mubang'a* is communicated to a homoeopathic medicine made from it which will cure stiff neck.

There is no attempt to distinguish between medicines whose effect is thought to depend on one kind of sensorily distinguishable property and medicines dependent on other kinds and to reserve one kind for a single curative procedure. All kinds are interlinked in a single procedure. The procedure itself may often contain actions and episodes that we in the West might consider to be " religious ". I refer to the invocations made by doctors to the principal medicine trees (*see* pp. 670, 687), to the formal washings, aspersions and anointings. The prescribed, stereotyped behaviour of the curative specialists seems often to fall more within the sphere of ritual than of therapeutic action. This consideration brings me back to Ackerknecht's query with which this paper began: " What are the ideas underlying these therapeutic acts, and under what circumstances (with or without ritual) are they performed ? ".

We have partly answered these questions in commenting on specific treatments. The central idea behind both Ndembu therapy and Ndembu ritual is that the visible world is permeated by and perhaps is but a manifestation of a series of " powers " (*jing'ovu*), assembled ultimately

---

[1] Ackerknecht, E. H., " Problems of Primitive Medicine," *Bulletin of the History of Medicine*, XI (1942) 503–21 (Quoting im Thurn on Indians of Guiana).

[2] *See* p. 696 above, and my *Chihamba, the White Spirit*, Rhodes-Livingstone Paper, No. 33, 1962.

under the treble rubric of white-red-black, and capable of being evoked by those with specialised knowledge either for good or ill. Such powers, conceived sometimes as personal, sometimes as animate but without purposiveness or rationality, may be evoked by various means. In the first place, there must be a specialist, a *chimbuki* or *chimbanda* who " knows " (*weluka*) what medicines are efficacious against a given disease, how they should be administered, and why they are used. Knowledge among the Ndembu is far more literally " power " than it is with us. To know more is to *be* more fully, and to possess greater power with respect to the field of action to which that knowledge pertains. It is also to increase in social status and authority in that field of action and knowledge. Knowledge, in short, has existential implications. It may be acquired by participation in a full-scale *rite de passage*, where the novices or candidates are taught the properties of herbal and other medicines, it may be taught by a senior relative—and this is particularly common where therapeutic knowledge is concerned— or it may be bought from another, unrelated specialist. In whatever way such knowledge may have been obtained, it confers some kind of mystical power on its possessor, gives him or her an affinity with the *materia medica* used, and enables the herbalist to activate the latent virtues in the herbs he uses.

But it is not enough merely to possess power and knowledge. He must take positive steps to awaken—and here the term *ku-tonisha*, " to awaken ", is actually employed—the powers hidden and slumbering in herbs. Sometimes he and his assistants do this by singing traditional songs, associated in some way with the disease, as they go into the bush to collect medicines. Sometimes the herbalist may " address " the principal medicine tree before he cuts portions from it for his special *lwalu* basket. I have given an example of such an address on p. 32: " O tree, I received you from another doctor. The medicine we will collect from you here must have the power of killing disease ". After making the address (*mpandula*), the doctor often takes a leaf from the tree, places it on the back of his clenched left fist and bangs his flattened right hand down on it. The sharp report thus made—sometimes compared with a gun shot—is also intended to " wake up " the medicine or—in rites proper—the ancestral spirits who act as tutelaries to the doctor-adepts.

This right–left contrast has importance in a number of ritual contexts, where it may represent: male/female, husband/wife, arrow (held in the right hand)/bow (held in the left)—and indeed the " arrow " may symbolise the male genital and power of begetting while the " bow " represents female fertility.

[710]

Again, right may be associated with whiteness while left may be associated with redness. Often they are conceptualised as a complementary pair in which the left hand is called *nkwashi*, " the helper ", the one which enables the right hand to accomplish its act, just as a wife helps her husband in his activities.

In medicine it is thought that the power of a *chimbuki* passes through his right arm into his axe when he cuts medicine from a tree. This power evokes the power possessed by the tree. The smell of the slashed bark or cut root, the gum or latex oozing from the excision, these too are regarded as expressions of roused power. Each tree is felt to have its specific " virtue " which is now informed by mystical power.

Such rousing preliminaries—which may also include the use of musical instruments, such as stridulators, drums, hunting bells and clashing bars of iron—are themselves only a part of a configuration of symbolic actions and symbolic articles, and it is the form of the total procedure which most signally evokes, contains and controls the mystical powers employed by the healer or herbalist. It is impossible to overstate the importance of the mode of arrangement of the parts of a curative procedure. Out of the randomness and incoherence of the environment the *chimbuki* selects certain items and arrays them in a coherent structure in accordance with his sensitivity to Ndembu evaluations and symbolism and in accordance with his intention of curing a specific, culturally defined disease. When I say that " the *chimbuki* selects " I mean no more than that he follows precedent, whether that of the doctor who taught him the medicine or of the tradition within which that doctor was working. Incidentally, it is no surprise to find that many doctors became so because they began as patients who learned the medicines and curative procedure for a particular disease in the course of being treated for it. But there are more than practical considerations at work here for Ndembu have a tendency to regard like or shared experience as creating a mystical bond between all persons (including, so Ndembu believe, the dead), things and activities comprising the experience or closely associated with it. From the point of view of Western science such a bond or association may be merely adventitious or superficial; from the point of view of the Ndembu, persons and things which " were together " in space and time at a moment of critical significance for an individual or a group may acquire a deep and permanent relationship of " mystical participation ", to use Lévy-Bruhl's useful term.

To understand Ndembu therapy, therefore, it is necessary to turn away from an atomistic consideration of particular symbolic and pragmatic items of medicine and treatment to an examination of the principles underlying the total procedure. From this standpoint it is unimportant that a particular medicine owes its employment to a particular mode of sensory or mental association. For behind the configuration of symbolic medicines and acts stand a few principles which articulate the separate items into a whole. This can be seen if a particular treatment is analysed.

ANALYSIS OF THE TREATMENT OF MUSONG'U WANYEMBU ('' SPLITTING '' HEADACHE)[1]

In this treatment there are five components: (1) the disease; (2) colour symbolism; (3) the medicines; (4) the mode of treatment; and (5) the times of treatment. These components are inter-articulated by a few ruling ideas. The disease is considered in this instance to be partly the result of witchcraft or sorcery. It has, in terms of Ndembu thought, a '' black '' character. This gives us the key to the colour symbolism for here white and red are regarded at one level as working in combination to rid the patient of the black, deathly taint of the witch's grudge (*chitela*) or malevolent action (*chisaku*). The white decoration of the pot represents the '' purification of the patient '', while the red line stands for '' blood '' or killing. Here it may represent the '' strength '' desired for the patient, and would link up with the '' strong '' medicines used (*mudyi, chikwata, chikoli*), for Ndembu say that blood is '' life '', though it also stands for the taking of life. It may stand here also for the taking of the '' life '' of the *musong'u*, the disease, regarded as an animate being. Red is an ambivalent symbol in Ndembu ritual and here would represent both a wish for the patient's recovery of life and a wish for the '' killing '' of the disease and the '' bad luck '' (*ku-halwa*). The medicines all have a '' strong '' (*-kola*) aggressive character, associated with redness and the level of colour symbolism. They have a '' bitter '' taste, they are '' hot '', they have thorns '' to pierce (or stab) the disease ''. But the disease itself has this very quality, for it is described as resembling '' the very bright light made when lightning falls on a hut—such a light comes suddenly, it is a sharp stab of pain ''. It must, so Ndembu seem to think, be fought by its own weapons. Hence the use of a lightning-struck tree as medicine, '' because lightning is like the pain of headache ''. Hence the mode of treatment by clinking axe blades together near the patient's head—not by any means a treatment that would strike us as soothing! Behind this simulation in the treatment of the supposed properties of the disease may also lie the notion (common in other aspects of Ndembu symbolic practices) that to reveal or portray is to expose, and that exposure of the '' true '' character of a disease or '' grudge '' is half the therapeutic battle, for the known is

---

[1] Described on p. 36.

not nearly so dangerous as the hidden and unknown. Action can be taken against something visible and classified in terms of traditional thought and belief, and positive action, as has often been said, reduces anxiety and promotes confidence. Nor can we rule out of the picture the possibility that noise and shock themselves may have a therapeutic value. As Lessa and Vogt[1] have said: " The typical primitive super-natural treatment involves elements of shock or stress analogous to modern shock treatment—treatment which stimulates an internal reaction capable of returning the organism to health ".

The times of performance—at sunset and sunrise—link up with the colour symbolism, with the medicines and with the disease. For the sun is considered a " white " object, and a symbol of *Nzambi*, the High God, source of all power. Here the rising of the sun seems to be associated with an increase in the effect of the medicines, while the declining sun is connected with the declining strength of the disease.

A number of symbolic actions, actually performed or implicit in the symbolism, represent the death or decline or elimination of the disease. There is the setting of the sun just mentioned—" diseases must die with the sun in the evening ". Then there is the sudden dropping of the axe blades at the patient's feet, " so that the disease may instantly leave him ". There is the *chikwata* thorn tree which can " pierce " the disease. And finally, there is the use of the pangolin's scale as *mpelu*, contagious magical medicine, for the reason that the pangolin eats up stinging ants, which are identified with the disease.

The symbolic contrast of " above " with " below " influences the procedure. We have noted the supposed effects of the rising and setting sun on the strength of medicine and disease. As the sun rises, the disease weakens, and as it sinks the disease dies. The white line *above* the red line on the pot may mean many things, but one of them is the wished-for ascendancy of " purification ", a term that embraces the curative procedure, over " bad luck ", a multivocal term that includes the disease and the witch's grudge that probably caused it. In the case of headache, it is, of course, the head (the " above ") that is itself being attacked by witchcraft which, with its necrophagous attributes, is associated in many contexts with the " below ". This is why the medicine pot is hung over the patient's doorway, head-high, why the axe blades are clinked in front of his head and why sun-symbolism plays such a major part. Healthful powers are thus enlisted against the " disease of the head ", wherein the patient's life (*wumi*) is felt to reside.

[1] Lessa, William A., and Vogt, Evon Z., *Reader in Comparative Religion*, New York: Row, Peterson and Co. (1958), p. 343.

But there are a number of echoes from Ndembu rites proper in the symbolic pattern of this treatment which indicate how deeply their pharmacopoeia is influenced by ritual beliefs and practices. For example, *chikoli*, *chikwata*, and indeed the *mudyi* tree itself, under which novices are circumcised, are important symbols in *Mukanda*, the boys' circumcision rites. *Chikoli* there represents *inter alia* an erect phallus, a tough, healthy body, and masculinity. *Chikwata* is thought to confer healing power on the boys' penes after the operation. Again, in *Mukanda*, the circumcisers' protective medicine has to be lifted above the ground or it will lose its efficacy, and when a certain song (the *ng'ung'u*) is sung by circumcisers, the novices must climb up trees or onto the shoulders of adult men, otherwise they will suffer, it is said, from incontinence of urine for the rest of their lives. Thus what is above is auspicious and what is below or on the ground is contextually inauspicious, as in the treatment of headache. It is probable that there is here a connection between a potent and erect male member and what is above, and a slack, impotent member and what is below. Pain is certainly associated with lying on the ground, for this is the posture of circumcision. Several informants have given me this interpretation. It might not be fanciful to conjecture that Ndembu associate the head of a healthy man with the glans of the potent member, and headache—produced by witchcraft—with impotence—also produced by witchcraft.

Other symbolic links with virility are perhaps provided by the use of *kapepi* and *kapwipu* medicines, for both these trees play an important role in the symbolism of hunting rites. I have discussed this role elsewhere[1] and here merely mention that in addition to their specific properties these trees are held to share the following characteristics:

(1) String cannot be made from their bark—thus they do not " tie up huntsmanship ", i.e. the hunter's power and skill in killing animals.

(2) They have a tough, termite- and weather-resistant wood—the hunter should possess toughness and power of endurance.

(3) Their wood is white and is thus an embodiment of the power of whiteness, supreme auspiciousness.

Kapepi and *kapwipu* are trees from which the most common type of shrine erected for the spirits of hunter ancestors is made—a forked branch stripped of leaves and adorned with trophies of the chase. Offerings of blood are smeared on the branches and poured at the base,

---

[1] " Themes in the Symbolism of Ndembu Hunting Ritual ", *The Anthropological Quarterly* (1962), pp. 47–48.

and portions of internal organs of the slain animal, consecrated to the use of hunters alone, are transfixed on the sharpened points. The sharpness of the points represents the acuity of huntsmanship (*ku-wambuka kwa Wubinda*).

Viewed in this wider framework, it seems likely that these medicines are not employed solely on account of their bitter taste or "heat", since they are believed to confer robustness and endurance on the person enfeebled by a splitting headache. If the connection between the treatment and hunting ritual is a valid one, there would be yet another reference to the relationship between white and red. For blood, the most direct expression of the principle of redness, is brought to the white shrine and the two are combined in the act of veneration.

The treatment of headache thus reveals itself as a formal procedure controlled by religious ideas that are expressed in symbolic actions and symbolic articles: whiteness/redness; above/below; strength/weakness; health/disease (a mode of blackness); sunrise/sunset; links between the power of God, the sun, whiteness, strength, endurance, virility; between lightning, metallic noise, stabbing headache, thorns, circumcision, the killing of animals. As in all diseases the aim is to restore the patient from a " black " to a " white " condition (one aspect of which is purification). In the particular case of headache this process of restoration is directed towards the head (with overtones of operations on the upper parts of other extremities). The notion of lightning plays an important part here because lightning is said to strike the top-knot of grass at the apex of a hut (resembling the head of a person) as well as on account of its analogy with sudden, splitting pain in the head. Lightning, in its suddenness and ferocity, is a symbol for sorcery/witchcraft, and indeed Ndembu believe that certain sorcerers use medicine (*wang'a wanzaji*, " lightning magic ") to bring lightning down (even from a clear sky) to kill their personal enemies. Violent headache, spreading out into constant pain, is for Ndembu a sign that an unknown witch or sorcerer is assailing them in their most vital centre. Against this assault must be mobilised medicines borrowed from rites which most signally promote health, strength and virility and other " white " qualities, such rites as girls' puberty (with its *mudyi* tree symbol), boys' circumcision and those of the hunting cults.

In these and other ways ultimate and axiomatic values of Ndembu religion and ethics enter into such an everyday matter as curing a headache. The *meaning* existence has for an Ndembu tribesman is present in many of his minor ends as well as in the great ends of a full-scale life-crisis rite. To restore order, health or peace the powers

[715]

that make for these must be brought into play by the correct use and combination of symbols, viewed as repositories of power as well as semantic systems. But for Ndembu, again unlike ourselves, to " know " something, to understand the meaning of a symbol or the use of a " medicine ", for example, is to increase in " power ".

CONCLUSION

After reading the above account people may ask: " Why do such treatments continue to be practised, since it is clear that they have little empirical derivation and are based on mystical ideas ? " One reason for their persistence lies, no doubt, in the very fact that they are part of a religious system which itself constitutes an explanation of the universe and guarantees the norms and values on which orderly social arrangements rest. To query the premises on which Ndembu medicine rests would be to query the axioms underlying the Ndembu *weltbild*. Another more practical reason would be that many diseases are self-curing; in the course of time, regardless of the treatment they are given, many people recover from illness, but the recovery is attributed to the treatment. Then again, psychological considerations must play a part in the case of mild psychosomatic conditions and in the milder cases of somatic illness. Such considerations would include the authoritative air of the doctor-herbalist, the purposive structure of the procedure, the " shock treatment " aspect mentioned above, and the sense that something traditional is being done about a known and named condition. Here we have an instance of the well-known " placebo " effect, where medicine is given to humour, rather than to cure, the patient, but where improvement in health nevertheless results.

Yet when all is said, the public health situation of the Ndembu, as of most Africans, is highly unsatisfactory. Charles C. Hughes, in an admirable conspectus of the topic in non-literate groups,[1] surveys a wide spread of literature bearing on health to reach the conclusion, with George H. T. Kimball,[2] that " in the African social drama sickness has a strong claim to being arch-villain ". Poor hygiene, malnutrition, dietetic imbalance—partly produced by food taboos of a ritual character, the presence of liver disease, worm infestations or other intestinal diseases which interfere with absorption or storage, famine—all these and other environmentally and culturally determined conditions maintain health

---

[1] " Hygiene and Public Health in Nonliterate Societies ", presented at the Conference on Medicine and Anthropology at Arden House, Harriman, New York, in November, 1961, and shortly to be published under the joint sponsorship of the New York Academy of Medicine Committee on Special Studies and the Wenner-Gren Foundation for Anthropological Research.

[2] *Tropical Africa*, New York: Twentieth Century Fund (1960), Vol. II, p. 159.

at a chronically low level. The fact that a rich and elaborate system of ritual and magical beliefs and practices provides a set of explanations for sickness and death and gives people a false sense of confidence that they have the means of coping with disease does nothing towards raising the level of health or increasing the life-expectancy. Only better hygiene, a bigger and well balanced diet, the widespread use of prophylactic medicine and the extension of hospital facilities will slay the "arch-villain" disease and free the African from its ancient mastery.

BIBLIOGRAPHY

ACKERKNECHT, E. H. 1. " Problems of Primitive Medicine ", *Bulletin of the History of Medicine*, XI (1942), 503-21.

 2. " Natural Diseases and Rational Treatment in Primitive Medicine ", *Bulletin of the History of Medicine*, Vol. XIX, No. 5 (May, 1946).

BAUMANN, H. ... ... *Lunda: Bei Bauern und Jägern in Inner-Angola*, Berlin: Würfel-Verlag (1935).

EVANS-PRITCHARD, E. E. *Witchcraft, Oracles and Magic among the Azande*, London: O.U.P. (1937).

GOODALL, E. B. H. ... *Some Wemba Words*, London: O.U,P. (1921).

HUGHES, C. C. ... ... " Hygiene and Public Health in Nonliterate Societies ", paper presented at the Conference on Medicine and Anthropology at Arden House, Harriman, New York, in November, 1961, and shortly to be published under the joint sponsorship of the New York Academy of Medicine Committee on Special Studies and the Wenner-Gren Foundation for Anthropological Research.

KIMBALL, H. T. ... *Tropical Africa*, New York: Twentieth Century Fund (1960), Two vols.

LESSA, W. A., AND VOGT, E. Z. (Eds.). *Reader in Comparative Religion*, New York: Row, Peterson and Co. (1958).

McCULLOCH, M. ... *The Southern Lunda and Related Peoples*, Ethnographic Survey of Africa, ed. Daryll Forde, London: International African Institute (1951).

RIVERS, W. H. R. ... *Medicine, Magic and Religion*, London: O.U.P. (1924).

TURNER, V. W. ... 1. *Lunda Rites and Ceremonies*, Occasional Papers of the Rhodes-Livingstone Museum, New Series, No. 10 (1953).

2. *Schism and Continuity in an African Society*, Manchester University Press (1957).

3. " Muchona the Hornet, Interpreter of Religion ", in *In the Company of Man*, ed. J. Casagrande, New York: Harper Bros. (1960).

4. *Ndembu Divination: Its Symbolism and Techniques*, Rhodes-Livingstone Paper, No. 31, M.U.P. (1961).

5. " Ritual Symbolism, Morality and Social Structure among the Ndembu ", *Human Problems in British Central Africa*, Rhodes-Livingstone Journal No. XXX (December, 1961).

6. " Three Symbols of Passage in Ndembu Initiation Ritual ", *Essays on the Ritual of Social Relations*, ed. M. Gluckman, M.U.P. (1962).

7. *Chihamba the White Spirit*, Rhodes-Livingstone Paper No. 33 (1962).

8. " Themes in the Symbolism of Ndembu Hunting Ritual ", *Anthropological Quarterly*, Vol. 35, No. 2 (April, 1962).

WHITE, C. M. N.   ...   *Elements in Luvale Beliefs and Rituals*, Rhodes-Livingstone Paper, No. 32, M.U.P. (1961).

WILSON, M.   ...   ...   *Rituals of Kinship among the Nyakyusa*, London: O.U.P. (1957).

16

THE MATERIAL CULTURE
OF
THE AMBO OF NORTHERN RHODESIA

BRONISLAW STEFANISZYN

1964

FOREWORD

This Occasional Paper on " The Material Culture of the Ambo of Northern Rhodesia " has been written by Father Stefaniszyn who was for many years a Jesuit missionary in Northern Rhodesia. In the course of his mission work, Father Stefaniszyn, like many of his fellow-missionaries throughout the world, became deeply interested in the life of the peoples among whom he was living, and decided to make a serious study of their culture. Through this study which was spread over many years, he has become the fore-most, indeed, the only, authority on the Ambo people. As he mentions in his Preface, the results of his studies have been embodied in a Ph.D. dissertation, the major part of which is being published by the International African Institute. The present Paper contains that part of the dissertation that relates to the material culture of the Ambo.

The Rhodes-Livingstone Museum is pleased to be able to publish this valuable ethnographic study which will be appreciated not only by anthropologists and others interested in the Ambo but also by all those interested in the material culture of the Bantu-speaking peoples of Africa.

GERVAS CLAY.

Livingstone,
    January, 1964.

PREFACE

The material on which this paper is based was gathered during the periods, September, 1938 to May, 1943, and November, 1950 to June, 1953, while the paper itself forms part of a Ph.D. thesis presented to the University of the Witwatersrand.

The major portion of this thesis has been published as a monograph by the International African Institute under the title, *Social and Ritual Life of the Ambo of Northern Rhodesia*.

A number of people assisted me during my fieldwork and in the subsequent writing up of my results. This assistance I acknowledge in the preface to the above monograph. I would, here, however, like especially to thank the Trustees of the Rhodes-Livingstone Museum for enabling me to publish my work on Ambo material culture and Mr. Barrie Reynolds, the Keeper of Ethnography of the Museum, for his help in preparing the paper.

BRONISLAW STEFANISZYN.

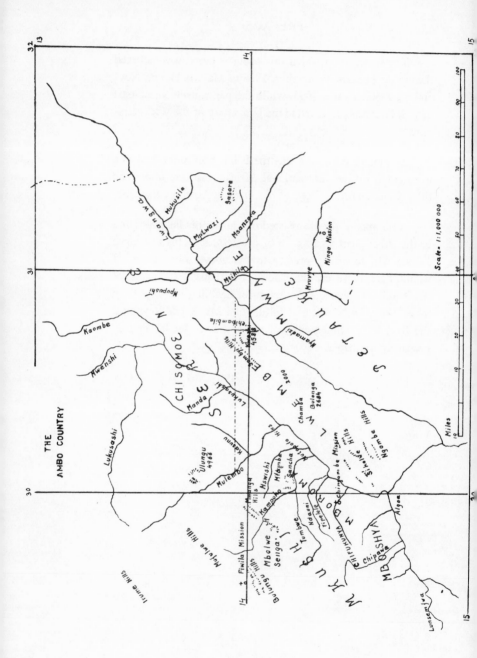

THE
AMBO COUNTRY

Scale = 1:1,000,000

Miles

Itume Hills

Mujelwe Hills

Lukusashi

Kaombe

Kwenshi

CHISOMO

Manda

Ulungu 4966

Katuna

Mulembo

+ Fiwila Mission

Mwenga Hills

Mbolwe

Bulunga

Senga'

Kampoko

Tumbwe

Ndauni

Firelele

Mbamba

Sancha

Sitahila

Mbolwe

Bulungu

Mulembo

Nswishi

Lwangwa

Mukusila

Mpukwazi

Sasara

Maanzara

FETAWA

Michilo

Mpupashi

Chibambila

4589

Emph.Hills

Namadzi

Mruye

Minga Mission

MBEL WA

Chamla

Bulenga 2684

Ngombe Hills

Sitahila Hills

Chigombe Mission

Chitukunya

Chipawa

Algoa

MBOSHYA

MKUSHI

Lunsenjya

CHAPTER I

INTRODUCTION

The Ambo occupy parts of three administrative districts of Northern Rhodesia, Mkushi, Serenje and Petauke. In the North, in the Chisomo country of Serenje District, they extend as far as latitude 13° 30' in the Lukusashi Valley and its tributaries. They also occupy the rest of the above mentioned valley which, in its lower reaches, lies in the other two districts, the right bank being in Mkushi District and the left bank in Petauke District. The rest of the tribe overflows eastwards to the Luangwa and beyond. To the west the tribe is settled on the left bank of the Lunsemfwa, from the Lukusashi confluence upstream.

The Ambo cultivate narrow strips of alluvial soils along the three main rivers, the Lukusashi, the Lunsemfwa and the Luangwa, and their tributaries. These coarse sandy loams passing to fine silts and clay-loams are characterised by mica particles and organic matter. They are covered with luxuriant thorn vegetation and form the mainstay of the valley agriculture. These belts of alluvial soils are less than a mile wide on the banks of the main rivers, and are even narrower along the tributaries. Since they retain moisture throughout the year the Ambo are able to grow four maize crops annually and to have available a plentiful supply of fresh vegetable relishes. In these gardens the Ambo also produce their main cash crop, tobacco.

The banks of the permanent streams and of those dry water courses which retain water below the ground during the dry season, are overgrown with luxuriant vegetation. This consists primarily of *Adina microcephala*, *Khaya nyasica* (*mululu*), *Trichilia emetica* (*musikisi*), *Acacia*, *Ficus* and *Kigelia pinnata* (*mufungula*). *Pennisetum purpureum* (*malenje*), buffalo grass, and *Phragmites communis* (*mitete*) grow close to the water.

On the western side of the Lukusashi, the valley spreads deeper inland, from five to eight miles and even farther along the bigger tributaries, till the range of Chifukunya is reached. This side of the valley is intersected by innumerable water-courses just as is the opposite side, but it is also enriched by quite a few rivers of considerable size and by streams which, in their lower reaches, flow for almost the whole of the year. The historic Mulembo, with a large number of villages along its banks and gardens, is navigable by canoe just as is its parallel neighbour, the Kampoko.

The belt adjoining the alluvial sandy loams is mature, heavy, brown soil of the *mopane* country forming at times nodules of lime concretions. This soil is covered sparsely with grass, and when soaked with rain becomes intractable. These clay soils are liable to large-scale sheet erosion. (Trapnell, 1943.)

Beyond the *mopane* belts rise numerous elevated tracts of barren shingle covered with scanty grass and dotted with sparse dwarfed *Mopane copaifera*, struggling for life. These give the valley a rather austere and arid outlook.

Among the *mopane* clays there are stretches of dark, grey-brown inferior and immature plateau soils, either colluvial from the escarpment rocks or residual from coarse grain sandstones with outcrops of underlying ferruginous sandstone. This soil, which covers flat stretches of the valley floor, is largely overgrown with *Brachystegia* (*musamba*) and *Bauhinia Thonningii* (*mufumbe*) and is left uncultivated.

Along the small streams, whole stretches of the banks are covered with *Oxytenanthera abyssinica* (*ntele*) or bamboo. This is used extensively in native building and homecrafts.

Game is represented by elephant, buffalo, a few eland, an occasional rhinoceros, roan antelope, kudu, impala in the *mopane*, water buck and a few reedbuck. Bushbuck are to be found by the streams and, in the *Brachystegia* woodlands, duiker; grysbok are also present in the area. Wild pigs are numerous and are a great nuisance to the maize growers. Warthogs roam everywhere. Zebra are found in the foothills of the escarpments, while hippopotami ravage winter gardens of maize. Lions pay a visit to each region a few times a year but maneaters are soon despatched. Leopards often take advantage of badly constructed hen and goat houses, as also do hyenas.

Cane-rats (*Thryonomys swinderianus*), though of smaller size than the above animals, are nevertheless very important in the valley economy. They perish in their thousands, especially in winter, and supply most families with meat several times a week.

Tsetse fly swarms on the left bank of the Lukusashi and on the Luangwa. In other parts it is found sporadically but it is seldom infected with sleeping sickness.

The rainy season begins in November and lasts till March. The average annual rainfall at Chingombe Mission in the Lukusashi Valley was 36.23 inches for the twenty-year period from 1929 to 1949. In Petauke, the mean minimum temperature is 64.5°F.; in Feira, 68°F.

[726]

The mean minimum temperature in the valleys lying between these two Government posts probably ranges between these two. In Petauke, the absolute maximum is 109°F. and in Feira 118°F. has been noted. April and May do not belong to the rainy season and do not constitute a part of the cold season, though the Ambo call these months *mwela* " winter ". Winter extends from June till the middle of August. After that period the dry hot season sets in till the rains. Chingombe Mission, although in the valley, is 1,700 feet above sea level. [1]

THE PEOPLE

The Ambo are considered to number some 10,000 and are distributed between the three administrative districts which they inhabit as follows:

District	Chiefdom	Population
Petauke	Mwape	
	Lwembe	
		1,000 (2)
Mkushi	Mboroma	2,980 ⎱ (3)
	Mboshya	1,918 ⎰
Serenje	Chisomo	3,955 (4)
	TOTAL	9,853

The density of the population of Chief Mboroma's country which measures 680 square miles, is five persons per square mile. Mboshya's chiefdom of 280 square miles has a density of seven per square mile. (Whiteley and Slaski, 1951). The density of the other three Ambo territories is about the same. The distribution of the population is, however, very uneven. Settlement is concentrated along the rivers

---

[1] and not 2,500 feet as stated in Trapnell (1943) and Whiteley and Slaski (1951).

[2] Tew (1951). The majority of the population in these chiefdoms is Nsenga. In 1957 I visited Mwape's country and found that only about three villages were of Ambo origin. I was informed that the adult population of these Ambo villages knew Ambo, but the younger generation spoke Nsenga and did not know Ambo. Even so, they are still proud of their origin and consider themselves Ambo.

[3] Information supplied by the District Commissioner's Office, Mkushi, based on figures collected in 1949.

[4] Based on Peters (1950). The chiefdom of Chisomo is not listed as Ambo in Whiteley and Slaski (1951) although the presence of Ambo in the chiefdom is mentioned as being probable. As a result of further enquiries the author now considers the chiefdom to be Ambo.

and streams, for the hills are forbidding, arid and stony and are cut by the gorges of watercourses. The stretches of *mopane* and *Brachystegia* country lying between the tributaries are also uninhabited. These areas are visited only by stray hunters and others in search of grubs, honey and building materials such as poles and bark strip.

On the rivers, however, life is bustling. People meet, children roam or fish, women wash and draw water, while men tend their weirs and fish traps. Beyond the immediate vicinity of the river or stream with its *Phragmites* and *Pennisetum* background, lie sorghum gardens. In these, agricultural activity goes on all the year round, with a brisk or slow tempo according to the season.

Beyond the gardens stand compact villages on elevated ground. These villages are linked by broad hoed paths running along the bank of the river or tributary. Each group of villages is linked by a similar hoed path with the next inhabited tributary. The pattern of habitation on big rivers is the same, except that the size of the river and the number of villages warrant a hoed path on each bank of the river, whereas on the streams one path is sufficient, crossing from one bank to the other and back again as the need may be.

The chiefdom of Chisomo lies on both banks of the Lukusashi. The territory extends, in the east, to the Luangwa where it borders on the chiefdom of Mwape. To the north and west, the boundary runs along the western escarpment. To the south, the boundary runs straight through the bush, parallel with and not far from the Chikufwe stream.

Most of the villages are at present to be found on the banks of the Lukusashi and on its eastern tributary, the Kaombe. The villages on the Manda, the Chikufwe and the right bank of the Luangwa have been abandoned.

Their geographical position enables the Chisomo people to maintain contact with the Lala to the west and to the north. In the latter direction they mingle with the Bisa. They show less interest, especially nowadays, in the districts down the Lukusashi. This social isolation of the Chisomo people from the rest of their tribe is accentuated by their modification of the Ambo dialect through Bisa influence. Their vocabulary often differs strikingly from that in common use in other Ambo chiefdoms.

South of the Chisomo chiefdom, mainly between the left bank of the Lukusashi and the right bank of the Luangwa, is situated the chiefdom of Lwembe. In the southern parts of this chiefdom, there is a compact group of Nsenga and only a few Ambo.

[728]

In pre-European times, the whole of the Ambo part of the Lukusashi Valley, below the confluence with the Mulembo, was included in the chiefdom which is now called Mboroma. The boundary between Mboroma chiefdom and what was, at that time, the Mwape chiefdom and is today the Lwembe chiefdom, was the Muchinga range, but the British Administration has now fixed the Lukusashi as the boundary. An old aristocratic Ambo once remarked to the author: " It is the Whites that made the Lukusashi a boundary. It is the Muchinga which divides the people, not the river ".

Opposite the Lwembe chiefdom, on the eastern bank of the Luangwa, another Ambo chiefdom, that of Mwape, extends in the regions of the Mvuvye River and the Mtikili stream. However, this chiefdom is considered Ambo only on historical and not ethnic grounds.

The chiefdom of Mboshya occupies the left bank of the Lunsemfwa with its centre along the Chipawa, one of the tributaries. To the west, the Mboshya chiefdom extends to the Lwano country, having as the boundary the watercourse of Tufinshi; to the east, the chiefdom reaches the Tumbwe stream which divides it from the neighbouring chiefdom of Mboroma. The northern boundary of the Mboshya chiefdom is the escarpment of the Chifukunya range. The speech of Mboshya's people shows occasional Soli elements.

The central Ambo chiefdom of Mboroma, of which some boundaries have already been indicated, extends in the south to the Lukusashi-Lunsemfwa confluence. In the west, it is enclosed by the same mountain range as the Mboshya country and, in the north, it stretches to the Mulembo.

History

The history of the Ambo is based on still recent and fairly reliable tradition.

As the original home of the Ambo, the country of the Luba is indicated. The Ambo left Luba country and settled on the Luapula River. The reasons given for this migration are scarcity of land and over-population. From the Luapula, the Ambo were led to Bukanda which lies in what is now the Congo. Later, the Ambo, under the leadership of the sons of the Aushi chief, Makumba Chawala, left Bukanda and moved to Nsenga country. Even today, the country of the Ambo is called Nsenga country. There is still a flow of immigrants from Bukanda and, in many villages, men and women are to be found whose parents were born in Bukanda. No doubt, the sons of the renowned chief of the Aushi set out to found new chiefdoms for themselves because, in their matrilineal society, succession to their father's office was denied to them. Even so their matrilineal clan, the Nyendwa, must have been of chiefly status, for the Nyendwa at that time seemed to have held sway over the Lala.

The first to settle on the Mulembo, was Mambwe Chisaka of the Mpande shell clan. Hence, the head of the matrilineage of this clan on the Mulembo acted like a feudal lord, a kind of sub-chief, because the chief did not exercise direct jurisdiction over the Mulembo country. (Such is the claim of the Mpande shell clan. As will be seen later, Lungo may have been the first Ambo settler. Lungo, however, was subject to the local Nsenga chief Mumba Chundu (Mbachundu) whom Mambwe Chisaka ousted). The head of the matrilineage of the Mpande shell clan on the Mulembo, with the hereditary name of Chikwashya, holds also a prominent ritual position as the burier of the chiefs, the senior sacrificer to the chiefs' spirits and the keeper of the chiefs' graveyard.

Kunda mpanda (patronymic: Tande)—When Mambwe Chisaka settled in his village on the Mulembo, his half brother, Kunda Mpanda of the Nyendwa clan, came to live with him for a time. Tradition has it that Kunda wanted to marry the daughter of Lungo of the Fish clan. Lungo was not agreeable to the marriage and fled with his family to the Mulembo River. The marriage of Kunda and Lungo's daughter, Kaluba of the Clay clan, was considered incestuous, because Kunda and Lungo were half brothers. Kunda was at a loss where to find Lungo and sought him over a wide area, even as far as the Zambezi and Chongwe rivers. Finally he found and killed him. The tradition, though embellished with stories, seems to be true. Offerings are made to this day to Kunda Mpanda, to Lungo, to Mambwe Chisaka, to Kaluba, the wife of Kunda, as well as to Mbachundu. The descendants of all these ancestors are still to be found along the Mulembo.

It is rather difficult to assign even an approximate date to this migration. Lane Poole (1934) quotes Lacerda's mention of the Ambo in 1798:

" According to the testimony of the natives of Kazembe, on the south are Alambas and the Ambos, peaceful friends of the Casembe who trade, they declare, with the caffres at Zumbo."

Lane Poole thinks that this is the section of the Ambo under Mboroma mentioned by Livingstone sixty years later. However, Lane Poole places the existence of the Ambo under Mboroma too early, according to his own calculations. Mboroma and all the Ambo under him are direct descendants of Kunda and Kunda's followers in Nsenga valleys. Lane Poole assigns the migration of Kunda to 1845. The Ambo mentioned by Lacerda can easily be identified with the Ambo of Chief Namupala in Bukanda. In Lane Poole's view, Lacerda's mention is conclusive evidence that the Ambo reached the Zambezi. There is no tradition, however, of their migration to the Zambezi. The explanation may be that the Ambo traded with the natives at Zumbo without actually settling on the river.

Kunda Mpanda did not stay long with Mambwe Chisaka but set out on an expedition against the Nsenga. In his three expeditions, he overcame and killed three Nsenga chiefs, Mumpanje, Munsingwa and Misaya. In his last expedition he lost his life in the war with Chief Nkana Yarobe. Lane Poole (ibid.) writes that the successor of Kunda, Chirimba Nondo, led the retaliatory expedition against Nkana Yarobe. The Lukusashi tradition, held by men not of the Mpande shell clan (such as Mulaku), is that Chirimba was still in Bukanda with Namupala, when the half brother, Mambwe Chisaka, with his clansmen and other auxiliaries such as Chief Chipepo of the Lenje, made the expedition. Chief Nkana Yarobe was killed in revenge for Kunda Mpanda. Thus ended the Nsenga wars. The head of Nkana Yarobe was taken to the grave of Makumba Chawala.

On the defeat of Nkana Yarobe, Mambwe Chisaka recovered the skin of Kunda Mpanda and buried it on the site of the village on the Mulembo where he and Kunda had lived. This was the beginning of the exclusive graveyard of the successors of Kunda Mpanda. The matrilineal descendants of Mambwe Chisaka, who are the heads of the matrilineage of the Mpande shell clan settled on the Mulembo have, since that time, acted as the official buriers and guardians of the graveyard of the chiefs. The name of the Mwimbwa River was then changed into the Mulembo in honour of the grave of Kunda Mpanda.

Kunda Mpanda gained the honorific name of Kankomba, which means, " Scraper of the (Relish) Pot " ! Western Lala and Swaka tradition refers this name to a fifth-generation ancestor of Kunda, but the Ambo refers it to Kunda Mpanda. The story goes that when young he indulged in scraping the relish pot. This name became a title of honour, with emotional content, for all successors of Kunda occupying the seat of the chiefdom now known as Mboroma. All the Ambo, of whatever chiefdom, call themselves " the subjects of the Kankomba " (*bene* Kankomba). This title is not applied to other Nyendwa chiefs, at least not by the Ambo (c.f. Munday, 1940. 436).

Chirimba Nondo—After the death of Kunda, his sister's son, Chirimba Nondo, succeeded him. During Chirimba's reign there was peace in the country. He is credited with having formed a chiefdom for his sister Mwape to be held in the female line. He also founded the chiefdom of Mboshya.

Mubanga—After the death of Chirimba, Mubanga was chosen as the great chief, but little is known of him. After his death, three brothers occupied the stool of the Kankomba, Bwashi, Chibuye and Lwembe. They were Chirimba's sister's sons.

Bwashi—The eldest of the three brothers was Bwashi. He lived, not in Nsenga country but among the Swaka at the hill of Katukutu. Bwashi ruled an extensive territory spreading to the Kabwe (the present Broken Hill), and to the Mulembo which divided his lands from those of Chibale. According to Chikwashya, Bwashi was killed by the Ngoni. His body was brought to the Mulembo where it was buried. During this time his younger brother, Chibuye, was chief of the Lukusashi Valley.

Chibuye—During Bwashi's reign, Chibuye made an important division of the territory he administered. He installed his sons on various streams as sub-chiefs. All who came to settle on these streams had to ask their permission. These sub-chiefs had hunting rights in the adjoining bush. To buy hunting rights from the owner cost three elands. The skins of lions and leopards killed in the area had also to be given to him. These sons of the chief offered sacrifices for rain to the chief's spirit. The sons of the chief had the privilege of sitting on a stone as a mark of distinction and, according to local explanation, as a symbol of their power. They could also afford to surround their villages with palisades.

Chibuye was hailed as " The Peace-maker ". He had, for his southern neighbours, the Chikunda under Kayetano and he must have come to an agreement with them. The Ngoni did not dare to encroach upon the Chikunda sphere of influence.

Chief Chibuye seemed to have reigned with deference to his elder brother Bwashi. After the death of Bwashi, Chibuye was accepted as the paramount, the Kankomba, but he did not reign for many years. Chibuye died when Chikwashya Kakote was about twelve years of age. Since Chikwashya died in 1955 at the age of about eighty, Chibuye must have died about 1890. After the death of Chibuye, his younger brother, Lwembe II Mukombola (the Hunter of Elephants), succeeded him but died after only one year.

Mboroma I—Chinda Mboroma Chontabunga was the sister's son of the three brothers who one after another occupied the seat of the Kankomba. Mboroma lived with Chief Namupala in Bukanda who, however, sent him away because he was quarrelsome. Mboroma entered the service of Bwashi in a capacity which seemed to have been congenial to him. During the reign of Bwashi as the Kankomba, Mboroma served him as his right-hand man. Mboroma was sent everywhere to carry out the Chief's orders. After the death of the three brothers, Mboroma, as their sister's son and having served them all for so many years, claimed the chieftainship. When Mboroma declared himself the Kankomba, the great chief, he toured the country but treated the nobles, that is the sons of chiefs, and the princes, members of the ruling Nyendwa clan, harshly, executing them on the least suspicion of plotting against him. Thus he made a reputation for himself of being a despot.

He fought Chief Namupala, Chief Mboshya and the sons of Lwembe, Chembe and Munsunki. The reason for the first two wars was that Namupala and Mboshya opposed his chieftainship. Mboshya used, as a pretext for his hostilities, the fact that Mboroma killed a Nyendwa prince, Chipwitima, on the orders of Bwashi. Mboroma fought the sons of Lwembe in order to restore the chiefly monopoly of ivory which they no longer respected. He was not successful in any of his wars. In the end, he settled on the Chisera Stream near Irume Hill in order to be far from the raiding Ngoni. In such a raid, however, the Ngoni burned the chief's heirlooms, the bows of his predecessors. Mboroma died in an accident at the Kangosa stream near the Lunsemfwa when he inadvertently pulled the trigger of a harpoon trap.

While Mboroma wandered, fought and then settled on the Lala Plateau at Irume Hill, the most important person with any political prestige on the lower Lukusashi was the remaining son of Chibuye, Nkumpa Nkowama. The lower Lukusashi and adjoining regions fell under the sway of the Chikunda. The Chikunda, of Maravi stock, are a branch of the so-called Nyungwe-speaking peoples, living along the Zambezi in Portuguese East Africa. Led by Portuguese half-castes, they were soldiers of fortune, the Bantu condottieri, and although originally drawn from many tribes, spoke Nyungwe. Unlike the Ngoni, they were all armed with flint-lock and percussion guns. While their own interpretation of the word "Chikunda" is "soldier", their main occupation was not raiding but trading in ivory, slaves, calico, guns and gunpowder, and probably beads. Occasionally, they had to fight to protect their trade and their friends, who were often business friends. Their renowned leader, Matekenya, operated on the eastern bank of the Luangwa. On the western bank was another leader, Kayetano, with the local nickname of Chilalamukoro or Chimtanda. The Ambo had to deal with either Kayetano or Matekenya and no Ambo chiefdom escaped the attentions of these warlords. Kayetano had his headquarters on the Nyonga stream, a tributary which joins the Lunsemfwa a few miles below the Lukusashi-Lunsemfwa confluence. Kayetano was probably active in the Ambo lands between 1870 and 1890. He was ousted by an Englishman, Harrison Clarke (Changa-changa).

[733]

The chiefdom of Mboshya was involved in hostilities with Kayetano, because his Chikunda killed a wife of Mboshya Mambwe Lukakanya in a raid. Therefore Mambwe sent his ivory to Matekenya for sale, by-passing Kayetano. This slight enraged Kayetano and caused a clash of arms between him and Mambwe. Hostilities dragged on for two years. Mambwe plotted to massacre a Chikunda settler on the Chingombe, Martinyu, with his people, but Martinyu, warned in time by his Ambo friends, fled. This incident is sometimes described as the burning of a Portuguese administrative post and resistance to Portuguese occupation.

After the death of Chinda Mboroma, Mubanga Kalutwa became the Kankomba. During his reign British Administration was established. He died in 1921 and was succeeded by his sister's son, Lubula Mpapilwa Komanga, who died in 1932. Komanga was succeeded by his sister's son, the present Mboroma, Chisenga Lishyoka.

Mwape—This sister of Chirimba lived near the Chibambira-Luangwa confluence. She gained a reputation for benevolence and good government but was, however, called Namutola, " who takes somebody's children ", and also Namukwanga, " who smashes people ". Her other name was Nachikwakululu, " who descended from heaven ". As her lands lay in an exposed position, she had her sister's son, Lwembe I, posted as her defender. Her principal husband was Katibula of the Elephant clan. (Lane Poole, 1934. 69).

Mwape Namutola was succeeded by her daughter, Changwe, whose official name was Mwape wa Chibambira, " Mwape of the Chibambira ".[1] She was a ruthless woman, assassinating her adversaries and rivals on the Luangwa. She was able to develop an imperialist outlook far above that of her Ambo contemporaries.

Her most notorious assassination was that of a headman, Mushyalira. This involved her in hostilities with Matekenya. She was defeated and had to flee to Bemba country. After her return to her lands, she quarrelled with and fought Chikwashya. During a pause in the hostilities she assassinated Mkwemba, the heir of Lwembe II. This deed aroused against her Kayetano who also supported his ally, Chikwashya. She was besieged in a stockade on the Chirumbu but her son-in-law, Ntimba, raised the siege. Lane Poole (ibid. 72) states that Mwape, after the victory over Chikwashya, reigned as the chief of all the Ambo.

---

[1] This is the current opinion. However, according to the chronicle of Richard Chimkoko, deposited in the Historical Collection of the Rhodes-Livingstone Museum, the second chieftainness was Chibuye Mtondo. Mwape's succession to the office probably took place about 1880. In 1888, Mwape came into contact with the German prospector Karl Wiese (Lane Poole, 1934. 72). Stephenson describes Mwape (II) of the Chibambira whom he had met in 1900 as being 30–40 years old. (Stephenson, 1937. 44). .

It has to be granted that she was supreme on the Luangwa but she was never the Kankomba, is not buried among the Kankombas, and never intervened in the Lukusashi Valley, except against Chikwashya.

Mwape II followed the practice of the chiefs' clan in choosing her own husbands. She used her right in her own manner, becoming a polyandrist with a harem of seven husbands (Stephenson, 1937. 84). Thus she became an exact counterpart of a male Nyendwa chief. The male children born to Mwape were put to death together with their fathers, though Lwembe III, Chimkoko, who was her son, seems to have been spared. Mwape II submitted to British rule and died in 1910. She was succeeded by her daughters, Nachilashya and Mwandu, and then by her grand-daughter, Chisenga, who became Mwape V.

Lwembe—Lwembe was not an independent chief but a defender of chieftainness Mwape in the east, as has already been observed. He was, however, a ruler of the lands he conquered and a colonising pioneer, building his first village on the Chifukuzi stream. His achievements gained him the honorific title, Lwembe Inyanja Inyalungu Intumpaula, which means " as large as a lake and as difficult to seize as a ball ". The Chisanga Valley was given by Chief Chirimba to his other sister, Kalimbangoma. This valley was taken over by another Lwembe, Mukombola ("the Hunter of Elephants "), brother of Bwashi and Chibuye. Lwembe III, Chimkoko, was established by the British as an independent chief.

Some Nyendwa princes built villages of their own but did not reach the full status of territorial chiefs. Such was Lwembe at the beginning and also Mairi, who settled on the Nyonga stream before Chimtanda and was killed by the Ngoni. There is no tradition, as Lane Poole maintains (1934. 68), of war between the Ambo and the Lala on account of Mairi's death.

Chisenga and Muliro founded two small Ambo chiefdoms under the Nyendwa, but these chiefdoms no longer exist. Similarly, on the lower Lunsemfwa there was a chieftainness, Chitambo wa Kalinda, who broke away from the Mboshya matrilineage of the Nyendwa clan. Her country was given by the British to Nyarugwe, a Chikunda elephant hunter.

Chisomo—Chisomo chiefdom differs from all other Ambo chiefdoms in that it has no genealogical link with Kunda Mpanda's segment of the Nyendwa, but was founded by Chief Chibale. There have been four Chisomo chiefs. The most famous was Nsangwe II Chitemwarwo (" who does the fighting "). He fought three wars against the Ngoni and repulsed them. He also fought the Bayongo (Bemba) and the Chikunda. He died at an advanced age in 1941.

[735]

CHAPTER II

PHYSICAL CHARACTERISTICS, CLOTHING AND DECORATION

Though there has been a large influx of foreigners, men marrying matrilocally, with an ensuing admixture of additional racial types, nevertheless the tribe shows, in certain respects, a marked tendency to develop some uniform and characteristic features. These valley people usually possess a rather poor physique and seldom does one meet tall, well-built men and women. Both are inclined to be short in stature by European standards. As a general rule, people are lean and thin, while men have markedly thin calves to their legs. Features are usually irregular and rugged in contrast to those of the neighbouring Nsenga and Chikunda.

The colour of their skin is, in the majority of cases, dark brown or nearly black, though there are individuals of somewhat lighter colour. They hardly ever attain the light brown complexion so common among South African tribes. The Ambo themselves are well aware of these colour differences and make distinction between the *baswesi*, the " brown ones ", and *bafisi*, the " black ones ". Jet black individuals are fairly common. The Lwano people, and there are many of them among the Ambo, have the reputation of being very dark. Newly-born babies are of very light colour but in a few days the pigment appears. Albinos are rare.

The hair of a new-born babe is soft and wavy, and grows hard and curly only after it is cut. Some children are born without hair, some with brown hair and some with black hair. In former times, there were a number of traditional hair styles. For *cilafuteni*, which was worn only by chiefs, the temples and the back of the head were shaved and hair was left only on the top of the head. *Mwala* consisted of a ridge or mane of hair, one and a half inches in width, which ran from the forehead to the back of the neck. If the mane was smeared with castor oil and red powder, the style was called *cisome*. These two styles were used only by women. *Cikuba* was the same as *mwala* but with the addition of hair tufts on the temples. For *kasusu*, which was worn by men, a tuft of hair was left at the front. Nowadays, men and women also shave their heads or trim their hair, so that it is about half an inch in length above the forehead and shorter towards the crown. Youths try to imitate European hair styles, straightening their hair with a hot brick. Hair clippings are carefully buried to prevent witches or sorcerers stealing them.

[736]

Ambo men shave their faces clean. Pubic hair and hair in the armpits of the husband is shaven by his wife who does the same for herself. A hairy man is looked upon as strong though prolific body hair is seldom seen.

Finger nails are cut short with razors and the parings are buried for fear of sorcery.

Some men and women chip off parts of the two upper incisors to make a triangular notch. Nowadays this is done with a file but formerly a flint was used. He who has a space between his two upper front teeth is called *mucena*, while *mpiki* is the name given to one whose teeth are not in a straight line. In the morning, before washing the face the mouth is rinsed (*kusukasa*), and the teeth are rubbed with a stick of *rempundu* split to make a toothbrush. (c.f. Lagercrantz, 1950. 324). Sticks of *funde* (*Vellozia retinervis*) and of *mucenje* (*Diospyros mespiliformis*) are also used. While washing in the river, the mouth is rinsed with water and sand. After meals it is rinsed with cold water.

When cleaning the nose (*kufyora*), the nostrils are squeezed slightly between the thumb and forefinger, the nose is blown and the mucus is rubbed off with a small stick drawn upwards from the upper lip. Another way is to press one nostril while the other nostril is blown and then repeat the action for the first nostril. The fingers are cleaned by rubbing them on the forearm or against the sole of the foot. The mucus is covered with earth if it is cast in the village for people are loath to tread upon it.

When micturating, men stand with legs apart; women bend a little forward with legs also apart, though when there are people about as at beer drinks, they kneel.

When defecating both sexes stamp the grass or earth flat, crouch, and afterwards draw their buttocks over the ground (*kusinda*). The excrement is not buried.

On sneezing (*kwentimuna*), a person mentions his or her father's clan, or rather the bystanders do it for him. The author was unable to discover any reason for this custom.

When sleeping, people usually lie on their side (*kulala mukabeya*) with legs slightly bent. To lie on one's back (*buisaneme*) or on the stomach (*bwifuneme*) is less common. The traditional wooden pillow, ornamented or artistically carved, is falling into disuse, a short log being used instead. All sleep naked, wrapping themselves with a blanket and completely covering the head. Small boys sleep near the fire (*mutuntumina*) in the boys' huts, though without blankets.

[737]

Although at home men like to sit on stools, at beer parties they sit on the ground or on mats with their legs outstretched (*kutambalala*) or with one leg laid upon the other. A comfortable posture in company is *bukankala*, sitting with the legs bent at the knees and held apart at a wide angle, the elbows resting on the knees. This way of sitting is considered most virile. Women do not sit so and it would be arrogant to sit *bukankala* in front of a chief.

Another way of sitting is *kusonkama*. The buttocks rest on the heels and the knees are kept apart. This is commonly employed at meal-times. Another form of *kusonkama* is for one buttock to rest on its corresponding heel and for the other leg, though sharply bent at the knee, to be pushed forward in front of the crouching body. The knees are kept apart. This second form of *kusonkama* is used for a short time when greeting or making a request as well as when eating. The most respectful position, used especially in sacrifices and before the chief, is to sit crosslegged on the ground (*bukunda*). To sit European fashion, with one leg crossed over the other, is considered arrogant.

Women as a rule avoid sitting on stools, preferring the bare ground or a mat. The most popular and comfortable position is sitting on the ground with legs outstretched, or with one leg bent at the knee, which rests on the ground, and the shin turned towards the other thigh. When greeting a chief, elders, or their husbands, women kneel, sitting on their heels. This is done for a few moments when clapping a salute to the chief or passing something to the husband. Then the position is changed; the woman sits sideways on the ground with her knees bent. Women may also sit sideways with their knees bent and their legs tucked beneath them. They may also sit *bukunda*. The last two positions are rather informal and are infrequently practised.

Men can walk much farther and faster than can women, therefore when a journey together is planned, the men shorten the length of the day's walk for the women's sake. Villagers like to set out just at dawn. They are loath to walk at mid-day, and in the hot season, when returning home from a neighbouring village some distance away, they will wait until the sun " softens " (*kanaka kasuba*). The Ambo do not like to travel in the rain but wait till it stops. " The rain has blocked us " (*mfula yatusinkira*) is the excuse.

In the hot season, women may pound meal as early as three a.m., going at dawn to their gardens to heap stalks and weeds into piles ready for burning. At about nine a.m. they cease work and seek shelter in the village from the scorching sun. Both men and women bathe between noon and two p.m., being careful to bathe below the spot where they draw water.

[738]

Women carry loads on their heads, though seldom without a head pad or ring (*nkate*) made of cloth or of twisted grass bound with string. Men also carry loads in the same way but were observed to do so only for Europeans. It is more common for them to use a forked carrying stick (*mumani*), the load, perhaps of tobacco plugs, salt or grain, being tied in the fork. The stick rests on the shoulder, with the load behind. The stick is supported in front with one hand; the other holds an axe, spear or stick across the other shoulder to support the load. Game animals or a human corpse are suspended from a pole (*kutemba*) carried by two men.

When walking, Ambo men like to hold, with both hands, a spear, a gun or an axe across their shoulders, at the back of the neck, in a horizontal position. An axe is frequently carried with the head hooked over the shoulder. Elderly men on a journey often wear sandals (*sapato*). These nowadays are made from a motor-car tyre; formerly hide was used. Two thongs run from between the first and second toes, across the foot, and end, one on each side of the instep. Both ends of these thongs are tied or sewn to the sole. Another thong is tied to the rear end of each thong and passes behind the heel.

Although there is nothing wrong in pointing a finger at somebody, this is avoided in a quarrel for it is considered provocative. Ambo children have an equivalent for sticking out the tongue in defiance. They make a sound not unlike the squeak of a mouse by sucking air between pursed lips (*kusyora*). Young women also do this. Men fight with sticks, women with open palms, clinging and biting.

During a proposal a girl looks in the other direction. Kissing is unknown but a mother will touch the child with her face as if she were smelling it.

Women carry their babies on their backs supported by a cloth (*cipapilo*). This is tied above the breasts, passed round the back of the child and fastened again in front round the woman's belt. Another less common way of carrying is for the cloth to run over one shoulder and under the opposite armpit, the ends being knotted over the breasts. This is called " the Ngoni way " (*cingoni*).

Surprise and sorrow are both expressed by opening the mouth, covering it with the right hand and saying, " Mama, mama " (the first is high-pitched). Disgust is shown by frowns and adverse comments. In shame, the eyes are cast down.

Before the advent of European goods men and women wore bark cloth. All women, from early childhood, wear a string of beads (*cinkole ca rubunda*) round their waist, claiming that without them they would look like men. The shape and size of the beads are described later in this chapter. Although beads of various colours are used, these colours are of no special significance. From a cloth band or the bead string hangs a flap of cloth to cover the private parts (*bukusi*).

Nkunsa is a cloth skirt wrapped round the body and tucked in at the waist. With men it reaches the knees as does the loin cloth; with women it falls to the ankles. *Mfundafwale* is a long cloth wrapped round the body above the breasts and falling to below the knees. At the waist the cloth is bound with a handkerchief. This handkerchief is folded in half to form a triangle which covers the buttocks, two corners being brought round the waist and tied at the front. This fashion is the most common dress of needy women such as divorcees, widows and young girls. Blue print is preferred though black is also popular. The handkerchief is usually white. Young women with wage-earning husbands wear blue blouses with *nkunsa*. Some fifteen years ago *mfundafwale* was the most common form of dress. Today, however, European dresses are becoming fashionable among girls and young women.

For a *mubinde* skirt, a cloth is wrapped over the buttocks and is tied at the front of the waist by two corners. The flowing part at the back is brought forward between the legs and tucked over the initial knot. The end of the cloth is then left dangling free in front of the legs. *Mubinde* is worn nowadays by small boys. Many boys wear only the last remnants of a *mubinde*, a triangular rag a few inches wide.

Munkonda—The end of the *mubinde* cloth, comprising two corners, may be tucked away under the frontal knot. If it is too long, it is not left hanging free but is brought upwards over the chest and tied by the two remaining corners at the back of the neck. Another variation is practised when one of the two remaining corners is passed under one shoulder and across the back, and is tied over the opposite shoulder with the first corner coming up across the chest. *Munkonda* is used nowadays by boys.

The most common garments for young and middle-aged men are khaki shorts and a shirt, either white or black. The latter is often worn outside the shorts. Elderly men prefer the *nkunsa* loin cloth, mostly of white, sometimes of black, occasionally of blue print, with a khaki shirt flowing free. The younger generation have taken to trousers, jackets and shoes.

At present, tiny seed beads of varied colours with a diameter of less than one-sixteenth of an inch are in vogue. The girls and the women make wristlets, necklaces and headbands of them. A necklace

[740]

of a single string has a few similar bead string pendants, two to three inches long, attached at the front. The necklace is worn close to the throat. Girls plait head pendants which hang at the back of the head. At the front of a bead necklace a large triangular bead is often inserted. Such may in fact be inserted anywhere in the necklace. *Makosa* wristlets, wire bangles made of twisted thin brass, copper or aluminium wire spaced with beads of beaten pieces of metal, are still worn. These metal beads are made by cutting thicker wire. Anklets (*minkonka*) of the same twisted wire were worn a few years ago but they have now gone out of fashion.

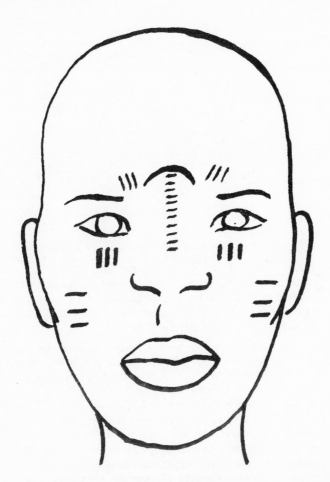

Fig 1—Tattooing on an Ambo woman's face

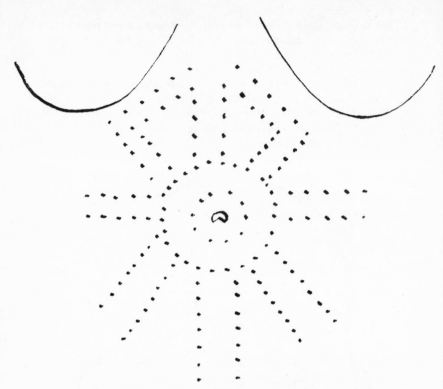

Fig. 2—Scarifications on the abdomen, focussed on the navel

All Ambo termed *bene Kankomba*, the subjects of the founder-chief Kankomba, display tattoo marks (*musibula*), comprising four groups of four vertical cuts on the forehead. They are worn by both men and women and run the whole breadth of the forehead. Women also cut rosettes (*kacebula*) under the eyes.

Scarification is preferred for the body, tattooing for the face. From the Nsenga women was adopted the *citopole*, a bow or an arch between the eyes above the nose. Under the bow, which is a curved line half an inch long with the bulge upwards, there are two or three vertical dashes. *Citopole* is very common. Tattooing is done by rubbing powdered charcoal into a cut. These are, or were, ornamental scarifications. Actually, the Ambo are much more scarified for medicinal purposes, which for them include magical purposes as well. Medicinal and magical scarifications are simple scars not blackened with charcoal. Women are elaborately scarified all over the body especially on the chest, stomach and thighs.

[742]

In former times, women had the upper and lower lips pierced. While still girls they enlarged the holes so that a disc of ivory, almost an inch in diameter, could be inserted. It is doubtful whether the Ambo women practised this custom widely. It seems to have been more a Nsenga custom. The Ambo chieftainness, Mwape of the Chibambira, is reported to have had these lip perforations. (Stephenson, 1937. 45). More common are smaller perforations in the upper lip in which leaden nails or ivory plugs, three-sixteenths of an inch or more in diameter, are inserted. In the 1930's, middle-aged women still wore these ornaments in their lips, but by the 1940's young women had ceased this practice. This disc and later the nail was called *cinanta*.

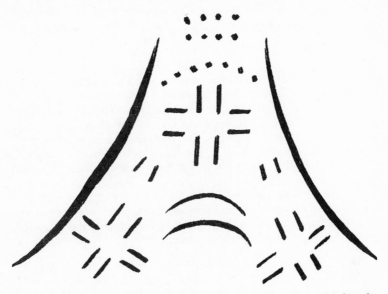

Fig. 3—Scarifications on the upper part of the body, between and below the breasts

CHAPTER III

THE VILLAGE

Villages shift every few years though usually they keep to one stream or one stretch of a big river, and few move more than three miles from the old site. It is difficult to assess the average time that a village stays in one place because no records are kept. The village of Kaumbo at the confluence of the Chingombe and the Lukusashi stayed in one place for fourteen years. The village of Markopo, however, shifted in 1939 and by 1950 was already on its fourth site including the site of 1938.

The reason for the sudden shifting of a village and its partial dispersal may be frequent deaths within a relatively short period—for example, three to four deaths within a year. Thus the village of Markopo on its new site in 1939 was big and prosperous. It won a reputation for having a plentiful food supply. Then within a year and a few months some four or five deaths occurred. The alarmed villagers said: " There is a sorcerer at work in the village. We shall all soon be finished ". New large houses were abandoned and villagers built rough shelters (*matungu*), each in his own garden. The gardens were still used because they were new and fertile. After a year or more, and when the spate of deaths had apparently ceased, fear subsided and the villagers reassembled in a new place.

The change of a village site, however, can usually be traced to two factors combined. Firstly, after several years the dwelling huts become dilapidated and are not worth repairing. The dwellings are eaten by termites and infested with cockroaches and ticks. Secondly, the gardens have become exhausted and new ones must be sought. Ambo villages are seldom far from their gardens; therefore, the village has to move nearer to the new gardens. Apart from rational grounds for moving a village, sometimes motives are advanced which do not sound rational, such as the suggestion that the village would be happier on another site.

Headman Mulaku of the village of Nkumpa planned to move from the Lukusashi to the Lunsemfwa, a good day's march, in order to have better hunting grounds. His men, however, refused to shift, threatening to desert the village. The village was then moved only one mile.

[744]

When in 1942, at the village of Kaputi, the crops failed owing to drought, the headman suggested shifting the village a distance of some three hours' walk to the Kanyansa stream. In 1950 his people grumbled when they suffered another setback due to drought, hinting that a drought is not a sufficient reason to move a village because it may happen anywhere. While soil suitable for the cultivation of sorghum may easily be found in any area, only on the old site did they have plenty of fish and game.

Before choosing a new village site many factors are considered. A permanent supply of drinking water must be within easy walking distance; the ground must not be so stony that hut-poles cannot easily be driven into it; the place must not be muddy nor subject to floods, whilst an area overrun by buffalo beans or other pests is avoided. Therefore, as a rule an Ambo village will be found near a river or a stream on raised but not stony ground. When a village is due to shift the disadvantages of the new site are fully discussed. If possible two major tasks, the making of new fields and the building of the new village, are not done at the same time. However, this may be necessary when crops fail and there is no good soil nearby. Such was the case with the village of Kaputi mentioned above.

A decision to move the village is taken one evening after supper by all the villagers assembled in the village shelter of the headman (*citenge*). All are supposed to agree. The women usually reserve their judgment and approval until they have seen and tried the new place. If it is far away men are sent there after the meeting to examine the new site, unless this has already been done. As has already been pointed out, a village usually moves only a mile or so along the stream, so often there is no need for this.

Men choose their fields under the leadership of the headman, marking the boundaries by cutting saplings. The headman has the first choice. Old women, widows and divorced women, lacking male assistance, choose lands where few trees have to be felled. Strong men like the land with big trees, the sign of fertile soil.

The cutting of trees for new gardens begins in March, at the end of the rainy season. If the new gardens are distant, men go to the new site and put up rough shelters of branches (*mitanda*). They stay at the new place some four days at a time, cutting trees until their provisions are exhausted.

The new site of a village is called *musokorwe;* the old village when abandoned is referred to as *matongo*.

[745]

Villagers move their village to the new site in the cold season, in July or August, after having gathered the harvest. Before the women move, the men put up shelters or construct the walls of the huts. Poles are driven into the ground at intervals, and between them grass is placed vertically and fastened with withes and bark strings, running from one pole to another on both sides of the grass wall. Roofs are not needed at this time of year. Proper huts are built slowly and at intervals, when garden work is less urgent and there are fewer beer parties.

Before a hut is built, the ground is first marked out. A peg is driven into the ground and a bark rope is fastened to the peg. A hoe, a stick or an axe is attached to the other end of the rope. Stretching the rope and holding the hoe, a man marks a circle on the ground. On the circumference of the circle holes are dug with a special tool, *cisonkero*, or the butt of a spear into which a small axe blade has been inserted. *Cisonkero* is a pole into which the tang of an axe blade has been vertically driven. The earth from the holes is scooped out with the hands. Then two bamboo stems are stood upright in each hole so that they project some nine feet from the hole. Afterwards, long split bamboos are plaited between the warps of the double bamboo uprights in a wicker-work pattern. During plaiting, the weft is beaten down with a small log to make a compact basket wall. Half way up this giant basket cylinder, poles are laid horizontally on top of the weft to act as scaffolding for further plaiting until the walls reach the desired height. These poles are removed when the wall is finished. Next, poles of three to four inches in diameter are sunk, three feet apart, into the ground on the outside of but close to the basket walls. Some of these poles have a small fork at the top. The reason for surrounding the basket walls with these strong upright poles is firstly, to keep the walls vertical and secondly, to provide supports for the roof. On the top of the upright poles a composite circular withe of several split bamboos bound together is laid. When the basket is finished a doorway some two feet wide is cut out. Then door posts, similar to the poles described above, are erected. A few poles or bamboos are laid across the basket cylinder, and on these is spread a little grass to keep out the sun. The house at this stage is called *nanda ya rupopo* and is ready for the family to move in. The next step is to put a row of forked poles some three feet from the walls and between two and three feet apart to form a verandah. They are lower than the basket walls. On the top of the verandah poles is put another composite withe similar to that described above.

Now the roof has to be made. Four bamboo poles (*tukoli*), notched at the butts, are bound together at the notches, the binding string being twisted between each bamboo. These bound poles are then opened out, the bound ends converging and the free ends spreading out. Two withes (*kankondwa*), one inside, the other outside the cone near the top, are fastened together to hold the four main roof poles in position. The skeleton of the roof is ready and may be hoisted on to the walls and fastened to the withes which rest on the wall supports. Now new poles are inserted between the roof withes, and new withes are added until an openwork cone is fashioned.

After the first rains, when the villagers have felt some discomfort, men are stirred to thatch the houses. Such unplastered houses are called *nanda ya musasa*. The thatching commences from the bottom of the cone. Grass is laid on with the heads upwards and is fastened with bark rope to the rafters and withes. The first thatching is thin, about five inches deep.

The peak of the roof (*nsunga*) is made by binding a small bundle of grass at the butt end, the grass being bound about five inches from the end. The rest of the bundle, being loose, is spread out conically. Into the apex of the roof a pointed stick is driven. On this stick the bundle of grass (*nsunga*) is placed. There is another kind of peak bundle that is finely coiled throughout with palm leaves (*nsunga ya kuruka*). The one described above is *nsunga ya kuteka*. The loose grass of the bundle covers the top of the roof, spreading downwards not unlike a spread-out skirt.

Usually, towards the end of the rains when some early crops have eased the food position, all major work in the gardens is at an end, and water is near at hand, the huts are plastered. The first smearing, we may call it plastering (*kumasa*), is the work of men though their wives and children help. Wives and daughters bring water to the pit. The subsequent smearing, a kind of polishing of the floor and of the walls outside and inside (*kusiburura*), is often repeated, and is done entirely by women. All building operations are the work of men, except for the thatch which is cut and brought to the village by women. Thatch is cut with sharpened hoes.

There are two styles of door (*cibi*). The first form of door is of Nsenga origin (*ca cinsenga*). The bark rope is elaborately twilled into the warp reeds. The Ambo type is much simpler and much more common. The door is usually made of *Phragmites* reeds, less often of bamboo or sorghum stalks. Four pairs of bamboo sticks are fixed in the ground some twelve to fifteen inches apart, their height being the width of the proposed door. They will form the cross-pieces. Between these sticks two layers of reeds are laid, separated by three other sticks inserted crosswise between the layers. These dividing sticks are

[747]

placed at the ends and in the middle. Between the two layers of reeds a layer of grass is inserted. Each reed of the layer is tied to the outside crosspiece of the door. Thus the door looks like a stiff double mat.

Outside, in the middle of the door, there is attached a loop of twisted bark string which is tied to a pole (*munkuru*). To lock the door this pole is set so that each end lies in front of a door-post. Behind each door-post, inside the hut, there is another post or two (*bupiringu*), about five feet long, driven into the ground less than one foot away from the door-post. Another pole (*mupindo*) leans obliquely against the door and a second pole (also *mupindo*) is laid crossways, pressing between the lean-to pole and the standing uprights. This allows the door to be closed from the inside.

Nowadays, in order to raise the standard of living, the chiefs, acting as Superior Native Authorities, under the persuasion of the Administration, have introduced verandahs for all dwellings. Formerly, however, only middle-aged men of importance had houses built with verandahs. For verandahs, additional roof poles have to be inserted. The floor of a verandah in a finished house is raised a few inches above the ground and it is mud plastered from time to time.

Some men close in part of the verandah with an outside wall made of smaller poles or bamboo wicker work. This wall or screen is constructed between the verandah poles. The enclosure sometimes serves as a store room. A house with such an outside screen is called *nanda ya cikuku*.

Bamboos grow on good soil in wet, sheltered ravines and along the banks and streams. Villages on the banks of the big rivers, if they happen to be situated far from such bamboo groves, lack this useful material and have to resort to poles and sticks. A village built of poles does not present such a neat and fine appearance as does a village constructed, together with all its outbuildings, of bamboo. Such a village offers a striking view before the walls are plastered.

When a house is built of poles a circle is marked out on the ground and a small trench, some four inches wide, is dug along the marked line. Into this trench the poles for the house-wall are set, about a foot and a half apart. Two withes, an outer and an inner one, are tied to the tops of poles. Other poles are inserted between the withes so that they fill all the spaces. Crooked poles are notched on the bends and forcibly straightened. The house of poles has about six lines of withes. The fourth withe from the bottom marks the top of the door-way. The threshold is made up of short uprights sunk into the earth and cut evenly. The remainder of the house is finished in the same way as a bamboo house, except that the roof poles are thin and that the withes are of specially pliable long sticks. The Ambo always prefer a bamboo house to a pole house if they have the material.

Minkunka, lean-to dwellings, are never popular in the village and are derided as indicating laziness. The form of such a house is a steep and strong conical roof set on the ground. This type of dwelling is made of poles bound with withes and covered with grass.

THE INTERIOR OF A HUT

To the left as one enters, and close to the wall, is the hearth (*siko*) made of three stones (*mafwasa*) as supports for pots. Near the wall and opposite the door are pots and baskets of every description. To the right is the bed. Weapons are leant against the wall at the bed-head. which is the end of the bed farther away from the door.

In some houses, a square platform (*rwino*) is erected on four forked poles. The height is that of a man plus that of a stool, because to reach the top of the platform one has to climb on to a stool. This platform is usually built when the grain bin is far from the village. Food can then be stored upon it.

It will be seen that present-day dwellings differ slightly from the old types. As has been stated, verandahs have been enforced through administrative measures while the lean-to dwellings have disappeared from the village under the impact of similar regulations, though they are still sometimes to be found in the gardens. The houses are far taller than in previous times. Only the front of the house used to be plastered (i.e. from the door post to the next support pole). Nowadays the whole outside wall is plastered except the space above the last but one withe.

The village yard is, in course of time, cleared of all trees except one or two small ones which are left for guests and travellers to lean their weapons against. Three reasons are given for the removal of trees: trees cast down leaves thus making rubbish where a snake may hide; a thunderbolt may strike a big tree; on a big tree an owl (the sorcerer) may perch at night thus causing misfortune.

THE GRAIN-BIN (*butala*)

Six short forked poles are driven into the ground in three lines, so that a foot or more of each is left showing. Upon these forked poles a platform (*butantwe*) is constructed. A basket cylinder, similar to that described for the hut of split bamboo sticks but of smaller dimensions, the diameter being from four to five feet, is prepared and is placed on the platform. Now a few poles (*manciriciri*) are set in the ground close to the basket cylinder and tied to it to act as supports and to prevent the basket from leaning over sideways.

A small rectangular opening is cut in the basket near the top of the bin. A rough small mat overhangs the opening and acts as the door. A conical bamboo-grass roof, similar to that on the houses, is made on the ground and hoisted onto the bin. In order to fill the granary a ladder is constructed from a forked pole, the two forked branches being long and crossed with rungs. The bottom of the fork is fixed in the ground, the main stem of the fork being short. A hand rail is provided from a bent sapling. When bamboo is lacking, the bins are constructed from poles and stalks. The technique differs slightly from the above and resembles that of other tribes.

THE SMALL BIN (*cimpaka* or *kandungu*)

A small platform is built about a foot off the ground. On the platform is placed a conical basket (though lacking a pointed apex). The bin is about two feet in diameter at the base and some three feet high. The basket is plaited from split bamboos in wicker-work but has no pole supports at the sides, the conical shape and small height being sufficient to keep it erect. The basket is plastered. The top hole is covered with a tiny mat and also plastered. This opening is about six inches in diameter. The basket is used to preserve ground-nuts, ground-beans and cow-peas. At the bottom are ground-nuts covered with a small mat, then there is a layer of ground-beans similarly covered and on the top are cow-peas.

THE HEN-HOUSE (*cinka ca nsumbi*)

Much the same technique is used as in the building of granaries. Four forked poles, some five feet long, are set in the ground and on them a platform is built. A small basket cylinder is placed on the platform, and four uprights are fixed in the ground, reaching to the top of the basket, to which they are tied. An entrance is cut; two uprights fixed in the ground and reaching to the top of the basket make the frame of the doorway which can be closed by inserting sticks between the wall and the two supporting poles. A small rough ladder is provided for the fowl to reach the entrance. The roof is similar to that on the grain-bin.

THE DOVE-COT (*cinka ca nkwirimba*)

There is not much difference between a dove-cot and a fowl-house except in a few details. The dove-cot is much broader than the fowl-house, the diameter being some four feet. There are two openings;

these are round and four inches in diameter with a circular frame in the form of a pad. They are closed by blocking them with a short, thick peg. Near the opening, at the corner of the platform, is a separate three-forked pole on which a potsherd containing water is placed. In front of the dove-cot is a kind of stepping bench, a two-foot pole lying in two forked poles, one and a half feet high. The owner climbs on to this bench when pouring water into the potsherd and while opening and blocking the entrance holes.

THE GOAT-HOUSE (*cinka ca mbusi*)

It is made of big logs, four or five inches in diameter, and is circular in shape. On top of the circular wall there is a withe fastened. The roof has first a ceiling made of logs laid horizontally on the walls. These logs are fastened to the walls with three withes. Such a flat roof is called *bwa nsulo*. In the rainy season the usual conical roof is put on top of the flat roof. Opposite the door-posts are two other posts, fixed separately. When closing the goat-house, logs are laid horizontally between these outside posts and the door-posts.

A DAY IN THE VILLAGE

A day in the village is fairly uniform in the two dry seasons, the hot and the cold, except when the monotony is broken by a beer party or a funeral. Village life in the rainy season has its own rhythm which is quite different from that of the dry seasons.

At dawn people begin to talk in the huts; doors creak and now and then somebody comes out. Fowls appear. When it is light people wash their faces and hands on the verandah. A man with business in a distant village slips out of his hut, hardly noticed, and sets off with his weapons. Other men go out to inspect basket traps in the weir or game traps. Many go to their tobacco gardens.

Soon women are busy threshing grain, grinding and pounding. At about ten o'clock they go in small parties to draw water and to pick vegetable relish for the evening meal. The relish for the mid-day meal is already cooking. At about eleven o'clock a stranger may come to the village shelter (*citenje*) and sits down, leaning his weapons against one of the small trees. Men who have returned from the bush, the river or the gardens, greet the stranger and chat with him for he is anxious to excite interest. The traveller is found to be on his way to retrieve his gun from the gunsmith. He is asked first whether there is " peace " in his village, i.e. no serious illness or death. He relates any news—deaths, grave sickness, abundance or shortage of fish in the weirs, any important arrival from the town and the coming beer parties. He will report passing game, the appearance of a lion or of elephants. Then women acquaintances will come to the edge of the shelter, kneel or more often sit, greet the guest, exchange a few words and go back to their work of stamping, grinding grain or preparing vegetables. It is almost certain that at least one man, after returning from his tobacco plot or weir, will be making a basket, and other men around will be chatting. From noon to two o'clock a small girl or boy will bring to one of these men some food. He will invite those present to share his meal. Nowadays he is more likely to be called to come to his house for a meal. From one o'clock to three o'clock most of the men go to bathe. Women will also go to the river to fetch water, to look for relish and to bathe between one o'clock and four o'clock. Small relish pots are on the fire. By now the strain of the day is over. Small boys come back from the bush, the riverside or the gardens where they have trapped birds or caught fish, and bathed. Men also return, including those who have been on distant visits. Women put bigger pots on the fire to cook the porridge. At dusk, people in small family groups are taking meals, women with children separately, and men together with their sons. After the evening meal, people chat by their fires in front of their huts, mostly in family groups, and are joined by other relatives. First the babies and little children begin to doze and are promptly taken to their beds. This occurs at about seven o'clock. The adults stay a little longer. About nine o'clock almost everyone turns in, taking with them firebrands for the fires inside their houses. The outside fires are extinguished and slowly, as the voices in the huts are stilled, night and silence set in. This silence is broken now and again by the animals of the bush. This is a picture of village life from July until November when the people stay in the village having withdrawn from the garden shelters.

For the rest of the year, however, people love to stay for the major part of the day in their garden shelters where they enjoy a greater measure of privacy. In the rainy season the order of the day is different. Early in the morning everyone leaves the village and the whole day is spent in the garden shelters. Until ten o'clock all weed and hoe. In their free time men trap fish with cone baskets which they place in the smaller streams and in the channels of the big rivers. This free time is mainly at the end of the rainy season. The evening meals are taken before sunset in the garden shelters. People return to the village at dusk, each family in single file, carrying mats, baskets and often fowl cages. This way of life is followed from March till June, when the presence of people is required in the gardens to guard the crops from birds and monkeys. In the other months people go early to the gardens and return to the village at ten o'clock.

CHAPTER IV

AGRICULTURE AND DOMESTIC ANIMALS

The making of new gardens was discussed in connection with the shifting of the village. Sorghum is the main crop and the major part of the garden land is given over to its cultivation. Sorghum, however, exhausts the best soil in a few years, usually in about six. The soil must create each year a thick stalk eighteen feet high, without manure and with shallow hoeing.

The Ambo carefully select the soil for the sorghum garden (*mabala*), by observing the kinds of grasses and trees growing thereon. The following grasses grow on good soil: *mulungwe* (*Rottboelia exaltata*), *marokoto* (*Andropogon gayanus*), *rwiba* (*Digitaria scalarum ?*) and *rucira*. The trees indicating fertile soil are: *mufumbe* (*Bauhinia Thonningii*), *combwe* (*Acacia campylacantha*), *musebe* (*Sclerocarya caffra*) and *cipumamboo*, a shrub. Infertile soils support such grasses as *rusoce, risempya, kasindandufu* and *risankani*. The trees found on poor soil are: *ruswati, mopane, musika kapempe* and *mungasenje*.

The old fields are left fallow and are termed *filala*. The sorghum growing there unattended is *makoko*.

The bush destined for a garden is called *cisompe*. The trees are cut at breast-height, though saplings are felled close to the base. The Ambo prefer to cut their gardens in bamboo thickets. Big trees are only lopped while *kusaira, mufungura* and *musikisi* are left intact to give shade. Some maintain that these trees do not hinder crops. The branches of the felled trees are lopped and piled round the stumps. Such plots covered with piled wood are called *mutemwa*. With the approaching rains these piles are burnt and the burnt patches are called *fisita*. The felling of trees is finished in May. Now begins the rough hoeing (*kukula*) of the ground between the piles of branches. Bundles of tall grass together with their roots are thrown on the wood piles. On the spots where the branches have been burnt the soil is not hoed, as it is maintained that fire makes the ground soft and light. In October the stalks (*misati*) of sorghum are gathered, piled and burnt; this is done mostly by women. Any shrub coming up is cut and burnt with the sorghum stalks. Men have already in the cold months cut a quarter of an acre or so of adjoining bush, thus every year enlarging (*kurunda*) their gardens.

Many people plant their seeds before the rains but it is risky, for the seeds may germinate and wither in the drought that may follow the first rains; then the seeds that have not sprouted have to be protected against doves and guinea fowls. More experienced agriculturists know the time of planting by the state of certain trees—for example, when *cintungulu* and *kasakokanduba* are in blossom, or when *musepa* bears fruit. Planting is done by digging a small hole two inches deep with one stroke of the hoe, dropping the seeds into the hole, then covering the hole by another stroke of the hoe in front of the first hole. The holes are about twenty-five to thirty inches apart without any special order. In one hole there may be between fifteen and thirty seeds of sorghum dropped. These seeds are mixed with those of cucumber (*fyakaka*), marrow (*malikere*) and cow-peas (*nyangu*). In the first year many people plant maize between sorghum; some maintain that if the soil is good this can be done even in the second and third years. Generally, sorghum grows alone with the undergrowth of cash crops mentioned above. Within a fortnight all gardens are planted, though it takes an individual cultivator seven to ten days to plant his garden. After the planting the cultivators wait some ten days till the sorghum has begun to sprout and is strong enough not to be disturbed by weeding. There are two weedings during the whole season. The first weeding is harder because the weeds grow more than in the second period. Weeding is done by hoeing and uprooting the weeds. When the weather is dry, weeds are left scattered in the garden. When it is raining, they are piled to rot and so to improve the soil (*musiri uwamye*— " that the soil may become better "). When sorghum is over a foot high and there is no drought, the smaller plants are uprooted and transplanted to gaps where seeds have failed. The ends of the leaves of such transplanted seedlings are pulled off. In the end, only four to six plants are left in each spot. Many under-developed or stunted plants are also thinned out.

Pumpkins (*cipusi*) and water melons (*cinamunwa*) are planted after sorghum but amidst it, on the patches where the stalks from the previous year have been burnt (*fikuka*). On the same places, tomatoes, *sunta* and *sansya*, kinds of native spinage, are broadcast. Soon after planting the main crops of sorghum, maize and pumpkins, women plant a quarter of an acre of ground-nuts around the shelters at the edge of the sorghum gardens, where they may be guarded from monkeys. Ground-beans (*buleya*) are not very common but some people plant them on about an eighth of an acre. From the middle of January to the middle of February, mounds (*mputi*) for sweet potatoes (*bware*) are thrown up near the garden shelter. The soil is piled ten inches high, three feet broad and about fifteen feet long. Each household has from five to ten mounds. Four kinds of sweet potatoes are grown: *Rufwansi* (red, leaves red at the edges), *ciburwe* (white roots, big leaves), *kasonta* (white roots, small leaves) and *syacisungu* (red roots).

Sorghum (*masaka*) is grown in five varieties: *Nyakapanda* ripens early with maize (i.e. in February) and is grown in small quantities by many. It is planted in the rainy season in maize gardens in separate holes, or in the same holes as the maize.

Njasi is the most common variety on the Lukusashi and its tributaries. It ripens in April and is harvested in May. *Mpande* ripens very late, in June, but it has large grains. It is grown on the Mulembo and on the Luangwa. *Kasera* (*cinande*) is an early variety; it ripens about Easter-time at the beginning of April. It is grown on the Lunsemfwa and generally in Mboshya's country, because it was taken over from the neighbouring Soli who like this variety. A sweet variety (*misare*) is grown primarily for the stalk which is chewed. The majority of the Ambo on the Lukusashi prefer *njasi* to *kasera* because *njasi*, though ripening a few weeks later, has bigger heads.

Sorghum is preferred to maize, which by Ambo standards does not make as substantial a meal as does sorghum. Therefore most work and land are devoted to sorghum. New fields measured in one village amounted to 1.5 acres, but at the same time the village shifted the huts as well. A big garden amounted to 4.86 acres after a few years of additions, but included an adjoining dry season maize garden of 0.37 acre which was not planted in the rains.

Sorghum is consumed from the time of its harvest in May till December and January. Though sorghum is so appreciated and desired, it does not last throughout the year and so recourse is had to maize (*mataba*). Maize is grown in much smaller patches (*cipoka*) hardly amounting to an acre but usually two crops a year are obtained. It is possible to have three or even four crops in a year and many do have them.

There is a different economy on the main rivers and along small streams. As a rule, the banks of these rivers have in the dry season no wet patches (*nsansa*) suitable for maize growing because the banks are high. Therefore, drought hits harder the fields lying on the high banks of the big rivers, damaging even sorghum. The banks of the small streams are often low, the moisture comes up and the crops survive drought. In 1951, most of the crops failed badly along the Lukusashi through prolonged drought, or rather an early end of the rains, so much so that sorghum did not even produce heads, for the rains stopped in February. At the same time the villages and their gardens along the tributaries were hardly affected by the drought.

[755]

If they had poor sorghum crops they hurried to cut *Pennisetum* on the streams, and in clearings they made big maize gardens. The village of Lusale on the Lukusashi-Kampoko confluence had very bad crops that year, the banks of the Kampoko being high there. The village of Masonga, on the small stream of Fiperere, had also lost its sorghum crop along the adjoining water course. The Masonga people left their sorghum fields unattended in the middle of the rainy season and made big maize gardens on the Fiperere stream. Lusale village on the Lukusashi had a good fishing season having made money from the sale of fish. With this money the villagers bought maize from the villages situated on the small streams. In 1951, the Lukusashi had exceptionally low water so that there was no moisture in the side channels nor in the lower shelves of its banks. The people living along that river and other big rivers could not have additional maize gardens in those lower shelves after the rains. As their main crops from the rainy season are not usually sufficient to last till the new crops of the next rainy season, they were faced with a shortage of food.

The people along the big rivers are able to grow another maize crop on the low moist patches along the banks, planting the seeds at the end of the rains, the crop being *akupwa-mainza* (" of the end of the rains "). The maize is planted in March. The cultivators on the big rivers can also find moist plots along the river banks for a third crop of maize, " the winter maize " (*mambwera*), planted in April and harvested in June and July. In most cases, the villages on the small streams have winter maize, although this may not be possible on the big rivers when there is a poor rainy season, or when the water level has been low and does not moisten the banks. The fourth drop of maize is that " of the wet place " (*ansansa*), which is mostly the privilege of the cultivators on small streams. Maize is planted in September and gathered in December. Maize grown in moist ground during the hot season is so timed that when the rains fall it is half grown. The maize gardens worked on moist ground and without the need of rain are made on places, usually sandy on the surface and overgrown with *Pennisetum-Phragmites*, which has to be cut, thrown out, or dried and burned. The ground is hoed, and maize is planted like sorghum though only five to six grains are dropped into a hole. These holes are dug deep in the sand. However, there are many moist sandless places along small streams. In the winter gardens, between the maize, sweet potatoes and pumpkins are planted for their leaves which are used as a relish.

Two kinds of pumpkins are grown. *Muzungu* which has leaves with stripes and big flowers (*bulongo*) appreciated as relish, and *cipusimusya*, characterised by its big fruits.

Cow-peas (*nyangu*) are of four varieties: *Matobo*, with big peas, ripens with sorghum in May; *kansankwa* is an early variety; *kanyense*, a very early variety, is grown from March till June.

Gourds (*lungu*) are of two kinds: *nkombo*, with excrescences (*nsolo*) which in the early stages are boiled and eaten. Later they are used for making drinking gourds with a handle. *Mitesi* are big gourds used for gourd drums (*malimba*).

Yams (*cirungu*) are rare. Some people grow a few plants of cassava (*tute*) for its leaves which they use for relish. Bulrush millet (*malembe*) is grown in small quantities, usually on burnt spots at the outskirts of the gardens, and used as an addition to malt to make the beer stronger.

THE GUARDING OF CROPS

It is not enough for the Ambo to cultivate their crops conscientiously and to have favourable weather. Much energy is spent in guarding the crops against numerous enemies. The author has seen many acres of fine grown maize on the Mulembo in June trodden down by herds of elephants. Nowadays, the Administration has at its disposal official hunters who are sent to help against such ravages. Again on the Kampoko in the village of Chitubula all the winter maize was eaten up by a stray hippo, when the crop was one to two feet high. This disaster was accentuated by the fact that in the neighbouring villages, especially on the Lukusashi, there was at the time a grave shortage of food.

The Ambo have most problems when guarding crops during the ripening of maize. In the day-time the garden is liable to attack by baboons and monkeys, while men have also to stay awake at night-time in shelters on high platforms (*rubingwe*), ringing bells or drumming to drive away wild pigs. *Rubingwe* is a lean-to hut as described above, but not as strong, resembling rather a makeshift roof laid on a high platform some eight feet high. It gives a good view over the fields and furthermore, it is safer against lions than any construction on the ground. If, however, a watchman falls asleep or falls ill the crops are damaged or ruined.

Until freshly-planted sorghum is established it must be guarded against doves and guinea fowls. The guarding is done by children under the supervision of women or by the women themselves.

Against the hippopotamus a fence of forked poles is erected, the latter being four feet apart and six feet high with cross-pieces so as to look like an aggregation of gates. Over each such gate a sausage tree fruit or similarly shaped piece of wood is suspended to resemble a fall trap, so that a hippopotamus will fear that it will hurt him if he passes beneath it. An alternative precaution is for a man to stay in the high sheltered platform (*rubingwe*) and shout or strike (*rinkubala*) two little resonant boats at night.

In many places elephants ravage the gardens. A lean-to hut may be erected in the garden and men watch the crops at night—drumming and making booming sounds through the partly closed palms of their hands (*kakoba* or *ngorwa*) which is supposed to be very effective in frightening away elephants.

In other places buffaloes threaten the crops. They are not easily frightened, but a rope stretched round the field with various pieces of iron so arranged as to ring when disturbed is considered to be effective. Some men even try to ambush buffaloes.

Rice is seldom protected against cane-rats, but when it is, the protection consists of a plaited low fence of split bamboos about a foot high.

When sorghum grain appears, it requires continual protection during the day-time against birds (*kuamina tuni*). The villages are then abandoned (*kukuka*) and every family spends the whole day in the garden shelter (*citenge* or *citenje*). A garden shelter is a conical roof supported on a few forked poles. The exodus to the fields takes place in the second half of March when the sorghum comes to seed. The population abandons the garden shelters in June, when the sorghum is brought to the granaries in the village. However, meals are again taken in these shelters from planting-time about the end of October. Some people stay in the shelters the whole day, taking all their meals there. Most people return to the village at dusk. During the day-time for several weeks birds have to be scared away by everybody. They are, however, more numerous in some regions than in others. Birds are less numerous along big rivers than along some tributary streams. Children are again mainly employed under the supervision of women for the scaring of birds, but men also help to guard the crops against the birds. Boys make small bows and arrows of *marokoto* grass stalks, to drive away birds. Sometimes they swing a bull roarer (*cibubibubi*) or else shout continually. The watchers know the time of day when the birds are most active in feeding. This is in the morning and the early afternoon (i.e. seven o'clock in the morning and three to four o'clock in the afternoon). Sometimes a part of the field is not harvested but given up to the birds to save the rest of the crop.

A few people have unplastered huts with walls mostly of poles in their gardens, where they live permanently. Such huts are called *ku nkutu*. This mode of life is practised when the gardens are very far

[758]

from the village. When a villager for personal reasons does not wish to live in the village he also resorts to this practice, ostensibly to guard his crops. Headmen do not like this mode of life for it disturbs the unity of the village community. Further, they would be held responsible before the court if any accident befell such a garden dweller.

If a family has an extensive maize garden in the winter it may take meals there, while guarding the crops the whole day. This practice occurs only when the cobs are ripening and baboons are a nuisance.

Not all these enemies of the garden make an equal nuisance of themselves. Buffaloes, hippopotami and elephants are rare and of local importance. Night watching against the wild pig is done by men only while the maize is in cob, which then means several weeks of sleepless nights. The maize gardens along the big rivers are generally immune from such vermin which does not frequent these places. Monkeys relish maize crops, but they attack the gardens only in the day-time. They are chased and driven far into the bush by a man or a boy. People are not averse to a lion making his appearance while they are pestered by wild pigs. The scaring of birds from sorghum is universal in the above-mentioned seasons.

THE HARVEST

The first crops to ripen are cucumbers and pumpkins which are eaten for the mid-day meal, the former being eaten raw. At about the same time the rainy season maize (*mataba a mainsa*) ripens. The cobs are broken off from the stalks and carried home in baskets. The drying of the rainy season maize crop presents a minor problem. If the garden is far from the village and the crop is fairly big, there is a special shelter, *cituula*, built for the drying and temporary storage of the maize crop. The *cituula* structure consists of a roof, not conical but made of two sloping rectangular sides joined at the top ridge. The slope is fairly steep. This roof, called " the back of the elephant " (*musana wa nsofu*), acts as the walls as well, resting on very low forked poles of less than a foot in height. The interior is occupied by a low platform on which maize is spread. Maize may also be dried on the inner platform of a dwelling house (*rwino*), on the floor of the house or on the floor of a garden shelter. When dry it is stored in a small grain bin differing only in size from the sorghum granary. The maize bin has a special name, *cimpaka*.

Cow-peas are gathered before the harvest of sorghum.

[759]

The most important harvest is that of sorghum. This harvest starts at the beginning of May and is rushed through in a few days because the birds flock to the standing sorghum of those who lag behind. The stalks are cut (*kutebula*) at the bottom with sharpened hoes, and laid in irregular but orderly rows (*ruyande*), the head of each stalk being laid on the preceding stalks. This method facilitates the cutting off of the heads, and later, the stacking (*kubunga*) of the stalks to be burnt. Men and women cut the sorghum stalks (*kutebula*). After a few days of drying, men cut the heads of sorghum from the felled stalks with knives (*kusesa*) and put them in small heaps. These are taken in baskets by women and girls to the low platform (*cisansa*) standing near the garden shelter. Women cut off the sorghum heads only of necessity. The grain is left piled on the platform for some two weeks or longer to dry, then it is carried by women to the granaries. If the granaries are far, men may help to carry the grain in big, oblong makeshift baskets (*cisekebere*), but this is hardly ever done. In exceptional cases, dugout canoes are used for the transport of grain. To store the grain, the roof is taken off the granary, and women climb the ladder which is placed against the wall and empty the baskets into the bin. Sorghum is stored unthreshed in heads, as in such a state it is held to be safer against weevils.

Ground-nuts are dug up after the sorghum harvest. Sweet potatoes are dug up when wanted during the whole cold season.

Industrious people grow small patches of rice (*mpunga*), on marshy spots during the rainy season where such places are at hand. The size of a patch hardly exceeds that of a ground-nut plot.

Plantains and bananas are grown along streams but rarely on the big rivers. Clusters of plantains are often found in the gardens of former cultivators, having been abandoned together with exhausted fields. The villager is satisfied with a few clusters of plantains scattered haphazardly throughout his garden. A few pawpaw plants are found in the village. The Ambo cultivator practises a limited crop rotation. The rainy season maize is grown on newly-tilled ground every year. Ground-nuts are grown for only one year in each place either on new ground or else in succession to sweet potatoes. Sweet potatoes are planted each year on new mounds, which are afterwards levelled and planted first with maize and the next year with sorghum. The loamy winter gardens for maize are used indefinitely.

TOBACCO CULTURE

Tobacco growing among the Ambo plays an important part in their economy as this is their main and most popular cash crop. They distinguish four kinds of tobacco (*fwaka*):

Kandyanga—dark green, with short leaves and short stem. This variety is most common because it is the strongest. Trapnell lists it as *Tobacco N. rustica*, not mentioning the other varieties.

Cipotomoka—with leaves long but narrow at the ends. This kind being mild is not grown much.

Kalemba—with long leaves.

Mulakule—is hairy, with big light-green leaves. It takes second place to *Kandyanga*.

The soil most suitable for tobacco is sandy and moist. This kind of soil is found along big rivers, some smaller rivers and medium-sized streams. Though some streams have excellent, moist and fertile sites for winter maize gardens, these fertile sites lack sand and therefore are considered by the growers as unsuitable for tobacco cultivation. The banks of the Chingombe River afford an example.

Tobacco is grown in the cold season. In February, a seed bed is prepared, the seeds are broadcast, and the plot is watered and covered with straw supported on rough platforms as protection against the sun. The seedlings are planted in May. The plot is prepared in the same way as for the winter maize.

While the tobacco is growing the cultivator must pluck the tops and side shoots of each plant so that it may develop large leaves. A few tops are allowed to flower in order to provide seed. Tobacco plants are cut when ripe in September. The leaves, stripped of the central hard rib, are spread upon strewn grass, covered with sacks, and are left for four days to ferment. The leaves are pounded in mortars, squeezed free of juice and put into small relish dishes to shape them into loaves, *cambwa*, which are then dried in the sun. After a week the loaves are smeared with the expressed juice until it is completely absorbed. Again the loaves are left in the sun, this time for a month. Then they are stored on the platform inside the hut, and are ready for sale.

HEMP (*Rubange—Cannabis indica*)

The seeds are sown broadcast and the seedlings are transplanted when they have begun to grow strongly. The plants are cut when full grown and are tucked into the roof of the hut.

DOMESTIC ANIMALS

Fowls seem nowadays to be more popular than goats because of their commercial value. They figure largely as presents at funerals and are given to important visitors, such as the chief, by the headman.

[761]

A fowl is killed for relish for a visiting relative, while a fowl is also used at the marriage feast as relish with a ritual connotation. Nowadays, however, fowls are kept largely as a source of income. Many young men, who do not want to go to labour centres and do not relish the drudgery of tobacco growing, take fowls to towns or sell them to hawkers. A fowl fetches a shilling on the spot. A number of old widows keep fowls and sell them to visiting hawkers to obtain money for clothes.

Some people feed their fowls with bran, mixed with water, even giving them maize and sorghum. Some give the fowls water, but many do not trouble to give anything. Usually the only trouble taken with fowls is to let them out of the hen-house in the early morning and to shut them up after the sun has set, though when people stay in the fields during the day, they take their fowls with them.

The hen-houses are often either in a bad state of repair or of such flimsy construction that they are easily broken into by leopards, wild cats, genets, hyenas and snakes. Genets and wild cats often catch fowls in the day-time in the open. Hawks also take a heavy toll.

Though goats are valued as wealth, the villagers are not keen on keeping them any more. In very few villages are they found and even there only one or two men keep them, for although goats entail much care there is hardly any profit from them.

Goats are not usually herded or milked. However, they have to be shut up in the evening and let out in the morning. When the gardens are near the village, the goats are kept penned at the time the crops are standing in the gardens and are only let out in the late afternoon so that they may not wander to the crops. They are not sold, owing to the distance to the market and the formidable nature of the escarpment. Thus their sale value is contrasted unfavourably with that of fowls. Goats are killed at funerals for the mourners and when their owner, feeling the so-called " meat hunger ", has a fancy for meat. When the owner is short of grain he may kill a goat, smoke the meat and barter it for grain. The labour migrant going to work may do the same, bartering the dried meat for flour.

A goat skin (*rufunga*) was formerly used as a flour bag for journeys, and is still used for blacksmiths' bellows.

Leopards, lions and hyenas take a steady toll of goats. These predatory animals can fairly easily force their way into goat-houses, especially if these are not new, when the poles and the bark rope have rotted. Depredations by wild animals are helped by the custom (which is now enforced by an Order of the Native Authority) of placing goat-houses on the outskirts of the village.

[762]

Pigs were formerly reared in many villages. The author has not seen a pig-sty since 1938, and then there were no pigs in it. At the present time there are no pigs in the country, though the village nearest to Chingombe Mission has again taken to keeping them, as some say, with a view to selling meat to mission teachers. It seems that the decline in pig-keeping is due to the same financial considerations as were noted about goat-keeping. Pigs also cannot be exported and sold. When killed they have to be distributed to all the villagers and to close clansmen and clanswomen living in the vicinity. When the amount of care in feeding pigs, watching them during the day, shutting them up and letting them out, is considered, it really does not pay to keep them. Pig-sties are of the same construction as goat-houses.

Of all domestic animals most care is lavished on pigeons. It is thought that if pigeons are neglected, they may fly away to live somewhere else. There is no apparent usefulness in keeping pigeons, but it is a hobby of elderly men. There is hardly an Ambo village without one or two dove-cots. The pigeons are also regularly fed for the same reason, though some men give them away when they are short of grain. Dove-cots have charms [1] to make the pigeons prolific and to stop them from settling elsewhere. Young pigeons are killed for relish by breaking their necks, when it is thought that the numbers have multiplied sufficiently. Women may own pigeons but they do not look after them.

Muscovy ducks are occasionally found in some villages but are not numerous.

Sheep were kept formerly, but now none are to be found in the valleys. Tsetse fly is given as the reason for their disappearance.

Cats are not often found. The reason for the small number of cats is the fear that the wild cat population may increase and become a menace to the fowls for it is maintained, probably rightly, that the domestic cat and the wild cat interbreed. Kittens are killed and thrown into the bush, one being left from each litter. Nevertheless, in some villages people greatly desire a cat when mice and rats become a nuisance, especially in the granaries. Cats are not given food; they must fend for themselves and they seem to do well, much better than dogs.

Dogs are plentiful, at least they were so until the recent dog tax put a check on their numbers. There is hardly a village without a couple of them. The dogs look miserable, thin, small and under-nourished. They are given a little food now and then but not regularly.

---

[1] I hope to discuss these charms fully elsewhere.—AUTHOR.

The author remembers the indignation of his carrier when the carrier commented with others on the new tax on dogs, saying, " dogs are of no use, they eat only excrement and that is their work ". The fact is undeniable that dogs survive. No wonder that they steal eggs found on the outskirts of the village and occasionally snatch a chicken. They are keen to attack any visitor to the village, but a word of displeasure from a villager sends them scurrying away. No doubt they learn discipline the hard way. Dogs are treated with medicine[1] to make them fierce, especially in hunting.

Dogs are useful in that they give warning when lions and other dangerous beasts are in the neighbourhood, and men dare to sleep outside in the village in the hot season when there are many dogs. Dogs also bear the unenviable brunt of the attacks of wild beasts. Four such dogs, at the village of Chendamukanwa in the neighbouring country of the Soli, cornered a leopard which sought refuge in a tree where it was stabbed to death by the men of the village.

Men are also keen on dogs because they are useful for the chase. More will be said about this in Chapter VII.

Dogs have nowhere to hide, especially from leopards to which they fall an easy prey. On cold nights they sleep on the warm ashes of extinguished fires. When a dog has a litter, a burrow is made for it. This consists of a hole over which sticks are laid and covered with earth. The opening to the burrow is blocked with a stone slab.

Domestic animals, fowls and goats may be owned by men or women. Many children receive fowls as a gift. Occasionally a monkey is caught and kept chained as a pet.

There have been attempts to keep cattle, but these have died from tsetse fly attacks.

---

[1] I hope to discuss these medicines fully elsewhere.—AUTHOR.

CHAPTER V

FOOD

The Ambo usually have two meals a day, one at mid-day and another at about six o'clock in the evening. Both meals consist of very thick porridge (*nsima*), made of sorghum or maize meal. This dish never changes but is accompanied by another additional dish of relish (*bucisa*) which if possible should vary from meal to meal.

Almost every year there is a shortage of food in some regions due to the failure of crops. Disasters sometimes happen when the whole crop is lost, but fortunately there is usually only a partial failure. Crops fail mostly through drought, but occasionally through floods, locusts, disease or vermin. As has been explained in the chapter on agriculture, people in certain areas are not able to harvest maize four times a year in fair quantity, and these areas are liable to food shortages. Again, there are areas which are safe from any food shortage and usually these have surplus grain available for the famine-affected areas. Thus a general famine, covering the whole of the Ambo country, is unlikely. By a food shortage, the Ambo usually mean a grain shortage.

Because of the varied agricultural possibilities of different areas, the inhabitants of famine-affected villages rely in the first instance on the generosity of their more fortunate relatives. Another solution is to buy grain. Nowadays, when a food shortage occurs, the young men either emigrate with their families to towns and labour centres or leave their wives and parents in the villages while they themselves set out to seek employment. They then send their earnings home for the purchase of grain. We have also witnessed instances of the bartering of native salt, fish, baskets, meat and clay pots for grain. Borrowing of grain among neighbours occurs too. If anybody is too poor to buy or barter grain and also finds it difficult to exact more grain from relatives, he or she seeks work in another village in return for payment of grain. Such shortages only occur in the months immediately before the new harvest of rainy season maize when supplies in the granaries are low. This search for food, strictly speaking for grain, is virtually an institution among the Ambo and is designated by a special term, *kupumba*.

In times of food shortage, people try to obtain at least their evening meal. At noon they may have to forego a meal or to make do with roots as a substitute.

As the first meal of the day is as late as noon, children and to some extent women, try to have a snack during the morning. This may consist of wild fruits, roasted whole maize grain or a gruel (*munyece*) made from flour mixed with cold water. However, even children are accustomed, and able, to do without food till the evening meal. When in February, cucumbers, then pumpkins, cow-peas and finally sweet potatoes ripen, and when the housewife is too busy in her garden to grind flour, vegetables alone are taken for the mid-day meal. School children bring boiled or roasted maize in cobs, if available, for their snack before they go home in the afternoon.

The scarcity or abundance of grain are the most common topics of conversation when a guest or traveller comes to the village. Those with plenty are admired and envied. The conversation also includes, according to the time of the year, the amount of rain and the state of the growing grain. Then, after the harvest, the various areas, mostly designated by the rivers, are divided into the haves and have nots. Those who have suffered a set-back in crops are pitied. The same anxious and intensely interested attitude towards the food-grain position is reflected in correspondence between the villagers and their relatives in schools and labour training centres.

Prayers at sacrifices deal entirely either with health or with food to which is added a request for *buswete*, the "red thing", by which is meant game meat if the sacrifice is not specifically offered for a hunt.

Very enlightening is a comparison of the attitudes to food of the Bemba and that of the Ambo (Richards, 1961). Unlike the Bemba the Ambo do not speak freely of relish foods. Children questioned about the relish they have eaten are always shy and rather secretive.

As may be inferred from the foregoing, the Ambo are not subject to seasonal starvation or "hunger months" as are the Bemba. Food shortage when it occurs among the Ambo is only local and accidental; further, it is met through the institution of *kupumba* which does not seem to exist among the Bemba. The comparison is interesting because of the common culture and close relationship in language, and because of the different agricultural systems. The Bemba set-backs are traced to one staple food, namely finger millet, which is harvested only once a year, coupled with the absence of green vegetables during the larger part of the year. The Ambo on the other hand enjoy ecological advantages over the Bemba as is evident from Chapter IV.

The preparation of flour from sorghum is a lengthy process though sorghum threshed in the morning may be consumed at noon as porridge. A woman takes a quantity of sorghum heads and, kneeling,

PLATE II

Paddling an Ambo Canoe

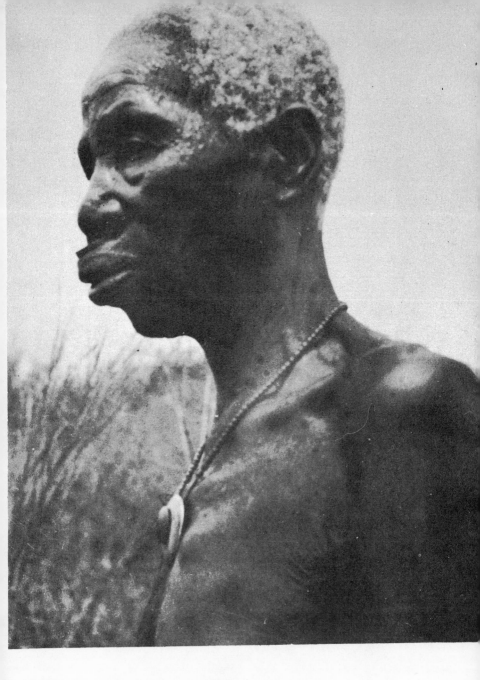

PLATE III

An old woman wearing a *cinanta* lip plug
An *mpande* shell is hung on the bead necklace

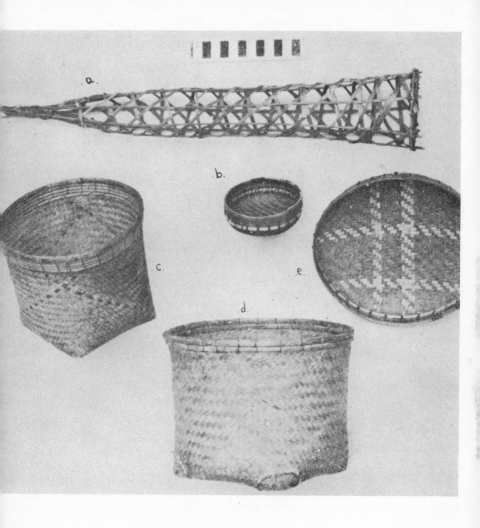

PLATE IV

BASKETRY

    (*a*) Cane rat trap (*kakoba*)
    (*b*) Eating basket (*kasere*)
    (*c*) Small carrying basket (*musako*)
    (*d*) Large carrying basket (*citundu*)
    (*e*) Winnowing basket tray (*rubango*)

PLATE V

POTTERY AND GOURDS

    (a) Washin basin (*cibate*)
    (b) Cooking pot for porridge (*citaro*)
    (c) Beer pot (*cibiya*)
    (d) Water pot (*nongo*)
    (e) *Citaro*
    (f) Cooking pot for relish (*cinkombe*)
    (g) Gourd dipper (*nkombo*)
    (h) Drinking gourd (*mutesi*)
    (i) *Nkombo*
    (j) Relish dish (*musero*)

PLATE VI

An Ambo smith demonstrates his bag bellows

PLATE VII

Noose-net-spring hunting trap set in a brush fence

PLATE VIII

Inspecting fish traps

The traps are single-valved cone baskets (*mono*)

PLATE IX

Fishing with a drag net (*cikulo*)

strikes them gently with a stick (*murupwisyo*). This is done near the grain bin, on a floor which has been swept clean for the purpose. The ears are turned over and over when threshed. Any grain that falls outside the threshing floor is left for the fowls to eat. When finished, the grain, together with a good deal of dust, is swept into a heap and the empty heads are picked out and thrown away. The woman puts the grain into a high *citundu* basket and standing, pours down the grain into the broad *rubango* basket set on the ground. The breeze blows away the light chaff, *mungu*, and some of the dust. Now the woman shakes the grain to the right and left side in the broad basket; the chaff comes to the surface in the middle and is picked out and thrown away (*kubungula*). Some grain still in heads may be found, but these are stamped (*kusokola*) instead of being threshed.

The grain is now put in a mortar, sprinkled with water and stamped (*kutwa*) with a pestle. Usually only women stamp, one to a mortar; sometimes two combine to stamp in the same mortar. For a big beer drink several women combine to stamp in pairs. The crushed grain is taken from the mortar and placed in a broad basket where it is shaken sideways as before or tossed gently upwards. Now and then, the bran is tossed forwards with a jerk so that it falls on to the ground. This winnowing is done kneeling. When the bran is thrown out, the big and small grains are separated. The big ones (*tunturu*) are stamped again and winnowed. By now all the grains are in fragments (*ntimbira*), and they are carried to the stream to be washed clean of any refuse. Much of the dust left after threshing is thus removed. After washing, the groats are spread out on mats to dry in the sun. When they are dry, a woman takes a few handfuls, places them on the back of a grinding stone, puts another handful in the middle and works over it (*kupera*) with a smaller oblong stone, moving it forwards and backwards. The flour falls into a basket set at the farther end of the nether grinding stone. The next handful of groats is supplied from those heaped at the back of the nether stone.

Porridge is cooked in a special pot (*citaro*). When the water is boiling, flour is gradually thrown in and the pot is continually stirred (*kunaya*) with a ladle (*munko*) until the porridge is quite thick. Salt is never added to the porridge. The pot is taken off the fire for the final stirring. Then the porridge is taken out of the pot with a scoop (*cipakiro*) and placed in eating baskets (*cipe* or *kasere*).

Fresh sorghum (whole grain) is boiled with crushed ground-nuts, under the name of *lunkubi*. Sorghum (again whole grain), boiled with salt or pounded ground-nuts, is sometimes eaten when there is no time for proper porridge. This meal is called *musaku*. Light porridge, from maize or sorghum, is prepared for children or for the sick.

Maize Flour

The difference between the preparation of sorghum flour and maize flour is that, after washing, the maize is again pounded and sifted. Some of it, after sifting, is already flour. Maize, if it is dry, is soaked for some two days before stamping.

Men eat their meals in groups of two to four. All the wives send in their contribution to a meal. Thus each man consumes as much as if he ate alone. The advantage is in the variety of relish dishes coming from the various households. The disadvantage appears to be that the participants may not have enough food, when they are numerous. However, this form of communal eating is on the decline. It is difficult to give a reason for the change. Certainly migrant labour disrupts the eating arrangements. The reason put forward by the local people themselves is the opposition of the women, who complain that some partners bring more sons than do others.

The Ambo love variety in food. That is why they grow such a variety of crops, but many do not go in for all the available crops. Some cultivators restrict themselves to a few plants only, like cassava or sesame.

Cucurbits

PUMPKINS: Fresh-cooked pumpkins are never eaten as relish.

> *Musungu* cut up and boiled may be eaten alone when there is a famine or much work to be done.

> *Cipusimusya* is eaten and prepared as above. This kind of pumpkin ripens in May and may be stored. To preserve it, it is cut, the seeds are taken out, and the fruit is exposed to the sun. In the hot season it is boiled with crushed ground-nuts and served as a relish (*makopa*).

Gourds

Mungu
Mitesi } Both kinds are prepared as above.

Cucumbers

> *Fyakaka* medium size, smooth skin.

> *Nakasongo* small and spiny.

> *Citungusa* warty cucumber. *Fyakaka* is eaten raw. *Fyakaka* and *Nakasongo* are peeled, cut, the seeds taken out, boiled and eaten alone. *Citungusa* are preserved in the same way as *cipusimusya*.

[776]

MARROW

Malikerere is eaten raw in the same way as *Fyakaka*.

WATER MELON

Cinamunwa is eaten raw in the same way as *Fyakaka*.

PUMPKIN SEEDS

Rungu are roasted, pounded and added to spinach-like vegetables except to the wild spinach itself, *mulembwe*.

SEEDS OF CUCUMBERS

Mufumbu marrow and water melon are prepared in the same way as are pumpkin seeds.

PULSES

Matabo

Syacisungu—Both are ground-nuts and are shelled, roasted, winnowed and pounded; salt is added and then they are used as the relish called *mundundu*. Ground-nuts may be pounded raw, winnowed and added to all vegetables and dried cucurbits except *mulembwe*, wild spinach. Ground-nuts prepared in this way are called *ntwiro*. Ground-nuts may be roasted and salted then eaten alone. Raw ground-nuts are pounded, winnowed, then poured upon hot water and used for a relish called *mulebe*.

Cow-peas (nyangu, menso a nombe)—When fresh they are boiled in water and eaten alone. When cow-peas are dry, they are ground, winnowed and boiled in water with salt added; then they are known as *cimperwe* relish.

OTHER KINDS OF PULSES

Kansankwa—Green grain *kanyense*.

GROUND-BEANS

Buleya.—These are shelled by pounding and added, when crushed and ground, to spinach-like vegetables except those of the *mulembwe* group. Ground-beans are eaten in the same way as cow-peas, and they are also boiled and eaten alone as are *nyangu*.

[777]

LEAF RELISH (*bucisa bwa matepo*)

Leaves of various vegetables and wild plants are used for relish. They are prepared like spinach. Generally the rib of the leaf (*kwangula*) is thrown away; the rest of the leaf is boiled in a little water. Ash soda is often added to most of these leaf relishes to soften them. They provide the common everyday relish.

The desired quality of every relish is that it should be gruel-like, so that lumps of porridge may be dipped in it (*kutowera*). Because porridge is not salted, all kinds of relish are strongly salted (*kurungira*). Porridge may be eaten in time of need without a relish (*kataula*).

Solid pulses, cucurbits and root crops are not used as relishes because they cannot be prepared in the desired form, but they make a solid meal by themselves.

The stems of some leaves are stripped of their outer cover, broken in pieces, and then boiled, together with other leaves.

To make cooking soda (*kusumika*), ashes from the hearth are placed in an old basket and strained. Water percolates through the ashes and the basket and the solution gathered beneath is the soda, *fikungu*.

Cassava leaves (*saasa*) are stripped from the middle rib, pounded and boiled with soda, salt and, if available, crushed ground-nuts.

Leaves of cow-peas (*taambe*) are prepared in the same way as cassava leaves but are not pounded. The leaf stem is stripped of bark, cut in pieces and added to the leaves. Soda is added.

Leaves of pumpkin (*msampala*) are cooked in the same way.

Leaves of sweet potatoes (*kalembula*) are prepared as above but the stem is not added; neither is soda.

Leaves of cucumbers (*narubimbi*) are prepared as above but without soda.

Sansya, also called *bondwe* or *bodongwe*, is cooked in the same way as *taambe* but the leaves are not stripped from the central rib, and soda is not used.

Musira is a marsh plant, cooked like *taambe*, without soda. It is served as an ordinary relish or is added to fish.

Ciniinina—The stem is broken, the bark is stripped and crushed— ground-nuts may be added. Otherwise it is cooked like *taambe* without soda.

[778]

Kamwerere	
Chipopo	
Kanunka	All these plants are cooked like *ciniinina* but
Fimpwimpwi	tomatoes may be added to *kamwerere*, as also
Kabwantoro	may crushed ground-nuts.
Sungwe	
Kanyangunyamo	

WILD SPINACH (*mulembwe*)

A group of plants each known by its own name, of which the leaves alone are picked and boiled like *taambe*. The central rib of the leaves is thrown away. The characteristic of this kind of relish is its slimy nature. Roasted and crushed cucumber pips may be added but not crushed ground-nuts, for these would make the spinach even more slimy. Spinach is eaten very often though it is looked upon as the least desirable of relish and scornfully referred to as *fibebebe*. Ash soda is very important for these plants.

Six kinds of spinach are counted: *Kamunwe, katate, sopyo, tindingoma, namwape* and *cilungutaŋde* (ochra ?) (cultivated).

Mwanya (Mukungu)—Leaves are stripped of their central rib, from which the outer coat is removed; the leaves and the stem are stamped but no potash is added. It is a very sour relish.

ROOT-CROPS

Cassava may either be eaten raw, or scraped and cooked whole, boiled in water or roasted. It provides a useful meal when porridge is short.

Sweet Potatoes—These may be eaten raw. More often they are stewed, roasted or baked in hot ashes. Livingstone potatoes, *Coleus esculentus*, are not grown as it is considered they need damp depressions, *dambos*; these are not found in the Ambo valleys.

Yams—These are grown only along the Dauni Stream.

Tomatoes—Small tomatoes are squeezed to press out the seeds and are then stewed. They may themselves be served as a relish or be added to one of the spinach relishes, even those of the *mulembwe* group. Tomatoes flavoured with crushed ground-nuts are considered a very tasty relish called *kaliri*. Tomatoes may be preserved like *cipusimusya*.

[779]

Sesame (bwengo) is roasted and used as a relish like *matabo* and *syacisungu*.

Rice (mupunga) is washed in cold water, then in warm water and boiled; it is served with meat. A porridge may be prepared from rice which has been ground. Rice is boiled whole with salt and crushed ground-nuts. Chillies *(mpirimpiri)* are added to meat.

Mushrooms (bowa)—Mushrooms are not plentiful in the valleys and certain kinds are found only on anthills. If the valley people want to gather mushrooms they usually have to walk to the escarpment hills. The Ambo know of the following varieties of edible mushrooms: *mfuti, kabofuka, munomba, bwitondwe, terya, kabansa, bowacuru, nyonswe, kayimbwe, butesi, colanswaswa, bwebwe, bunkungwa.* The stumps of *munkumbi, kabansa* and *bwebwe* are eaten raw or they may be boiled. *Terya* and *mfuti* are grilled and boiled. *Mbusi, longwa* and *ciyongoli* are boiled and dried. All mushrooms may be dried in the sun after boiling and thereby preserved.

Insects

Ntowa grubs, so named from the *mutowa* tree on which they live, are squeezed, washed and either roasted or stewed. They may also be preserved by boiling and afterwards drying in the sun. They are eaten during the busy bird-scaring time.

Bwendalongo are found on the tree *kasasa* after the rains. They are not squeezed but grilled.

Kapale are found at the beginning of the cold season in May. They are prepared like *ntowa*.

Fisololo are found the whole year round in *Acacia* trees. Men only can gather them because they have to split the trees to get at the grubs. They are not squeezed.

Rupole are found in *mopane* trees before the rains. They are not squeezed but may be roasted or stewed.

Locusts (sombe) are caught in the early morning, roasted, stewed, salted and used as relish.

Finyense is a kind of locust. The entrails are squeezed out and the insects washed and stewed with salt. They may also be roasted.

The Lala and Bisa have a much greater variety of edible grubs and caterpillars, but many of the trees that harbour those insects do not grow in the Ambo valleys. The valleys, on the other hand, are richer in fish and in green vegetables all the year round.

> *Flying Ants* are caught at the beginning of the rains. Torches of sorghum stalks or of grass are lit on an ant-hill; a small hole is dug and nearby an earthen pot with water is placed. The ants fall into the hole and fall into the water. They are roasted, stewed, salted and served as relish.

ANIMALS

Meat is the most prized relish. Its appreciation is enhanced by its rarity. This rarity is explained in Chapter VII. The gap is partially filled by a large and steady supply of cane-rats trapped in both the cold and the hot seasons. Other attempts to procure meat, such as the digging out of mice by women or the setting of traps by men, are either of minor importance or are not generally employed. Meat hunger, which has a special term, *nkasya*, is to some extent eased by supplies of fish. The relish of meat or fish is termed *munani*. All other kinds of relish, especially vegetable which is the most common, are disparagingly referred to as *fibebebe*. However, meat is more appreciated than fish.

If there is a large amount of meat to be stored, it is cut into strips of varying lengths and approximately one and a half inches thick called *mutendu*. Flesh is dried alone, without bones. These strips of meat are spread out on a platform two to three feet high and there smoked over a slow fire. This meat, *nama va kukanga*, when the smoking is finished is hard and dry. Later, when used, it must be boiled; it is never roasted. Fresh meat is preferably first roasted a little in a dry earthen pot over a fire and then stewed, though it may also be stewed without this preliminary roasting. Fish are cut open lengthwise along the belly, and then laid on platforms to be smoked.

As has been pointed out in Chapter I, the fauna of the valleys is less varied than that of the plateau. The following animals are eaten: elephant (*nsofu*), hippopotamus (*mfubu*)—some people do not like this meat because of its smell, eland (*nsongo*), rhinoceros (*cipembere*), roan antelope (*mpewa* or *twakanwa*), zebra (*mbisi*), water buck (*cusu*), duiker (*insya*,) klipspringer (*cipomo*), reedbuck (*mpoyo*), bushbuck (*cibawara*), wild pig (*ngurube*), wart hog (*njiri*)—the skin is also eaten, the hair being scraped off with a knife, porcupine (*nunji*)—the entrails are not eaten, ant-eater (*mpendwa*), goat (*mbusi*), baboon (*korwe*)

[781]

—many do not eat baboon, giving the reason that it has hands and is therefore a human being, and monkey (*karusoko*)—this is more widely eaten than is baboon. The genet is not eaten. The Ambo say they do not eat any wild beast (*ciswango*) which has claws. Some eat only the legs of tortoise. Old people are said to eat civet (*katumpa*), the gland being cut out and given to the dogs to make them fierce in hunting. Hare (*kalulu*), lemur (*canga*), ratel (*kambole*), and *bumbe* and *turukonko* both unidentified, are not eaten. Some eat *impuru*. The three last named may be mongoose.

The hair of mice is singed or washed in hot water and then plucked. The flesh is boiled. Cane-rat (*ntika*) and other rats (*cibuku, mfumbe, citute, ngali, kamungu* and *ntondo*) are eaten. It is said that when a *ntondo* is caught, one has to blow into its ears which then swell and the animal dies. *Citwitwi* rat is eaten (of this it is said that it dies when it tries to cross a road). *Kampanda* is also eaten.

BIRDS

The feathers are plucked in hot water, the entrails removed and the carcase then grilled or stewed. The following birds are eaten: Domestic fowl (*nsumbi*), dove (*ciba*), pheasant (*musokosi*), guinea fowl (*nkanga*), partridge (*nkware* and, more rarely, *cintalatala*), thrush (*pwere*) (common), quail (*kaundu*), parakeets (*candwe*), lark (*kamutyengu*), " wailing " dove (*katutwa*), *mukwe, ceso, isipi, cipampa, mulongwe, isebe, lurie, ndubaruba, mukuta, funkunkanana, mutongola* and *tukonge*.

FISH

Fish is boiled in water, salt is added and the entrails are discarded. Small fish may be grilled. The following fish are eaten: *Ntongo* (*Mormyrops deliciosus: Mormiridae*). *namuroroma, kalondo* (*Sweta serranochromis, kafuensis: Cichlidae*), mbele (*Alestes imberi: Characinidae*), *kabangalala, nkupe* (*Mormylidae*), *moola, sampa* (*barbel, Heterobranchus longifilis: Clariidae*) *cituku* (*Tilapia spermani: Cichlidae*), *mpata* (*Synodontis nigromaculatus: Mochochidae*), *ntandala, lupumbu manje* (*Hydrocjon lineatus; Charcinidae*), *namusyanga, makobo, lutukula, mukunga, cimpulutumba* (*Barbus paludinosus*), *malemba* (*Snathonemus nonteni: Mormyridae,*) *mulombwelombwe* (*Mormyrus cabullus Mormyridae*), *mumbalala, cintole* and *mita*.

FRUIT

In the hot season, *musokolobe*. In the cold season: *cikuyu, makole, tumbulamuseke, nsense, tupuku, tusimbilili, mabuyu, masoa, mpundu, tumutambacipota*.

In the rainy season: *misesa, munyamenda, mufungufungu, matondo, tulyabapulu, nteme, kapotopoto, kalumbisya, kamuyakamuseka, citobe, ngayingayi, mukolongwa, manomba, mampuli, misepa.*

WILD FRUITS

In times of famine whole villages may live on *busika* (*Tamarindus indica*), in the hot season and at the beginning of the rains. This dish is usually prepared for the mid-day meal. The seeds are squeezed in water, potash is added to neutralise the sourness and the fruit is boiled to a mash. It is said that this fruit affects the stomach.

Mabuyu, the fruit of the baobab (*Adansonia digitata*) is very much sought. It is crushed and squeezed, and then flour and water are added. This juicy liquid may be added to thin porridge.

Though the *musuku* (*Uapaca kirkiana*) does not grow in the valley, women and girls from some nearby villages make expeditions to the escarpments to gather its fruit.

WILD ROOTS

Busabo, musepo and *makulubwi* are boiled. *Nsasa* is peeled and eaten raw. *Kasabo* and *rukonongo* are peeled, sliced, boiled, tied in a bundle of grass and put in running water for a day and night. Then a porridge is made of them. Otherwise they are poisonous.

SALT

The use of local salt is on the decline but needy people still use it. Salt bought in stores is much preferred and some young people complain that the local variety adversely affects their stomach.

Salt is extracted from the following: *Rweresi*, which grows in water; *cikonkoti*, which is plentiful in *mopane* forests, and which is the most commonly used; *kapuku* palm, of which the stem is burnt; *muntambala*, a creeper, of which the stem and the leaves are used; *kalungabusaneme* from *mopane* forest, of which the salty sap is used; *kasanga* and *musoke*, herbs which are found along rivers; *ndabe* which grows in wet places, and *cilungila*, which is saline soil.

To extract the salt, the plants are dried, sometimes spread on a platform of sticks over fire, and then burnt. A percolator, consisting of a conical funnel, resembling in shape that of an ordinary roof, is constructed. The funnel, which at the base is fifteen inches in diameter, is set on four forked sticks, two feet tall. The ashes are placed in it, water poured on them and the solution collected in an earthen pot below. This salty water may be boiled and, as it evaporates, fresh

[783]

salty water added until the whole pot is filled with a residue of salt. The pot is then broken and the salt stored. The loaf of salt is called *cipala*; a piece of salt, *cikumu*. The saline solution may also be used.

Though all the above grow in the valley, only *rweresi* and *cikonkoti* are usually exploited since they yield more salt than all the rest. Salt from *cikonkoti* is alleged to be so strong that it may cause death when eaten in large quantities by a child.

HONEY

Some people use magic to find honey. At the beginning of the rains men go into the bush and even into the escarpment hills in search of honey. A man knocks on the trees until a honey guide hears the knocking and begins to twitter. The man is led by the bird to the hive. A fire is made under the tree where the hive has been found and then a hole is cut in the tree to reach the hive. Only *nsimu* stinging bees need to be smoked out. If the bees are very angry, a rag is torn from a shirt, twisted and put to the opening of the hollow. The grubs of the bees are eaten. First they are stewed, then roasted; salt is added and they are used as relish.

The following honey-making insects are known: *Nsimu, cipasi* the honey of which is eaten with rice or alone and *cibonga*, dug out from the earth. *Kantolola* is the name of the honey made by small bees, *tumpunyunyu*, also known as *tumanina*, which live in *mopane* trees; *mwande* honey is made by bigger *mopane* bees; *cinsuku* is made by a third kind of *mopane* bee (these stingless bees are varieties of *Trigona, Meliponinae*).

BEVERAGES

Honey beer (*mbote*) is not drunk, *kasubia* is a beverage made of ground sprouted grain (*mimena*), to which water and a little fine flour is added. This beverage is drunk by girls and children. *Mpwima* is made of *mimena* to which hot water and more flour is added, and is drunk warm. For *fisunga*, dry malt (*mimena*) is pounded and winnowed and mixed with hot water and flour. This concoction is boiled. After boiling, the liquid is set aside for a day and is then ready to be served. A wife prepares it for her husband as refreshment after heavy work, like felling trees. This is the so-called light Kaffir Beer.

BEER (*bwalwa*)

There are two kinds of beer, *kanjanji* and *cipumu*. The Ambo, however, never brew *cipumu*; firstly, because it can be made only from finger millet which they do not grow, and secondly, because it needs the constant mixing of malt and water during drinking. This the Ambo find annoying. It is said that the Lala and the Bemba make this *cipumu* beer and drink it through reeds.[1]

BREWING OF BEER

There are seven stages:

1. Sorghum or maize is soaked in water for two days until it sprouts. This is called *kusabika* or *kwabika* (to soak).

2. *Kusabula* (*kufundula*)—The sprouted grain is taken out of the water and put into a pot (without water). The leaves of sorghum (*fipumbu*) or the leaves of *mwenge* are put over it to keep it hot and fermenting. Leaves of *mwenge* are used as it is maintained that they are of the same taste as the beer and so do not affect the flavour. This stage lasts four or five days.

3. *Kusimpula*. Now the fermented grain is pounded in a mortar, and fine flour, called *cipandwa*, and boiled water are added.

4. *Kuipika mukupa*—After one day this mixture is called *fisunga*. It is boiled and is given the name of *cinya*. *Cinya* is kept fermenting for from three to five days. The pot containing *cinya* is covered with a smaller pot and the edges are plastered.

5. *Kuposa*—Malt is pounded, winnowed and mixed little by little with *cinya*. The mixing is done in the evening. This mixture is left for one day.

6. *Kukumba* (" to brew ")—A mixture of gruel, made of fine *cipandwa* flour and pounded malt with cold water, is mixed with hot boiling water and with the fermented liquid, *cinya*. This beer is called *kanjanji*.

7. *Kunwa*—The morrow of the *kukumba* stage is called *kunwa* (" to drink "). The technicalities of beer brewing end at the former stage. This stage is the stage of consumption. The guests judge the flavour of the beer which they may describe as good (*bwa bila*) or sour (*bwa sasa*). The beer, the day after, is called *mulala* (" which slept "), the next day *kacekuru* (" the little old man ") and the last day, *kaswalulu*.

---

[1] Richards, 1961. 76 sq. does not make this distinction between the two kinds of beer. However, Bemba women questioned knew the word *cipumu*.

CHAPTER VI

HANDICRAFTS

BASKETRY

Basket-making is a specialised craft and few men practice it (in a sample of five villages only 26.6 per cent of men were basket-makers). Of those who do, not all are able to make all varieties. For example, there are men who can make two kinds of flat baskets but are unable to weave the tall carrying baskets. Women never attempt to make baskets or mats, contrary to what has been observed in other tribes.

The material for baskets is split, scraped bamboo strips as thin as palm leaves. The width and length of these strips depends on the type of basket the maker is going to weave. There are basically two types of baskets, though the Ambo distinguish four kinds according to size.

EATING BASKET (*kape* or *kasere*)

The breadth of each of the strips is an eighth of an inch and the length is according to the local measure from one bamboo notch to another (*malundu*). The strips are twilled into a kind of stiff mat, each strip of the weft being passed alternately over two and under one strip of the warp. The following types are twilled in the same way. First a round rim (*mumpangu*) of bamboo lath is made. The mat is splashed with water and pressed over the circular rim until it is convex. Holes are pierced in the rim, which is then sewn on to the body of the basket. The rim has another inside ring, separate from the external ring. Thus the edge of the basket is sewn between two rings. For sewing, a creeper (*bwasye*) is used. For all the basket work only one tool is employed, a chisel-awl (*cengo*). The holes in the rim are made with the pointed end. The finished product is usually smeared with crushed bark of the *musikisi* to make it a deep brownish red. It measures some ten and a half inches in diameter and three and a half inches in depth.

This kind of basket, the smallest, is used mostly for porridge. It is also used as a measure and as a container for agricultural produce as well as for general domestic use.

WINNOWING BASKET (*rubango*)

This is made in the same way as the above but is twice as large and is put to different use. Therefore the length of the strips is two *malundu* and their breadth is a quarter of an inch. One specimen measured was eighteen inches in diameter and three inches deep. This kind of basket is indispensable for winnowing but is also used as a measure and container for grain and flour.

CARRYING BASKET (*citundu*)

This basket has a square bottom gradually passing into the round. It is rather tall and cylindrical as against the preceding baskets which are flat and shallow. The bamboo strips prepared for the plaiting are of the length between the outstretched hands. This measure is called *mukwamba*. The width of the strip is the same as that for the winnowing basket. The finished carrying basket is about fifteen inches in diameter and of the same height. When the square base of the basket has been plaited, the outstanding strips are worked vertically from the base. The rim is made in a manner similar to that of the winnowing basket. This basket is used by the women for carrying, especially for carrying grain.

SMALL CARRYING BASKET (*musako*)

There is a smaller variety of the same type, differing, apart from size, only in that the rim is made of split reeds and not of bamboo. The size is about one foot in both diameter and in height. Both these kinds of carrying baskets have the corners of the base reinforced with small pieces of skin sewn over them. The only ornamentation is whitish or blackened strips used in the twilling so as to form a large diamond figure. In the winnowing basket these strips of different colours form crossing squares.

BEER SIEVE (*rusanso*)

There are two types of beer sieve. One is of the same pattern and size as the eating basket, though with two differences. In the first sieve, the bottom is moulded into a cone and a handle is attached to the rim, so that the latter looks like a frame of a tennis racket except that it is round not oval. The second type is of wicker-work, made of bamboo sticks not much thicker than a match. It has a round convex bottom and the rim is provided with a handle as in the first type. Sieves are used to sift dregs from beer.

MATTING

Much simpler to make are mats (*mpasa*). *Phragmites* reeds are split into strips, three-eighths of an inch wide, the length being that of the height of a man. The reed strips are soaked, laid flat and sewn together with a long flat needle (*ntungo*) threaded with a twined bark string, one-eighth of an inch thick. On the edges of the mat, two strips are tied together by wrapping them at intervals with the string mentioned earlier (*bwasye*). The width of the mat is the *mukwamba* described above. These mats serve for sleeping or for sitting. Damp flour is also spread on them to dry in the sun.

Lower mat (*cisengere*)—The *mpasa* mat is not used by itself for sleeping as it is too fragile. Another stronger mat is laid beneath. This underneath mat is made of scraped bamboo laths, half an inch wide and, in the middle, about one-twelfth of an inch thick. These laths are tied together with twined strings. The rows of string are at intervals of about eight inches.

Whole reed mat (*cisando*)—Another kind of mat may be made by plaiting whole reeds or even bamboos. This rough mat is resorted to when the finer lower mat is not available. It is also used in fish weirs.

POTTERY

Before a woman makes pots from any clay she tests it, making a small pot which she fires to see if it will crack. The potter brings the clay to the village, stores it in a hole or in an old pot and pounds lumps of it on a stone, using a small pestle (*munsi we roba*). The dry clay is sprinkled with water. She pounds also some potsherds, *nsibe*. The clay is mixed with this crushed potsherd (to stiffen the clay) and also with more water. The clay is now called *misuma ya kuponda*. A ring of clay (*misuma ya kupeta*), two inches thick, is moulded to the size required for the pot. The ring is set on a potsherd covered with leaves, and upon it are set two more rings. Four rings are required for large pots and five rings for out-size beer pots. The shaping of the rings into a pot is done with the fingers, the surplus clay being brought upwards. The inside of the pot is smoothed and thinned with a piece of gourd (*cipamba*), and the outside with a flat stick. When the upper part of the pot is finished, it is set for a few hours to harden. Then the pot is turned upside down, and the bottom is filled in with the clay drawn from the lower part of the vessel. Ornamentation is now added by pressing a flat stick, indented at the end, round the mouth of the pot. On the neck of the pot, triangular lines are drawn with a fragment of gourd, and the indented stick is pressed all over alternating triangles. On the third day, the pots are covered with dry bark and fired.

Cracked pots are sealed with the juice of *cintimbiri* or *mopane*.

The majority of women are unable to make pots. (In a sample census of four villages having seventy-one women, only five could make pots, i.e. 7 per cent.). Those unable to make pots have to barter grain for them.

Relish dish or saucer (*musero*)—This is the smallest kind of pot made. It has a wide mouth, a diameter of five inches and a depth of three inches. Sometimes there is a ridge round the base to support and steady the pot. Relish is served in this kind of dish.

Relish pot (*cinkombe*) The second smallest kind of pot, with a slightly narrower mouth, is eight inches in diameter in the middle of the body and five inches deep. It is used for cooking relish.

Water pot (*nongo ya mensi*)—The mouth is small to lessen the spilling of water. It is seven inches wide at the mouth, twelve inches in diameter at the middle of the body, and eleven inches tall. Water is fetched and kept in this kind of pot.

Washing basin (*cibate*) has a wide mouth, is nine inches in diameter but only six inches deep. It is used to hold water for washing.

Cooking pot (*ntaro*) is taller than the preceding pot but also has a wide mouth. It is eleven inches in diameter at the mouth and seven inches deep. This pot is used for cooking porridge.

Beer pot (*citaro ca bwarwa*)—This is often covered with a bark strip and serves for the brewing of beer. These pots are large, sixteen inches in diameter at the mouth and sixteen inches tall.

WOODWORK

The few objects that are made of wood are all carved from the round. Again most of these objects are made by specialists, though hoe and axe handles are made by everybody. One interesting case was noted of a ladle, expertly carved and ornamented, being made by a woman. However, the usual kind of ladle is a flat piece of wood with a long, straight, simple, stick-like handle. Normally women are unwilling to work with an adze or axe and disdain all handicrafts except pot-making.

DRUM (*ngoma*)

Few men can undertake to hollow out a drum, for this requires delicate skilful work. The drum-workers use a special tool, a giant chisel (*mpampo*). This tool is prepared by bending an axe blade along its sides so as to make a straight but convex chisel which is then hafted vertically in the butt of a handle, three feet in length and some two inches thick. The log of wood is pounded vertically with this chisel.

In common with their neighbours the Ambo use single membrane drums. These are rarely decorated though towards the foot of the drum a ridge may be left in which triangles are indented. The length of the drum is measured from one shoulder to the outstretched finger tips of the opposite hand. The diameter of the broader end is the local measure from the finger tips to about three inches above the wrist. At the narrow end, the size of the opening is measured by putting together the tips of the first fingers and thumbs of both hands and bending them to form a circle. The hide of the griesbuck (preferably with the hair outside) is stretched over the wider opening and fastened to the sides with pegs. Drums are made of *mupapa*, *mukusa*, *musumba*, *mufungura*, *ntebentebe*, *mutupa*, *mubambangoma* and *musebe*.

MORTAR (*mpondo*)

This is also made with the chisel described above. In height it reaches the middle of the thigh as the Ambo measure it. The thickness of the walls is measured by putting the fingers of both hands together. There is no attempt at ornamentation, except at the narrow neck towards the bottom, where a round collar may be left. This is not found, however, on every mortar. The same trees are used as for drums but *mupapa* is considered to be the best.

PESTLES AND HANDLES

The length of a pestle is the *mukwamba*, while the thickness is that of the arm below the elbow. A hoe handle is as long as one's arm to the neck; the axe handle is somewhat shorter. Their thickness should be such as to enable the user to grasp them conveniently. Usually the head and butt of a hoe handle are scorched black.

LADLES, SPOONS AND STIRRERS

The ladle (*mwinko*) or stirring stick consists of a handle, some eighteen inches long, with a spade-like stirring end. It is ornamented with burnt spots and lines. Another cooking implement is the porridge scoop (*cipakiro*). This consists of a short, sharply-bent handle and of a convex, round bowl. The Ambo measure for a bowl is both palms concavely bent and joined together so as to imitate a bowl. The bowl of the scoop is as thick as the fingers held together. The scoop is usually ornamented with burnt dots, lines and triangles. The former cooking implement is used to stir the porridge while it is boiling. With the scoop, porridge is lifted from the pot and placed on dishes, the eating baskets. Nowadays scoops made of thick beaten aluminium sheet are seen.

HEAD-REST (*musao*)

There is a great variety of head-rests. The most common type has the same cross-section as a stool. One specimen observed was in the shape of a small thick disc with a diameter of over four inches and three inches in thickness. Another was a foot-long stick with three branches on one side, cut short and acting as legs. The commonest form of the stool type is narrow, flat, six inches long and about five inches tall. It serves as a pillow for the side of the head, the cheek and the ear. The use of head-rests is on the wane; only a few old people still use them. Many young people use nothing, or just a piece of wood.

STOOLS (*cipuna*)

These are not numerous. Usually there is only one in a village, though there is almost always a deck chair too. Stools are not very elaborate and are carved out of one piece of wood. The round seat is concave, and there are six legs, bent outwards at an angle and joined at the bottom in a circle. The legs may also be curved inwardly. Some ornamentation, mostly triangles, may be burnt in the stools, which are about one foot tall, the diameter being some ten inches.

DUGOUT (*bwato*)

When cutting big trees for dugouts, certain ritual precautions involving the use of medicines must be taken. The bark is scraped off the log, and notches (*turangu*) are cut along the top of it. The spaces between the notches are the length of a man's arm to the elbow, and the length of the notches is the same. The notches reach as deep as the centre of the palm. The wood between these notches is ripped off. The distance between the sides of the canoe is measured so that the buttocks may enter (*kwesya matako*). When the spaces between the notches have been levelled, the log is turned over. Now the outer surface of the bottom is likewise notched and levelled. Next the place for steering and paddling (*cisuka*) is cut out. Then the canoe is carefully hollowed with an adze. When finished, it is rolled on logs down to the river.

The parts of the canoe have a special nomenclature of their own. The rope with which the canoe is tied to a pole on the bank is called *mukungo* and is of *ruburukutu* creeper, one and a half inches thick. *Mibeya*, the sides of the canoe, should be as thick as the middle of the palm of the hand. *Cisuka* is the stern. The stern is narrower than the prow, for the prow is where the foot of the tree was, while the stern is where the top of the log was. Probably the stern is narrower because it is easier to steer from there, changing the paddle from one side to another. The gunwales are *miromo*, " the lips ". The bottom of a canoe is called *rukasa*, " the foot ". The prow is *mutwi*, " the head ". Canoes are used mainly for crossing rivers, but also occasionally for the transport of grain and for fishing. When the current is strong, the canoe is hauled upstream by the paddler pulling on the reeds on the bank. Wherever possible a punting pole (*musundo*) is used. Where the water is too deep for punting, a paddle (*nkafi*) is used. The paddler uses the punting pole standing, the paddle sitting. The paddle blade is as broad as the palms of both hands; the handle is as thick as the arm above the wrist. The length of the paddle is a *mukwamba*. A canoe rots fairly quickly for the inner, hard core of the tree has been hollowed out. Each canoe is owned individually, it is not communal property.

ROPES, KNOTS AND NETS

Ropes (*miando*)

Two strips of inner bark are rolled separately on the thigh in the same direction; then they are rolled together in the reverse direction. Even small boys know how to do this. Though the women know it, they seldom do it. Twined strings are used for binding luggage, parcels and for traps. Otherwise raw bark strips are used, especially for all building purposes. The most common supply of fibre is the *musamba* tree (*Brachystegia*) though the best twined ropes are made of young baobab (*Adansonia digitata*). Thin twine for bird snares is made from wild *mukusa* sisal (*Sansevieria*), rarely from cultivated sisal.

Knots

1. Reef knot, *cikaka banarume*, or the " male knot ".
2. *Cikaka banakasi*, the " female knot ".
3. Slip knot, *citwi ca mbwa*, *kamforomwena*, *cikonkoli canbwa;* this is used to tie dogs and goats. It is used also for trap nooses.

Net-Making

Nets are made from the creeper, *bwasye*, and the shrub, *kapapi*. *Bwasye* is cut at the joints and placed on the hearth in the sun for thirty minutes; the bark then comes off, and the fibre is taken out and used as yarn (*mposo*), which is rolled on the thigh (*kupiata*). *Kapapi:* the twigs are broken, dried in the sun and put in water for a day. When dry, the bark is taken off. The string is twisted.

After the material for the net has been prepared, a small bow is made. This bow is held between the toes of both feet, so that the bow string is stretched between the feet. To the end at the left another string is attached with a slip knot and now the plaiting of the knot begins. (Fig. 4). When the first line of meshes has been plaited, the bow is upturned, the nether side becomes the upper side and now a slightly different knot is used. This knot is kept on throughout, but the bow is turned after each row of meshes.

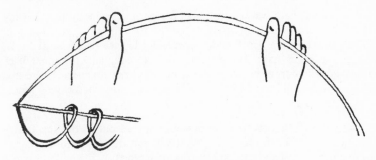

Fig. 4—Making a fishing net; the first stage

SPINNING, WEAVING AND BARK CLOTH

SPINNING

A little cotton, one or two shrubs, is grown in most villages. The Ambo have developed a spindle which is a stick, one foot long and as thick as the little finger, with a disc or rather a flat cone at one end. On the top of the disc there is a wire hook or a hole may be burnt through the stick. Yarn, thinly stretched for the length of a foot, is put through the hook or the hole. The yarn is caught at the hook and the spindle is rolled, slowly at first, on the thigh. When the thread has been spun, the spinner gives a last strong twirl to the spindle on the thigh. The finished length of thread is wound round the disc and the next stretch of cotton wool is spun in the same way.

WEAVING

The Ambo did attempt a form of weaving (*kupika*), probably in imitation of European fabric, but the art did not develop and, soon after the introduction of European goods, was discontinued.

A mat was used instead of a loom and was partially folded in order to shorten it. The warp was stretched by catching the protruding ends of reed strips with thread. The warp threads had a spacing of less than a sixteenth of an inch thick. This cloth was said to be stronger than that obtained from traders but was not so compact.

BARK CLOTH (*nansa*)

Bark cloth used to be made from the inner bark of the *Brachystegia*. A party of a few men would go into the bush where they would make a shelter and sleep, if the distance from the village was too great.

First the bark was tested by breaking it in the hands and chewing it. Young trees only were sought, for the bark of old trees is too stiff. When suitable bark was found, a three-foot log was cut from the tree. Then the outer bark was scraped with an adze and the inner bark removed whole from the log. All the pieces of raw inner bark were tied into a bundle and brought home. This process was called *kusumo'nkwa*. A man could gather ten pieces a day.

In the village, the bark pieces were spread out in the sun to dry for two days. When each was dry, it was put into black mud (*buleru*) to dye it black. Then the bark was again scraped with a knife to make it smooth, soaked in water, and spread on large flat logs (*mukunu*) where it was beaten with a tool in the shape of a blunt axe (*cipamba*) with a double edge. The bark was then wrung out, spread out in the sun and trimmed, and the pieces were sewn together. This cloth is no longer used, as it is not durable; it lasts only a month.

METALWORKING

IRON SMELTING

The traditional way of smelting iron was for a party of men to go where iron ore was to be found, and to build a shelter there. A hole was dug to the depth of the knees, its diameter being about two feet or, by Ambo measurements, such a circle as that made by both arms bent into a circle with the finger-tips touching. At the bottom, firewood and charcoal were piled, as high as the middle of the calf of the leg. A layer of iron ore, eighteen inches thick, was laid on top, then one layer of charcoal; then a second layer of iron ore, and on top of this again charcoal was spread. The whole kiln was thickly plastered with mud, except at the bottom where there are two holes for the bellows. In the evening the kiln was lighted, and the bellows pumped until the fire became strong.

The smelting of iron soon stopped when ready-made material and iron goods became available in the trade stores.

SMITHING

Nowadays, in almost every village there are bellows which are used only when it is necessary to heat hoes and axes in order to sharpen them and to set them into new handles. When red-hot, the metal is hammered, often with an old native-made hammer (*cifulo*), mainly on the edge, so that it needs only a little honing. When an axe or hoe needs a new handle, it is heated at the tang and driven into the head of the handle.

The bellows are made of goat skins flayed whole. They are made in pairs. Each of the pair has two openings, one for receiving the air and the second for expelling it into the fire. The first opening has an edging of two bamboo laths, sewn to the bellows edges. The fingers are inserted between the laths and the skin. Using these fingers, the bellows are opened, closed and pressed down, driving the air through the second opening into a bamboo pipe leading into a clay tuyere set in the glowing charcoal. The two bellows are worked alternately.

MISCELLANEOUS

ROUGHING GRINDING STONES

When grinding stones become smooth through constant use, women roughen them by striking their surface with a small round stone, called *nsono*.

DYEING

Ambo women like to dye their cloth black, especially white calico. The cloth is boiled in a brew of *businwe* fruit and soaked in black mud for two days. Men blacken bamboo strips, in the same way, for ornamental purposes when making baskets. They keep a few strips in black mud to interplait them with strips of natural colour.

EXTRACTING CASTOR OIL (*kwenga mafuta a mbono*)

The seeds of castor oil are exposed to the sun to dry them. When the shells burst, the seeds are winnowed, placed in a potsherd on the fire and roasted. After being stamped, they are boiled in water and stirred with a ladle. As the water evaporates, and the oil comes to the surface the woman gently dips the palm of her hand in and gathers the oil. She draws her palm, now covered with oil, over the edge of a pot.

FIRE-MAKING (*kusika muliro*)

To make fire, two sticks are prepared: one, six inches long and half an inch thick; the other eighteen inches long and thinner than the first. The first stick is *cipantu*; the second is *ruteya*. A hole is drilled in the middle of the shorter stick, and a channel-like notch is cut at the side of the hole. This stick is laid on the ground and held fast by one man. His companion inserts the pointed end of the longer stick into the hole, holding it vertically, and twirls it between the palms of his hands. While twirling, he continually slides his hands down the stick, at the same time pressing it gently into the hole in the nether stick. After two minutes, black powder begins to form round the base of the twirled stick; the powder begins to smoulder and falls down the channel. This powder is gathered into a rag serving as tinder, and is blown upon; the rag begins to smoulder and a little grass put upon it easily catches alight.

The nether stick may be of any wood; the upper stick is made of *musikaliro* or bamboo. In the rainy season the lower stick is carried in the travelling bag; the longer stick is inserted in a bamboo to keep it dry. Nowadays matches are widely used and can be bought at any village store. Matches are among the few items from Western civilisation which are generally accepted in village life.

CHAPTER VII

HUNTING, TRAPPING AND FISHING

The Ambo love hunting. It is the most honourable, useful and fascinating occupation for a man. Formerly he hunted with a bow and arrows, carrying a hatchet and spear as subsidiary weapons. Today, however, the muzzle-loader gun has ousted the bow.

WEAPONS

Bows

The bow was made of *mukole* or *kasasa* wood (*Thespesia rogersii*). The string was made of the gut of roan antelope or of baboon, and was inserted into holes burnt into the stave one and three-quarter inches from its ends, and then wound round them. The arrow heads were given two " ears " (barbs) or were barbless. They were smeared with poison from *Strophanthus* roots (*bulembe*). The bow string was smeared with castor oil. The length of the bow was from the ground to the forehead. When aiming, the butt of the arrow reached the chin.

Spears (*fumo*)

There was only one kind of spear. It is still in general use and is carried by men when going on a journey or to the bush. Those who own guns prefer to carry them, though usually with an axe or spear as well. These weapons are termed *fyensyo*, " the things to walk with ".

A spear is used as a javelin against buck. Against savage beasts, however, it is held in the hands and used for stabbing.

The shaft of a spear is made of bamboo. Into the butt of this shaft, a small axe head, called *coco*, is driven vertically. This tool is used for digging holes in the ground for the uprights and forked poles which are used in the building of all structures. The length of the spear is from the ground to a man's shoulder. The blade should be the length of the palm of the hand. There is a tendency to have the foreshaft between the blade and the tang from six to eighteen inches in length. Around both ends of the shaft, where the spear tang and the axe blade are inserted, a spiral iron tape is wound.

Fish spears (*musumbo*)

The shaft is made of bamboo, the length of the whole spear being a little less than a man's height. Into the shaft, a round, sharp, iron spike, some eight inches long and a quarter of an inch thick in the middle, is driven. At the joint the shaft is wound with string. The shaft

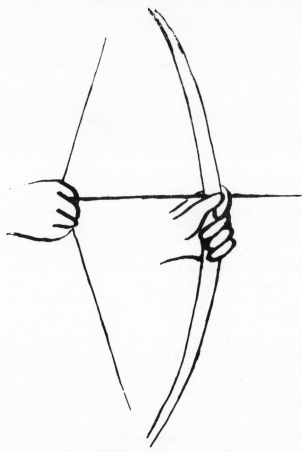

Fig. 5—Holding a hunting bow and arrow

is much thinner than that of an ordinary spear, being about half an inch in diameter.

AXES

These are of the same shape as those of other central Bantu peoples of Eastern Province. The helve is of an arm's length. The butt end and the head of the helve are scorched black. The difference between the axes of the Ambo and those of neighbouring tribes is that the Soli make the head of the handle sharply differentiated from the helve (i.e. the head suddenly thickens from the rest of the helve). The Ambo handle imperceptibly grows bigger from the helve to the head. The Nsenga axe blade is inserted into the head at a sharp angle;

the Ambo blade is a little less than 90 degrees. It is argued that a blade with a sharper angle is more liable to cut into the leg on a faulty stroke or if the blade slips out of the helve.

Many have guns but many more do not. Yet an outstanding hunter is comparatively rare. A large percentage of men try to acquire guns, muzzle-loaders. Though a shotgun has become more and more popular, it is hardly within the reach of a common villager, partly because of Government restrictions on fire-arms and partly on financial grounds. (The percentage of men owning guns in a sample census was 24.6 per cent. The sample was taken from seven villages of seventy-seven men. Two men had two guns each, but in one village of twelve men, only one gun was found and, as it was owned by a woman, it was left out of the count).

Some sixty years ago the bow was the standard war and hunting weapon. Through early contact with the Portuguese Chikunda, the use of the gun spread rapidly. more rapidly than among many other Rhodesian tribes, and the bow fell into disrepute. The author saw one man with a bow in 1938 and another in 1949. The latter was an old man, however, of Aushi origin, who used his bow to chase baboons from his garden. With the coming generation, hunting with the bow will become a lost art.

All hunting is closely connected with a knowledge of magical " medicines " and religion as has been described elsewhere.[1] The present chapter is concerned only with the technical use of the gun and other weapons and traps.

There are gunsmiths in the country who can turn a more or less suitable steel pipe taken from the mines into a muzzle-loader. Two most famous gunsmiths were trained in Tete long before the coming of the British Administration. One of them is still living, Kalubangwe-Mulaku, a son of Nkumpa Nkowama, mentioned in Chapter I.

It is no wonder that fatal accidents happen with guns bursting when fired. A gun fetches about £5 in the villages, a sum far less than that charged for a new gun at a store.

Ammunition is home-made. The bullets are round, ball-like or cylindrical, one inch long, with the front end shaped the same as the back end without any streamlining. Round bullets are hammered from pieces of lead, taken from the mines. The long bullets are cast. Instead of ignition caps, Belgian-made sulphur matches are used.

Saltpetre (*cikulo*) is now bought from Indian stores. In olden times it was gathered in the hills and boiled. The scum was skimmed with a piece of gourd until only pure saltpetre was left. This was spread out

---

[1] Stefaniszyn, 1964.

to dry. The saltpetre is mixed with finely-ground charcoal from the *cintimbiri* tree. A sample of this gunpowder is tried on a hot potsherd to see if it explodes. The gun butts are made of *mucenje* tree which does not crack.

HUNTING

The villager is not usually a good shot,[1] for the muzzle loader is not an accurate weapon, especially when in the condition in which it is commonly used. He has very little training in shooting, and most of the muzzle loaders have no back-sight. Therefore, many animals which are wounded get away. Those men who have guns and are keen on hunting, walk through the bush where they are likely to come across game. They walk all the year round, but not much at the end of the rainy season or at the beginning of the cold season when the grass is high, except in the *mopane* bush where the grass is always low and impala abound. The proper hunting season starts with the hot season, when the grass has been burnt, and lasts until the rainy season when the new grass grows too high for the game to be seen easily.

The hunter works upwind. Some carry little bags with fine ashes which they shake out to test the direction of the wind. If ashes are not available, the wind is tested by dropping sand. These are precautionary measures against scaring away game. To find game the hunter uses his eyes. The African, even should he not be a hunter (and even if he is a mere youth), is very quick to see game amongst the undergrowth and trees. On sandy or muddy ground the hunter looks for the tracks of animals. He can distinguish old tracks from the more recent ones of the day before and from the fresh ones of the same day. Recent rain obliterates all tracks and clearly shows up fresh ones made after the rain. The hunter distinguishes between different tracks in dry sand, noticing whether they are blurred by wind and by insects crawling over them. Very helpful in tracking are the urine and the dung left by game. This determines, even more accurately, the time which has passed since the tracks were made. Some hunters even examine the grass on which passing game has browsed. When the hunter goes upwind, it is not surprising that he can smell game from some two hundred yards, especially if he has a large herd before him.

On sighting game, the hunter slowly sinks down and considers the direction of approach. He will test once more the wind and examine the bush for cover. He may retreat and approach the game again from some direction where there is more cover. The secret of

---

[1] Among nearly a hundred men, working on the road through the escarpment in 1953, there were only three first-class hunters, good trackers, keen and good shots.

success is the close shot. The hunter will crawl imperceptibly, making sure that there is a shrub or a tree between him and his quarry. The Ambo likes to fire standing, and without leaning the gun against a tree, when he is some thirty to fifty yards away from the animal.

There is only one method of hunting; that described above. There are, however, two ways of organising a hunt. One is when a solitary hunter with possibly a boy companion walks through the bush in the neighbourhood of his village, preferably early in the morning or late in the afternoon. The Ambo is really seeking the larger varieties of game. Duiker and griesbuck are too wary to be surprised. They are more easily trapped. Bushbuck may be found standing in the thicket and shot. Larger game also give the hunter a larger target and more meat in addition to being more easily seen.

This is why buffalo hunting is so much appreciated. The interesting feature of it is that a close shot from a distance of some twenty yards is thought necessary for success; then, after the shot, the hunter throws down his gun and scurries away for his life. Some who stalked a wounded beast have paid with their lives.

The second way is the group hunt. A party of three to five men, relatives or co-villagers, combine for a hunting expedition to some distant place where game abounds. They take provisions for two or three days, and erect a shelter of branches (*mutanda*) to sleep in. Small boys accompany them to carry the food. From this base the hunters scour the bush, each going in a separate direction to avoid their accidentally shooting one another.

When game is killed it is divided according to a conventional scheme. The scheme is not strictly adhered to, but is followed in most details:

The neck is given to the carriers, and one front leg to the hunter's companions. One hind leg goes to the headman, the rump (*bukome*) to the hunter's mother-in-law, and the other front leg to his sister. The other hind leg is presented to his mother. The hunter takes the entrails and the liver (*ryanga*—" hunter's meal "), which are eaten on the spot, and the head. The back goes to the hunter's wife, while the sides are given to those who carry the kill.

Small game, suspended by the legs, is carried on a pole. If the game is killed far away from the village, it is smoked at least partially at the place of the kill. Otherwise the carcase is cut up and carried to the village. If a man kills two or three animals in a year, he is reckoned a good hunter. Many, having killed a few animals, rest on their laurels. The need to give away practically all the meat to the rest of the village is not a good incentive for the arduous toil of tracking game.

DECOY FLUTE

A duiker pipe, or decoy flute, is fashioned in the shape of a miniature native drum, from an antelope's horn. The best pipes are made from the horn of the sable antelope, kudu and roan antelope, though inferior specimens are made from duiker or bushbuck horn. Over the bottom or the larger opening of the pipe, a membrane is stretched and glued with the sap of *mwenje* (*Diplorrhynchus mossambicensis*). The membrane is either the wall of a spider cocoon, a white paper-like substance, or else the film-like underskin of any antelope. The hunter makes a sound by blowing across the narrower opening so that the air strikes the opposite rim. The air which enters the pipe makes the membrane vibrate, producing a screeching sound. The hunter plays four to six notes, alternately rising and falling. This sound is a perfect imitation of an antelope's call, especially that of a duiker. A male antelope comes running at full speed, supposing it to be the call of a female. A female duiker approaches slowly and hestitatingly at the supposed call of a kid either lost or in distress. The hunter repeats the notes two or three times and then awaits the result. If a duiker is within hearing, it cannot resist the call and runs in the direction of the sound. The hunter leaves intervals of about half a minute's silence between calls, so as to draw the duiker by degrees. During the long interval the duiker loses its direction and awaits a new call. Thus gradually it comes within shooting distance of the hunter, at last stopping in full view. If the intervals are too short or the calls too frequent, the duiker, especially if a male, runs without stopping in the same direction, approaches too close to the hunter, and on seeing him swerves to one side and runs away.

The hunter usually has a boy companion who whistles for him. If the hunter is alone, he may keep the pipe suspended round his neck. After blowing it, he drops the pipe and stands with his gun ready, especially if he hears the rustling of oncoming game.

Duiker come most often to such calls because it is very common. The same response to the call is made by griesbuck, klipspringer and reedbuck. Cases are known of roan, kudu and impala also coming, but the responsiveness of this last group is restricted to the times when they are accompanied by their young. It is more customary to track and stalk the bigger antelope without calling them. Bushbuck seem to be somewhat indifferent to the call.

The Ambo maintain that pythons, hyenas, lions and leopards also answer the call in order to catch the decoyed game. The author has himself observed a jackal and a hyena doing this.

The decoy flute is doctored with magical medicines, and it is believed that such a doctored flute cannot attract a lion. In spite of this magical precaution, the hunter is careful not to blow the flute after sunset lest a savage beast be attracted.

ANT-BEAR HUNTING

The Nsenga country abounds in such a good supply of meat relish in the form of cane-rats and fish that ant-bear hunting, though known, is hardly practised except by strangers coming from the Lala plateau. Few dare to face the danger of ant-bear hunting, except skilled hunters who have the necessary magical medicine. The hunter must have the medicine of *ntesi* (*kutesimuka*—to slip), to be passed by and not be bitten by a snake. It is known that the burrows of ant-bears abound in snakes. The hunter enters the burrow usually with three spears, since the animal, being hardy, may not succumb to one spear, or the spear may bend and snap. The lair of the animal is large enough for a man to turn round in. The most dreaded danger is that the animal may burrow round towards the exit corridor and block it. It is said that a man may die by being trapped in this way. The pursued animal may also block the corridor in front of the pursuer and thus stop him short. Then he knocks, and his companions dig a shaft to the burrow and so the pursuit goes on. When the hunter has killed the ant-bear, he either drags it backwards or knocks on the ceiling of the burrow. His companions hear him and dig a shaft to extricate him together with his kill. If it is found that the animal has gone too deep, men will watch the whole night until it comes out.

HUNTING BABOONS WITH NETS

The net is some fifty-five inches high and may be fifty yards long. The mesh is made of the best fibre known, that of young baobab bark. As nets are scarce, they are often hired. The headman pays five shillings or a goat (information from the early 1940's) while every villager contributes sixpence.

First the bush is cleared so that the net may be spread out without hindrance. This is done in the evening, on supporting sticks and trees near the tree where the baboons sleep. Men go in the early hours and take up their positions before sunrise. Baboons are not early risers for they dislike the dew. Men encircle the side which is not blocked by the net and advance noisily towards the baboons. A few men are placed in front of the net. The baboons in a panic are entangled in the net and killed with knobkerries. Guns are not used but some are taken in case a lion is met.

After the grass has been burnt, a few men go into the bush with their dogs, keeping them close by. When an animal is scented the dogs rush at it and bring it down. Hares and griesbuck are often caught in this way. Larger game such as warthog, is harassed by the dogs, which try to encircle it while the hunters attempt to stab it with their spears. Less often do they use guns, fearing the accidental shooting of a dog or of a companion.

Before the acquisition of guns, elephants were hunted with spears. A group of men, making a great noise, would drive a herd of elephant towards spearmen perched on trees. The spearmen struck the elephants as they passed beneath.

HUNTING OF CANE-RATS

When a bush fire passes through the *Phragmites-Pennisetum* belt along the river, men and boys set out with dogs and fish-spears. When the dogs scent a cane-rat in a clump of unburnt reeds the men encircle it. The dogs drive out the rat which is then speared. Men also take conical baskets (*kakoba*), three feet in length, and place them on the rat tracks leading out from unburnt clumps of thicket. The dogs chase out the rats which, following their customary runs, enter the long narrow baskets. Near each basket a hunter waits to spear the rat.

TRAPPING

Many Ambo, especially the elderly and the middle-aged, love trapping (*kusonsola*), for those who have no guns have no other means to satisfy their meat hunger. Women look approvingly on trapping and trappers and many, for obvious reasons, prefer husbands who are good trappers. The ingenuity displayed in capturing wild animals is prodigious as will be seen. Due to interference and control by the Administration, trapping will soon be a thing of the past.

NOOSE-SPRING TRAP (*mupeto wa nama*) (Fig. 6)

This trap is used for the smaller kind of buck, such as duiker, griesbuck, bushbusk and reedbuck. First a rough fence of branches is constructed in the bush. At frequent intervals there are openings in which the traps are set. A sapling, either growing naturally or brought specially and set in the ground (sometimes supported with a short forked pole as a prop), is bent by means of a cord. The sapling acts as a spring. Where the cord coming from the top of the sapling reaches the ground, a small hole (one foot in diameter and six inches

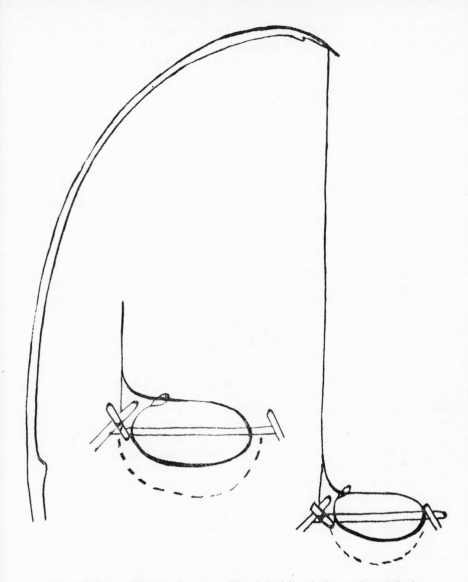

Fig. 6—Noose-spring hunting trap. The dotted line indicates the small pit dug beneath the trap. *Inset:* A close-up of the trap to show the trigger mechanism

deep) is dug. Round the rim of the hole, a noose (*nsanga*) is attached to the cord of the spring. A loose stick (*musalabwe*) is laid across the hole and is propped against two pegs (*mpopo*), which are to hold the trigger (*kapirinyonso*). The trigger is attached to where the cord of the spring and the noose meet. The hole is covered and camouflaged with grass, sticks and earth. The loose stick, when pressed by a passing animal, falls down, easily releasing the trigger. The sapling straightens up, tightening the noose round the leg.

Ordinary nooses are used extensively, for the noose is the most common device for catching guinea fowl. A fence of branches and twigs, though much smaller than that for game and hares, is constructed, and nooses suspended at intervals in places where guinea fowl are usually seen, as in burnt-out patches of bush strewn with grass seeds. The nooses for guinea fowl are made of sansevieria (*agave*), and are like those used for birds though much thicker.

The spring noose-trap, as described above, may be constructed in the gardens at planting-time, to catch guinea fowl. A head of maize is tied to the releasing stick. The guinea fowl pecks at the grain, disturbs the releasing stick, thus freeing the trigger and the spring and is caught by the neck in the noose. This practice does not seem, however, to be widespread. It has been seen to be used only by a Bukanda immigrant, a great trapper.

Nooses of thick rope, nowadays preferably of wire, are set for wild pig and the larger buck. Often, however, though a pig may be caught by the neck or by the foot, it is able to extricate itself because its neck, being thick, narrows evenly towards the head, while its foot similarly narrows smoothly towards the hoof. Unforeseen incidents also sometimes happen. A strong noose of wire was once attached to a big log and set for big game, but a lion was caught and strangled itself. In another instance the same thing happened, but the lion disappeared with the whole contraption. It was surmised that the lion died, because soon afterwards vultures were seen hovering over the hills in the direction whither the tracks of the lion led.

NOOSE-SPRING-NET FOR HARES (*masebayo*) (Fig. 7)

A fence of branches and felled saplings is constructed, three feet high and running straight through the bush. At frequent intervals traps are set for hares. The hare first pushes the net thus causing the loose stick above, the releasing stick, to which the net is attached, to drop. This stick releases the trigger which holds the sapling spring by the rope above and by the noose below, spread on the edges of the rectangular

[806]

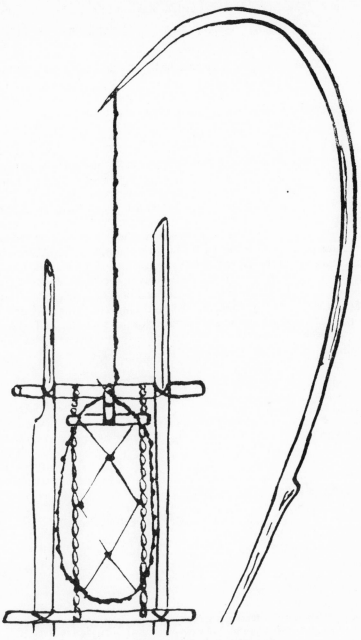

Fig. 7.—Noose-spring-net hunting trap.

opening. The trigger is set in position and is held there by two sticks; one stick, a crosspiece, is tied to uprights to a frame for the entrance. The second stick is loose and leans against the strings tying the uprights to the cross-piece. This second stick is the releasing stick holding up the net. One successful trapper claimed he had caught twenty hares during one season.

Noose-spring Trap for Genet (*cinkoloto*) (Fig. 8)

This trap is only a modification of the hare trap and of the noose-spring trap for small buck. There is the same spring made from a bent sapling and a trigger held in position by the inclined corner formed by a peg and the releasing stick. A noose is also attached to the trigger as in the above constructions. The difference is that in *cinkoloto*, the releasing stick, to which a dead rat is tied, is in a small hole. The hole is encircled with the noose. When the genet or mongoose seizes the rat and shakes the releasing stick loose, the trigger and the spring are released, tightening the noose round the animal's neck. A second, different feature of this trap is that it consists of two open holes connected by a tunnel. The first hole containing the bait is as described above. Through the tunnel passes the end of the noose and the rest of the releasing stick. In the second hole is the main releasing mechanism —the trigger, the peg, the end of the releasing stick, the end of the noose attached to the trigger and the rope leading upwards to the bent sapling.

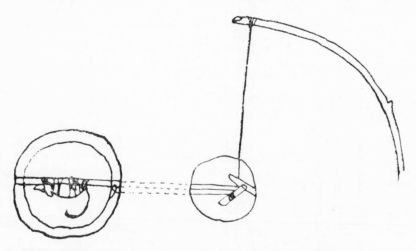

Fig. 8—Noose-spring hunting trap for genet and civet. The larger pit is 6 in. in diameter and the tunnel between the two pits is 4 in. long

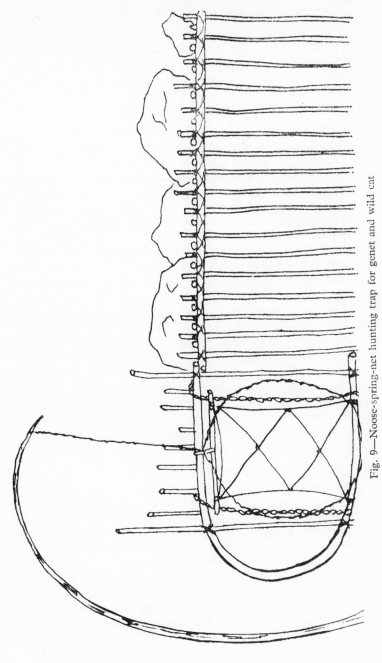

Fig. 9—Noose-spring-net hunting trap for genet and wild cat

Usually, although genets and wild cats play havoc with fowls, nothing is done. Sometimes, however, an energetic and industrious man tries to combat these vermin. A hutch is added to the hare trap, described above, with two compartments. In the second compartment a chicken is placed as a bait. The genet is caught by the noose at the entrance.

GAME PITS (*macinga*)

A circular game pit (*bucinga bwa kumufule*)[1] had a diameter of six feet. The pit was as deep as the height of a man with his raised hands. A *mwafi* pole was laid across the middle of the top of the pit to support the covering of sticks, grass and soil. *Mwafi* was chosen because it breaks easily. To weaken it even further a notch would be cut in the middle of the pole. The pit narrowed down to the bottom, where a pointed pole of hardwood, the core of a *mopane* tree, three feet long and three inches thick, was fixed. This kind of pit was made for large animals such as the elephant and hippopotamus.

The long game pit (*bucinga bwa rutanto*) was a ditch, three feet broad and four hoe handles (eighty inches) long; the depth was seventy-five inches. At the bottom, the pit was as narrow as the width of the hoe blade. The covering was the same as that of the circular pit.

The small game pit (*kapasaya*) was one hoe handle broad and as long as the long game pit, but was meant for small animals. Three poles were placed across the pit at each end. At these ends the top of the pit was covered with earth but in the middle only grass was strewn. In this game pit the legs of the animal could not reach the bottom because it was very narrow. Game pits were dug near salt pans or were placed in gaps left in a branch fence. Usually they were dug near the village so that their daily inspection was not difficult.

LOG TRAPS FOR CANE-RATS (*munkuru*) (Fig. 10)

Cane-rats roam at large through the whole bush in the wet season, unhampered by the lack of food. When the grass withers and dries, however, they flock to the succulent *Pennisetum*, buffalo grass and *Phragmites* reeds along rivers and streams. Then on these green banks are erected reed fences in which traps of falling logs are set. The cane-rats fall an easy prey to these traps or to the chase.

In a fence a passage, six feet long, is constructed of reeds. Over this passage a heavy log is suspended horizontally from the ends of two sticks, balanced on two forked supports. At their other ends these sticks cross each other and, at the intersection, are held by a cord

---

[1] Game pits are no longer dug.

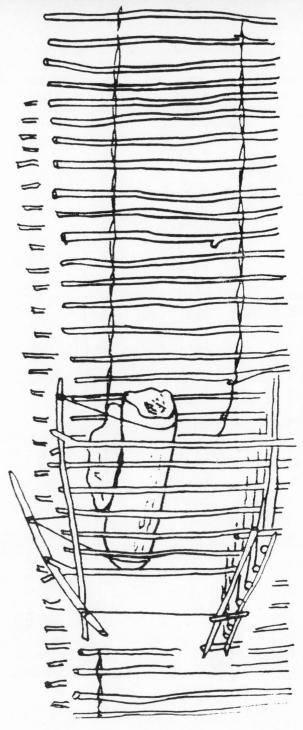

Fig. 10—Cane-rat trap, *munkuru*

leading to a trigger. The two forked supports and the trigger mechanism are set outside the passage. The trigger is held in position according to the general principles of Bantu traps. There are two short supports and a cross-piece tied to them at its ends. Thus the trigger is held in position by the weight of the log, suspended from two sticks and linked to them by a cord. The weight pulls the trigger against the cross-piece, which is set close to the ground. The other end of the trigger is pressed

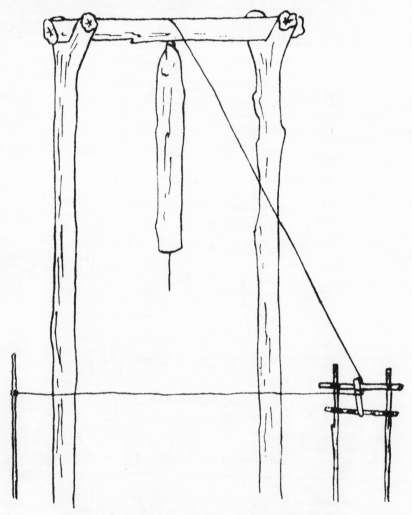

Fig. 11—Harpoon trap for elephant, buffalo and hippopotamus

against the releasing stick, which in turn is pressed by the trigger against the supports of the cross-piece. A layer of reeds is laid across the floor of the passage and on top of the releasing stick. The heavy cane-rat walks over them, releases the hidden stick and sets off the trigger. The heavy log, weighed down with several big stones, crushes the rat. Almost every family consumes several cane-rats a week during the season.

Harpoon Trap (*cisumpi*) (Fig. 11)

This trap, which is similar in principle to the *munkuru* trap, is the biggest and most powerful of all traps. It was the first, therefore, to be forbidden by the Administration. It was extensively used by the Chikunda on the Lower Luangwa, and by all the tribes on the Lunsemfwa. The Bemba group of tribes, however, may not have used this trap to any great extent, while Doke (1931) does not mention it for the Lamba. The Ambo used a pitfall, as described above, for large game.

The harpoon trap was used for elephant, buffalo and hippopotamus. Instead of treading on a releasing stick as in the cane-rat traps, the animal pushed a string stretched across his path. The string was connected to a trigger set at the side of the trap in a manner similar to that of the log trap. There was also a frame made of two uprights and a cross-piece. Below the cross-piece was a loose releasing stick, kept in position only by the pressure of the trigger pulled by the suspended weight of the harpoon. From the trigger a rope ran over a frame holding a pointed log over the path and over the outstretched string. The trigger was released when the string was disturbed, causing the rope to slip off the trigger. The harpoon had a small iron blade, poisoned (*strophanthus—bulembe*) at the tip.

Falling Basket Trap for Monkeys (*cuumba*) (Fig. 12)

This trap is again similar in principle to the log trap and to the harpoon trap. It differs in that, on seizing the bait, the monkey causes a coffin-like basket to fall upon him. The sides of the basket are blocked and fenced with branches so that it completely encloses the monkey but does not fall across him. If this happens, the monkey would probably lift the basket and extricate himself.

The bait is a maize cob which is linked by a cord to a releasing stick. The stick is loose but is kept in position against a frame by the trigger, as in the preceding traps. The trigger is itself kept in position by the weight of the trap-basket and by means of a stick. This stick is balanced at one end by the basket and rests on a frame. At its other

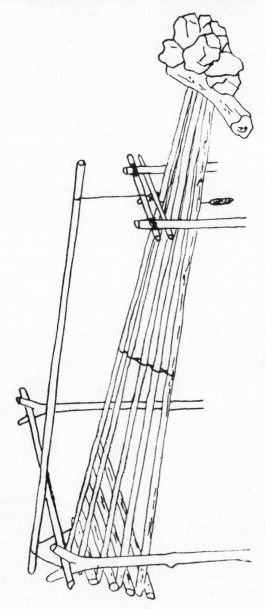

Fig. 12—Monkey trap; side view

end this stick supports the trigger. When the monkey pulls at the maize cob, he disturbs the releasing stick and the trigger. The trigger goes up, weighted by the basket, which falls and covers the animal. The sticks of the basket are made spring-like by piling across the end of them a log and a few small rocks. One monkey trap observed caught nine baboons before it rotted.

The traps are set in the shade under big trees.

There is another kind of trap for monkeys in the form of a huge cylinder plaited of split bamboo of wicker-work. The basket is narrower than a house but taller. On the top a conical valve, similar to the valve in a conical fish-basket, is inserted and a bait of a few maize cobs is thrown inside. The baboons squeeze themselves, òne after another through the valve, but cannot get out again (in a similar way to that in which fish enter the conical basket trap with inverted valve). This second trap was found on the borders of Ambo country. The Ambo prefer the former type *cuumba*.

HUTCH TRAP (*sense*) FOR LIONS AND LEOPARDS

A hutch is built with two compartments. A goat is put in the second (inner) compartment, and a door of planks is suspended over the entrance. The trigger is set at the back of the first compartment, in much the same manner as in the harpoon or log trap. Inside the first compartment, a layer of sticks connected to the releasing stick is set. The lion knocks down the releasing stick, much in the same way as the cane-rat does in the passage of the log trap, thus causing the trap door to fall behind him.

This trap was probably employed long ago before the use of guns. Nowadays a dog is tied as a bait and the beast is shot from an enclosed verandah, for the hutch trap entails a great deal of work.

A lion is always left unmolested unless he is a man-eater, in which case the village tries to destroy him.

HUTCH GUN TRAP

A hutch is built and a goat is placed in it. In front of the goat a gun is fastened. In the entrance a rough net is tied with a releasing string across it which goes round the butt of the gun and is tied to the trigger. When the lion, seeking the goat, pushes the net he disturbs the releasing string, thus pulling the trigger.

MOUSE TRAPS

Field-mice are extensively hunted by women and girls who roam the bush adjoining the village, especially in both disused and culti-vated gardens, digging out mouse nests. Women also trap field-mice in pots. This trap has the name, *cintimbwi*. An ordinary pot is sunk into the earth and is filled with water. The inner sides are smeared with roasted ground-nuts and, when mice go to lick this paste they fall into the water.

There is a variant of this trap: the pot is set on the ground between two forked sticks and a cross-piece is laid on the forks. Over this scaffolding a potsherd is placed, the concave side being turned downwards towards the pot. The cavity is smeared with a paste of roasted and pounded ground-nuts. Mice, seeking the paste, overturn the potsherd and fall into the water.

Small boys also trap mice with slabs of stone (*see below*).

TRAINING OF BOYS

Boys are trained or rather train themselves from an early age in all three methods of gathering proteins. Enough has been said about how they are made familiar with hunting, mostly by accompanying the hunters with whom they learn stalking and experience the thrill of the chase. There is also a game of spear throwing, using a moving target. Such a game is preparation and training for hunting.

Boys set mouse traps (*ciliba*), consisting of a weighted slab of stone set on a cross-piece and forked stick. A grain of maize is tied as bait to a string encircling the slab and also holding it in position. This string is tied at one end to the grain and at the other end to the balancing stick. When the grain is disturbed, the slab falls and crushes the mouse.

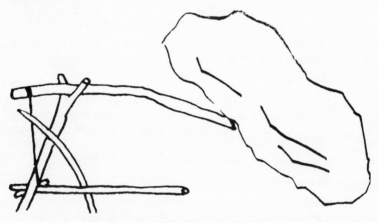

Fig. 13—*Ciliba* slab trap for birds

[816]

Boys set several kinds of traps for birds including the *ciliba* slab trap (Figs. 13 and 14). The position of the slab at first glance is similar to that poised for mice. The mechanism is, however, different. The balancing stick is in a similar position as in the mouse trap but it is

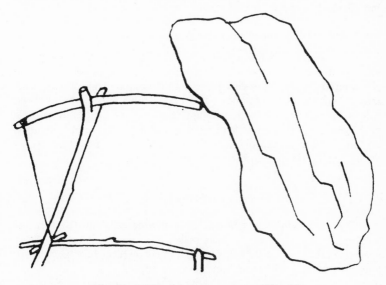

Fig. 14—*Ciliba* slab trap; variant of Fig. 13

connected by a string to a trigger set near the ground. The trigger is held in position in the same way as many of the other traps described. It is wedged between a peg and a releasing stick. The bird knocks down the releasing stick, thus freeing the trigger. A bait of grain or bran is scattered under the slab.

Spiny cucumbers are hung on trees and a circular hole, one inch in diameter, is cut in the side. Round this hole a noose of *Sansevieria* fibre twine is set. Birds, particularly thrushes, come to peck the pips from the cucumber and are caught by the noose. Small nooses are also set at intervals in the paths in the gardens after harvest. A long stick is laid some three inches above the ground and a noose is suspended from it. A fence of twigs is created on each side of the noose.

All nooses for birds have to be prepared from fine *Sansevieria* twine or the coarser *agave* twine. The technique of making twine has been described in Chapter VI.

[817]

It must be borne in mind that trapping, which is carried on in both dry seasons, in the cold and in the hot one, fills only a part of a boy's time. He engages also in fishing even when bush trapping is not possible, as in the wet season. He uses small basket traps, fixed nets and fish hooks, and works both the streams and the channels of the big rivers.

BIRDS' " SWEEP " (*cimpangu*)

A reed screen is put up, usually after the harvest. Some thirty yards from the screen a clear and even place is prepared on which bran is scattered as bait. On this place a split bamboo some three yards long is laid, and is tied at one end to a peg driven in the ground at the side of the clearing. A cord, leading to the screen, is tied to the middle of the bamboo. When a flock of birds is feeding on the bran a man or a boy pulls the cord sharply, and the bamboo sweeps the clearing, revolving round the peg and injuring the birds' legs.

FISHING

One of a man's chief duties is to provide relish in the form of meat and fish, while the woman makes sure of a regular supply of vegetable relish. Even though vegetables may be plentiful, the villagers long for protein. Whereas hunting and trapping yield scanty results, except for cane-rat trapping, fishing usually repays much more the labour spent on it, though this does depend on the size of the river and on the season; the bigger the river, the better the yield of fish. Thus, the villages on the Lunsemfwa have ample fish, the Lukusashi villages have much less, while the villages on small tributaries have very little. The methods of fishing also vary according to the size of the river. The most usual methods of fishing depend on two implements, the cone basket trap and the net. Other methods are of less importance.

CONE BASKET (*mono*)

The basket, which is in the form of a conical cylinder, is made of split bamboo tied to a few circular frames. The walls of the basket are of open work, and in the mouth a conical valve is inserted. The fish squeeze in through the valve but cannot come out again. They are taken out through the apex of the basket, which can be untied.

The size of the basket varies according to the depth of water. In small streams the diameter may be eight inches, and the length two and a half feet. In deep water, the basket may be as much as three or four feet in diameter and eight feet in length. When the cone basket is laid on its side in a weir, the upper rim of its mouth should just reach the surface of the water.

The valveless cone basket (*kansa*) is narrower and longer than the valved one, being eight inches in diameter at the entrance and five to six feet long. This basket is tied to stakes in swift running water, so that the strong current acts like a valve to prevent the fish from escaping. Cone baskets are liable to be torn by otters seeking the fish trapped in them.

Weir (*cipanda*)

Weirs are built only where river conditions warrant them. They are not built, for example, in very deep water or on sand. In practice, they are concentrated on the Lukusashi where almost every village has its communal weir right across the river. On large rivers weirs are built only in side channels after the rains. These weirs are individually owned. So are weirs on lesser streams. On the Lukusashi, the time for constructing weirs is in June, when the water subsides. In the side channels and streams the time is just after the end of the rainy season, when there is no danger that the weir will be swept away by a sudden flood. Openings are left in the weirs, wherein conical basket traps are set. Each man may have one or two cone basket traps in the communal weir, which the whole village community combines to make, as one man would find it hard to block up some hundreds of yards of river. The combination of weir and traps set at intervals, like that in animal trapping of fences and traps set in the escape holes, is sound, ingenious and efficient. Mere technical efficiency is, however, not sufficient; to ensure success, the weir is treated with magical medicines. The goodwill of the local spirit is also sought by offering him a sacrifice. Thus the construction of a weir proceeds along three lines, the technical, the religious and the magical.

First, posts are driven into the river bed about a foot apart, their heads showing just above the water. To these posts mats, made on the pattern of very rough twined basketry but of whole reeds, are tied. The posts are buttressed against the current with forked poles, while every few feet an opening is left in the weir for a cone basket trap to be inserted. The opening is made in the form of a channel, which is also of mats. A few feet downstream from the channel are two posts that support the cone basket trap, which may be turned to face either upstream or downstream.

The cone basket may also be used independently of a weir as a " submerged basket " (*mono wa cirambira*) in deep water. A few stones are put inside to hold it down, together with some thick, roasted porridge for bait.

[819]

NETS

The making of nets was discussed in Chapter VI. There are three types of nets and several methods of using them. The small net (*kombe*), which has a half-inch triangular mesh and is from ten to fifteen yards long, is used in small streams. It is stretched on sticks from the bank to the middle of the stream, and boys with sticks and fish spears drive fish into it.

Such a net may also be stretched on sticks to form a horseshoe (*cisinkiro*). Bran is scattered on the enclosed water and stones are laid along the bottom edge of the net. The net is stretched in still water and a man slowly approaches the entrance, thus frightening the fish through it; the fish, in trying to escape, entangle themselves in the net.

Another method is to stretch a small net in front of the overgrown bank of a pool. All the men and boys of the village wade in and prod under the bank with fish spears. This is done when the river is at its lowest level just before the rains.

The drag net (*cikulo*) has a triangular mesh over one inch long. At the end of the hot dry season, when the big rivers are at their lowest and the weirs have fallen into disuse, men and boys from the village, accompanied by their relatives, fish with such a net. Stones are tied to the bottom of the net, which is stretched on supporting sticks (*rupa*), to a height of about three feet. The distance from one stick to another is that of the outstretched arms and a man stands at every second stick. In front of the net a few men go with fish spears to look for crocodiles. If one is met, a fish is passed to him on the end of a spear. If he eats it he is considered dangerous. A crocodile lying with a bent tail is also looked upon as being vicious. If the situation is awkward, the fishermen may shift to another spot but usually crocodiles in shallow water are killed, while in deep water the net is merely lifted over them. Two men with fish spears move along each bank, chasing fish from their holes and from behind roots into the path of the net. All the men are armed with fish spears. The party moves downstream towards a second net (*musinkira*) which has been set on sticks to block the fleeing fish. This second net is stationary. At the end of the drive, when both nets meet, they are tied together and dragged, together with their catch, to the bank.

A *kokota* net has a smaller mesh than the *cikulo*, the size of each mesh being only one inch. It is also a drag net but without the stick supports and without men to hold it at the middle. This kind of net is used in deep pools or deep rivers when it is dragged by its two ends from canoes. As it has a small mesh, the fish are swept up rather than entangled.

" FESTOON " FISHING (*kukula candwe*)

Women, and especially girls, catch small fry during the dry season, by dragging a long, festoon-like bundle (*candwe*), made of reed roots and riverine creepers, through shallow water. The dragging is done downstream and the fish are swept to a sandbank. This activity is jokingly referred to as " women's hunting " (*bupalu bwa banakasi*).

When small streams cease to flow, women and children gather in the drying pools that are left and scoop out the water with all kinds of baskets, thus stranding any fish that have been trapped there.

POISONING (*kutwira*)

Kanyense leaves or the roots of *buba* (*Tephrosia*), a cultivated shrub, are pounded and thrown into pools or even into small streams. The fish become paralysed and are caught. *Fute* is used in a similar way after being chopped, beaten and washed in water.

SPEARING

When the level of the water is low, men go and spear fish at random in holes and under the banks of rivers.

LINE FISHING

Fish hooks are eagerly sought for use in deep water such as in the Lunsemfwa. Even before the introduction of European-made hooks, barbless hooks (*ndobo*) were in use. Women, especially girls, do not disdain fishing with hooks.

[821]

CHAPTER VIII

RELAXATION

Beer drinking is the most common, most popular and the most important form of tribal relaxation, especially for men. It is said that nobody drinks beer alone, but only with friends. Though women drink far less than men, they also attend beer parties for the sake of the social intercourse that is offered. This is particularly true of older women, the widowed and the divorced, who are free to go where they please.

The beer season begins in March after the rainy season maize harvest, when small beer parties are first held. These beer parties are quite private affairs confined to the villagers, and are usually held in the gardens. Beer brewing increases both in volume and frequency after the main harvest of sorghum is stored, and lasts till the end of October, the end of the hot season. Every household is socially obliged to provide a beer party in return for attending the parties of their neighbours. Men are welcome to beer. If a man avails himself, however, of every opportunity of beer drinking in the neighbourhood, he gets a bad name, especially among his in-laws, who are all the more resentful if, in doing so, he neglects to keep his buildings in repair or to contribute his share to garden work.

Beer drinking ceases with the fall of the first rains, for the women must plant the crops and have to hoe continually. The more affluent still contrive to arrange beer working-parties for the first weeding of sorghum in December, but in January and February, at the height of the rainy season, there is hardly any beer; the women are too busy in the fields and grain is scarce.

There are three kinds of beer parties. The biggest beer drink is that in commemoration of the dead, called the " funeral beer " (*bwarwa bwa maliro*). The second is the ordinary beer party, which differs from the commemoration beer drink only in that guests need not stay up the whole night nor play gourd drums. Similar beer parties are arranged for the festivals that follow initiation ceremonies.

The third kind of beer drink is the working beer party. Two days before a commemoration beer drink or even an ordinary beer party, a married man is sent round to invite people, especially the headmen, to attend. He does not mention beer, unless it is the commemoration or initiation beer. For the former, people arrive in the evening and stay up all night.

[822]

People come and, when seated on the ground, are courteously greeted. Only headmen may sit on stools; all the others sit on mats or on the ground, though nowadays old men are allowed to sit on stools even in the presence of a member of the chiefly clan or of a headman.

The men of each neighbouring village receive a pot of beer (*mutondo wa bwarwa*) from " the owner of beer " who presents it through their headman.

" The owner of beer " ladles out some of the beer with a dipper and tastes it saying, " Let me remove the medicine of sorcery " (*nka-fumyepo bwanga*). Then he gives the dipper to a fellow villager who goes round each group from the other villages, tasting the beer in the same way. At last a special pot of beer is offered to the men of the local village with the same ceremonial, the headman or his younger brother accepting the present on their behalf. This tasting of the beer by " the owner of beer " is to prove that no *bwanga* (poison or medicine) has been put in it.

The youngest man in the party acts as a kind of steward. He mixes the beer, strains it, and pours it into a drinking gourd (*cipanda*). This he passes to the next man. Every man takes a long draught from the gourd and passes it to his neighbour. Beer is drunk thus by groups, especially at the beginning. Those who have been given pots of beer freely share them with men of other communities and even with complete strangers. Old women sit to one side in a compact group, especially at the start of the drinking when a big gourd of beer is passed to them. Young women keep at a distance. They remain fairly sober and do not really take part in the communal drink. They receive their own gourd of beer which they drink apart and very moderately. All the more this refers to the unmarried girls who prefer non-intoxicating beverages. Young people, particularly girls, do not drink much beer and indeed it would be difficult for them to obtain much of it from their elders. Youth is more interested in dancing. While dancing at night the boys fondle the girls' breasts and may pass from harmless dancing figures into more suggestive and indecent contortions.

The drinking is usually quiet and without brawling. The local headman sees to it that the unpleasantness of brawls with their ensuing litigation and fines is avoided. Weapons are hidden, and guns unloaded to prevent accidents. Old men and women, when intoxicated, begin to dance, one at a time. After a few hours, people scatter all over the village, groups mix and become hilarious, voices are raised, but all the same the drinkers remain orderly. The singing of beer-songs goes on for the most of the time.

[823]

When the local headman sees people growing drunk and rowdy, he brings out a single pot of beer, calls all present and says, " It is finished " (*casira*). This is the last pot offered and is a sign for all guests to go home. Only intimate friends, who have been specially invited to stay for more beer, remain. The end usually comes about three o'clock in the afternoon. All the guests gather in the village shelter, closely packed together, for an hour or so. There the last pot is drunk, the gourd drums and ordinary drums are beaten, solo dancing of intoxicated elders takes place, and songs are sung by the whole gathering. The groups are quite mixed; even some middle-aged women may join the men. Then suddenly the party breaks up and all go home.

WORKING BEER PARTY (*mbire*)

Three or four pots of beer are brewed for those men and women who have responded to the announcement of a working beer party.

The tasting of the beer (*cisulo*) takes place in the early morning, and one pot is drunk at home in the village. Then the people go off to work, two or three pots being carried to the garden to be drunk during working-time.

Works stops at about two o'clock and the workers return to the village, unless the family who employs them wishes to stay the whole day in the garden. Beer is distributed in gourds among the people who worked. If women have worked, they get one pot of beer to share among them, while their husbands come to drink from other pots.

Beer parties are arranged for plastering a hut, cutting trees for a new field, the first hoeing (*kukula*), weeding, cutting down the stalks of sorghum, cutting the heads of sorghum from the stalks, and carrying sorghum to the grain bins.

Once I watched an all-night dance held without any beer by a group of young people. The occasion was the presence of a professional dancer. Two boys were each beating a drum, while a few other boys, followed by one or two girls, danced round them in single file. Round this moving circle of dancers stood a ring of spectators, mostly women of all ages. From time to time the professional dancer halted in front of the drums and performed his solo dance, which consisted of short steps danced in very quick succession. This the crowd admired greatly. The girls during this solo performance stood still in their section of the circle, swaying the upper part of their bodies to right and left, and shuffling their feet backwards and forwards. The boys swayed their whole bodies backwards and forwards. Whistles were

[824]

blown and songs with a choral refrain were sung. When the professional dancer became tired, the circling was resumed. So the dance
went on and on till dawn.

Nsoro

This game, the African draughts, is known and played, though
not assiduously. The Ambo villager, when he might be expected to
play it after the harvest, has such a variety of pursuits that he rarely
ever finds sufficient time. When there is no beer drink, he goes to
attend to his tobacco plot. He has to inspect his cane-rat trap every
day for much of the year; he has to see to his weir basket traps; he is
continuously making baskets and mats if he knows the craft; and also
he must spend much of his time in his dry-season maize garden. When
he comes back to the village, he finds that his fellows are all busy with
similar pursuits.

The principles of this game are much the same as those of the
Ila except in minor rules. (Smith and Dale, 1920 II. 232–237).
The most common system is to have four rows of holes, each row
containing twelve holes, with two pebbles each. Each player sits at
the side of the board. At the start, the two holes at his extreme right,
one in the front row and the other in the back row, are left empty.
The third hole in the front row on the left is also empty, while the
first hole on the left in the front row contains only one pebble. In the
first move all the pebbles of five holes of the adversary are taken by
the player, but in later successful moves only four holes of the adversary are emptied, the two opposite the hole where the player stops
and two additional holes by choice. The direction of the moves is
opposite to that of the Ila; in other regards the Ila " *ku suntula* "
method is used.

The second method is the " woman's *nsoro* ", of which the main
feature is that the winner takes over for her own use the pebbles
which she wins, instead of removing them from the board.

[825]

BIBLIOGRAPHY

BARNES, J. A. ... ... *Politics in a Changing Society.* Rhodes-Livingstone Institute, London, 1954.

DOKE, C. M. ... ... *The Lambas of Northern Rhodesia.* London, 1931.

LAGERCRANTZ, STURE ... *Contribution to the Ethnography of Africa.* Studia Ethnographica Upsaliensia, Lund, 1950.

LANE POOLE, E. H. ... *The Native Tribes of the East Luangwa Province of Northern Rhodesia.* Livingstone, 1934.

MUNDAY, J. T. ... ... " Some Traditions of the Nyendwa Clan of Northern Rhodesia." *Bantu Studies*, Vol. 14, No. 4, Johannesburg, 1940.

PETERS, D. U. ... ... *Land Usage in Serenje District.* Rhodes-Livingstone Paper No. 19, London, 1950.

RICHARDS, A. I. ... ... *Land, Labour and Diet in Northern Rhodesia.* London, 1961.

SMITH, E. W., AND DALE, A.M. ... ... *The Ila-speaking Peoples of Northern Rhodesia* (2 vols.). London, 1920.

STEFANISZYN, B. ... ... *The Social and Ritual Life of the Ambo of Northern Rhodesia.* International African Institute, London, 1964.

STEPHENSON, J. E. ... *Chirupula's Tale.* London, 1937.

TEW, MARY ... ... *Peoples of the Lake Nyasa Region.* International African Institute, London, 1950.

TRAPNELL, G. C. ... *The Soils, Vegetation and Agriculture of North-Eastern Rhodesia.* Lusaka, 1943.

WHITELEY, W. AND SLASKI, J. ... *Bemba and Related Peoples of Northern Rhodesia; Peoples of the Lower Luapula Valley.* International African Institute, London, 1951.